Food for Today

Fifth Edition

Food for Today

Fifth Edition

HELEN KOWTALUK

Alice Orphanos Kopan

GLENCOE

Macmillan/McGraw-Hill

New York, New York   Columbus, Ohio   Mission Hills, California   Peoria, Illinois

Send all inquiries to:
GLENCOE DIVISION
Macmillan/McGraw-Hill
3008 W. Willow Knolls Drive
Peoria, Illinois 61614

ISBN 0-02-676162-9 (Student Text)
ISBN 0-02-676163-7 (Teacher's Wraparound Edition)

Printed in the United States of America

2 3 4 5 6 7 8 9 10 AGH 99 98 97 96 95 94

Nutrition Consultant

Elizabeth Shipley Moses, M.S., R.D.

Contributors

Gwen Bagaas
Jamestown, New York

Gayle Gardner Erskine, M.S., C.H.E.
Home Economics Department Chair
Cherry Creek Schools
Aurora, Colorado

Brenda Barrington Mendiola, M.S.
Home Economics Teacher
Irion County Schools
Mertzon, Texas

Elise Zwicky
Pekin, Illinois

Reviewers

Pamela M. Baggett, C.H.E.
Home Economics Teacher
Middleburg High School
Middleburg, Florida

Ann Branch, M.Ed.
Personal and Family Life Science Instructor
Jefferson Senior High School
Alexandria, Minnesota

Patricia Brodeen, M.S.
Home Economics Department Chair
Roosevelt High School
San Antonio, Texas

Jeannine C. Campbell, M.S., C.H.E.
Home Economics Teacher
F.J. Reitz High School
Evansville, Indiana

Judith Egolf, M.A., C.H.E.
Home Economics Teacher
Warsaw Community High School
Warsaw, Indiana

Ann Larkin, P.H.E.C.
Family Studies Teacher
Clarke Road Secondary School
London, Ontario

Mary Helen Mays, Ph.D., R.D.
Coordinator, Coordinated Program in Dietetics
University of Texas Pan American
Edinburg, Texas

Vicki McClung
Home Economics Teacher
Trumann High School
Trumann, Arkansas

Paula McKee
Home Economics Teacher
Middleburg High School
Middleburg, Florida

Brenda Barrington Mendiola, M.S.
Home Economics Teacher
Irion County Schools
Mertzon, Texas

Wanda Menghini, M.S.
Home Economics Teacher
Olathe South High School
Olathe, Kansas

JoAnne S. Rowe, M.S.
Research Associate and Instructor of
Home Economics
Indiana State University
Terre Haute, Indiana

PHOTO CREDITS

American Dry Bean Board (NE)/Peter Monge, 445
447, 448.
American Egg Board, 471, 476.
American Gas Association, 373.
Angelo's/Brent Phelps, 295.
Arnold & Brown, 135, 149, 170, 177, 375, 415, 475.

Ballard, James, 25, 81, 171.
Bean, Roger B., 33, 299, 321, 332, 637, 681, 684,
685, 686.
Bemis Company, Inc., 397.
Berry, Keith M., 9, 150, 328, 449, 682.
Bettmann Archive, 43, 141, 158.
Black Star
Holbrook, Andrew, 365.
Turnley, Peter, 365.
Blake, Anthony, Photolibrary
Gerritt Buntrock, 600.
Brooks, J.R. & Son, Inc., 37, 69, 410, 411, 532.
Burns-Milwaukee, 366.

Carter, Tom, 237.
Circle Design/Carol Spengle, 74, 81, 82, 83.
Cupboard, Denton, TX

de Wys, Leo, Inc.
Lavine, Arthur, 649.
Naclivet, Jean Paul, 641, 651.
Phillips, Van, 414.
Denton West/Ann Garvin, 184, 223, 250, 441.
Dillard's Department Store, Golden Triangle Mall,
Denton, TX/Christine Rowell, Trish Steinmetz,
and Karen Washington
Dotter, Earl, 84, 328, 349, 475, 676.
Dry Bean Advisory Board, 127.

Florida Dept. of Agriculture and Consumer
Services/Bureau of Seafood & Aquaculture,
68, 312, 512, 533, 541.
Flow Rehabilitation Hospital, Denton, TX/ Ann
Garvin, 194.
Frazier, David R., Photolibrary, 251, 340, 344, 351,
354, 367, 405, 429, 444, 451, 456, 458, 500, 554,
586, 599, 601, 624, 627, 632, 635, 667, 687.
Frazier, David R., Photolibrary,
Kevin Syms, 547.
Jim Patrico, 624.

Garvin, Ann, 9, 10, 11, 12, 13, 14, 15, 16, 20, 22,
40, 47, 57, 61, 63, 67, 71, 80, 88, 104, 108, 109,
112, 123, 126, 128, 129, 133, 138, 146, 152, 153,
159, 162, 166, 168, 169, 188, 191, 200, 205, 211,
220, 231, 232, 236, 245, 249, 254, 266, 273, 277,
278, 280, 281, 284, 285, 286, 290, 291, 292, 293, 296,
304, 307, 309, 319, 326, 345, 370, 372, 387, 389, 394,
402, 403, 404, 408, 421, 423, 424, 428, 432, 437, 443,

454, 462, 463, 465, 466, 470, 473, 474, 477, 478, 479,
482, 505, 511, 513, 515, 518, 522, 525, 527, 528, 532,
534, 538, 540, 545, 550, 557, 561, 563, 564, 565, 568,
570, 571, 573, 574, 575, 578, 584, 585, 588, 590, 597,
598, 603, 604, 605, 606, 613, 615, 616, 620, 623, 624,
626, 628, 631, 640, 642, 652, 654.
Greenberg, Jeff Isaac, 321, 420, 494, 634.

Hamptons/Arnold & Brown, 371, 234.
Hershey Foods Corporation, 31, 377.
Hopkins, John, 172, 179, 676.
Human Issues Collaborative/Ron Chapple, 55, 321.
Hutchings, Richard, 48, 680.

Idaho Bean Commission, 130, 134, 630.

Kiss the Chef Gourmet Shop, Lewistown, TX/
Ann Garvin, 380.
Kraft General Foods, 13, 461, 464, 468, 524, 558,
559, 646.

Marshall, James M., 17, 294, 364, 472, 498, 604,
607, 611, 617.
Maytag, 185, 256, 257, 272.
Merillat, 10, 41, 186, 187, 189, 383, 385.
Mishima, 38, 143, 151, 322, 328, 362, 665.
Morse, P.C., 222, text/cover design

National Broiler Council/Newman, Saylor and
Gregory, 427, 442.
National Live Stock and Meat Board, 485, 489,
490, 492, 493, 507, 516, 517, 524, 538, 664.
National Pork Producers Council, 11, 268, 269,
491, 506, 514, 539.
National Turkey Federation, 498, 535.

Peerless Photography, 100, 101, 182, 183, 437, 658,
660.
Peterson, Judith, 433, 531.
Phelps, Brent, 30, 45, 56, 59, 62, 66, 68, 78, 90, 92,
93, 94, 95, 107, 113, 114, 116, 117, 124,125,128,
131, 132, 156, 157, 165, 167, 176, 190, 192, 196,
197, 201, 207, 210, 212, 214, 224, 225, 227, 228,
230, 233, 239, 243, 244, 259, 262, 263, 264, 265,
274, 275, 276, 279, 293, 298, 306, 312, 315, 316,
318, 328, 332, 333, 337, 338, 340, 341, 342, 352,
356, 379, 381, 395, 396, 397, 398, 400, 401, 415,
416, 417, 425, 426, 442, 447, 450, 457, 460, 463,
469, 499, 510, 514, 524, 526, 529, 530, 536, 537,
543, 544, 551, 555, 557, 643, 650, 652, 663, 666,
670.
Photo Edit
Aron, Bill, 587, 594, 597, 602.
Conklin, Paul, 364.
Denny, Mary Kate, 321.
Dreyfess, Hermine, 364.

TABLE OF CONTENTS

Unit One
Food, Nutrition, and You

Unit Two
Workspace, Tools, and
Techniques

Chapter 9. Cooking Methods ··············254

Chapter 10. Mealtime Customs ··········290

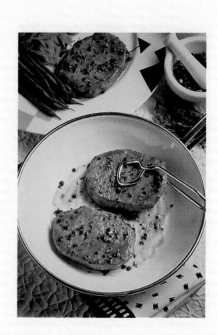

Unit Three
Consumer Decisions

Chapter 11. Planning Meals ···············304

Unit Four
Foods for Meals and Snacks

Unit Five
Expanding Your Horizons

Chapter 25. Careers in Food and Nutrition ··························674

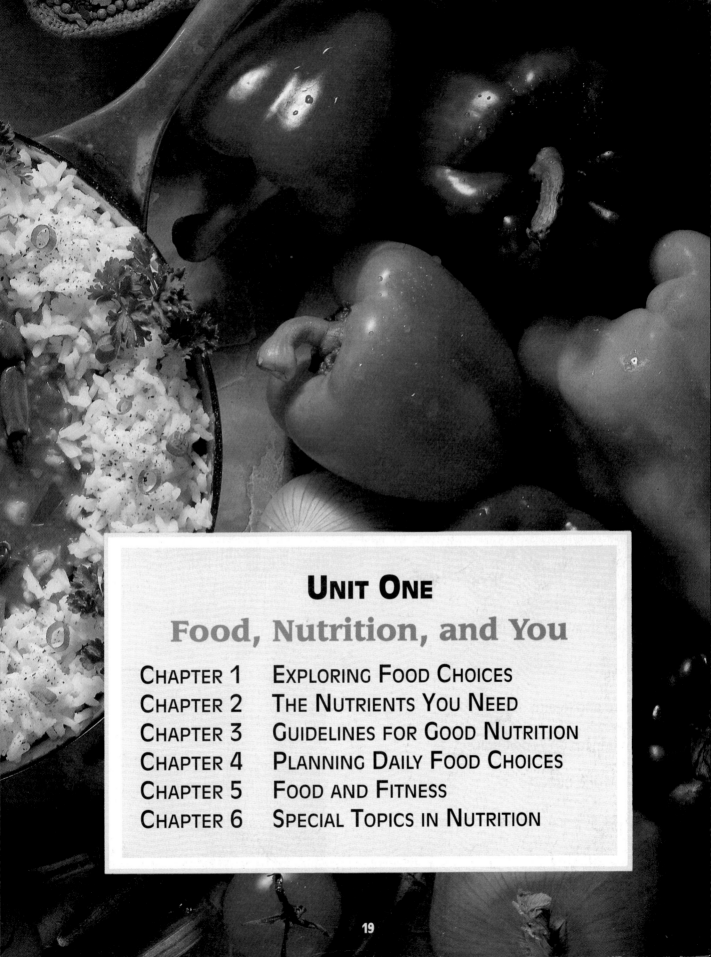

UNIT ONE

Food, Nutrition, and You

CHAPTER 1

Exploring Food Choices

Food and Health

Look for These Terms

nutrients
nutrition
wellness
psychological
self-esteem

Troy was headed out the door of the school when he saw a group of his friends. "Hey, how about stopping for something to eat? I'm starving."

Justin shook his head. "I can't. I promised Dad I'd pick up a few things at the supermarket."

Isabel said, "Sorry. It's my turn to get dinner ready."

"I'd like to, but I've got a pep club meeting," said Brian. "We're going to plan our next spaghetti supper."

"I'll go with you, Troy," said Jamal. "We can talk about the weekend while we eat."

On this particular afternoon, the activities of Troy and his friends all revolve around food. Why does food play such an important role in people's lives? As you will see, food helps people meet a variety of needs.

Physical Needs

Food is necessary for survival. When your body needs food, it lets you know—you feel hungry. You begin to think about getting something to eat.

However, food does more than fill the stomach to stop hunger pangs. Food supplies the human body with chemicals called **nutrients.** The human body is a living organism that needs nutrients to carry on its functions.

Nutrition is the study of nutrients and how they are used by the body. The term "nutrition" can also refer to the effect of your food choices on your health. If your food choices provide all the nutrients you need in the right amounts, you are practicing good nutrition.

Good nutrition has many benefits. It can help you feel your best and look your best. It helps you grow and become strong. It helps you stay energetic and healthy, both now and in later life. As part of your study of food, you will learn more about good nutrition and how to make wise food choices.

Wellness

Good nutrition is an important part of wellness. **Wellness** is a philosophy that encourages people to take responsibility for their own health. That means it's up to you to take the necessary steps to have and enjoy good health throughout your life.

Of course, practicing wellness doesn't guarantee that you will never have a health problem. However, wellness will help you attain the highest level of health that you possibly can.

Wellness involves taking care of yourself in many ways for good physical, mental, and emotional health. By developing good health habits now, you have a better chance of staying healthy throughout your life. Making wise food choices is an important part of anyone's wellness program.

Getting the most out of life depends on feeling your best. Do your daily routines and decisions promote wellness?

Healthy Attitudes

In addition to making nutritious food choices, you can practice wellness by:

- Exercising regularly.
- Getting plenty of rest and sleep.
- Practicing good hygiene.
- Getting regular checkups and routine medical care when needed.
- Following safety practices.
- Avoiding health risks such as tobacco, alcohol, and other drugs.
- Learning to manage stress.

Psychological Needs

Psychological (sie-kuh-LAHJ-ih-kuhl) means having to do with the mind and emotions. Psychological health is part of wellness and is just as important as physical health. Though you may not realize it, food also helps you meet psychological needs. These include the need for security, a sense of belonging, enjoyment, and self-esteem.

Security

Security is a feeling of being free from harm, fear, and want. One type of security comes from knowing you have the basic necessities of life. Thus, having a good supply of food helps you feel secure.

Security can also be related to emotional needs and desires. In times of stress, people may turn to certain foods that they believe will make them feel better. For example, they may crave favorite foods from childhood because they associate them with feelings of being cared for or rewarded. Later in this chapter you will learn more about how emotions influence food choices.

A Sense of Belonging

People need to feel that they are accepted by others and belong to a group, whether it's a family or friends. Food can help create a bond between people, giving them a sense of belonging.

Food is associated with hospitality. At parties, weddings, family reunions—even when people just "stop by"—guests are usually offered something to eat or drink. This helps people feel welcome and at ease.

Foods that give a sense of security are sometimes called "comfort foods." Many people turn to chicken soup when they don't feel well. Scientists have found that it also offers some physical relief—it can help clear a stuffy head.

There are real advantages to involving the whole family in food preparation. The work is shared, but so is the fun. It also provides opportunities for passing on family traditions.

Food can also help strengthen family relationships. For instance, Isabel often helps out with meal preparation. She is proud to be making a contribution to her family. She also enjoys the companionship of sharing mealtime with her mother and two younger sisters. It gives them a chance to talk and laugh together.

Food can also help you feel a part of a larger group—all the people with whom you share customs and traditions. Section 1.3 will look at the relationship between food and culture.

Enjoyment

What are your favorite foods? Imagine their appearance, taste, texture, and aroma. It's easy to see that food satisfies the senses. In addition, trying new foods may appeal to your sense of adventure.

Preparing food can bring pleasure as well. Many people enjoy the chance to be creative and the challenge of learning new skills. Turning an assortment of ingredients into a delicious dish for yourself and others to enjoy can bring a great sense of satisfaction.

Self-Esteem

Brian has been volunteering to help with the pep club's fundraising dinners for the past two years. Half of the money raised goes toward club activities and the rest to a local charity. Brian is glad he got involved. He's made some new friends and is learning to overcome his shyness. The fact that he has a valuable skill to contribute helps him feel good about himself.

Brian may not realize it, but he is developing a strong sense of self-esteem. **Self-esteem** is a healthy recognition of your strengths and weaknesses and the ability to accept yourself as you are. It doesn't mean you're better than anyone else, but you're just as good. Developing your skills, including skills in food and nutrition, can help strengthen your self-esteem. People with good self-esteem not only have confidence in themselves, but respect and support others.

As you can see, food helps people meet a variety of physical and psychological needs. These basic needs are shared by everyone. However, experience tells you that people's food choices differ dramatically. Why do people eat the foods they do? How can the same food be liked by one person and disliked by another? The next section will help you think about the answers to those questions.

Learning new skills boosts your self-esteem. You will feel more confident.

Section 1.1 Review

RECALL THE FACTS

1. What is nutrition? Why is good nutrition important?

2. What are four psychological needs that food can help meet?

3. What psychological need is being met when family members share a meal together?

DISCUSS YOUR IDEAS

4. How might a natural disaster threaten food supplies? How would this affect people's sense of security? How might they react?

5. Do physical and psychological needs for food ever conflict? Explain.

APPLY YOUR LEARNING

6. List foods you might serve at a gathering of family or friends. Identify how these foods could help meet physical and psychological needs.

Objectives

After studying this section, you should be able to:

❖ Identify social influences on food choices.
❖ Describe how food choices are influenced by available resources and technology.
❖ Identify personal influences on food choices.

Look for These Terms

culture
media
resources
lifestyle

You probably have some very definite ideas about what foods you like and dislike. Where do these preferences come from? You may not be aware of it, but when you make food choices, many influences are at work.

Social Influences

Although you are an individual, you are also a member of various social groups. Many of your preferences begin with the influence of culture, family, friends, and the media.

Culture

Culture refers to the shared customs, traditions, and beliefs of a large group of people, such as a nation, race, or religious group. The distinctive customs help the members of the group develop a common sense of identity.

Food customs are one aspect of culture. Members of different cultures often enjoy distinctive foods. They may also have their own traditional ways of preparing, serving, and eating meals. You will learn about the food customs of many different cultures as you read this book.

Cultural differences are not as pronounced today as they have been in the past. Modern communication and transportation have allowed food customs to be shared and blended much more rapidly than before. Today people can choose from a wonderful wealth of food traditions from around the world. At the same time, they can uphold and celebrate the unique food customs of their own culture to express pride in their heritage.

Cultural influences can change throughout life. For example, Jin Soon was born in Korea but now lives in the United States. Her favorite foods include both traditional Korean dishes, such as *kimchi,* and typical American foods, such as hamburgers.

Food customs are part of any culture's traditions. These women in Bali are bringing offerings of food to a local temple.

Kimchi is a spicy-hot Korean relish. It is made from cabbage mixed with ingredients such as onions, hot peppers, and spices. Traditionally, the mixture is put into sealed pots or jars and buried in the ground. Commercially made kimchi can be purchased in Korean markets.

Family

Your family probably has had the greatest influence on your food choices. When you were very young, family members made most of your food choices for you. As you grew, you learned food habits by following your family's example. You saw them enjoying certain foods at certain times of day, for instance.

A family's food customs often reflect cultural background. For instance, the Masinelli family always has two main dishes at Thanksgiving—turkey and lasagne.

In addition, many families have developed their own unique food traditions. In one family, pancakes are a traditional Saturday night meal. Another family wouldn't think of serving pork chops without applesauce. Birthdays might call for a cake served on a special plate.

People tend to feel comfortable with foods that are familiar. If certain foods were never served in your home, you may think you dislike them. However, part of the adventure of eating is trying new foods and finding some that you enjoy.

Nutrition experts know that families shape the food habits of young children. That influence often lasts a lifetime. How have your food choices been influenced by your family?

Friends

Food is usually an important part of friendships. You and your friends might get together for pizza, eat at the same table in the school cafeteria, or share a bag of pretzels from a vending machine. It should come as no surprise, then, that you and your friends influence each other's food choices.

As part of the group, you help make the decision as to where and what to eat. Sometimes you may not agree with your friends, but you go along with them anyway. If your friends are from different cultural backgrounds, you might learn to enjoy the foods they commonly eat. What kind of foods do you eat because your friends choose them?

The Media

Newspapers, magazines, television, and radio bring information to large audiences. Together these channels of communication are referred to as **media.** Today, they are major influences in making food choices.

Nutrition has become a popular topic for newspapers, magazines, and television shows. The media also report on new products and new trends in foods. You might make food choices just to try the new foods or be part of the trend.

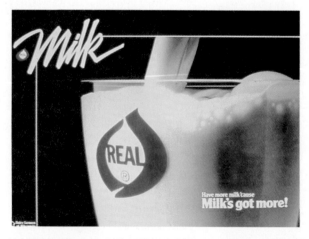

Think about how often food is mentioned in the media.

Advertising is an especially powerful influence on food choices. Does watching a television commercial for hot, juicy hamburgers or chewy chocolate candy make you hungry? Have you ever chosen a particular cereal or snack food just because the ad made it sound so good?

If you are to make wise food choices, be aware of how the media influences you. Think critically about what you see and hear. You'll learn how in Section 3.3.

Available Resources

Your choice of foods depends a great deal on the resources that are available to you. **Resources** are objects and qualities that can help you reach a goal. For example, this textbook is a resource that helps you learn about food and nutrition.

Many resources are involved in getting the food you need. Money is an obvious one. Time, knowledge, abilities, equipment, and a place to buy food are equally important.

One reason people make different food choices is that their resources differ. No one has an endless supply of all resources, but everyone has some. You can often substitute a resource you have for another that is in short supply. For instance, if you have time and skills, you can save money by cooking at home instead of eating out.

Technology and the Food Supply

One of the resources that influences your food choices is the basic food supply. In other words, the choices you make depend on what you have to choose from. Technology influences the food supply and therefore your choices.

Imagine that you have stepped back in time two or three hundred years. How would your food choices change? In this world of the past, almost everything you eat must be grown by your family or your neighbors. In warm weather, foods are plentiful but spoilage is a problem. In cold weather, the challenge is to make food last until the next harvest.

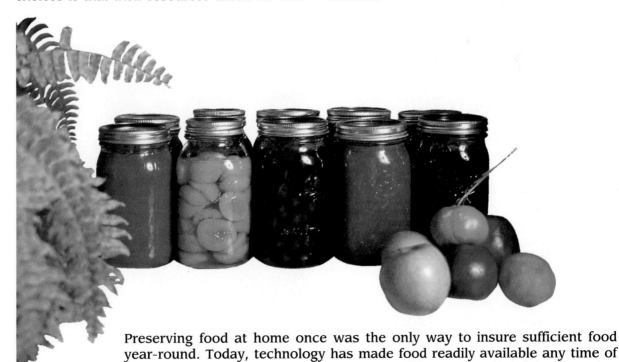

Preserving food at home once was the only way to insure sufficient food year-round. Today, technology has made food readily available any time of the year. People who preserve food at home usually do so by choice, rather than necessity.

Technology Tidbit

Did you know that some of the foods you buy may have been prepared with the help of robots? For instance, at some large commercial bakeries, robots take baked loaves out of the pans. This technology helps food companies provide high-quality products.

Today, modern technology has greatly increased the options that are available to you. Jet planes and trucks bring food from around the world to the local supermarket. You can take a frozen, already-prepared main dish out of the freezer and pop it in the microwave. In just minutes it will be hot and ready to eat.

New technology will continue to add to people's food choices. Can you imagine what foods might be available two hundred years in the future?

Personal Influences

Your lifestyle, values, priorities, and emotions also influence your choice of foods. They are part of the reason that your food choices are uniquely your own.

Your Lifestyle

Lifestyle refers to a person's typical way of life. Your lifestyle includes how you spend your time and what is important to you. Lifestyle has a strong influence on what and where you eat, how and where you shop, and how you prepare food.

Today, your lifestyle might include school, a part-time job, family activities, and hobbies. Your busy lifestyle can affect your food choices. For instance, you may buy a snack from a vending machine just because the food is available, easy to carry, and easy to eat quickly.

Values and Priorities

Not everyone spends time or money in the same way. People make different choices based on their own values and priorities.

Food choices, too, depend on your values and priorities. Some people enjoy the time they spend preparing meals. Others would rather spend the time on another activity, such as a hobby or community service. Some people may choose to eat out, even though it costs more than preparing food at home.

It's not always easy to juggle your priorities. Time, money, health, enjoyment—all are important to most people. As you continue your study of food, you will learn ways to meet the challenge of a busy lifestyle.

What are the most powerful influences on your food choices?

Most celebrations call for special foods. They make such occasions more enjoyable and memorable.

Your Emotions

Emotions and moods can also influence food choices. Some people believe certain kinds of food make them feel better if they are sad or depressed. They may choose different foods if they are happy or celebrating an event.

Food often carries strong associations, which may be pleasant or unpleasant. For instance, Jarod can still remember being forced to eat spinach as a child. He does not like spinach to this day. On the other hand, Tonya loves spinach. It reminds her of meals at her grandmother's house and feelings of comfort and security.

As you can see, even a decision such as what to have for lunch, though it may seem simple, is influenced by many factors. Your background, your lifestyle today, and the world around you all play a part in your food choices.

■ Section 1.2 Review ■

RECALL THE FACTS

1. What is culture? How does it relate to food choices?

2. What is a resource? Name five resources that are involved in obtaining food.

3. What is lifestyle? How does it influence a person's choice of foods?

DISCUSS YOUR IDEAS

4. How has your family influenced your food choices? What are some of your family's food traditions?

5. Imagine that you are an inventor in the 22nd century. Describe a new food product or kitchen appliance that you would like to invent. How would it affect people's food choices?

APPLY YOUR LEARNING

6. Find three food advertisements in magazines. Do they make you want to buy the product? Why or why not?

Objectives

After studying this section, you should be able to:

* Describe the characteristics of a multicultural society.
* Give examples of cultural food customs.
* Explain how food customs have evolved through history.

Look for These Terms

ethnic group
multicultural
cultural diversity

Eric, Cyrise, Joel, and Amber decided to have lunch in the food court at the mall. Each went to a different food stall. Eric returned with wonton soup and chicken fried rice. Cyrise chose a burrito, while Joel decided on pizza. Amber had a shish kebab and pita bread.

The foods they chose were all made from basic ingredients, such as grains, vegetables, and meat or poultry. However, each dish was distinctly different. Each represented the food customs of a specific culture.

Understanding Culture

As you learned in Section 1.2, "culture" refers to the shared customs, traditions, and beliefs of a group of people. But what makes up a "group of people"?

One example of a cultural group might be the people who live in a particular part of the world. The various nations around the globe have developed many unique customs, including those related to food.

Corn has special significance in some Native American cultures. It is used for ceremonies, as well as for food.

A cultural group may also be defined by a common heritage, or past. For instance, Native Americans are descendants of the original dwellers in America. Some people now living in the United States were born in other countries. Most Americans can trace their ancestry back to other parts of the world. A cultural group based on common heritage is often called an **ethnic group.**

Religion is another basis for defining cultural groups. Members of a particular faith usually have a common set of beliefs and follow specific practices.

As you can see, a person may belong to more than one cultural group. In addition, many different cultural groups may exist side by side. The term **multicultural** describes a society that includes many cultures.

The United States has always been a multicultural society. Today it has become even more so, and the trend will almost certainly continue in the future. Many people see this **cultural diversity,** or variety of cultures, as a great strength. In a multicultural society, people are free to share and enjoy the customs of many cultures. At the same time, it's important to respect other people's beliefs and practices, even though they may differ from your own.

Understanding Cultural Food Customs

Food is essential in the everyday life of individuals and families. In addition, food can play an important role in celebrations and ceremonies. It's no wonder that food customs are often a focal point in cultural traditions.

Food-related celebrations are common in this country. One town's annual pumpkin festival offers everything from pumpkin ice cream to pumpkin chili.

Examples of Food Customs

Food customs usually involve certain kinds of foods, but that's just the beginning. They also include the way food is prepared, how it is served, and how it is eaten.

Unique Foods

In the example you read at the beginning of this section, the foods chosen by Eric, Cyrise, Joel, and Amber each trace their roots back to a different part of the world. For instance, Eric's wonton soup originated in China. Wontons are dumplings filled with minced vegetables and meat. Amber's shish kebab, made with chunks of meat threaded on a skewer, originated in the Middle East. So did pita bread, a distinctive flat bread that forms a pocket. You can find many other examples of foods from around the world in Chapter 22.

Within a nation, there may also be distinct regional food traditions. In the United States, well-known regional foods include cornbread and grits from the South, chili and barbecue from Texas, sourdough bread from San Francisco, and clam chowder from New England. Although these foods are now available all over the United States, each was developed in a particular section of the country. You can read more about regional foods in Chapter 23.

Dietary Laws

Religious beliefs often include dietary laws, or rules about what foods may be eaten. For example, Jews who follow a kosher diet do not eat meat and dairy products in the same meal. Hindus do not eat beef because they consider cattle to be sacred animals. Muslims eat no pork.

Etiquette

Social customs for serving and eating food also vary, depending on the culture. For instance, not all cultures use forks, knives, and spoons for eating. In China and Japan, chopsticks are the traditional eating utensils. In some countries, such as India, Pakistan, Algeria, and Morocco, it is considered proper to eat many foods using the fingers. In Mexico, food may be scooped up with a tortilla.

Food customs affect not only what is eaten, but how foods are served. How does this scene from a restaurant in China differ from what you might see in an American restaurant?

WORLD of variety

If you were a guest at a meal in Laos, a country in Southeast Asia, you would sit on a mat on the floor. The host would bring in the food, crouching to keep his head below the level of yours as a sign of respect. The food would be in small pieces and served in one dish from which everyone would eat. You would eat with a fork in your left hand and a spoon in your right. However, to eat rice you would use your fingers, then wipe them on a napkin.

Special Occasions

Many food customs relate to holidays, festivals, and religious observances. To celebrate Chinese New Year, Judy Chen helps her mother make New Year's dumplings. The small, smooth, round dumplings are made of rice powder and water and filled with a sweet soybean paste. Their shape symbolizes good fortune. For Easter, Poles and Ukrainians color eggs in complex designs. In Italy, a popular Easter food is a ring-shaped coffee cake with colored eggs tucked into the top.

Holiday food customs do not always involve special foods. On Yom Kippur, the Jewish faith observes the Day of Atonement by fasting. Catholics refrain from eating meat on certain church holy days. During Ramadan, a month-long religious observance, Muslims do not eat or drink during the daylight hours. Instead, they eat anytime after sunset and before sunrise.

Easter is celebrated in some countries as both a signal of spring and a religious feast. These intricately decorated eggs from the Ukraine are a symbol of both.

Sometimes food itself is the theme for a festival. Harvest festivals have been common since ancient times. In the United States, Thanksgiving is the official harvest festival. Many communities also have their own festivals to celebrate the harvest of locally grown foods.

How Food Customs Evolve

As you can see, there are as many different ways of preparing, serving, and eating food as there are cultural groups. None of these food customs can be considered "better" than any other. Different customs arise naturally because of different circumstances.

For instance, you may be used to eating leftovers for lunch or dinner. In Japan, this would be considered unusual, even strange. This cultural difference can be understood if you realize that most Japanese do not have large refrigerators for food storage. Food is purchased fresh daily to be eaten that day. Dining on leftovers would be viewed as eating "old" food.

Food Customs Through History

A journey through history can help you understand many other food customs. In the distant past, geography greatly influenced the development of food customs. Differences in climate and soil affected the foods that could be grown in an area. Without modern transportation, food choices were limited. How the foods were cooked often depended on the types and amount of fuel available. For example, in many Asian countries, cooking fuel was scarce. To conserve it, food was cut into small pieces that would cook quickly.

In many cultures, economic conditions created two types of food customs. One was for the rich, who could afford the finest foods prepared by talented chefs in the most elegant manner. The rest of the people were poor and ate only a few basic foods. A typical daily meal might be soup, made with whatever food was available, and coarse, dark bread made from ground whole grain.

Stir-frying small pieces of food probably developed as a way to save scarce fuel. The ingredients used depended on available foods.

However they originated, food customs were passed down from one generation to the next. Still, changes occurred along the way. Explorers took some of their own foods with them on their journeys and brought strange foods from distant lands when they returned. Invading armies often brought new food customs with them.

European explorers who reached the Western Hemisphere found an abundance of foods eaten by the Native Americans. The explorers brought back samples and seeds of foods that were not found in Europe, such as dry beans, corn, tomatoes, potatoes, sweet potatoes, and cassava, a type of root. Over the centuries, some of these foods became popular in the Eastern Hemisphere.

As food customs traveled around the world, they were often changed and adapted. Perhaps the original ingredients were not as commonly available in the new locale, or people adapted dishes to suit their own tastes. Sometimes an entirely new dish resulted. For example, chop suey is not authentic Chinese food, but an American dish based on the Chinese style of cooking.

A World of Food Choices

Today, the world is becoming "smaller." People and foods can be flown thousands of miles in a few hours. Satellite links allow almost instant communication with any part of the globe.

As a result, food customs travel the world faster than ever. Foods grown halfway around the world are sold in your local supermarket. Television programs can show you the sights of another country or tell you how to prepare dishes from remote parts of the world.

Of course, as discussed earlier, you don't have to turn to another part of the globe to find examples of different cultures. You can find many examples right here. Whenever people gather to share food and fun, they also share each other's food traditions.

It's not surprising, therefore, that ethnic and international foods are now an everyday part of American life. Supermarkets routinely stock a wide variety of ethnic foods, and many restaurants include an assortment on their menus. You probably enjoy many such foods, from tacos to pizza, without thinking of them as being different. They have become as familiar to Americans as steak and potatoes.

This is one of the benefits of living in a multicultural society. Consider the mingling of international flavors in this meal, which Katie's family ate recently. They had chicken curry over rice (India), garlic French bread (France), steamed snow peas and water chestnuts (China), and a dessert of fresh papayas and bananas (Caribbean).

Global flavors are also being combined in recipes. Rachel makes pizza with chili-seasoned ground meat and tops it with grated cheese and salsa (SAL-suh), a spicy, Mexican fresh tomato sauce. At the same time, American fast foods such as fried chicken, french fries, and hamburgers are known around the globe. Fast food places have become popular in major cities around the world, such as Moscow and Tokyo.

Such global diversity enriches everyone's lives. No matter where people go, they can find foods they enjoy and experience the adventure of new flavors.

Mangoes were once available only in tropical climates. Today, they can often be found at the neighborhood supermarket. How often do you try new foods?

This fast food restaurant in Tokyo shows that food customs are being shared around the world.

RECALL THE FACTS

1. What does "multicultural" mean? What are some advantages of living in a multicultural society?

2. Name four categories of cultural food customs. Give an example of each.

3. What often happens when food customs are introduced into new areas? Why?

DISCUSS YOUR IDEAS

4. Do you think it is important for members of a particular culture to retain some distinct food customs? Why or why not?

5. Do you think differences in food customs will continue to exist in the future? Why or why not?

APPLY YOUR LEARNING

6. List some of your own or your family's favorite foods. Indicate the cultures that are represented.

Look for These Terms

science
food science
ergonomics
technology

Stacey wandered down the supermarket aisles, trying to decide on food for her party Saturday night. Finally, she chose a few old favorites but also several new items that looked good. They included fat-free cookies, mini-pizzas made for the microwave, and red, tomato-flavored chips.

It never occurred to Stacey that science and technology were responsible for the wide variety of foods that made her choices so difficult. Science and technology have had a great effect on food, from the kind of food available to how it is prepared.

Scientific Aspects of Food

Science involves research to develop knowledge of a particular part of nature. The study of food and nutrition is related to a number of basic sciences, such as chemistry, biology, and physics. Here's a brief look at some of the ways in which science is directly related to food.

Food technologists help develop new foods and improve existing ones. They rely on knowledge of food, nutrition, science, and technology.

Nutrition

The science of nutrition is a continuing process. So far, about 40 nutrients have been identified. No one knows how many other nutrients still remain to be discovered. Once nutrients are discovered, scientists continue to research the role they play.

In recent years, scientists have made amazing discoveries about the relationships between nutrition and health. For instance, research shows that beta carotene (BAY-tuh CARE-oh-teen), a form of vitamin A found in fruits and vegetables, may be helpful in preventing certain kinds of cancer.

The Science of Food Preparation

Moira's friend Keisha is a whiz in the kitchen. Inspired by Keisha's example, Moira tried making biscuits and gravy. She followed Keisha's recipes exactly—well, almost exactly—but the biscuits were flat and hard and the gravy was greasy and lumpy. "I guess I just don't have Keisha's magic touch," Moira decided.

What makes the difference between light, flaky biscuits and hard ones, or between smooth and lumpy gravy? The answer isn't found in magic, but in science.

Food preparation is governed by natural laws. When certain foods are heated, chilled, mixed together, or manipulated in other ways, they undergo chemical and physical changes. In fact, you can compare a recipe to a chemistry experiment. If you change the conditions of an experiment, the results are likely to change. In the same way, even a small change in a recipe can cause the final product to turn out differently.

Courses that help you learn about food from a scientific angle are often called **food science** courses. Knowledge of food science can help you understand why certain instructions in a recipe are important. If something doesn't turn out right, food science can help you understand why. Then you'll be able to keep the problem from happening again.

Fresh pineapple contains an enzyme that prevents gelatin from becoming firm. However, the enzyme is destroyed by heat in the canning process. Knowing about science can help you in food preparation.

This book will introduce you to some of the scientific principles of food preparation. For example, you'll learn:

❖ Why fresh pineapple makes a gelatin salad turn out more like fruit soup.
❖ Why fried chicken is so brown, crispy, and flavorful, and how you can get similar results using other cooking methods.
❖ Why an angel food cake recipe has so many egg whites.
❖ Why some fruits turn brown when you cut them and how you can prevent it.

Ergonomics

Have you ever felt stiff or sore after sitting in a chair that just didn't seem to fit you? If so, you've experienced the need for ergonomics. **Ergonomics** (urr-guh-NAHM-iks) is the study of how to make tools and equipment easier and more comfortable to use.

Ergonomics plays a key role in the design of kitchens, appliances, and food preparation equipment. For instance, cookware and kitchen tools are ergonomically designed to make food preparation easier and faster.

"Work simplification" is an important part of ergonomics. It means looking for the fastest, easiest method for getting a job done. Using work simplification in the kitchen or foods lab can save time and energy, as you will discover.

Technology and Food

Technology is the practical application of scientific knowledge. Through technology, new or improved products and processes are developed. Examples can be found in the food industry and in the home.

The Food Industry

Technology plays a major role in how foods are produced, processed, packaged, and shipped. For instance:

❖ Food processors are using computers and robots to help control the quality of their products.
❖ New forms of packaging have been developed to keep food safe longer. In some cases, special packaging methods allow foods that traditionally required refrigeration to be stored at room temperature.
❖ Food scientists continue to develop new fat and sugar substitutes and new ways to use them in foods.
❖ Scientists are learning how to "design" plants with certain traits, using a technique called *genetic engineering* (also known as *bioengineering* or *biotechnology*). For instance, they have developed a variety of tomato that stays firm longer after ripening. This will allow ripe tomatoes to be shipped long distances without rotting or being damaged.

An ergonomically designed kitchen includes conveniently placed equipment and easy access to stored items.

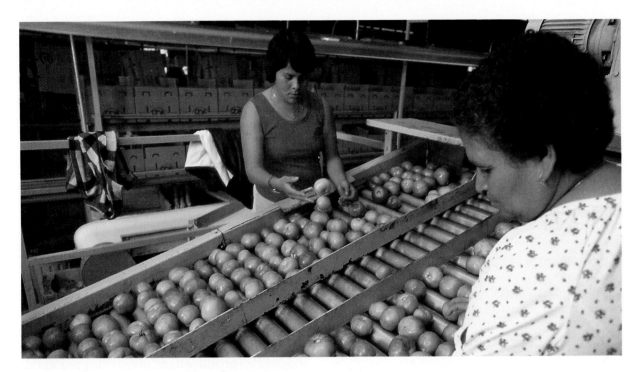

Tomatoes are often shipped green so they won't spoil before they reach the stores. Through genetic engineering, new varieties are being developed that can be left on the vine until they are ripe.

Science Connection

Biology:

Genes and genetic engineering

A *gene* is a tiny chemical unit in a living organism, such as a tomato. Genes allow traits to be passed on from parent to offspring. Each gene carries information about a specific trait. Genetic engineering involves making changes in the gene structure to produce desired characteristics.

■ ■

In later chapters, you will learn more about the food industry and the products that have been developed as a result of technology.

Technology in the Home

Many examples of technology can be found right in the home. These examples show that new technology can have far-reaching effects on people's lives.

The Microwave Oven

The microwave oven was not an instant success. The first models, sold in the 1950s, were about the size of a large refrigerator and cost about $2,500. Many people questioned their safety. The one advantage of the microwave oven was its cooking speed.

As their lives became more fast-paced, people wanted quicker ways to cook. Scientists improved the microwave oven, making it safer. New technology made the ovens smaller and more automatic. The fast-cooking microwave oven gained popularity and became more affordable.

Today, microwave ovens can be found in about 90 percent of U.S. homes and in many workplaces. Hundreds of new food and cookware products have been developed for the microwave. Some people predict that microwave ovens will someday be found in cars.

Other Kitchen Appliances

Like microwave ovens, other appliances—such as ranges, refrigerators, dishwashers, and small appliances—have changed over the years. Designers and manufacturers continually search for ways to make appliances that perform better, are more reliable, require less energy, and are easier to use. Many of today's appliances contain a "brain" in the form of computer chips. Some even alert the user when repair is needed.

New technology does have its drawbacks. Appliances with advanced features are more costly than basic models, making them out of reach for many consumers. In some cases, the advanced features may add to the difficulty and cost of repairs. Learning to use new features and controls can be time-consuming. Still, technology has made many modern conveniences possible. Most people feel that the benefits of technology outweigh the drawbacks.

Microwave ovens are smaller, less expensive, and give better results than when they were first introduced. Many appliances are now available with special features, such as Braille touchpad controls, that make them adaptable for people with physical limitations.

Personal Computers

A relatively new technology that is finding a place in many people's lives is the personal computer. One of the ways computers are proving helpful is in the area of planning meals. For instance, some people use a computer to store recipes and plan menus. With the right software, they can evaluate whether they are getting a nutritious diet. A computer can also help keep track of food spending and supplies. As home computers become more common, the uses are sure to expand.

Food for Tomorrow

What you have read is just a sample of the ways in which science and technology relate to food. You'll find additional information in the "Science Connection" and "Technology Tidbits" features throughout this book.

New discoveries are made every day. Stay informed about the latest developments in science and technology. They have a great influence on what your life will be like in the future.

A personal computer can help you manage food selection and preparation. A computer program was used to calculate the nutritional content of the recipes in this book.

■ Section 1.4 Review ■

RECALL THE FACTS

1. What is the difference between science and technology?

2. How is a recipe like a chemistry experiment?

3. What is meant when a kitchen tool claims to be ergonomically designed?

4. Give an example of recent technological advances in the food industry.

DISCUSS YOUR IDEAS

5. How do you think the drawbacks of technology compare to the benefits?

6. What are the advantages and disadvantages of using a personal computer to help with meal planning?

APPLY YOUR LEARNING

7. Using a catalogue, compare the price and features of a basic model and a "high-tech" model of a common kitchen appliance, such as a toaster. Draw conclusions.

Look for This Term

management

In her foods class, Lawanda is learning to make healthful food choices. Even though she keeps busy with school, a job, and after-school activities, she makes time to eat three nutritious meals a day. As part of her studies in foods, she has learned decision-making and management techniques which help her to live more successfully.

What Is Management?

Management refers to specific techniques that help you use resources wisely. As you learned in Section 1.2, resources are objects and qualities that can help you reach your goals. They include time, money, equipment, food, knowledge, and abilities, such as your ability to think and imagine.

With good management you can use whatever resources you have most effectively.

Scientists are concerned that destruction of the tropical rainforests could change the global climate. What might be the effects on food production?

As you study food and nutrition, you will find many ways in which management techniques can be useful. For instance:

❖ **Managing time and energy** can help you accomplish what you really need and want to do without wearing yourself out. You'll find that time management is an essential part of working in the school foods lab.

❖ **Managing your money** can help you meet financial goals and get the most value for your dollar. Unit Three of this book looks at the consumer decisions involved in buying food and kitchen equipment.

❖ **Record-keeping** can help you to make plans and evaluate how well you use your resources. For instance, later you will learn how keeping a record of the food you eat for a few days can help you make better food choices.

❖ **Organizing** means arranging items in an orderly and logical way. A good way to organize a kitchen is to put items near where they are used. You might organize a shopping list by grouping similar items together. Being well-organized saves time and effort in the long run.

Another very important management technique is knowing how to make decisions.

Making Decisions

Throughout this course, and in your daily life, you will be making many decisions related to food and nutrition. For example, what foods will you choose from the lunch menu? Which recipe will you try? Which package of meat will you purchase? What equipment will you use to prepare the recipe?

People often make decisions without thinking them through. They may "flip a coin," picking an option at random. Sometimes they put off making a decision until they no longer have any choices. However, important decisions deserve more careful thought.

Steps in Making Decisions

Here is a simple seven-step process that can help you make better decisions:

1. ***Identify the decision to be made and your goals.*** In other words, what do you want the end result to be? For instance, "I need to choose what food to bring to the potluck dinner. It should be easy to fix, easy to keep hot or cold, and something most people will like."

2. ***List your resources.*** What do you have available that could help you in this situation? A resource for finding recipes might be a cookbook. A resource for keeping food hot at the potluck might be an electric slow cooker.

3. ***Identify your options.*** Be creative and open to new ideas. As you think of solutions that might work, make a list.

4. ***Consider each option.*** Imagine the results of each possible choice. If you need to, gather more information. Now list the advantages and disadvantages of each option. How well would it meet the goals you originally set?

5. ***Choose the best option.*** Often there is no perfect solution. Weigh and compare, then choose the one that seems best. What if none of the choices is acceptable? Try going back to step 3—perhaps there's a solution you've overlooked.

6. ***Carry out your decision.*** Make a plan based on your choice. For instance, if you decide to take baked beans to the potluck, plan when and how you will make them. Then put your plan in action.

7. ***Evaluate the results.*** How did your decision turn out? If it worked well, take pride in what you accomplished. However, don't be discouraged if things didn't work quite the way you planned. Accept the fact that you did your best, then try to learn from the experience. As you continue to make decisions and carry them out, the process will become easier.

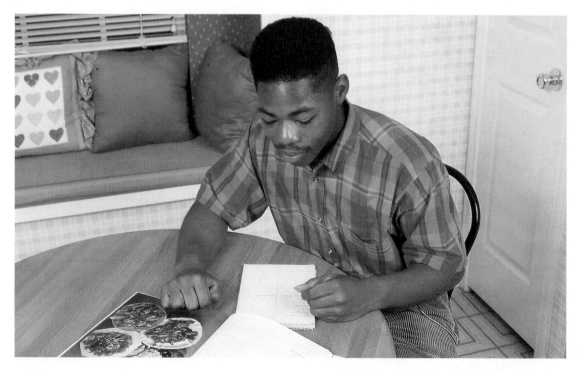

With practice, the decision-making process will become automatic. You will be more satisfied with the choices you make.

Decision-Making and Food Choices

A lifetime of good or poor health depends, in part, on the many small decisions you make each day. Often poor food choices are made as a matter of habit, but remember that good choices can also become a habit.

As you continue in this book, you will learn more about the nutrients in foods and how to eat nutritiously at home and away. That knowledge, along with the decision-making process, will help you evaluate and improve your day-to-day food choices.

The food industry offers diverse career opportunities. The need for food workers is expected to increase steadily.

Career Decisions

One of the most important decisions you will ever make is choosing how you would like to earn your living. When making career decisions, identifying the options is especially important. Too often, people decide on a line of work without really knowing much about it. They are unaware of many other possible careers, any one of which might prove even more satisfying to them.

You might be surprised at the wide range of careers related to food and nutrition. This book can help you learn about the possibilities. At the end of each chapter, you'll find a "Career Profile" describing a particular worker and his or her job. The last chapter of this book provides more information to help you think about and prepare for a career.

Section 1.5 Review

RECALL THE FACTS

1. What is management?

2. Name three management techniques. Tell how each relates to food and nutrition.

3. What are the seven steps in the decision-making process?

DISCUSS YOUR IDEAS

4. Why is the seventh step in the decision-making process important?

5. Why do you think some people dislike making decisions? What advice would you give them?

APPLY YOUR LEARNING

6. Imagine that your class has been asked to cook a meal for a local senior citizen's group. Identify at least three decisions that would have to be made. Choose one and explain how you would use the decision-making process in this situation.

CAREER PROFILE

Rita Johnson
Caterer

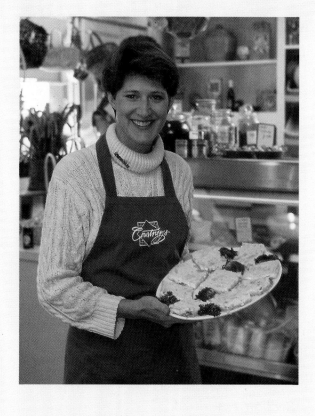

Current position:

"I own a small deli/catering service specializing in parties and receptions."

Why I chose this career:

"I've enjoyed cooking since I was 11 years old. I'm the type of person who takes cookbooks to the beach instead of paperbacks."

Skills:

"Of course it's necessary to be a good cook in this business. It also helps to be well-organized and personable."

Education:

"I've taken community college courses in culinary arts, as well as in business management and advertising."

Typical day on the job:

"My days vary, depending on the kind of jobs I have lined up. Some days are spent meeting with potential clients, while other days are spent in the kitchen. Because most clients have slightly different needs, no two days are exactly alike!"

Favorite part of the job:

"The flexibility of owning my own business is a real plus. Also, I get a lot of satisfaction from hearing my clients say what a great time their guests had, and would I be available to cater their sister's wedding reception in April?"

- What might be the benefits and drawbacks of owning your own business?
- What aspects of Rita's job do you think you might enjoy? Why?

Summary

Section 1.1

Food and Health: Good nutrition is an important part of physical health. Food can also contribute to psychological health by providing security, a sense of belonging, and enjoyment. Developing skills in food and nutrition can help build self-esteem.

Section 1.2

Influences on Food Choices: Social influences on food choices include culture, family, friends, and the media. Food choices also depend on available resources. Technology has increased the options available. Personal influences also affect your choice of foods.

Section 1.3

Food and Culture: Today's world is becoming an ever more multicultural and global society. Different cultures have distinct food customs. Many food customs originated in the distant past, although they have changed and mingled along the way.

Section 1.4

Food, Science, and Technology: The study of food has many scientific aspects. Nutrition is a science in itself, while chemistry and ergonomics play a role in food preparation. New technology is changing the way food is produced and processed, as well as the way people plan and prepare meals.

Section 1.5

Managing Resources and Making Decisions: Management techniques help you use resources wisely and are useful in studying food. The decision-making process can help in situations ranging from choosing food to choosing a career.

REVIEWING FACTS

1. Define: nutrients, nutrition, wellness. (1.1)

2. Give an example of how food can help provide a sense of belonging. (1.1)

3. Name four forms of media. How does the media influence food choices? (1.2)

4. Give an example of how two people might make different food choices because of differences in lifestyle. (1.2)

5. What is meant by "cultural diversity"? How does it relate to food customs? (1.3)

6. How did geography affect the development of food customs in the past? Why does it have less influence today? (1.3)

7. What do natural laws of science have to do with food preparation? (1.4)

8. Discuss the changes that have resulted from the invention of the microwave oven. (1.4)

9. What is the first step in making a decision? (1.5)

10. What should you do if a decision doesn't turn out as well as you expected? (1.5)

LEARNING BY DOING

1. **Taste-test lab:** Wearing a blindfold, taste food samples prepared by your teacher. Describe the aroma, texture, and flavor. Try to identify the food. Discuss how the senses contribute to the enjoyment of food. What role do they play in making food choices? (1.1, 1.2)

2. **Food science lab:** Cut an apple or banana into slices. Coat half the slices with lemon juice. Let all the slices stand at room temperature for thirty minutes. Observe the appearance of the slices. How does this experiment reinforce the idea that food preparation is governed by scientific principles? (1.4)

3. **Foods lab:** Prepare popcorn in the microwave oven, on the range, and in a popcorn popper. Compare the methods for time, cost, and taste. What are the advantages and disadvantages of each method? Which would you be more likely to choose in the future? (1.4, 1.5)

THINKING CRITICALLY

1. **Identifying evidence:** How might a person determine whether food is successfully meeting physical and psychological needs? (1.1)

2. **Recognizing values:** Some people, if asked to bake a cake, would choose to bake it from scratch. Others would use a cake mix. What values and priorities are reflected by each approach? (1.2, 1.5)

3. **Comparing and contrasting:** Working with a partner, compare and contrast the eating habits of each of your families. Discuss the reasons for similarities and differences. (1.2, 1.3)

4. **Identifying cause and effect:** In what ways has the microwave oven changed daily life? (1.4)

MAKING DECISIONS AND SOLVING PROBLEMS

What Would You Do?

1. You're working in the foods lab, rolling and shaping dough for yeast rolls. You notice that one of your lab partners seems to be having trouble. Most of her rolls are lopsided or falling apart. "I don't know why I even try," you hear her mutter. "I'm no good at anything." (1.1)

2. A new student at your school has invited you home for dinner. When you sit down to eat, you learn that your friend's grandmother has prepared a meal of authentic foods from her native country. You don't recognize any of the foods on your plate. (1.2, 1.3)

3. You are helping your family shop for a new microwave oven. There is a basic model in your price range that looks easy to use. However, you think your family would like some of the special features found in higher-priced models. (1.4, 1.5)

LINKING YOUR STUDIES

1. **Writing:** Describe your favorite food in a paragraph. Focus on details of taste, texture, appearance, and aroma. (1.1)

2. **Social studies:** Choose five foods that originated in five different cultures. Prepare a display that tells what part of the world each food came from and how it came to this country. (1.2, 1.3)

3. **Business:** Explain how the management skills described in the chapter would apply to someone who is a business owner or employee. What other management skills are used in business? How might they apply to food and nutrition? (1.5)

CHAPTER 2

The Nutrients You Need

Objectives

After studying this section, you should be able to:

❖ Name the six major types of nutrients.
❖ Explain the purpose of RDAs.
❖ Give guidelines regarding calorie needs and calorie sources.
❖ Evaluate the use of supplements to meet daily nutritional needs.

Look for These Terms

carbohydrates
fats
proteins
vitamins
minerals
dietary fiber
nutrient deficiency
malnutrition
RDA
calorie

As you learned in Chapter 1, food provides essential chemicals called nutrients. Nutrients play a vital role in your ability to enjoy life and reach your potential. They work in three basic ways:

❖ They give you energy.
❖ They are needed for growth, maintenance, and repair of the body.
❖ They keep the different systems in your body working smoothly.

Nutrient Teamwork

As you may recall, more than 40 nutrients have been identified so far. Each has a specific job to do to keep the body healthy. You can't substitute one for another, and one nutrient alone can't keep your body healthy. All the nutrients work together to contribute to good health.

You might compare good nutrition to a football team. One player carries the football for a touchdown, but it takes the whole team to make sure that player gets to the goal. The coach decides who will play on the team.

Nutrients work together as a team, each one playing its role. Some are major players, and some are minor, but all are essential to good health. Think of yourself as the coach of the team. Your role is to choose the foods that will provide all the nutrients you need.

Good nutrition is essential for good health.

A team relies on each member's contributions. The food you eat must include all vital nutrients in order for your body to function smoothly.

What Nutrients Do You Need?

The nutrients are divided into six major types.

- The body's main source of energy is **carbohydrates** (kar-bo-HY-drates).
- **Fats** are a concentrated source of energy. They are needed, in moderate amounts, to perform important functions in the body.
- The main job of **proteins** is to help build and repair the body. They also provide energy.
- **Vitamins** are chemicals needed in small amounts to help the body function properly. They also help other nutrients do their jobs.
- Like vitamins, **minerals** help the body work properly. Many also become part of body tissues, such as bone.
- Water is considered a nutrient because it is essential to life.

You will learn more about these nutrients in the next two sections of this chapter. You'll also learn about **dietary fiber,** a mixture of plant materials that are not broken down in the digestive system. Like the nutrients, fiber is important for good health.

Effects of Poor Nutrition

When people make poor food choices or do not have enough to eat, they may not get the right balance of nutrients. Poor health can result.

A **nutrient deficiency,** or severe shortage of a nutrient, can cause illness. For instance, a lack of vitamin D can keep children's bones from growing properly. Their bones become weak and they develop bowed legs. In adults, a lack of vitamin D weakens bones so they break more easily. It may also cause muscle spasms.

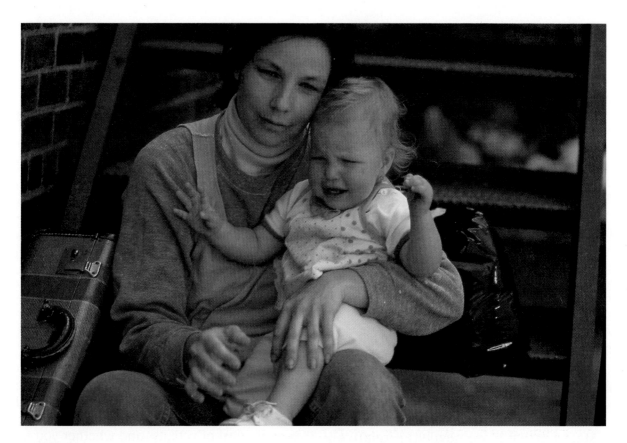

Children are at particular risk from malnutrition. Lack of adequate, nutritious food during childhood can have lifelong effects. What programs are available in your area to fight malnutrition?

Malnutrition refers to serious health problems caused by poor nutrition over a long period of time. Generally, malnutrition occurs when people do not have enough to eat. Bad weather, poor transportation, political problems, or other factors can cause food shortages.

Many people around the world simply cannot afford to buy the food needed for good health. In the United States, it's estimated that 20 percent of children live in poverty.

Poor nutrition can also occur among people who have an abundant food supply and can afford to buy whatever they want. Their problem stems from poor food choices. They choose foods that do not supply enough of the nutrients needed for good health. They may also eat too much or get too much of some nutrients, such as fat.

The food choices you make today will have long-term effects on your health. Poor food choices increase the risk of diseases that can shorten life or reduce the quality of life. By making good choices, you can increase your chances of staying healthy, strong, and active throughout life.

How Much Do You Need?

Scientists have established how much of certain nutrients people need. They have developed **RDA** values, which stands for *Recommended Dietary Allowances*. The RDAs are divided into 18 groups based on age and gender (male or female). They include recommended amounts for protein, 11 vitamins, and 7 minerals. Researchers have enough information about these nutrients to be able to recommend specific amounts. Not enough is known about other nutrients, so they are not included. The RDAs are updated periodically as new information is available.

The RDAs are used by professionals such as nutritionists and dietitians. They are an important tool in shaping U.S. nutrition policy and for developing educational programs. They are also used by industry when adding nutrients to foods and developing new products.

The Food and Drug Administration has used the RDAs as the basis for another set of guidelines. These are known by their new name, *Reference Daily Intakes (RDIs),* or by their original name, *U.S. Recommended Daily Allowances (U.S. RDAs).*They are used in nutrition labeling.

How Nutrients Are Measured

Most nutrients are needed in relatively small amounts. It's easier to measure them using the metric system, the system of measurement used by scientists. The metric system includes small units of measure, such as the milligram (mg).

The amount of iron you need each day is small—less than the weight of a single raisin. A cup of raisins contains 3 milligrams of iron.

For example, teenage females need 15 milligrams (mg) of iron each day. That's equivalent to about 0.0005 ounce.

Energy from Nutrients

As you have learned, some nutrients—carbohydrates, fats, and proteins—supply your body with energy. This energy is measured in units called *kilocalories* (KILL-oh-KAL-uhrees). For consumer use, kilocalorie has been shortened to **calorie,** the term that will be used throughout this book. (In the metric system, energy is measured in kilojoules [kJ].)

Your Energy Needs

Your body needs energy to carry on basic processes, such as pumping blood, and to fuel activities, such as walking. Therefore, you need a certain number of calories each day. The number depends on your age, weight, level of activity, and whether you are male or female.

Science Connection

Nutrition Science:

Measuring Kilocalories

One kilocalorie is the amount of energy needed to raise the temperature of 1 kilogram (a little more than 4 cups) of water 1 degree Celsius. An instrument called a *calorimeter* is used to calculate the energy content of foods. A measured amount of food is placed in the calorimeter chamber and burned. Scientists calculate how much heat was given off in the process. The results tell them how many kilocalories the food contains.

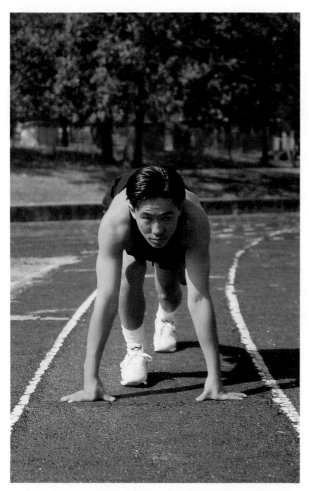

Vigorous exercise, such as running or swimming, uses large amounts of energy. That is why athletes usually need more calories per day than nonathletes.

If the number of calories used by the body balances the number of calories from food, your body weight will stay about the same. However, if the calories do not balance, over time you will gain or lose weight. In Chapter 5, you will learn more about weight management.

Recommended Sources of Calories

Scientists have calculated the number of calories provided by each of the three energy-producing nutrients in their pure form. (See the chart below.) Notice that fat is a concentrated source of energy. It has more than twice the number of calories per gram as carbohydrate and protein.

Health experts recommend that you get 30 percent or less of the calories you take in from fat, 55 percent or more from carbohydrates, and 12 to 15 percent from protein. This ratio provides the healthiest balance of the three nutrients.

For instance, Julie, who needs about 2200 calories a day, should get no more than about 660 of those calories from fat (2200 x 0.3 = 660). How many grams of fat will supply 660 calories? There are 9 calories in one gram of fat, so divide 660 by 9. The answer is about 73 grams. For comparison, a double cheeseburger and fries from a fast-food restaurant provide about 47 grams of fat.

The U.S. Department of Agriculture, as part of its nutrition guidelines, offers the following suggestions for calorie intake:

- ❖ 1600 calories is about right for many sedentary (inactive) women and some older adults.
- ❖ 2200 calories is about right for most children, teenage girls, active women, and many sedentary men. Women who are pregnant or breastfeeding may need more.
- ❖ 2800 calories is about right for teenage boys, many active men, and some very active women.

Nutrient	Calories	kJ
1 gram carbohydrate	4	17
1 gram protein	4	17
1 gram fat	9	37

**Carbohydrates
(55% or more)**

**Fat
(30% or less)**

**Protein
(12 to 15%)**

It's not just the number of calories you take in that's important. The sources of those calories also affect nutrition and health. As the chart above shows, health experts recommend that more than half your calories come from carbohydrates, 30 percent or less from fat, and only 12 to 15 percent from protein.

Technology Tidbit

Computer software is available that can check for a balanced diet. After a list of daily food choices is entered, the computer calculates the percentage of calories from carbohydrates, proteins, and fats. It displays the results in comparison to the recommended goal.

Who Needs Supplements?

Supplements are nutrients people take in addition to the food they eat. Supplements are generally available as pills, capsules, liquids, or powder.

Supplements may be useful for people who are taking certain kinds of medication, pregnant and nursing women, those recovering from illness, the elderly, and people on special diets. In such cases, the people may not be getting enough nutrients from the food they eat.

Most people, however, do not need supplements. They can get all the nutrients they need by eating a variety of nutritious foods. People who rely on supplements to make up for poor food choices may be short-changing themselves.

Nutritional supplements are not a substitute for eating nutritious food. Never take large amounts of any supplement without checking with a physician.

Some people believe in "megavitamin therapy," which means taking extra-large amounts of supplements to prevent or cure diseases. This should be done only on the advice of a physician. Excess amounts of many nutrients can accumulate in the body and cause harm. For instance, taking large amounts of vitamin A can lead to liver damage.

Some nutrients are not stored by the body. The excess amounts simply pass out of the body unused. Thus, taking unneeded supplements is a waste of money.

Try to get all your nutrients from food. If you do decide to take supplements:

❖ Avoid mega-doses and single nutrients (unless prescribed by a health professional).

❖ Read the list of ingredients to make sure of what you're getting. Avoid unrecognized nutrients.

❖ If you're taking supplements "just to be safe," consider taking them every other day instead of daily.

Safety Check

Children often confuse vitamin and mineral pills with candy. They can be harmed by large doses of supplements. If there are children in the home, make sure nutrient supplements are stored in child-resistant packages out of the reach of children.

Section 2.1 Review

RECALL THE FACTS

1. What are the six major types of nutrients? What are the main functions of each?

2. What purpose does the RDA serve?

3. Which nutrients supply your body with energy? How is food energy measured?

DISCUSS YOUR IDEAS

4. Why do you think nutrient supplements are so popular? Do you think people who use supplements would change their minds if they better understood the drawbacks?

APPLY YOUR LEARNING

5. Jonathan is 15 years old. Approximately how many calories does he need to take in each day? How many of those calories should come from fat? How many grams of fat would supply that many calories?

Objectives

After studying this section, you should be able to:

❖ Name sources of simple and complex carbohydrates.

❖ Tell why soluble and insoluble fiber are needed.

❖ Distinguish between complete and incomplete proteins.

Look for These Terms

refined sugars
insoluble fiber
soluble fiber
amino acids
complete proteins
incomplete proteins

As you read in section 2.1, for good health you need six basic nutrients, plus fiber. Read on to learn more about these, beginning with carbohydrates, fiber, and proteins.

Carbohydrates

The body's main source of energy is carbohydrates. You may know them as starches and sugars. They are found mainly in foods from plant sources, such as fruits, vegetables, grain products, and dry beans and peas. For good health, eat a variety of these foods every day. Generally, they are the least expensive form of energy you can buy.

If you don't eat enough carbohydrates, your body will use the other energy-producing nutrients for energy. When it does, however, it keeps those nutrients from doing their specialized jobs.

Carbohydrates include starches, natural sugars, and refined sugars.

Science Connection

Chemistry:

Simple and Complex Carbohydrates

Carbohydrates get their name from their chemical structure. They are composed of the elements carbon, oxygen, and hydrogen. Simple carbohydrates (sugars) are made up of single or short chemical units. Complex carbohydrates (starches) are made up of long chemical units.

Grain products, dry beans and peas, and fruits and vegetables are important sources of carbohydrates. The starches and sugars they contain provide energy for the body.

Starches

Starches are also known as *complex carbohydrates.* They are found in dry beans, peas, and lentils; vegetables, such as potatoes and corn; and grain products, such as rice, pasta, and breads. These foods are also good sources of proteins, vitamins, minerals, and dietary fiber.

Natural Sugars

Sugars, also called *simple carbohydrates,* are a natural part of many foods. There are several types of natural sugars. *Fructose* (FROOK-tohs) is found in fruits, *maltose* (MALL-tohs) in grain products, and *lactose* (LACK-tohs) in milk. These foods also provide other nutrients, such as proteins, vitamins, and minerals.

Refined Sugars

Refined sugars are sugars that are removed from plants and used as sweeteners. *Sucrose* (SUE-krohs), or table sugar, comes from plants such as sugar cane or sugar beets. It is used as a sweetener in many foods, such as desserts and candy. Other refined sugars include corn syrup, honey, maple syrup, molasses, and brown sugar.

Studies show that refined sugar does not directly pose any health risk. It can, however, lead to tooth decay. Eating large amounts of sweetened foods can lead to excess weight, which can contribute to health problems.

Refined sugar does not supply nutrients other than simple carbohydrates. To meet your energy needs, rely on the starches and natural sugars found in vegetables, dry beans and peas, fruits, and grain products.

Although you need carbo-hydrates, you don't need refined sugars. Besides these obvious sources, refined sugars are ingredients in many products.

Dietary Fiber

As you learned in section 2.1, dietary fiber consists of plant materials that are not digested. Fiber is found only in foods from plant sources, such as fruits, vegetables, grain products, and dry beans and peas. Foods from animal sources do not contain fiber.

There are two kinds of fiber. Most plant foods contain different amounts of both.

Insoluble fiber will not dissolve in water. It absorbs water and contributes bulk. It helps food move through the large intestine at a normal rate. It promotes regular bowel movements and helps prevent constipation. This type of fiber appears to lower the risk of colon cancer. It is found mainly in fruit and vegetable skins and in whole wheat or wheat bran products.

Soluble fiber dissolves in water. It does not contribute bulk. Studies show it appears to lower blood cholesterol levels. (You will learn about cholesterol in Section 2.3.) Soluble fiber is found in fruits; vegetables; dry beans, peas, and lentils; and oat products.

The National Cancer Institute recommends 20 to 35 grams of dietary fiber a day. To make sure you get enough fiber, eat a wide variety of plant foods such as fruits, vegetables, and whole grain products every day. Increase the fiber gradually and be sure to drink enough liquids. Otherwise, you might develop digestive problems, such as abdominal cramps.

Wheat bran is high in insoluble fiber, which helps move food through the body. The soluble fiber in oat bran seems to play a role in lowering cholesterol.

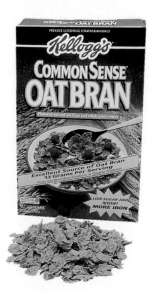

Proteins

Proteins are used mainly to help the body grow and to repair worn-out or damaged parts. About one-fifth of your body's total weight is protein. Your hair, eyes, skin, muscles, and bones are made of protein. The proteins you eat help maintain them in good condition.

Proteins also regulate important body processes. For instance, they play a major role in fighting disease because parts of the immune system are proteins.

Proteins can do their job only if the body has enough carbohydrates and fats for energy. If not, the body uses proteins for energy instead of for building and repairing.

Proteins are found in all foods from animal sources, such as meat, poultry, fish, eggs, and dairy products. They are also found in foods from plant sources, especially dry beans and peas, peanuts, vegetables, and grain products. Most Americans eat more protein than they need. Excess amounts are stored by the body as fat.

Many foods are good sources of protein. Those from animal sources (left) are called complete proteins because they contain all the essential amino acids the body needs. Many plant foods are also good sources when used in combination.

Complete and Incomplete Proteins

Protein is made up of chemical compounds called **amino acids** (uh-MEE-no). There are about 22 different amino acids. They can be combined into millions of different kinds of protein.

The body can manufacture most of the amino acids it needs to build protein. However, nine amino acids cannot be made in the body and therefore must come from the food you eat. These nine amino acids are called *essential amino acids.*

Complete proteins supply all of the essential amino acids. Foods from animal sources, such as meat, poultry, fish, eggs, and dairy products, provide complete protein.

Incomplete proteins are lacking one or more essential amino acids. Foods from plant sources supply incomplete proteins. However, it is possible to obtain all of the essential amino acids by eating a variety of foods from plant sources.

Many dishes from around the world make use of plant proteins. For instance, meals in India often include *dal,* lentils cooked and seasoned in a variety of ways. *Dal* is often served with rice, a combination that provides complete protein.

For example, dry beans and peas are high in proteins, but they lack certain essential amino acids. Grain products, nuts, and seeds also lack some essential amino acids. However, they provide the ones that dry beans and peas lack. If dry beans or peas and any grain products, nuts, or seeds are eaten during the same day, they provide all the essential amino acids needed for good health. Each supplies what is missing from the other.

Most Americans get the largest amount of their protein from animal sources. Health experts recommend that people get more of their protein from plant sources. Why? Plant sources have less fat, and low-fat food choices are recommended. You will learn more about fat in the next section.

Section 2.2 Review

RECALL THE FACTS

1. List three foods that supply natural sugars and six foods that supply complex carbohydrates.

2. Why is it important to obtain both soluble and insoluble fiber?

3. What is the difference between complete and incomplete proteins?

DISCUSS YOUR IDEAS

4. In general, Americans eat more refined sugar than is needed for good health. What are some possible reasons?

APPLY YOUR LEARNING

5. Think back to the last meal you ate. Which foods supplied carbohydrates? Fiber? Proteins? What types of carbohydrates, fiber, and proteins were they?

Objectives

After studying this section, you should be able to:

* Describe the functions and sources of fats.
* Identify three basic types of fatty acids.
* Discuss the effects of cholesterol and the different fatty acids on health.

Look for These Terms

cholesterol
saturated
polyunsaturated
monounsaturated
hydrogenation

Fats are in the news a great deal these days. You may have heard or read about cutting down on fats. That's sound advice, as you will see. However, even health experts do not recommend that you avoid fats altogether. This section will help you understand fat's role as a nutrient.

Functions and Sources of Fats

Fat is an essential nutrient that has several important functions.

* You need some fat in your diet for healthy skin and normal growth. Specifically, your body needs certain substances called *essential fatty acids,* which are found mainly in vegetable oils.
* Fat in the body carries vitamins A, D, E, and K to wherever they are needed.

In addition, the body stores fat to provide a reserve supply of energy. This stored fat also acts as a cushion to protect vital organs such as the heart and liver.

Fat not needed immediately is stored in body tissues for later use. These are fat cells in bone marrow.

Oil, butter, and margarine are obvious sources of fat. However, many other foods also contain high amounts of fat.

Fats also add flavor to food. Because they move through the digestive system slowly, they have satiety (suh-TIE-uh-tee) value. In other words, your hunger remains satisfied for a longer time if you eat foods that include some fat.

The problem with fat is that most people eat too much. Eating too much fat increases the risk of illnesses such as heart disease and cancer. It can also create a health risk by causing the person to become overweight. (Remember, fats have twice as many calories as carbohydrates or proteins.)

Foods high in fat include butter, margarine, oils, cream, sour cream, salad dressings, fried foods, some baked goods, and chocolate. Large amounts are also found in some cuts of meat, nuts and seeds, peanut butter, egg yolk, whole milk, and some cheeses.

Fats cannot be eliminated from the diet completely. However, it is important to moderate, or limit, their use. To cut down on fat, eat more complex carbohydrates and choose low-fat foods. You will learn more about making food choices in Chapters 3 and 4.

Health experts also advise people to pay attention to the types of fats that are eaten. As you will soon discover, some fats create more of a health risk than others.

Cholesterol, Fats, and Health

"My dad is watching his cholesterol." "Brand X oil is high in polyunsaturates." Statements like these can be heard frequently. What does it all mean?

Cholesterol in the Bloodstream

Cholesterol (kuh-LESS-tehr-all) is a fatlike substance present in all body cells. It is needed for many essential body processes. Your body manufactures cholesterol in the liver.

A certain amount of cholesterol circulates in the blood. It does not float through the bloodstream on its own, but in chemical "packages" called lipoproteins (LIH-po-PRO-teens). There are two major kinds of lipoproteins: LDL and HDL.

❖ **LDL** stands for low-density lipoprotein. The LDL "package" takes cholesterol from the liver to wherever it is needed in the body. However, if too much LDL cholesterol is circulating, excess amounts of cholesterol can build up in artery walls. This increases the risk of heart disease or stroke. Thus, LDL cholesterol has come to be called "bad" cholesterol.

❖ **HDL** stands for high-density lipoprotein. Studies suggest that HDL picks up excess cholesterol and takes it back to the liver, keeping it from causing harm. For this reason, cholesterol in the HDL "package" has come to be known as "good" cholesterol.

Medical tests can determine the amounts of total cholesterol, LDL cholesterol, and HDL cholesterol in the bloodstream. The risk of heart disease is believed to increase if LDL and total cholesterol levels are too high and if the HDL level is too low.

Making wise food choices can help reduce the amount of harmful cholesterol in the bloodstream. As you will see, both cholesterol and fat in foods may affect blood cholesterol levels.

Cholesterol in Foods

In addition to being manufactured in the body, cholesterol is found in some foods. Cutting down on high-cholesterol foods may help reduce the level of harmful cholesterol in the bloodstream.

High levels of cholesterol in the bloodstream can increase the risk of heart disease or stroke. Foods from animal sources contain cholesterol. Limiting how often they are eaten can help reduce cholesterol levels in the blood.

Foods such as fish, poultry, and meat contain saturated fats. Polyunsaturated and monounsaturated fats are found in vegetable oils and foods such as peanuts, olives, and avocados.

Cholesterol is found only in foods from animal sources. Meat, poultry, and fish all have about the same amount of cholesterol. Foods especially high in cholesterol include liver, egg yolks, and a few types of shellfish.

Saturated and Unsaturated Fats

For most people, the amount and types of fats eaten have an even greater effect on blood cholesterol levels.

The different fats found in food, such as butter, chicken fat, or corn oil, are made up of different combinations of *fatty acids.* There are three basic kinds of fatty acids. Each has a different effect on cholesterol levels. All fats include all three kinds of fatty acids, but in varying amounts.

Saturated (SAT-chur-ay-ted) fatty acids appear to raise the level of LDL ("bad") cholesterol in the bloodstream. Foods relatively high in saturated fatty acids include meat, poultry skin, whole-milk dairy products, and the tropical oils—coconut oil, palm oil, and palm kernel oil.

Polyunsaturated (PAH-lee-uhn-SAT-chur-ay-ted) fatty acids seem to help lower both HDL and LDL cholesterol levels. Many vegetable oils, such as corn oil, soybean oil, and safflower oil, are high in polyunsaturated fatty acids.

Monounsaturated (MAH-no-uhn-SAT-chur-ay-ted) fatty acids appear to lower only LDL ("bad") cholesterol levels. Foods relatively high in monounsaturated fatty acids include olives, olive oil, avocados, peanuts, peanut oil, and canola oil.

In general, a fat that is solid at room temperature, such as butter or lard, has mainly saturated fatty acids. Fats that are liquid at room temperature, such as vegetable oil, have mainly unsaturated fatty acids.

Vegetable oils can be made solid through a process called **hydrogenation** (hi-DRAH-juh-NAY-shun). Shortening and margarine are examples of hydrogenated fats. The hydrogenation process makes the fat more saturated.

Many people are switching from saturated fats to unsaturated ones in an effort toward better health. They should remember, however, that it's also important to limit the total amount of all fat eaten.

Healthy Attitudes

Besides eating less fat and cholesterol, here are some other health habits that can help lower blood cholesterol levels:

- Eat plenty of soluble fiber (the kind found in dry beans and oats).
- Exercise regularly.
- Maintain a healthy weight.
- Don't smoke.

Section 2.3 Review

RECALL THE FACTS

1. Name two functions of fat.

2. List six foods high in fat.

3. What is cholesterol? Why is LDL cholesterol called "bad" cholesterol?

4. Name three types of fatty acids. Which is considered least healthy? Why? Where is it mainly found?

DISCUSS YOUR IDEAS

5. Suppose you are shopping for peanut butter. One brand has "No Cholesterol" in large letters on the label. The kind you usually buy does not. Would you switch brands? Why or why not?

APPLY YOUR LEARNING

6. Design a magazine ad encouraging people to cut down on fat and cholesterol.

Objectives

After studying this section, you should be able to:

❖ Identify the types of vitamins and minerals, their functions, and their food sources.

❖ Explain the importance of water in the diet.

Look for These Terms

fat-soluble vitamins
water-soluble vitamins
macrominerals
electrolytes
trace minerals
osteoporosis

As you have learned, carbohydrates, fats, and proteins are the only nutrients that directly provide energy. However, they are not the only nutrients you need. Vitamins, minerals, and water are just as important.

Vitamins

Although vitamins are needed in very small amounts, they are essential for good health. They help keep your body's tissues healthy and its many systems working properly. They help carbohydrates, fats, and proteins do their work.

Scientists are still learning about the functions of vitamins. Recent studies suggest that some vitamins may protect against illnesses such as heart disease and cancer. More research is needed before scientists can say for certain.

Vitamin C, shown here under a microscope, plays a key role in keeping the body healthy and repairing wounds. Good food sources include citrus fruits, potatoes, and tomatoes.

Chemistry:

Chemical Names of Vitamins

When vitamins were first discovered, they were given letter names: vitamin A, vitamin B, and so on. Later, scientists were able to analyze the chemical makeup of the vitamins. For example, vitamin C is ascorbic acid. Today, many vitamins are still commonly referred to by their letter names. Others are known by their chemical names, such as riboflavin and niacin.

■ ■ ■

Types of Vitamins

So far, scientists have identified about 13 different vitamins. They fall into two main groups. **Fat-soluble vitamins** dissolve in fat. They include vitamins A, D, E, and K. **Water-soluble vitamins** dissolve in water. They include vitamin C and the B vitamins, which are actually a group of eight different nutrients. The charts on pages 72 and 73 list the functions and food sources of these nutrients.

One important difference between fat-soluble and water-soluble vitamins is how the body handles extra amounts. If you eat more fat-soluble vitamins than you need, they are stored in the body's fat and in the liver. The body can draw on these stores if needed. In contrast, water-soluble vitamins remain in the body for only a short time. Therefore, you need them on a daily basis.

Meeting Your Vitamin Needs

Remember, it's best to obtain vitamins and other nutrients from foods rather than from supplements (unless supplements are advised by a physician). Some vitamins can be found in a wide range of foods. Others are limited to just a few.

Here are some hints for getting the vitamins you need. For more information, refer to the vitamin charts.

❖ To help meet your need for vitamin A, eat plenty of dark green and deep yellow-orange fruits and vegetables. These foods contain *beta carotene* (BAY-tuh CARE-oh-teen), which is used by the body to make vitamin A. Beta carotene may also help lower the risk of certain types of cancer.

❖ Vitamin D is available in fortified milk. It is also made by the body through the action of sunlight on the skin, but this is an unreliable source. If you don't drink fortified milk, be sure to get enough vitamin D from other sources.

❖ Vitamin C occurs only in fruits and vegetables. Be sure to eat some every day.

Foods high in vitamins usually contain substantial amounts of other nutrients as well.

Water-Soluble Vitamins

Vitamin/Functions	Food Sources
Thiamin ❖ Helps turn carbohydrates into energy ❖ Needed for muscle coordination and a healthy nervous system	❖ Enriched and whole grain breads and cereals ❖ Dry beans and peas ❖ Lean pork
Riboflavin ❖ Helps the body release energy from carbohydrates, fats, and proteins	❖ Enriched and whole grain breads and cereals ❖ Milk products ❖ Vegetables ❖ Dry beans and peas ❖ Meat, poultry, fish ❖ Dark green, leafy vegetables
Niacin ❖ Helps the body release energy from carbohydrates, fats, and proteins ❖ Needed for a healthy nervous system and mucous membranes	❖ Meat, poultry, fish ❖ Liver and kidneys ❖ Enriched and whole grain breads and cereals ❖ Dry beans and peas, peanuts
Vitamin B6 ❖ Helps the body use carbohydrates, fats, and proteins ❖ Needed for a healthy nervous system and mucous membranes ❖ Helps protect against infection	❖ Poultry, fish, meat ❖ Dry beans and peas ❖ Whole wheat products ❖ Some fruits and vegetables ❖ Liver
Vitamin B12 ❖ Helps the body use carbohydrates, fats, and proteins ❖ Helps build red blood cells and form genetic material ❖ Needed for a healthy nervous system	❖ Found only in animal foods, such as meat, poultry, fish, shellfish, eggs, and dairy products
Folate *(Folacin, Folic acid)* ❖ Helps build red blood cells and form genetic material	❖ Fruits ❖ Enriched and whole wheat breads ❖ Dark green, leafy vegetables ❖ Dry beans and peas ❖ Liver
Pantothenic acid ❖ Helps the body release energy from carbohydrates, fats, and proteins ❖ Helps the body produce cholesterol ❖ Needed for healthy nerves	❖ Meat ❖ Dairy products ❖ Eggs ❖ Dry beans and peas ❖ Whole grain breads and cereals ❖ Dark green, leafy vegetables

Water-Soluble Vitamins (continued)	
Vitamin/Functions	Food Sources
Biotin ❖ Helps the body make fatty acids and use carbohydrates	❖ Dark green, leafy vegetables ❖ Nuts ❖ Liver, kidney ❖ Egg yolk
Vitamin C (Ascorbic acid) ❖ Helps maintain healthy capillaries, bones, skin, and teeth ❖ Helps the body heal wounds and resist infections ❖ Aids in absorption of iron ❖ Helps form collagen, which gives structure to bones, cartilage, muscle, and blood vessels ❖ Protects other nutrients from damage by oxygen	❖ Fruits and vegetables, such as citrus fruits, cantaloupes, kiwis, mangos, papayas, cabbage, kale, plantains, potatoes, tomatoes

Fat-Soluble Vitamins	
Vitamin/Functions	Food Sources
Vitamin A ❖ Helps ward off infections ❖ Helps form and maintain healthy skin, hair, mucous membranes, bones, and teeth ❖ Essential for reproduction ❖ Needed for normal vision, especially in dim light	*Beta carotene:* (converted to Vitamin A in the body) ❖ Dark green, leafy vegetables, such as broccoli ❖ Deep yellow-orange vegetables, such as sweet potatoes ❖ Deep yellow-orange fruits, such as cantaloupes and mangos *Vitamin A:* ❖ Dairy products ❖ Liver
Vitamin D ❖ Helps the body use calcium and phosphorus ❖ Helps body build strong bones and teeth	❖ Fortified milk ❖ Egg yolk ❖ Fatty fish, such as salmon and mackerel ❖ Liver
Vitamin E ❖ Protects vitamins A and C and essential fatty acids from damage by oxygen and mucous membranes ❖ Helps form red blood cells and muscles	❖ Vegetable oils ❖ Whole grain breads and cereals; wheat germ ❖ Dark green, leafy vegetables ❖ Dry beans and peas, peanuts ❖ Nuts and seeds
Vitamin K ❖ Necessary for normal blood clotting	❖ Dark green, leafy vegetables ❖ Cauliflower, cabbage, turnips ❖ Egg yolks Liver

Minerals

Minerals are essential for good health. Most minerals become a part of the body, such as teeth and bones. Others are used to make substances that the body needs.

Types of Minerals

Minerals can be divided into three groups:

❖ **Macrominerals** (MACK-ro-MIHN-uh-ruhls) are needed in relatively large amounts. They include calcium, phosphorus, and magnesium.

❖ **Electrolytes** (ee-LECK-troh-lites) are minerals that work together to help maintain the body's fluid balance. They are potassium, sodium, and chloride.

❖ **Trace minerals** are needed in small amounts, but are just as important as other nutrients. They include iron, copper, zinc, iodine, and selenium, as well as many others. Scientists continue to research trace minerals and their functions.

The charts on pages 76-77 show the functions and food sources of minerals.

Meeting Your Mineral Needs

Even though some minerals are needed in very tiny amounts, getting the right amount is important to health. For example, getting too much or too little iodine can cause thyroid problems. The thyroid gland, located in the neck, produces substances needed for growth and development. Getting too much sodium, or too little potassium, may be linked to high blood pressure.

Getting the right balance of minerals is not difficult. The key is to eat a wide variety of healthful foods. However, you may need to pay special attention to whether you are getting enough calcium and iron.

Calcium and Strong Bones

As you can see by the chart, calcium has several important functions. One of these is to maintain bone strength. Lack of calcium throughout life is one of the factors that can lead to **osteoporosis** (AH-stee-oh-puh-RO-sis). This is a condition in which the bones gradually lose their minerals, becoming weak and fragile. As a result, posture may become stooped and bones can break easily.

Through good nutrition and sufficient exercise now, you can help reduce the risk of osteoporosis later in life. Calcium is a key mineral in building bone mass.

Loss in Height

Normal

Osteoporosis

Although it can affect either gender, osteoporosis is most common in women. It's estimated that about 25 percent of women over 65 have osteoporosis.

If you want to reduce your risk of osteoporosis, it's essential that you start now. Bone mass is built up during childhood, the teen years, and young adulthood. The more you do to build strong bones now, the less likely you will be to develop osteoporosis when you are older.

To build strong bones:

❖ Eat plenty of calcium-rich foods. These include dairy products, dry beans and peas, and dark green, leafy vegetables.

❖ Follow other basic guidelines for healthy eating. Remember, nutrients work in teams. Many nutrients, such as vitamin D, work together with calcium.

❖ Exercise regularly. Weight-bearing exercise, such as walking or jogging, helps build and maintain strong bones.

❖ Avoid smoking, alcohol, and excess caffeine (found in coffee and soft drinks). All may contribute to osteoporosis.

Iron and Red Blood Cells

Iron is essential in making hemoglobin. *Hemoglobin* (HEE-muh-glow-bin) is a substance in red blood cells that carries oxygen to all the cells in the body. If you don't get enough iron, the blood may not be able to carry enough oxygen to the cells. This condition is called iron-deficiency anemia (uh-NEE-me-uh). People with anemia are often tired, weak, short of breath, and pale.

Some sources of iron are lean red meat, dry beans and peas, dried fruits, grain products, and dark green, leafy vegetables. (Other sources are listed in the chart on page 76). Eating foods rich in vitamin C at the same time as iron-rich foods helps the body absorb more of the iron from plant foods. Iron utensils used to cook food are also a good source of iron.

The hemoglobin in blood carries oxygen to the body's cells. Iron from food is needed for the formation of hemoglobin.

Trace Minerals	
Mineral/Functions	**Food Sources**
Iron ❖ Helps carry oxygen in the blood ❖ Helps the cells use oxygen	❖ Meat, fish, shellfish ❖ Egg yolk ❖ Dark green, leafy vegetables ❖ Dry beans and peas ❖ Enriched or whole grain products ❖ Dried fruits
Iodine ❖ Responsible for the body's use of energy	❖ Saltwater fish ❖ Iodized salt ❖ Dairy products ❖ Bakery products
Copper ❖ Helps iron make red blood cells ❖ Helps keep bones, blood vessels, and nerves healthy ❖ Helps the heart work properly	❖ Whole grain products ❖ Shellfish ❖ Organ meats ❖ Dry beans and peas ❖ Nuts and seeds ❖ Potatoes and sweet potatoes
Zinc ❖ Helps the body make proteins, heal wounds, and form blood ❖ Helps in growth and maintenance of all tissues ❖ Helps the body use carbohydrates, fats, and proteins ❖ Affects the senses of taste and smell ❖ Helps the body use vitamin A	❖ Meat, liver, poultry, fish, shellfish ❖ Dairy products ❖ Dry beans and peas, peanuts ❖ Whole grain breads and cereals ❖ Eggs
Selenium ❖ Helps the heart work properly ❖ Protects cells from damage by oxygen	❖ Whole-grain breads and cereals ❖ Vegetables (amount varies with content in soil) ❖ Meat, organ meats, fish, shellfish
Fluoride ❖ Helps strengthen teeth and prevent cavities	❖ In many communities, small amounts are added to the water supply to help improve dental health

Macrominerals	
Mineral/Functions	Food Sources
Calcium ❖ Maintains bone strength; helps prevent osteoporosis ❖ Helps regulate body processes such as blood clotting and nerve activity ❖ Needed for muscle contraction, including the heart	❖ Dairy products ❖ Canned fish eaten with the bones ❖ Dry beans, peas, and lentils ❖ Dark green, leafy vegetables such as broccoli, spinach, and turnip greens ❖ Grain products
Phosphorus ❖ Works with calcium to build strong bones and teeth ❖ Helps release energy from carbohydrates, fats, and proteins ❖ Helps build body cells and tissues	❖ Meat, poultry, fish ❖ Dry beans and peas ❖ Dairy products ❖ Grain products
Magnesium ❖ Helps build bones and make proteins ❖ Helps nerves and muscles work normally ❖ Helps regulte body temperature	❖ Whole grain products ❖ Dark green, leafy vegetables ❖ Dry beans and peas ❖ Nuts and seeds

Electrolytes	
Mineral/Functions	Food Sources
Sodium ❖ Helps maintain the fluid balance in the body ❖ Helps with muscle and nerve action	❖ Salt ❖ Many foods
Chloride ❖ Helps maintain the fluid balance in the body	❖ Salt
Potassium ❖ Helps maintain the fluid balance in the body ❖ Helps maintain the heartbeat ❖ Helps with muscle and nerve action	❖ Fruits such as bananas and oranges ❖ Vegetables ❖ Meat, poultry, fish ❖ Dry beans and peas ❖ Dairy products

Water

Your body needs a regular supply of water to carry on its many life-supporting activities. You may be able to live for weeks without food, but you can live only a few days without water.

About 50 to 60 percent of the body is water. Even your bones contain water. Your blood is 80 percent water.

Water plays a role in the many chemical reactions that constantly go on in the body. It also helps keep your body temperature normal. Think of what happens when you get too warm. You begin to perspire. As the perspiration evaporates into the air, it cools your body.

On the average, the body uses about 2 to 3 quarts (2 to 3 liters) of water a day. To help replace it, be sure to drink about 6 to 8 cups (1.5 to 2 liters) of liquid daily. In hot weather, when you perspire heavily, you might need even more.

Liquids that can help supply your body with water include plain water, fruit juices, milk, and soups. The foods you eat also help meet your need for water. Most foods contain water, with fruits and vegetables having the largest amounts. Watermelon and lettuce, for instance, are about 90 percent water.

Even "solid" foods such as bread and meat contain water. However, you also need to drink plenty of liquids daily.

Healthy Attitudes

Don't wait until you are thirsty to drink water. By the time you feel thirsty, your body may have already lost a quart (liter) of water or more.

Section 2.4 Review

RECALL THE FACTS

1. Which vitamins are fat-soluble? Water-soluble? Why is this distinction important?

2. Why do you need calcium? Iron? What foods provide these nutrients?

3. How much liquid do you need to drink each day to replenish your body's water supply?

DISCUSS YOUR IDEAS

4. Why are trace minerals just as important as other minerals, even though they are needed in such small amounts?

APPLY YOUR LEARNING

5. List ten of your favorite foods. Using the charts in this section, identify the vitamins and minerals they provide.

How Your Body Uses Food

Objectives

After studying this section, you should be able to:

❖ Outline the process of digestion.
❖ Explain how nutrients are absorbed, transported, and stored.
❖ Tell how the body uses food to produce energy.

Look for These Terms

digestion
esophagus
peristalsis
glucose
glycogen
oxidation
basal metabolism

While you are reading this, your body is busily working. You are inhaling oxygen from the air and exhaling waste products. Your heart is recirculating blood with every beat. In the time it has taken you to read this paragraph, about 100 million of your body cells died and new ones took their place. If you had a meal or snack in the last several hours, your digestive system is breaking down the food into nutrients.

Digestion

The process of breaking down food into usable nutrients is known as **digestion.** It takes place in the digestive system, a long tube that extends from the mouth through the entire body. Here is what happens to food on its journey through the digestive system.

The Mouth

The digestive process starts before you even begin to eat the food. Just smelling and seeing food, or even thinking about it, can start saliva flowing in your mouth. Saliva is the first of many digestive juices that act on food to break it down chemically.

Science Connection

Chemistry:

Enzymes in Digestion

Enzymes are an important part of the digestive process. An *enzyme* helps cause a chemical reaction, but does not actually enter into the reaction. At different stages of the digestive process, specific enzymes go to work to help break down food.

Saliva contains an enzyme called *ptyalin* (TIE-uh-luhn). As food is chewed, ptyalin begins to digest starch, turning it into sugar.

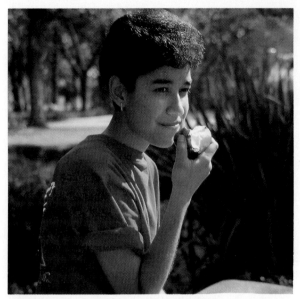

Digestion begins in the mouth as food is chewed and mixed with saliva.

Food is also broken down physically as your teeth grind it into tiny pieces. Chewing food well is important. It mixes the food with saliva and makes it easier to swallow and digest. Solid food should be chewed until it is the consistency of applesauce.

The Esophagus

Once the food is swallowed, it passes into the **esophagus** (ih-SOFF-uh-gus), a long tube connecting the mouth to the stomach. The muscles of the esophagus contract and relax, creating wavelike movements that force the food into the stomach. This muscular action is called **peristalsis** (PAIR-uh-STALL-suhs).

The Stomach

The stomach is the widest part of the digestive system, a pouch located on the left side of the body inside the rib cage. On the average, it can hold about 2½ pints (1.2 liters) of food.

The walls of the stomach manufacture gastric juices—a combination of acid and enzymes that helps in the chemical breakdown of the food. In addition, the stomach breaks food down physically through peristalsis. The food is churned until it turns into a thick liquid called chyme (KIME).

Different kinds of food take different amounts of time to break down and leave the stomach. Carbohydrates take the shortest amount of time, usually one to two hours. Proteins take longer, about three to five hours. Fats take the longest time to digest, about five to seven hours. That's why a food with fat will keep you from feeling hungry for a longer time.

The Small Intestine

From the stomach, chyme is released into the small intestine a little at a time. The small intestine is a long, winding tube between the stomach and the large intestine. Here, the chyme is acted on by three types of digestive juices:

❖ Bile, a substance that helps your body digest and absorb fats. It is produced in the liver and stored in the gall bladder until needed.
❖ Pancreatic (pan-kree-AT-tick) juice, which contains enzymes that help break down carbohydrates, proteins, and fats. It is produced by the pancreas (PAN-kree-us), a gland connected to the small intestine.
❖ Intestinal juice, produced in the small intestine. This digestive fluid works with the others to break down food.

When fully broken down, carbohydrates are turned into a simple sugar called **glucose.** Glucose, or blood sugar, is the body's basic fuel supply. Fats are changed into fatty acids. Proteins are broken down into amino acids. Vitamins, minerals, and water do not need to be broken down. They can be used by the body in the same form in which they appear in food.

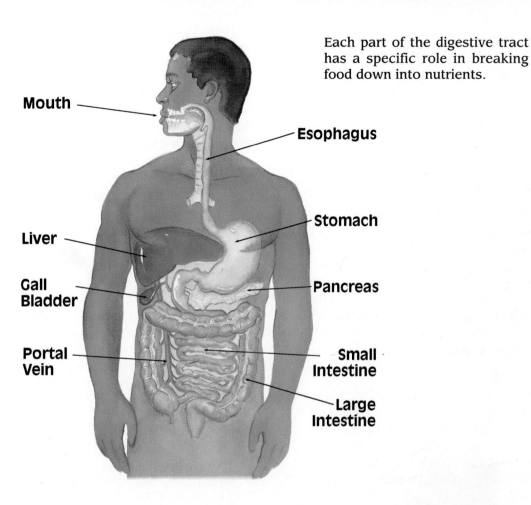

Each part of the digestive tract has a specific role in breaking food down into nutrients.

Mouth

Esophagus

Liver

Stomach

Gall Bladder

Pancreas

Portal Vein

Small Intestine

Large Intestine

Healthy Attitudes

At one time or another, most people have digestive problems. Possible causes include food choices, smoking, and alcohol. Emotions such as worry, fear, anger, and depression can also cause digestive problems.

Here are some guidelines that can help lead to good digestion:
- Eat regular meals every day.
- Chew food thoroughly before swallowing it.
- Relax while you eat.

Negative emotions are one possible cause of digestive problems.

Using the Nutrients

Once food has been broken down into nutrients, digestion is complete. However, the body still has work to do. It must absorb the nutrients and take them to where they can be used or stored.

Absorption

After digestion, the nutrients are absorbed into the bloodstream. Most absorption takes place in the small intestine. The lining of the small intestine is arranged in folds. It is lined with billions of tiny finger-like projections, called villi (VILL-eye), like velvet cloth or shag carpet. The villi increase the surface area of the intestine so that more nutrients can be absorbed.

Villi

Intestine Wall

This is a cross-section of the lining of the small intestine. The many small projections, called villi, create a large surface area for absorbing nutrients.

After absorption, some waste material, including fiber, is left in the small intestine. This waste material is moved into the large intestine, also called the colon. The colon removes water, potassium, and sodium from the waste. The remainder is stored as a semi-solid in the rectum (REK-tum), or lower part of the intestine, then eliminated.

Processing and Storing Nutrients

After the nutrients are absorbed by the villi of the small intestine, they are carried through a blood vessel, called the portal vein, to the liver.

One of the liver's many jobs is to turn nutrients into different kinds needed by the body. For instance, it takes amino acids the turns them into different kinds of proteins. Then the proteins are carried by the blood to wherever they are needed.

Some nutrients, if not needed immediately, can be stored for future use.

❖ The liver converts extra glucose into **glycogen** (GLIE-kuh-juhn), a storage form of glucose. Glycogen is stored in the liver and the muscles.

❖ If there is more excess glucose than can be stored as glycogen, the rest is converted to body fat. Fats are deposited throughout the body as an energy reserve. Excess fatty acids and amino acids are also converted to body fat.

❖ Minerals are stored in various ways. For instance, iron is stored in the liver and in bone marrow.

❖ Fat-soluble vitamins are stored mainly in the liver and in body fat.

Some nutrients, including most water-soluble vitamins, are not stored for long periods. If not needed, they are removed from the body with wastes.

Muscle Cells

Nerve Cell

Cells differ in appearance. The shape of each type is related to its specialized function.

Red Blood Cells

Feeding the Cells

Nutrients and oxygen are carried throughout the body by the circulatory system. The smallest blood vessels, the capillaries, bring nutrients and oxygen to individual cells. They also remove waste products from the cells.

When they reach the cells, the nutrients are used for their specialized purposes. As you recall, one of these is to provide energy. This is done by combining glucose with water through a process called oxidation.

Skin Cells

Energy from Nutrients

Oxidation is a process in which fuel is combined with oxygen to produce energy. One example of oxidation is a log burning in a fireplace. The fuel in this case is wood. To keep burning, it must have oxygen from the air. Energy is produced in the form of light and heat.

In your body, the fuel is glucose. When glucose reaches the cells, it is combined with oxygen. The result is energy in the form of heat and power for the cells.

As explained in section 2.1, energy supplied by food is measured in calories (actually, kilocalories). The number of calories you need to take in each day depends on how much energy you use.

Your body uses energy for two basic purposes:

❖ *Physical activities,* such as work and exercise. The more active you are, the more energy you use. For instance, you would use more energy walking up a flight of stairs than riding in an elevator.

❖ *Automatic processes* such as breathing, digesting food, and creating new cells. Even when you are resting or sleeping, your body is using energy. This energy is called **basal metabolism** (BAY-suhl muh-TAB-oh-lih-zum).

Generally, about two-thirds of the calories you use are for basal metabolism. However, this varies from person to person. It depends on factors such as age, body size, and body composition (the amount of muscle or fat). The amount of energy used for basal metabolism is sometimes called the basal metabolic rate, or BMR.

As you can see, the human body is an amazing organism. Without your even thinking about it, the body carries on thousands of complex processes every moment. By now you should have a better understanding of how the food you eat provides nutrients and energy to every one of your cells, keeping you alive and healthy.

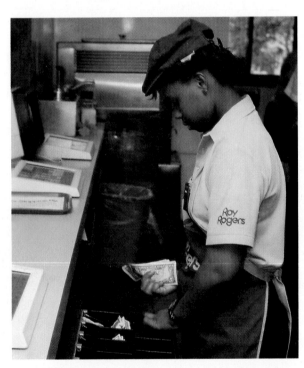

The energy you need can come only from the nutrients in food. Without good nutrition, you can't do your best.

Section 2.5 Review

RECALL THE FACTS

1. Summarize the steps in the digestive process.

2. How do nutrients get from the digestive system to the bloodstream?

3. Name two ways in which excess glucose can be stored.

4. What two substances combine to produce energy in the cells? What is this process called?

DISCUSS YOUR IDEAS

5. How might emotions such as worry or fear lead to digestive problems?

APPLY YOUR LEARNING

6. Sketch a design for a poster or bulletin board showing how food is broken down into nutrients and how nutrients travel through the body.

CAREER PROFILE

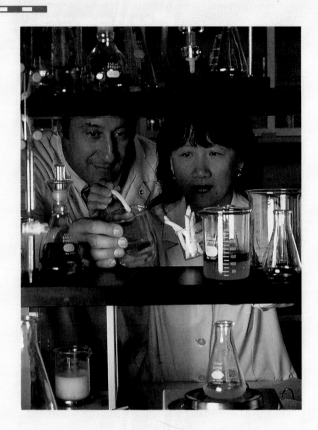

Lisa Yang
Food Scientist

Current position:

"I'm a scientist specializing in food research for the U.S. Department of Agriculture."

Responsibilities:

"My job involves finding ways to increase the nutrition of various foods, such as soybeans and grains."

Skills:

"Patience is a must in this field, as research can be very time-consuming and sometimes frustrating! You also need a strong background in science."

Education:

"I hold a bachelor's degree in chemistry, and master's and doctoral degrees in food engineering."

Work environment:

"I spend most of my time running experiments in the lab. Although several scientists may work on the same project, much of my day is spent working on my own. I also spend quite a bit of time documenting my findings."

Favorite part of the job:

"I've always had an inquisitive mind and a love of science, which are perfect for this line of work. I like knowing that my research leads to better tasting and more nutritious foods."

- Does Lisa seem well suited to this job? Why or why not?
- What aspects of Lisa's job do you think you might enjoy? Why?

Summary

Section 2.1
The Role of Nutrients: The six major types of nutrients work as a team. Lack of nutrients, or too much of certain nutrients, can result in poor health. Recommended amounts have been established for some nutrients. The energy supplied by carbohydrates, proteins, and fats is measured in calories. Most people do not need nutrient supplements.

Section 2.2
Carbohydrates, Fiber, and Proteins: Carbohydrates include starches and sugars. Refined sugars, which are added to many foods, are limited in nutrients. Both soluble and insoluble fiber are important for good health. Complete protein can be obtained by eating animal foods or combinations of plant foods.

Section 2.3
Fats: Fats perform several important jobs. However, eating too much fat is linked with several health problems. The three types of fatty acids—saturated, polyunsaturated, and monounsaturated—appear to have different effects on blood cholesterol levels. Experts recommend that people limit their intake of total fat, saturated fat, and cholesterol.

Section 2.4
Vitamins, Minerals, and Water: Each vitamin and mineral has specific functions and food sources. The body can store fat-soluble vitamins for long periods, but not most water-soluble ones. Some minerals are needed in relatively large amounts and others in very small amounts, but all are important. Every day you must replace the water lost by the body.

Section 2.5
How Your Body Uses Food: Digestion is the process of breaking down food into usable nutrients. As food travels through the digestive system, it is broken down by a combination of physical and chemical action. Then the nutrients are absorbed and put to use. Some nutrients can be stored if not needed right away. The bloodstream carries nutrients to all the cells in the body. Glucose and oxygen combine to produce energy for physical activities and basal metabolism.

REVIEWING FACTS

1. What does RDA stand for? What is included in the RDA chart? (2.1)

2. What percentage of daily calories should come from carbohydrates? From proteins? From fats? (2.1)

3. What are complex carbohydrates? In what foods can they be found? (2.2)

4. What are proteins made of? Why are plant proteins considered incomplete? (2.2)

5. What is the difference between HDL and LDL cholesterol? (2.3)

6. Which type of fatty acid is corn oil highest in? Olive oil? Coconut oil? (2.3)

7. How does your body use beta carotene? In what foods is it found? (2.4)

8. Which minerals are electrolytes? What do electrolytes do? (2.4)

9. Name four digestive juices. In what part of the digestive system does each do its work? (2.5)

10. What is basal metabolism? (2.5)

LEARNING BY DOING

1. **Taste test:** Taste samples of ripe fresh fruits provided by your teacher. Which do you think are highest in natural sugar? (2.2)

2. **Food science lab:** Rub a sample of butter or margarine on a piece of white paper. Label the spot left by the butter. Do the same with samples of ten different foods, such as cheese, a potato, an apple, and a cookie. Let the paper dry for 15 minutes. Which foods left a translucent spot that did not disappear? How does this compare to the spot left by the butter? What do you conclude? (2.3)

3. **Computer lab:** If nutrition software is available, use it to analyze a sample daily menu. How would you rate the menu's balance of carbohydrate, protein, and fat? How would you rate it on vitamins and minerals? After changing some of the foods in the menu, analyze it again. How do the results differ? Why? (2.1, 2.2, 2.3, 2.4)

THINKING CRITICALLY

1. **Recognizing fallacies:** An advertisement claims that a special nutrient supplement will "meet all your daily nutrient needs." What is wrong with this claim? (2.1)

2. **Identifying evidence:** A frozen dinner boasts "only 300 calories per serving." The nutrition information shows that the dinner contains 20 grams of fat. What do you conclude? (2.1, 2.3)

3. **Predicting consequences:** Janine is about your age. She doesn't like milk, and seldom eats vegetables except for corn and potatoes. Unless she changes her eating habits, what health problem is she at risk for? How can she reduce her risk? (2.4)

MAKING DECISIONS AND SOLVING PROBLEMS

What Would You Do?

1. One of your friends often skips meals and fills up on soft drinks, candy, and chips. She says that what she eats doesn't matter because she takes vitamin supplements every day. She encourages you to do the same. (2.1)

2. Your uncle tells you he has decided to increase the fiber in his diet. Since he hasn't eaten much fiber before, he plans to make up for it by eating twice the recommended amount for several days. He asks your opinion. (2.2)

3. The cafeteria supervisor at your school is considering whether to add a salad bar featuring vegetables, fruits, and pasta. Next week, students will be asked to vote on the idea. How will you vote? Why? (2.2, 2.4)

LINKING YOUR STUDIES

1. **Math:** Collect and bring to class three food labels that include nutrition information. Multiply the number of grams of fat by 9 to find the number of calories from fat. Divide by the number of calories per serving, then multiply by 100. The result is the percentage of calories from fat. Compare results with classmates. (2.1, 2.3)

2. **Social Studies/Health:** In regions of the world where food is scarce, certain nutrient deficiencies are common. Using library resources, find information about three specific deficiency diseases. What are the symptoms? How can each be prevented? Treated? (2.1, 2.2, 2.4)

3. **Reading and Study Skills:** Create a game to help you review the digestive process. Be prepared to explain your game to classmates. (2.5)

CHAPTER 3

Guidelines for Good Nutrition

Objectives

After studying this section, you should be able to:

❖ List six Dietary Guidelines for Americans.
❖ Tell how each Guideline contributes to good health.
❖ Describe ways of reducing fats and sodium in your diet.

Look for These Terms

Dietary Guidelines for Americans
moderation

New discoveries about nutrition and health are constantly being made. To help you take advantage of the latest nutrition knowledge, health experts have developed dietary guidelines—suggestions for making healthful food choices. Following these guidelines can increase your chances of living a long and healthy life.

Dietary Guidelines for Americans

The **Dietary Guidelines for Americans** were developed by the U.S. Department of Agriculture (USDA) and the U.S. Department of Health and Human Services. They include the six guidelines shown in the box on this page.

The Dietary Guidelines for Americans
1. Eat a variety of foods.
2. Maintain healthy weight.
3. Choose a diet low in fat, saturated fat, and cholesterol.
4. Choose a diet with plenty of vegetables, fruits, and grain products.
5. Use sugars only in moderation.
6. Use salt and sodium only in moderation.

Eat a Variety of Foods

As you have learned, scientists have identified about 40 different nutrients needed for good health. Many more probably occur in foods but haven't yet been identified. Eating a variety of foods is a good way to get all the nutrients your body needs.

No single food can supply all nutrients in the amounts you need. For instance, sweet potatoes are packed with vitamins A and C, copper, and fiber, but have little calcium or phosphorus. Skim milk is a good source of calcium and phosphorus, but has no fiber and little vitamin C. As you can see, for good health you need to eat a variety of foods.

Moderation, or avoiding extremes, goes hand-in-hand with variety. People often eat a few favorite foods regularly, sometimes in large amounts, and ignore others. Instead, eat moderately sized servings of many different kinds of foods. That way, you'll be getting a wider variety of nutrients for good health.

There are no "bad" or "good" foods. Any food that supplies nutrients can be part of nutritious daily choices. The key is to balance your food choices so that, overall, they lead to good health. Variety and moderation can help you do just that.

Maintain a Healthy Weight

Your chances of developing a health problem are greater if you are overweight or underweight.

Excess weight is a common problem in the United States. Generally, a few extra pounds are not harmful. Being truly overweight, however, is a health risk. It may contribute to illnesses such as high blood pressure, heart disease, stroke, diabetes, and certain kinds of cancer.

Being too thin can also be a problem. It may mean that you are not eating enough to meet your body's energy and nutrient needs. Some health problems are associated with being underweight.

Right now, there is no exact definition of a healthy weight. Researchers are still trying to find precise ways to determine the weight that is right for an individual.

In Chapter 5, you will learn more about today's guidelines for a healthy weight and how to maintain it.

Eating a variety of foods in moderation will help insure you get the nutrients you need.

Choose a Diet Low in Fat, Saturated Fat, and Cholesterol

There are several reasons why the Dietary Guidelines encourage people to eat less fat and cholesterol. A high-fat diet is linked with certain kinds of cancer. Fat—especially saturated fat—and cholesterol are linked with increased risk of heart disease. Choosing foods high in fat can lead to overweight.

Health experts have suggested the following goals for fat in making daily food choices:

* ❖ **Total fat:** 30 percent or less of the calories you eat. (Section 2.1 shows how to calculate the amount of fat that is equal to 30 percent of the day's total calories.)
* ❖ **Saturated fat:** 10 percent or less of your calories. Remember, the highest proportion of saturated fatty acids are found in animal fats (in meat, poultry, fish, eggs, and dairy products) and in the tropical oils (coconut, palm, and palm kernel oil).
* ❖ **Cholesterol:** Limit the amount of cholesterol eaten. Only foods from animal sources contain cholesterol.

Visible and Invisible Fats

Studies show that on the average, Americans get 37 percent of calories from fat. Many people are unaware of how much fat is in the food they eat.

Some fat is called *visible fat* because it is easily seen. For example, you can see the butter on a baked potato or the layer of fat around a pork chop. People are usually aware of these sources of fats in their diet.

Much of the fat people eat, however, is *invisible fat.* It is a part of the chemical composition of the food and cannot be seen. Foods such as whole milk, cheese, egg yolks, nuts, and avocado are loaded with invisible fat. So are fried foods and baked goods.

Lowering Fat

Eating low-fat foods can help reduce your risk of health problems. It also allows you to eat more food without increasing your total calories. Remember, a gram of fat has 9 calories, while a gram of protein or carbohydrate has only 4 calories.

It's not difficult to substitute low-fat food choices for high-fat ones. The chart on page 92 gives some examples. As you study this book, you will learn more about choosing low-fat foods and cooking methods.

Keeping your weight at a healthy level may reduce the risk of health problems such as high blood pressure.

Suggestions for Lowering Fat		
High-Fat Food	Low-Fat Alternative	Fat Savings
Whole milk (1 cup/250 mL)	Skim milk	8 grams less fat
Fried chicken (3 oz./84 g)	Baked chicken without skin	8 grams less fat
Regular salad dressing (1 Tbsp./15 mL)	Flavored vinegar, lemon juice, or fat-free dressing	9 grams less fat
Potato chips (1 oz./28 g)	Plain popcorn, air popped (1 cup/250 mL)	10 grams less fat
Premium ice cream (1 cup/250 mL)	Low-fat frozen yogurt	20 grams less fat
Cheddar cheese (1 oz./28 g)	Part-skim mozzarella	4 grams less fat
Sour cream on a baked potato (2 Tbsp./30 mL)	Plain nonfat yogurt	6 grams less fat

By becoming more aware of foods high in invisible fats, you can make better food choices.

Choose a Diet with Plenty of Vegetables, Fruits, and Grain Products

Vegetables, fruits, and grain products should be the foundation for your daily food choices. They provide valuable starches and fiber, which other foods do not have. They are also excellent sources of proteins, vitamins, and minerals.

Most starchy foods are low in fat (as long as you don't add high-fat toppings, such as butter, sour cream, and rich sauces). By eating more vegetables, fruits, and grain products, you can cut down on the amount of fat in your diet.

Use Sugars Only in Moderation

As you have learned, Americans eat sugar in many different forms. Natural sugar is a source of energy in many foods, such as fruits and grain products. These foods also provide other nutrients.

The refined sugars that are added to many foods also provide energy. However, they are limited in nutrients. Most healthy people should use only moderate amounts of these sugars. Very active people with high energy needs may be able to use more, as long as their food choices are nutritious ones. People with low energy needs should use refined sugars sparingly (that is, in very small amounts).

You probably expect to find sugar in foods such as candy, desserts, and baked goods. Other foods, such as cold cuts, ketchup, and peanut butter, may also contain refined sugar as a flavoring. Because there are many different kinds of sugars, you may not be aware that the product you are buying is sweetened. Here are some of the different sugars that may appear on food labels:

- ❖ sucrose
- ❖ brown sugar
- ❖ raw sugar
- ❖ glucose
- ❖ dextrose
- ❖ fructose
- ❖ maltose
- ❖ lactose
- ❖ honey
- ❖ syrup
- ❖ corn sweetener
- ❖ molasses
- ❖ high-fructose corn syrup
- ❖ fruit juice concentrate

Check labels for sugar in the ingredients. Remember that it may be shown under a variety of names.

Use Salt and Sodium Only in Moderation

Table salt contains sodium and chloride, both of which are essential nutrients. Most people, however, eat more salt and sodium than they need for good health. Salt is added to most foods and beverages during processing. Many foods also contain natural amounts of sodium.

Excess sodium in food choices has been associated with high blood pressure. People can lower their risk of getting high blood pressure by eating less salt and sodium. Here are some hints for cutting down on salt and sodium:

❖ Add little, if any, salt to food when cooking and at the table.
❖ Choose salted snacks, such as chips, crackers, pretzels, and nuts, only occasionally.
❖ Go easy on processed foods. They generally have more sodium than fresh ones.
❖ Check labels for the amount of sodium in foods. Choose those lower in sodium most of the time.

Many popular snacks have a high sodium content. What are some low-sodium alternatives?

Other Nutrition Guidelines

The U.S. government is not alone in issuing recommendations for healthful eating. For example, the National Cancer Institute and the American Cancer Society have issued dietary guidelines that focus on reducing cancer risk. These guidelines give much the same message as the Dietary Guidelines for Americans. They include recommendations to avoid obesity, eat less fat, and eat more fruits, vegetables, and whole grains. In addition, they recommend that people eat fewer smoked, salt-cured, and nitrate-cured foods, such as bacon and some cold cuts.

Dietary guidelines give you goals to help you improve your health. In the next section, you will learn about the Food Guide Pyramid, a tool that can help you meet your goal of good nutrition.

Making healthier choices doesn't mean giving up all the foods you enjoy. Frozen yogurt, for example, is as satisfying as ice cream—with significantly less fat.

In Japan, the Ministry of Health and Welfare has issued "Dietary Guidelines for Health Promotion." The guidelines recommend that people eat a variety of foods, at least 30 or more different kinds daily. They also emphasize weight management and cutting down on total fat, saturated fats, and salt. One guideline states, "Make all activities pertaining to food and eating pleasurable ones." It encourages Japanese families to sit down to meals together and to enjoy traditional home-cooked dishes.

Section 3.1 Review

RECALL THE FACTS

1. What are the six Dietary Guidelines for Americans discussed in this section?

2. Why must you eat a variety of foods for good health?

3. What is meant by "invisible fat"? Name three foods in which it is found.

4. List five examples of different sugars that may appear on food labels.

DISCUSS YOUR IDEAS

5. Which Dietary Guideline do you think is hardest for most people to follow? Why?

6. Discuss the fifth dietary guideline issued by the Japanese government: "Make all activities pertaining to food and eating pleasurable ones." Why do you think this was included?

APPLY YOUR LEARNING

7. Choose one Guideline and list five to ten suggestions for helping people to follow it.

Objectives

After studying this section, you should be able to:

❖ Describe the food groups in the Food Guide Pyramid.
❖ Give guidelines for using the Food Guide Pyramid to plan daily food choices.

Look for These Terms

Food Guide Pyramid
nutrient-dense

You probably grew up learning about the "four food groups." Did you know that there are now five food groups?

Over the years, different food group systems have served as tools for planning nutritious meals. Foods are placed in groups based on the major nutrients they contain. Choosing foods from each group gives you a variety of flavorful, nutritious foods every day.

As nutrition knowledge changes, food group systems have also changed. In 1992, the U.S. Department of Agriculture unveiled a food group system called the **Food Guide Pyramid.**

Understanding the Pyramid

The Food Guide Pyramid is designed to help you follow the Dietary Guidelines for Americans. It guides you toward eating a variety of foods in moderate amounts, including plenty of grains, vegetables, and fruits.

The Food Guide Pyramid includes five food groups:

❖ Bread, Cereal, Rice, and Pasta Group.
❖ Vegetable Group.
❖ Fruit Group.
❖ Milk, Yogurt, and Cheese Group.
❖ Meat, Poultry, Fish, Dry Beans, Eggs, and Nuts Group.

A pyramid shape was chosen to illustrate how each food group fits into a healthful eating plan. Look at the illustration of the Pyramid on page 97. As you can see, foods are arranged in the Pyramid according to the recommended number of servings. For instance, the Bread, Cereal, Rice, and Pasta

Food Guide Pyramid
A Guide to Daily Food Choices

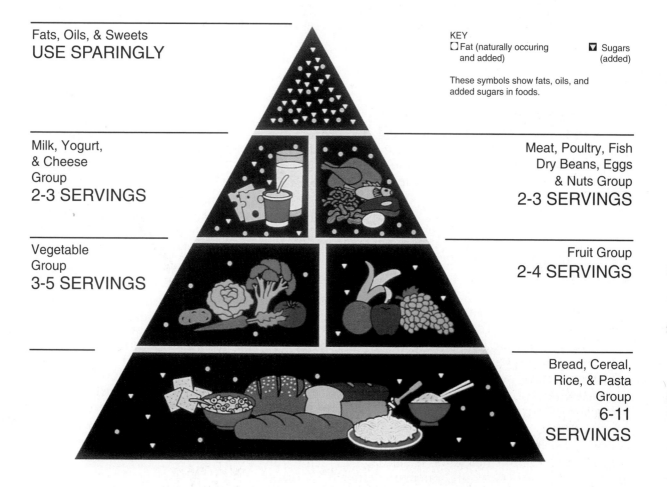

Fats, Oils, & Sweets
USE SPARINGLY

KEY
☐ Fat (naturally occuring and added)
◤ Sugars (added)

These symbols show fats, oils, and added sugars in foods.

Milk, Yogurt, & Cheese Group
2-3 SERVINGS

Meat, Poultry, Fish Dry Beans, Eggs & Nuts Group
2-3 SERVINGS

Vegetable Group
3-5 SERVINGS

Fruit Group
2-4 SERVINGS

Bread, Cereal, Rice, & Pasta Group
6-11 SERVINGS

Keeping the Food Guide Pyramid in mind can help you balance your daily food intake. Which three food groups have the highest number of recommended daily servings?

Group is located at the base of the Pyramid—the largest section—because you need more servings from this group than any of the others.

In addition to the five food groups, the Pyramid includes a section labeled "Fats, Oils, and Sweets." Foods in this category include salad dressings and oils, cream, butter, margarine, refined sugars, soft drinks, candies, and sweet desserts. These foods provide calories from fat and sugar, but little or no vitamins and minerals. Fats and sweets are placed at the small tip of the Pyramid to show that they should be used sparingly.

On the Pyramid diagram, fats are represented by small circles, and added sugars by small triangles. Notice that these symbols appear not only at the tip of the Pyramid, but also within the food groups. This is to remind you that fats and added sugars can be found in some of the foods within each group.

Using the Pyramid

Now that you are familiar with the basics of the Pyramid, here are some guidelines for putting it to use.

Choosing Nutrient-Dense Foods

Within each food group, there is a wide assortment of foods. They differ in nutrients and calories. Spinach, for example, has more vitamins and minerals than iceberg lettuce. French fries have more fat and calories than a plain baked potato. Peaches canned in syrup have more sugar and calories than fresh peaches.

A food that is low or moderate in calories, yet rich in important nutrients, is said to be **nutrient-dense.** Generally, nutrient-dense foods are low in fats and added sugars. Instead, they supply other nutrients such as complex carbohydrates (starches), fiber, proteins, vitamins, and minerals.

When selecting foods from the food groups, choose nutrient-dense ones. That way, you can get the important nutrients you need without getting more calories, fat, and sugar than you need. Later in this section, and throughout the book, you will find hints for choosing foods from the Pyramid. You may also want to use the chart at the back of this book, "Nutritive Value in Foods," to compare the calories and nutrients in different foods.

The Food Groups

All five food groups are important to health. Each provides some, but not all, of the nutrients you need. One group cannot replace another. You need a variety of food from the food groups each day.

Bread, Cereal, Rice, and Pasta Group

This group includes all kinds of grain products. They supply complex carbohydrates, fiber, vitamins, and minerals.

You need six to eleven servings from this group every day. Some examples of a serving are:
* 1 slice bread.
* 1 ounce (28 g) ready-to-eat cereal.
* 1/2 cup (125 mL) cooked cereal, rice, or pasta.

To get the fiber you need, choose as many whole grain foods as you can, such as whole wheat bread and whole grain cereals. This group includes many low-fat choices, but also some higher-fat ones, such as croissants and other baked goods.

Vegetable Group

Vegetables provide beta carotene, which your body uses to make vitamin A. They also supply vitamin C, folate (a B vitamin), and minerals such as magnesium and iron. They provide fiber and complex carbohydrates and are low in fat.

You should have three to five servings of vegetables daily. Each of the following counts as one serving:
- ❖ 1 cup (250 mL) raw leafy vegetables.
- ❖ 1/2 cup (125 mL) other vegetables, cooked or chopped raw.
- ❖ 3/4 cup (175 mL) vegetable juice.

Different types of vegetables provide different nutrients. For variety, include dark green, leafy vegetables, such as kale; deep yellow-orange vegetables, such as sweet potatoes; starchy vegetables, including corn, peas, and potatoes; dry beans and peas; and others.

Most adults need two servings of milk products daily. Three servings are recommended for pregnant or breastfeeding women, teens, and young adults up to age 24. One serving equals:
- ❖ 1 cup (250 mL) milk or yogurt.
- ❖ 1½ ounces (42 g) natural cheese.
- ❖ 2 ounces (56 g) process cheese.

Low-fat choices from this group include skim milk, nonfat yogurt, and nonfat dry milk. Go easy on high-fat cheese and ice cream. Remember, too, that some milk products, such as flavored yogurt, contain added sugar.

Fruit Group

Fruits provide important amounts of beta carotene, vitamin C, and potassium. Edible skins are good sources of fiber. Like vegetables, most fruits are low in fat and sodium.

You need two to four servings of fruit every day. One serving equals:
- ❖ 1 medium fruit such as an apple, banana, or orange.
- ❖ 1/2 cup (125 mL) chopped, cooked, or canned fruit.
- ❖ 3/4 cup (175 mL) fruit juice.

Be sure to have fruits rich in vitamin C regularly, such as citrus fruits, melons, and berries. Eat whole fresh fruits often for the fiber they provide. When choosing canned or frozen fruits, look for products without added sugar. Count only 100 percent fruit juices as a serving of fruit.

Meat, Poultry, Fish, Dry Beans, Eggs, and Nuts Group

This group is an important source of protein, vitamins, and minerals. Two to three daily servings are recommended.
- ❖ 2 to 3 ounces (56 to 85 g) of cooked lean meat, poultry, or fish equals one serving. This is about the size of an average hamburger or the amount of meat in half a medium chicken breast.
- ❖ Each of the following portions is the equivalent of 1 ounce (28 g) of meat: 1/2 cup (125 mL) cooked dry beans; one egg; or 2 tablespoons (30 mL) peanut butter.

The total of your daily servings should be the equivalent of 5 to 7 ounces (140 to 196 g) of cooked lean meat, poultry, or fish. For instance, you might eat one egg for breakfast, a cup of cooked dry beans in bean soup for lunch, and a lean hamburger for dinner. These foods would give you the equivalent of 6 ounces (168 g) of meat.

To limit the fat in your diet, select lean meats, fish, and poultry without skin. Have dry beans and peas often—they are high in fiber and low in fat. Go easy on eggs, nuts, and seeds.

Milk, Yogurt, and Cheese Group

Foods in the milk group are high in protein, vitamins, and minerals. They are also one of the best sources of calcium.

THE FOOD GUIDE PYRAMI

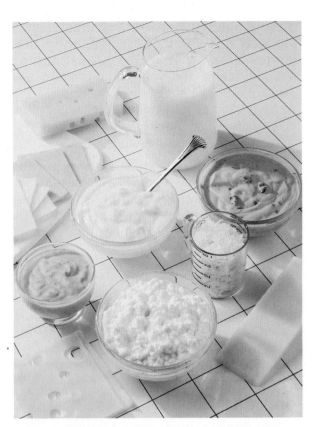

▲ **Milk, Yogurt, and Cheese Group**
Foods in the milk group are high in protein, vitamins, and minerals and are one of the best sources of calcium. (top left)

▲ **Meat, Poultry, Fish, Dry Beans, Eggs, and Nuts Group**
This group is an important source of protein, vitamins, and minerals. (bottom left)

▲ **Vegetable Group**
Vegetables provide beta carotene, vitamin C, folate and minerals such as magnesium and iron. They provide fiber and complex carbohydrates and are low in fat. (bottom right)

▲ Fruit Group
Fruits provide important amounts of beta carotene, vitamin C, potassium, and fiber. (right)

▲ Bread, Cereal, Rice, and Pasta Group
This group includes all kinds of grain products. They supply complex carbohydrates, fiber, vitamins, and minerals. (bottom right)

▲ Fats, Oils, and Sweets
Use these foods sparingly. They provide calories from fat and sugar, but little or no vitamins and minerals. (bottom left)

How Many Servings for You?

As you have seen, the Food Guide Pyramid does not give an exact number of servings for each group. Instead, it gives a range, such as three to five servings of vegetables. This is because people have different needs for calories and nutrients, depending on their age, gender, body size, and activity level.

In general, most teenage boys need the highest number of servings from each food group. For most teenage girls, the middle number of servings (such as nine servings from the bread group) is about right. However, all teens need three servings from the milk group.

You may be used to eating amounts of food that are larger or smaller than what the Food Guide Pyramid considers a serving. For example, if you eat 1 cup (250 mL) of cooked spaghetti, remember to count that as two servings from the bread group, not one.

Some foods include ingredients from more than one food group. If you're eating tacos, you would have servings from the bread group (taco shell), meat group (meat or bean filling), milk group (cheese), and vegetable group (lettuce and tomatoes). Depending on the amounts of the different fillings, you might have full or half servings from the different groups.

The Food Guide Pyramid makes it easy to plan for good nutrition. It is a valuable tool for getting all the nutrients you need in their proper balance.

Healthy Attitudes

The Food Guide Pyramid differs in several ways from the four food groups that were used earlier:

- Fruits and vegetables are placed in separate groups rather than combined.
- The number of recommended servings for fruits, vegetables, and grain products has been increased.
- The Pyramid places more emphasis on making low-fat choices.

All of these changes reinforce the Dietary Guidelines for Americans.

Section 3.2 Review

RECALL THE FACTS

1. List the five food groups in the Food Guide Pyramid. Give the range of recommended daily servings for each.

2. What does "nutrient-dense" mean? How does it relate to choosing foods from the Pyramid?

3. For each food group, give two examples of serving sizes.

DISCUSS YOUR IDEAS

4. Do you feel the pyramid design is an effective way to get the desired nutrition message across? Why or why not?

APPLY YOUR LEARNING

5. Name two combination foods (other than tacos). List the food groups that are represented by the food's ingredients.

6. Make up a one-day menu that provides the recommended servings from the Food Guide Pyramid for a female teen.

Objectives

After studying this section, you should be able to:

❖ Explain how to evaluate advertisements, news reports, and other information related to foods and nutrition.

❖ Name reliable sources of nutrition information.

Look for These Terms

critical thinking
quacks
study
myths

"Fish oil prevents heart attacks," exclaimed newspaper headlines in the mid 1980s. Studies of populations that eat large amounts of oily fish, such as natives of the North Arctic, Japan, and Greenland, showed low blood cholesterol levels and few heart attacks. Omega-3 (oh-MAY-guh-3) fatty acids were identified as the "magic" ingredient in the fat.

Almost immediately, omega-3 fatty acids were available in capsules and advertised as a cure for high blood cholesterol levels. Later studies were conflicting. Some verified the original report, but others raised many questions. In 1990, the Food and Drug Administration (FDA) banned the capsule manufacturers from making any health claims for omega-3 fatty acids. According to FDA, there was not enough scientific evidence to support the health claims on fish oils.

This is but one example of confusing nutrition claims. How can you, as a consumer, determine the facts behind the claims? Start by thinking carefully about what you see and hear.

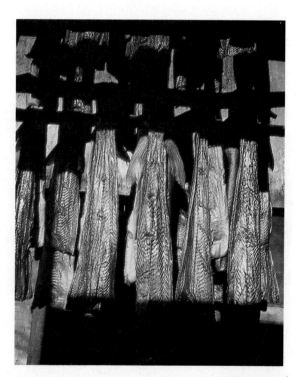

When it was reported that the oil in fish might reduce cholesterol, consumption of fish and fish oil increased sharply. For centuries, native peoples of the Arctic have relied on fish, like these dried salmon, as a main source of food. However, no one factor is responsible for their health.

The Need to Think Critically

Critical thinking means judging an idea on its soundness and truthfulness. It involves asking questions about a claim and the people who make it to decide whether you will accept it as true.

In a society where you have many choices, critical thinking is a valuable skill. It can help you recognize the ways in which advertisements, news reports, and nutrition fads may be misleading.

Evaluating Advertising

Many products related to health and nutrition are advertised on television and radio, in newspapers and magazines, and in other ways. Advertising can be informative and entertaining. Without it, many of the products you enjoy today would not be available.

At times, however, advertisements can be misleading. They can lead people to buy products without thinking about cost or nutrition.

How Advertisers Persuade You

Here are a few of the techniques advertisers use to convince you to buy their products:

❖ *Limited information.* Often, advertisements give you only the facts that will encourage you to buy. They may not tell the whole story.
❖ *Positive images.* An advertisement may use images of things that people feel positively about, such as friendship or good looks. The advertiser hopes you will associate these images and feelings with the product.
❖ *Appeal to basic needs.* Advertisers may focus on ways the product meets a need for security or self-esteem. They try to convince you that the product will make you look or feel better.
❖ *Celebrities.* Some advertisements show popular performers or athletes promoting the product. They don't tell you whether the person actually uses the product in real life.

Advertising can be a valuable source of information about products, but it can be misleading. Children tend to believe everything they see or hear. Thinking critically requires experience and practice.

Besides advertising, companies use other techniques to promote their products. A soft drink company may lend its name to a sports event or arrange to have its product shown in a movie. Coupons and eye-catching store displays encourage consumers to buy. Even product packages are a form of advertising.

The problem with these techniques is that they often don't give you the facts you need to make an informed choice. Instead, they appeal to your emotions. When evaluating advertising, ask yourself: What facts am I given? What needs or wants does the ad appeal to? What do I know about the people promoting the product?

Remember that the purpose of advertising is to get people to buy a product. Your goal is to get good nutrition at a fair price. Be sure your buying decisions are based on your own priorities, not the advertiser's.

Quacks and Frauds

Quacks are people who promote a particular food, diet, or supplement as a health aid without sound scientific evidence. Some quacks are deliberate frauds—their only goal is to make money in whatever way they can, even if the product hurts someone's health. Others are firm believers in the products they sell.

Understanding how quacks work can help you evaluate information. Here are some signs to look for. An advertisement or other product claim may not be truthful if it:

❖ *Guarantees fast results.* If the claim sounds too good to be true, it usually is.
❖ *Claims to be based on a "scientific breakthrough."* Legitimate scientific research takes time. The "miracle" discovery promoted in the ad may be complete fiction, or it may be based on early, incomplete studies.

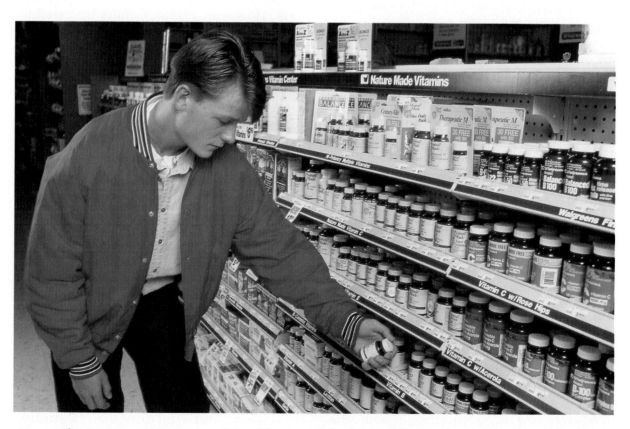

No product can guarantee good health or weight loss. Make your choices based on facts, not false promises.

- *Uses scare tactics.* For instance, it may play on people's fear of aging or becoming ill. Some ads suggest that common symptoms, such as headaches and fatigue, are signs of an illness that can only be cured by the advertised product. Yet there are many possible causes for such symptoms.
- *Relies on personal testimonials.* An advertisement may say that Ms. L.J., of Pine Grove, Oregon, used the product with fantastic results. But who is Ms. L.J.? You can't even be sure she really exists.
- *Encourages megadoses of vitamins and minerals.* As you have learned, excess amounts of vitamins and minerals can be a threat to good health.

Realistic expectations about nutrition are your best defense against false claims like these. Quacks are successful because many people are looking for shortcuts to good health. Remember, good health is attained by practicing wellness every day, not by "miracle" products.

Nutrition in the News

Reports of the latest health and nutrition studies appear in the media almost daily. A study is a scientific experiment conducted on a specific group of either people or animals.

There are several reasons why you should be cautious when reading about the latest research results.
- Many studies are poorly designed or show vague results.
- The people who performed or reported on the study may have been biased (swayed toward a particular conclusion). For example, research performed by a dental resource center reportedly showed that chocolate could fight dental plaque (PLACK), a cause of tooth decay. Investigation revealed that the center received most of its funds from a candy company.
- Even a well-designed, unbiased study usually is not the final authority. The results must be verified by other researchers.

Nutrition research can help health professionals learn more about how the body uses food. However, research must be carefully planned and carried out to provide valid information. Think critically about research results reported in the press.

- Most studies focus on just a small segment of the population. Some are done on animals. The results may not apply to people in general.
- Media reports are often too brief to provide complete information.
- News reporters may not have the scientific background needed to correctly interpret the details.

Stay informed about the latest research, but use critical thinking. When you read or hear about an interesting study, don't jump to conclusions. Look for the facts in the report. Get information from other sources. Be patient and wait for further studies instead of allowing yourself to be influenced by just one report.

Food Myths and Fads

Advertisements and news reports are not the only sources of information that call for critical thinking. People often spread stories about the latest food fad they've heard. They pass along myths, or unsound beliefs, about nutrition. Many books and magazine articles written by so-called "experts" give poor advice about nutrition and health.

Before you follow anyone's advice, ask yourself whether the source is a reliable one. Authors of books and magazine articles should be well-qualified, with an educational background in the particular subject from an accredited university or college.

Many people believe brown eggs are better than white. In fact, they are nutritionally the same. It's true that butter has more cholesterol and saturated fat than margarine, but they have the same amount of total fat and calories. Are muffins a good choice for breakfast? It depends. Many are high in sugar and fat. Check out the facts.

Healthy Attitudes

Here are just a few examples of nutrition myths and the facts behind them.

- *Myth: Eating grapefruit will help you burn fat and lose weight.* Fact: Grapefruit is low in fat and calories, but it has no special fat-burning qualities.

- *Myth: People who are under stress need extra vitamins.* Fact: Eating a balanced variety of nutritious foods, like other wellness habits, can help you handle stress. However, there is little evidence that everyday stress robs the body of vitamins.

- *Myth: If a food is cholesterol-free, it must be fat-free.* Fact: Cholesterol and fat are not the same thing. For instance, cholesterol-free crackers may contain coconut oil, which is high in saturated fatty acids. Remember, eating too much fat—especially saturated fat—may increase the risk of heart disease.

Where to Get the Facts

If you are suspicious about any nutrition information you have received or want more facts, here are some sources to contact:

❖ A local nutritionist or dietitian.
❖ Your local health department.
❖ Your home economics teacher.
❖ A professional organization, such as the American Dietetics Association.
❖ The nutrition department at a nearby university or college.

Remember that your health is your responsibility. Separating nutrition fact from fiction is an important part of exercising that responsibility.

Your local health department is one source of accurate nutrition information. Don't take chances by believing everything you see and hear.

■ Section 3.3 Review ■

RECALL THE FACTS

1. What is critical thinking?

2. What are two signs that an advertisement may be promoting a "quack" product?

3. Why doesn't any one scientific study provide enough evidence to draw a conclusion?

4. List three reliable sources of information about nutrition.

DISCUSS YOUR IDEAS

5. Why do you think some people continue to believe false claims and myths when there is no evidence for them?

APPLY YOUR LEARNING

6. Bring to class ads that you think are false or misleading. Identify the misleading statements or techniques.

CAREER PROFILE

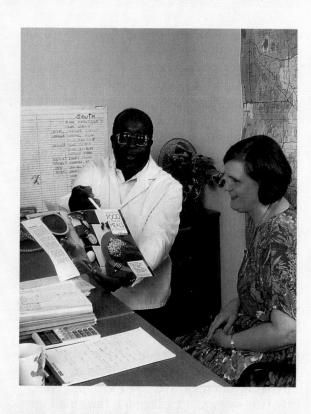

Larry Burke
Dietitian

Current position:

"I'm an administrative dietitian working for a large public school district."

Responsibilities:

"I supervise large-scale meal planning and preparation for the entire school district. It's also my responsibility to enforce safety standards and maintain a budget."

Skills:

"To succeed in this field, you must be able to work well with all types of people. Organizational skills are important, and of course, you need knowledge of nutrition and food service."

Education:

"I have a four-year college degree with a major in food service management. I'm also a registered dietitian and have a master's degree in business administration."

Work environment:

"I work about 40 hours a week. More than half of that time is spent at my desk, often in front of a computer. I also spend some time supervising the kitchen staff and food servers."

Favorite part of the job:

"I'm very people-oriented. I enjoy the challenge of giving school kids meals that are both good-tasting and healthy."

- Why is it important for Larry to be able to work well with many different people?
- What aspects of Larry's job do you think you might enjoy? Why?

Summary

Section 3.1
Dietary Guidelines: The Dietary Guidelines for Americans give advice for healthy eating. Included are recommendations to eat a variety of foods; maintain healthy weight; choose a diet low in fat, saturated fat, and cholesterol; choose a diet with plenty of fruits, vegetables, and grain products; use sugars only in moderation; and use salt and sodium only in moderation. Other dietary guidelines are issued by various groups.

Section 3.2
The Food Guide Pyramid: The Food Guide Pyramid is a tool to help you plan daily food choices. It shows the approximate number of servings you need each day from each of five food groups. Fats, oils, and sweets are placed at the small tip of the Pyramid and should be used sparingly. Choosing nutrient-dense foods from the food groups will help you get the nutrients you need without too many calories.

Section 3.3
Separating Fact from Fiction: Critical thinking can help you identify information that may be misleading. Advertisers use a variety of techniques to convince you to buy their products. Quacks promote products as health aids without sound scientific evidence. Avoid jumping to conclusions when reading news of a scientific study. Be wary of food myths and fads, and know where to get accurate information about nutrition.

REVIEWING FACTS

1. What are the recommended limits for fat and saturated fat in the diet? (3.1)

2. What are the benefits of choosing a diet with plenty of vegetables, fruits, and grain products? (3.1)

3. What problems are associated with excess sodium? Give three hints for cutting down on salt and sodium. (3.1)

4. Explain how the position of food groups in the Food Guide Pyramid diagram relates to the recommended number of servings for each. (3.2)

5. Briefly describe the main nutrients provided by each food group. (3.2)

6. Why does the Food Guide Pyramid give the recommended number of servings for each food group as a range instead of an exact number? (3.2)

7. Name three techniques used by advertisers to convince you to buy their products. (3.3)

8. What is meant by the term "nutrition myth"? Give an example. (3.3)

9. How can you tell whether the author of a book on nutrition is a reliable source of information on the subject? (3.3)

LEARNING BY DOING

1. **Taste test:** Heat three samples of a canned vegetable, such as green beans: one canned with salt and two canned without salt. Season one of the no-salt samples with a salt alternative, such as herbs or lemon juice. Compare the taste of the vegetables. Which do you prefer? Why? (3.1)

2. **Foods lab:** Compare the amount of fat in different types of ground beef. Weigh out 1/4 pound (112 g) of regular ground beef and the same amount of ground round. Form each portion into a patty. Cook each patty in a separate skillet over medium-low heat until done (about five minutes on each side). After cooking, weigh each patty again. Pour the grease from each pan into a separate measuring cup. Which patty contained more fat? How might you use this information? (3.1, 3.2)

THINKING CRITICALLY

1. **Determining accuracy:** Suppose a friend tells you that honey and molasses are better for you than white or brown sugar. How can you decide whether this is true? (3.1, 3.3)

2. **Predicting consequences:** What may be the consequences of eating too many foods low in nutrient density? (3.2)

3. **Recognizing bias:** Suppose a study on whether vitamin C is effective against colds is being paid for by a company that makes vitamin C tablets. Why does this suggest a possible bias? (3.3)

MAKING DECISIONS AND SOLVING PROBLEMS

What Would You Do?

1. Your sister has learned that carrots are very nutritious. Therefore, she has stopped eating most other vegetables and eats large amounts of carrots at almost every meal. (3.1, 3.2)

2. One of your friends is planning to go on a grapefruit-only diet for a few weeks. She asks you to go on the diet with her. (3.3)

LINKING YOUR STUDIES

1. **Fine arts:** Prepare a song, skit, puppet show, or poster that could be used to teach children about the Food Guide Pyramid. (3.2)

2. **Reading and study skills:** Find a newspaper or magazine article about a nutrition-related study. Identify the following information in the article: What was the purpose of the study? Who did the study and where? Who paid for it? What type of people or animals did the researchers study? How was the study carried out? (3.3)

3. **Writing:** Think of a nutrition claim you have recently seen or heard about. Write a letter to a dietitian asking for information and advice on the subject. (3.3)

CHAPTER 4

Planning Daily Food Choices

Objectives
After studying this section, you should be able to:
❖ Identify different eating patterns.
❖ Discuss how nutritional needs can be met through meals and snacks.

Look for These Terms
eating patterns
snacks
"grazing"

Barry greeted his friend at the door. "Hi, Manuel. I'm glad you stopped by. We were just sitting down to dinner—would you like to join us?"

"I'm sorry, I didn't know you hadn't eaten yet," said Manuel. "I've already had supper."

"Well, then, how about a snack?" Barry grinned. "Come on in!"

Has something similar ever happened to you? Because of differences in schedules, family background, and habits, people follow different patterns when it comes to meals and snacks.

Eating Patterns

The term **eating patterns** refers to when, what, and how much people eat. Today, many different eating patterns are becoming common. Some people eat three traditional

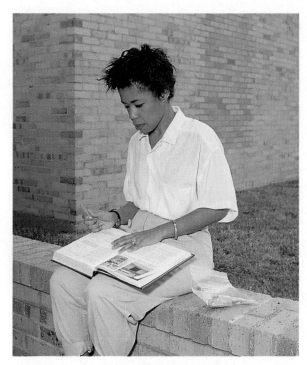

Your daily schedule is one of the factors that influence your eating pattern. What are some others?

meals a day, while others prefer to eat many small meals. People often eat snacks between meals. Some use different eating patterns from day to day, depending on their schedules.

No matter what your eating pattern is, the goal is to make nutritious food choices throughout the entire day. It's also important to eat regularly. If you try to go too long without food, your body won't have the fuel it needs. Studies show that people who skip meals make up for it by overeating later. Usually, meal skippers eat more in a day than they would if they chose to eat at regular intervals.

Traditional Meals

The traditional meals include breakfast, the midday meal, and the evening meal.

Breakfast

Studies continue to prove that breakfast is the most important meal of the day. You haven't eaten since the evening before, which means your body hasn't had a supply of energy foods for many hours. Breakfast gives you energy and helps you feel alert during the morning hours.

Eating breakfast makes a difference in how you feel all morning. Any of these nutritious choices can give your body fuel for a morning of activity.

Are you a breakfast skipper? If time is your problem, begin by getting up a few minutes earlier. Make a meal out of "quick" foods, such as:

- Low-fat flavored or plain yogurt, whole grain muffin or bagel, and a banana.
- Peanut butter and jelly sandwich and low-fat milk.
- A breakfast drink made by blending low-fat milk or yogurt, juice, and fruit.

If you skip breakfast, it's harder to concentrate on your schoolwork. Recent studies show that students who eat breakfast get to school on time and score better grades than those who don't eat breakfast.

Not all breakfasts are equal. A breakfast of starch, protein, and fruit, such as whole grain cereal or muffin, milk, and banana, gives you more lasting energy than a doughnut and a soft drink. You may feel fine after eating the doughnut and soft drink, but you will probably experience a mid-morning letdown.

Some people skip breakfast because they are bored with standard breakfast fare. However, any food can be breakfast food, so long as it is nutritious. Try having pizza, tacos, soup with crackers, or refried beans on toast for breakfast. Round out the menu with a serving of fruit and low-fat milk.

Midday and Evening Meals

The midday meal gives you energy and nutrients to carry out the rest of the day's activities. The evening meal is a good time to think about the food you've eaten for the day. It's your chance to fill in any food group servings that are lacking.

"Dinner" traditionally means the largest meal of the day. It may be eaten at midday or in the evening, depending on your personal preference and your schedule.

Some people prefer to eat dinner at midday and a lighter meal, sometimes called supper, in the evening. The larger midday meal provides fuel for the day's activities. Some people find they sleep better if the evening meal is light.

On the other hand, sometimes people prefer to have a light meal, or lunch, at midday. This pattern is often chosen by those who work or go to school. They may prefer to have the largest meal in the evening when all or most family members can eat together. On weekends or special occasions, they may follow a different pattern.

No matter when it is eaten, a dinner usually includes a main dish along with a grain product, vegetables, and a beverage. Sometimes people add dessert. A typical dinner might be stir-fried chicken, broccoli, and water chestnuts over rice; a tossed salad; low-fat milk; a whole wheat roll; and fruit for dessert.

For a lighter lunch or supper, popular choices include sandwiches, soups, main-dish salads, and similar foods. Accompaniments could include fresh fruits and vegetables, whole grain bread, and low-fat milk or yogurt.

In Mexico, the main meal is eaten at midday. A light meal or snack, called *merienda*, may be eaten in the early evening, followed by supper in the late evening.

Snacks

Snacks are small amounts of food eaten between meals. Snacking is not necessarily a bad habit. Well-chosen snacks can help you meet your energy and nutrient needs throughout the day.

However, many so-called "snack foods" are high in fat, sugar, and calories. These include candy, chips, granola, cookies, and other sweets.

For a nutritious snack, you can choose almost any nutrient-dense food from the five food groups. Try leftovers from the refrigerator, fresh fruits or vegetables, low-fat dairy products, or whole grain breads and cereals.

Also consider the timing of your snacks. If you snack too close to mealtime, you may not be able to eat the nutritious foods included in the meal.

Remember that snacks are as much a part of your eating pattern as breakfast, lunch, or dinner. Choose them wisely.

"Grazing"

Some people prefer to eat five or more small meals throughout the day instead of three larger ones. This eating pattern is sometimes called **"grazing."**

When you choose snacks, consider nutrient density. Snacks like those shown at the left can satisfy your hunger and provide important nutrients. The snacks shown below are high in fat, sugar, sodium, and calories. Which snacks do you choose most often?

Why might a person prefer smaller meals more often instead of three larger meals?

If grazing is your eating pattern, think about your food choices toward the end of the day. Are you lacking any servings from the food groups? If so, eat those foods so you'll be sure to meet the daily recommendations. On the other hand, check to be sure you are not eating too much. The day's total servings and calories should be the right amount for you, just as if you were eating three traditional meals.

As you have learned, eating patterns vary from person to person and day to day. In the end, *when* you eat is less important than *what* you eat. The eating pattern that helps you get the nutrients you need and the right number of calories is the one that's best for you. Identifying your eating pattern can help you plan for good nutrition.

Section 4.1 Review

RECALL THE FACTS

1. Give three examples of different eating patterns.

2. Why is breakfast considered the most important meal of the day?

3. How can you choose snacks that help meet your nutrient needs?

DISCUSS YOUR IDEAS

4. What eating pattern do you usually follow? How does it reflect your lifestyle?

5. What are some advantages of grazing? What are the disadvantages?

APPLY YOUR LEARNING

6. Make a list of 15 nutritious snack foods that require little preparation. Put a check mark by those you have tried before. Put a star by those you plan to try.

Objectives

After studying this section, you should be able to:

❖ Describe how to keep a food record.
❖ Suggest practical ways to succeed in changing eating habits for the better.

Look for This Term
food record

If you are like most people, some of your eating habits are healthful ones. Others, however, could be improved. The first step in improving your eating habits is to recognize the kinds of food choices you make now. Then you can keep your good habits and work on improving the poor ones.

What Are Your Current Habits?

People sometimes aren't aware of how often and what they eat. They may make sound food choices at certain times or in some situations, but not others.

You can become more aware of your habits by keeping a **food record.** This is simply a list of all the food you eat for a specific period of time. Start by carrying a small notebook or scratch pad with you. Each time you eat, no matter how small the amount, make a note in your record. Write down:

❖ The time you ate.
❖ The food eaten and the amount. You don't have to measure the exact amount—just make a reasonable estimate.

❖ A brief description of the eating situation. This might include where you were, what you were doing, your mood, and any other information that could help you understand your food habits.

Keep your food record for three consecutive days, including at least one weekend day. During this time, make your usual food choices. This is not a test you have to pass. It's just a way of letting you know the kind of food choices you are making now.

Reviewing Your Food Record

At the end of the three-day period, take a look at your food choices. For each day, count the number of servings you had from each group in the Food Guide Pyramid (page 97). Compare your totals with the recommended number of servings. Did you eat at least the minimum amount of servings? If not, which foods were you lacking? Were your food choices high or low in fats and added sugars? Remember, fats, oils, and sweets should be eaten sparingly.

Food Record

Thursday, Feb. 10

Time	Food and Amount	Situation
6:30 A.M.	1 small glass orange juice	home—breakfast—
	1 cup cornflakes	in a hurry
	1 glass skim milk	
10 A.M.	1 small bag potato chips	school—between classes
Noon	cheeseburger	school lunch
	tossed salad with dressing	
	soft drink	
	brownie	
3:30 P.M.	1 large bag french fries	mall—shopping
	1 diet soda	with Kara and Jason

How Can You Improve Your Habits?

Perhaps your food record shows that you are already following the Food Guide Pyramid and the Dietary Guidelines. If so, keep up your good habits.

Most people, however, find that their food choices leave room for improvement. For instance, Roberto discovered that he was not eating enough vegetables. He also saw that high-fat and sugary foods were often among his food choices.

Once you have identified poor eating habits, think about why they occur. Look at your food record again. Did you tend to make poor food choices in certain situations, such as while watching TV or when you were unhappy? Roberto's food record showed that he often snacked on cookies or french fries when he was at the mall with friends.

Roberto's food record made it easier for him to identify ways he could improve his eating habits. Consider keeping track of your own food intake for several days.

TIPS for Success

Developing New Eating Habits

❖ Begin to make changes in your food habits gradually. Work on them one by one.

❖ Allow plenty of time for each new way of eating to become a habit.

❖ If you find yourself slipping back into old ways of eating, don't give up. Review your plan and make sure it's realistic, then try again. If you continue to make the effort, eventually you will succeed.

In shopping malls, tempting foods seem to be everywhere. Look for nutritious choices.

Next, think about how to solve the problem. Some people just tell themselves, "I'll eat better from now on." That promise is hard to keep because it isn't specific. Instead, decide on specific changes you can make. (You may want to review the decision-making steps explained in Section 1.5.)

The next time he went to the supermarket, Roberto noticed how many different kinds of fresh vegetables there were. He decided to try at least one new vegetable a week. After he had done this for several weeks, he began to work on choosing healthier snacks at the mall.

Remember, eating is an enjoyable part of life. Don't take the pleasure out of it. You can make changes in your food habits and have fun doing it.

Every once in a while, keep another food record for several days. Use the same method to analyze your food choices. Compare it to your previous food record. You can see if you are making the necessary changes that will help you feel and look better. Keeping a food record and analyzing your food choices can help you stay on the track toward good health.

Section 4.2 Review

RECALL THE FACTS

1. What is a food record? What is its purpose?

2. When keeping a food record, what information do you need to write down?

3. Give two tips for successfully changing one's eating habits.

DISCUSS YOUR IDEAS

4. How could you give encouragement to a friend who is working on new eating habits?

APPLY YOUR LEARNING

5. The text describes two specific steps Roberto decided to take to improve his eating habits. List at least five other steps that could help him reach his goals.

Section 4.3

Eating Out Nutritiously

Objectives

After studying this section, you should be able to:

❖ Give guidelines for making nutritious food choices when eating away from home.

❖ Explain how eating out fits into overall food choices.

Look for These Terms

entree
a la carte

Eating out is growing in popularity. Recent studies have shown that Americans eat more than one-fifth of their meals away from home.

Most people enjoy eating out. When it comes to nutrition, however, eating out can be a challenge. Take care to make healthful food choices when eating at restaurants, at school, and on the go.

Restaurant Meals

There are many types of restaurants. Each has advantages and disadvantages when it comes to nutrition.

❖ **_Full-service restaurants_** offer table service, which means you sit at a table and a server takes your order. Nutrition varies depending on the menu. Some restaurants offer a wide variety of choices.

At full-service restaurants, you usually have many food options. That makes it easier to make healthful choices.

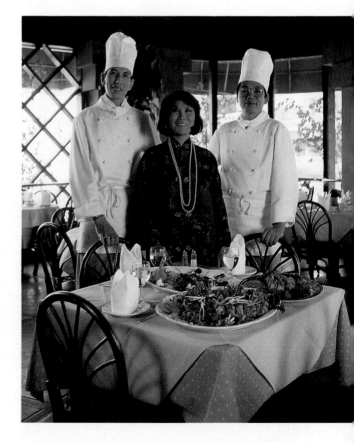

Others specialize in certain types of food, such as fish or steaks, or in certain cuisines, such as Italian or Chinese food. Since food is usually cooked to order, there's a good chance you can ask to have some items prepared the way you want—with less fat or salt, for example.

❖ **Cafeterias, restaurant buffets, and smorgasbords** (SHMORE-guhs-boards) are self-serve restaurants. A wide variety of food is displayed on counters, from which you make your selection. This can give you greater control over the kinds and amounts of food you eat. Buffet-type restaurants, however, generally allow you to return as many times as you want for second helpings. They often advertise "all you can eat" for a specific price. Such offers can tempt you to overeat and choose high-fat and sugary foods.

❖ **Fast-food restaurants** are changing to meet customers' requests for more nutritious food. Traditionally, fast food restaurants have offered a limited selection of foods, many of them high in fat, sugar, and sodium. Today, however, many fast-food restaurants are adding more healthful choices to the menu. You can now find broiled and roasted foods, salads, skim milk, and fruit juice. You may or may not have some choice in the way foods are prepared.

Many factors enter into your choice of restaurant, such as the price of a meal and how quickly you want to be served. Nutrition should also be a consideration. Try to select a restaurant that you know offers healthful choices.

Choosing from the Menu

As with at-home meals, wise choices can help you get the most nutrition when you're eating out. The guidelines that follow can help you.

Menu Clues

Pay attention to the way foods are described on the menu. For example, food described as "broiled," "baked," or "steamed" is probably relatively low in fat. On the other hand, the following terms are a clue that the food may be high in fat:

❖ fried
❖ breaded
❖ in its own gravy
❖ in a cheese sauce
❖ rich
❖ sautéed
❖ creamed
❖ au gratin
❖ scalloped
❖ batter-dipped

If you're in doubt, ask the server how foods are prepared. You might also ask whether your food can be prepared or served differently. Perhaps fish could be broiled instead of breaded and fried, for instance.

Many fast-food restaurants now have information available on the nutritional content of the foods on their menu.

Portion Size

Many restaurants give large portions—more than you may want or need to eat. How can you avoid this problem?

❖ If there is a choice of sizes on the menu, choose the smaller one. Even if there is no size choice, some restaurants will serve a smaller portion on request.

❖ Portions for the **entree** (AHN-tray), or main course, are often large. Try making a meal of appetizer or side dish selections, such as soup and a leafy green salad.

❖ If you are served a portion that is too large, don't force yourself to eat it all. Ask for a bag to take the leftover food home. Use it for a meal or snack.

Smart Side Dishes

In a full-service restaurant, the price of an item may include certain accompaniments. For instance, a sandwich may come with french fries and cole slaw. To avoid high-fat side dishes, ask if you can order items **a la carte** (ah-lah-CART), or individually. That way you can choose which side dishes you want.

The menu may offer a variety of accompaniments to the meal. Look for healthful choices such as whole grain breads, vegetables (not fried), and fruits. If you can, combine several of these foods with a moderate-sized serving from the meat group. Add skim or low-fat milk for a beverage, and you've put together a meal based on the Dietary Guidelines.

Topping It Off

In many cases, restaurant foods would be light and healthful if it weren't for toppings and other extras. Examples include rich sauce or gravy on an entree, butter or sour cream on a potato, dressing on a salad, and mayonnaise on a sandwich. There are a number of ways to get around the problem.

When the portion you receive is more than you need, don't hesitate to ask for a container to take the extra food home. The food won't be wasted and you won't overeat.

Salad dressing isn't the only way to enhance the flavor of a tossed salad.

seasoned with salt or with a flavor enhancer called *monosodium glutamate* (MSG for short). Both contain sodium. You may want to ask whether your food can be prepared without added salt or MSG.

Fast Food Suggestions

Many fast-food restaurants now supply nutrition information to customers. Ask for a brochure or look for a sign that lists the nutrient content of items on the menu.

The box below gives suggestions for items that, in general, may be nutritious choices. However, the nutrient content of similar items can vary quite a bit from one restaurant to another. Check the nutrition information to be sure. Also remember to watch out for those extra toppings that can add fat, sugar, and sodium.

You can:
* Ask for the food to be served without the topping.
* Use a substitute. For example, you could ask for a low-fat salad dressing or use lemon juice, vinegar, pepper, or herbs instead.
* Ask that rich sauces and salad dressings be served on the side (that is, in a separate container). Then you can add just a small amount.

Perhaps you're concerned about getting too much sodium. Often restaurant foods are

Healthy Attitudes

If you're hungry enough for a giant burger with all the fixings, consider having two small plain burgers instead. The extra bun gives you more carbohydrates without added fat.

Fast Food Suggestions

Main Dishes
* Small burger with lettuce and tomato
* Roast beef sandwich
* Grilled or roast chicken sandwich
* Chicken white meat (eat without skin)
* Salad made with lean meat or poultry

Side Dishes
* Tossed salad
* Plain baked potato
* Mashed potatoes
* Plain pasta
* Corn on the cob
* Baked beans

Beverages
* Low-fat milk
* Fruit juice
* Water

Breakfast Items
* Whole grain cereal with low-fat milk
* Bran muffin

Choosing from a Salad Bar or Buffet

Many restaurants have a salad bar. You can choose from a variety of ingredients and toppings to build your own salad. The salad bar may also include ready-made salads and perhaps other foods such as fruit, cottage cheese, or hot soup.

A salad bar is a good way to include fruits and vegetables in your restaurant meal. However, if you don't choose carefully you could also be adding more fat than you realize. Prepared salads that have a creamy or oily dressing, such as potato salad, macaroni salad, or marinated vegetables, can be very high in fat. So can salad dressings and cheeses. Take smaller amounts of these items, but help yourself to plenty of leafy greens, carrots, broccoli, melon, and other nutritious selections.

Buffets are similar to salad bars, but include a wider variety of items. As with salad bars, you can build a healthful or less healthful meal. It's all in what you choose and what toppings you add. Look for nutri-tious, low-fat foods such as fruits, vegetables, whole-grain breads, low-fat dairy products, and lean meat, poultry, and fish.

Eating at School

Most schools have a cafeteria that serves lunch, and often breakfast as well. Usually the cafeteria offers a complete meal that was planned with good nutrition in mind. In some schools, you may also be able to choose from items served a la carte. Be sure to follow the Dietary Guidelines when you choose.

Bringing food from home is also an option. You'll learn how to pack a nutritious lunch or snack in Section 20.1.

Eating on the Go

These days, busy schedules often keep people from sitting down to regular meals. While they are out, they buy ready-to-eat foods from vending machines, convenience

Look for salad bars that include plenty of choices low in both calories and fat. What healthful salad foods are your favorites?

Fruit juice makes a refreshing snack any time of the day.

stores, mall shops, or drive-through windows. They may eat while working, walking, or driving.

If you find yourself in such a situation, you can still make healthful food choices. For instance, if you're limited to a vending machine, choose fresh fruit, fruit juice, yogurt, or pretzels. Better still, if you know you're not going to have much time to eat, pack nutritious foods to take with you.

How Eating Out Fits In

Keep in mind that variety is one of the keys to good nutrition. When eating out, your choices are likely to be limited. You may be short on some of the foods needed for good health, such as fruits and vegetables. If so, make an extra effort to include many different types of those foods in other meals.

Whether you eat out twice a month or twice a day, the food choices you make at that time are important ones. Remember that the food you eat away from home counts as part of your overall eating plan. Make your choices as nutritious as you can.

In Japan, it's considered bad manners to eat while walking. Snack foods bought from street vendors must be eaten at the food stand.

Section 4.3 Review

RECALL THE FACTS

1. When it comes to nutrition, what is one advantage of an all-you-can eat buffet? What is a disadvantage?

2. Give three suggestions for making healthful choices from a restaurant menu.

3. Name two vending machine foods that would be relatively nutritious choices.

4. Why is it important to balance restaurant food choices with other food choices?

DISCUSS YOUR IDEAS

5. Why do you think eating out has become so popular?

6. What do you consider when deciding when and where to eat out?

APPLY YOUR LEARNING

7. Create a lunch menu for a fast-food restaurant that emphasizes foods low in fat, sugar, and sodium. Give names to the food items. What would you call your restaurant? Why?

Section 4.4
Vegetarian Food Choices

Inez and her friends were standing in the lunch line, trying to decide what to eat. After Jennie had made her choices, Inez looked at her tray and said, "What? No hamburger today?"

"No," said Jennie, "I'm thinking of becoming a vegetarian, so I thought I'd stop eating meat for a while and see how it feels."

Vegetarians are people who do not eat meat, poultry, or fish. In addition, some do not eat dairy foods or eggs.

A vegetarian diet can supply complete nutrition. However, as with any way of eating, the food choices require some thought and planning. Before Jennie changes her way of eating, she would be wise to learn more about making vegetarian food choices.

Facts About Vegetarians

Some people are confused about what foods vegetarians eat. In fact, there are several kinds of vegetarians, depending on what foods they include in their diet.

❖ **Vegans** (VEE-guns or VEE-juns) are also known as pure vegetarians. They eat only foods from plant sources, such as grain products, dry beans and peas, fruits, vegetables, nuts, and seeds.
❖ **Lacto-vegetarians** eat dairy products in addition to foods from plant sources.
❖ **Ovo-vegetarians** eat eggs in addition to foods from plant sources.
❖ **Lacto-ovo vegetarians** eat foods from plant sources, dairy products, and eggs.

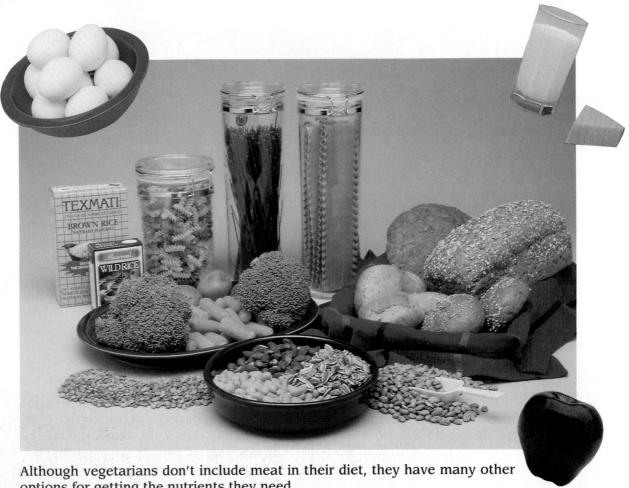

Although vegetarians don't include meat in their diet, they have many other options for getting the nutrients they need.

People choose to become vegetarians for many reasons. Close to 50 percent do so because they feel it is healthier. Of course, it's not necessary to become a vegetarian in order to practice healthful eating habits. Still, studies show that well-chosen vegetarian diets are healthier than the average American diet. For instance, most Americans eat too much protein and fat, whereas vegetarian diets can provide enough protein and be relatively low in fat.

Some people are vegetarians for religious reasons. Seventh Day Adventists, for instance, encourage their members not to eat meat. Many Hindus and Buddhists are vegetarians.

Some people become vegetarians because they are concerned about the world food supply. Animals can eat about 5 pounds (2 kg) or more of grain to produce 1 pound (500 g) of meat. Many vegetarians believe that eating meat contributes to the problem of world hunger. They think it would be better to use the grain to feed people around the world.

Others are vegetarians because they do not believe in killing animals. Still others are vegetarians for economic reasons. Vegetarian meals are usually less expensive than meat-based ones.

Good Nutrition for Vegetarians

If they make wise food choices, vegetarians can usually get all the nutrients they need. As with any other eating patterns, the key to good vegetarian nutrition is variety. Although vegetarians choose to avoid some foods, they still have plenty of others from which to select.

Today, the availability of many meatless convenience foods makes quick vegetarian meals easy to fix.

Specific Nutrients

It's helpful to take a look at how some specific nutrients are supplied in vegetarian food choices. Of particular interest are protein, fat, iron, calcium, and vitamins B_{12} and D.

Protein

Obtaining enough protein on a vegetarian diet is not difficult, even for vegans. As you may recall, proteins are made up of amino acids. Proteins from plant sources are called incomplete proteins, since they do not provide all of the essential amino acids. However, they can be combined to provide complete protein.

Safety Check

Some extreme vegan diets are too limited. For instance, "macrobiotic" diets recommend cutting out most foods until you are eating only brown rice. Such limited diets can lead to serious health problems.

Dry beans or peas, together with any grain products, nuts, or seeds eaten during the same day, can provide all the essential amino acids. In addition, vegetarians who eat dairy products or eggs can get complete protein from those sources.

Fat

You have learned in previous chapters that health experts recommend choosing foods low in fat. A well-chosen vegetarian meal pattern can be low in fat because it emphasizes grain products, fruits, and vegetables. However, vegetarians who rely heavily on whole milk, cheese, or eggs may be eating too much fat, especially saturated fat. Nuts and seeds are also high in fat.

When Angelo became a vegetarian, he enjoyed a wide variety of recipes using dairy foods and eggs. When his weight began to go up, Angelo realized that he was eating more fat than before, so he made some basic changes. He switched to low-fat dairy products and cut back on eggs. He discovered delicious recipes for cooked dry beans and peas and added a variety of whole grain products to his meals. He also ate more fruits and vegetables. Before long, Angelo's weight returned to normal.

Iron

Many fruits, vegetables, and grain products are good sources of iron, especially dry beans and peas and dried fruits. However, vegetarians run the risk of an iron shortage because the iron in foods from plant sources is not easily absorbed.

Vitamin C helps the body absorb iron from plant sources. It's best to eat foods rich in vitamin C at the same time as foods high in iron. If vegetarians eat a wide variety of foods, including rich sources of vitamin C, they will probably meet their iron needs. Another way to get iron is by using cast iron cookware.

Calcium

Getting enough calcium is of particular concern for vegans and others who do not drink milk. As you have learned, a good supply of calcium is essential for healthy bones and teeth.

Dry beans are used in many vegetarian dishes because they supply protein and other nutrients. Dozens of different varieties of beans are available.

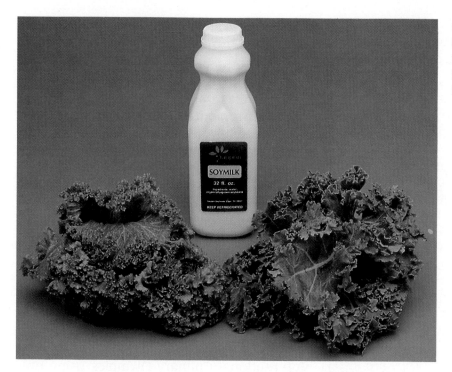

Green leafy vegetables and soy milk are important sources of calcium for vegans, who only eat foods from plant sources.

Calcium needs can probably be met by eating good plant sources of the nutrient. These include dry beans and green leafy vegetables, such as spinach, kale, and mustard greens.

Even so, it may be difficult for vegans to get enough calcium. They may be advised to drink fortified soy milk. Some health professionals recommend vegans use calcium supplements.

Vitamins B$_{12}$ and D

Another concern regarding vegan diets is vitamins B$_{12}$ and D. Vitamin B$_{12}$ is not found in foods from plant sources. Vitamin D is found mainly in fortified milk. Some health professionals recommend the use of supplements to help vegans meet the requirements for these vitamins.

Planning Vegetarian Meals

Planning vegetarian meals can be easy. Just follow the basic guidelines for meal planning you have already studied, but modify them. Here are some suggestions:

❖ Start with the Food Guide Pyramid (page 97). For servings from the meat group, choose dry beans and peas, nuts, and seeds (and eggs, if you wish). Remember that 1/2 cup (125 mL) of dry beans, or one egg, is the equivalent of 1 ounce (28 g) of meat.

❖ Look for food products made from soybeans and wheat that can be substituted for foods from animal sources. The box on page 132 lists some that can be found in supermarkets or health food stores.

❖ Get acquainted with the many varieties of grain products and dry beans and peas that are available. (See Chapter 17 for more information about these foods.) For instance, you might want to try grains such as millet, bulgur, and barley.

❖ Each day, make sure you have several good sources of vitamin C, such as citrus fruits, strawberries, and melons.

❖ Use dark green leafy vegetables, such as kale and mustard greens, liberally.

Products to Try

❖ **Soy milk,** a beverage made from soybeans, can be used as a milk substitute. Look for products that are fortified.

❖ **Tofu** (TOE-foo) is also known as soybean curd. High in protein, it has a bland flavor that blends well with other foods. Choose from firm or soft tofu to use in recipes. You can also buy tofu hot dogs, patties, and ready-to-eat frozen foods.

❖ **Seitan** (say-tan) is also known as wheat meat. Although it resembles cooked meat, it's made from wheat dough cooked in a flavored liquid. Seitan can be substituted for meat in many recipes and is also available as ready-to-eat foods.

❖ **Vegetable protein foods** are made of soy protein. You can buy them in granular form to mix in recipes. They are also commercially made into ready-to-eat meat and poultry substitutes, such as breakfast links.

Vegetarian Recipes

Many vegetarian recipe books are available. They range from basic information on getting started with vegetarian foods to gourmet and ethnic recipes. Since vegetarian recipes are sometimes high in fat, choose them carefully. You can also adapt favorite non-vegetarian recipes, substituting ingredients such as seitan or bulgur for meat.

Many ethnic cuisines, such as Asian and Central and South American, are based on vegetarian foods. They can provide you with a wealth of menu ideas and recipes as well as introduce you to new foods.

Vegetarian meals can be just as appealing as any others. One of the most famous American chefs is Brother Ron Pickarski, a Franciscan friar and certified executive chef. He heads the American natural foods team, which has won two silver medals at the International Culinary Olympics using only vegan foods.

Some vegetarian products are designed to replace meat and poultry in recipes.

Eating Out Vegetarian Style

Because of demand from their customers, many restaurants are offering at least one vegetarian meal on their menu. Except for vegans, most vegetarians should have no problems making food choices when eating out. They can usually find meatless meals made with milk, eggs, or cheese. Some food choices might include baked potatoes with cheese toppings, pizza, meatless lasagna, bean soup, and omelets.

Since vegans eat no animal products, their choices are more limited. Many restaurants offer salad bars or a selection of salads on the menu, but for those who eat out frequently, this can be tiresome.

Here are some suggestions for vegans when eating out:

❖ Choose self-serve restaurants, such as cafeterias or buffets, whenever possible. They usually have an assortment of hot vegetables and breads, along with fresh fruits and salads. If hot soup is offered, find out if it has meat or is made from a meat stock.

❖ Read the menu descriptions carefully. Sometimes the ingredients for each selection are listed. If not, and an item sounds as though it might be suitable, ask the server what it contains.

❖ Tell the server that you are a vegetarian and ask whether the chef would be willing to make up a plate of cooked vegetables.

❖ Ethnic restaurants, such as Chinese, East Indian, Mexican, and Mideastern, usually offer some vegan meals.

❖ If a restaurant does not offer any vegan meals except salads, talk to the manager. Restaurants are always looking for ways to attract new customers and may be receptive to your ideas.

Tofu, made from protein-rich soybeans, comes in several different forms. Because of its bland flavor, it blends well with many foods.

Vegetarian meals aren't just for vegetarians. This spicy bean pizza, for example, would please almost anyone.

RECALL THE FACTS

1. How are a vegan and a lacto-ovo vegetarian similar? How are they different?

2. List four reasons people give for becoming vegetarians.

3. How can vegetarians be sure to get enough protein? Iron?

4. Give three guidelines for planning vegetarian meals.

DISCUSS YOUR IDEAS

5. Do you think restaurants should offer more choices for vegetarian customers? If they did, would non-vegetarian customers also benefit? Why or why not?

APPLY YOUR LEARNING

6. Plan one day's meals and snacks for a vegetarian. Be prepared to explain the type of vegetarian the menu is for and why you chose those foods.

CAREER PROFILE

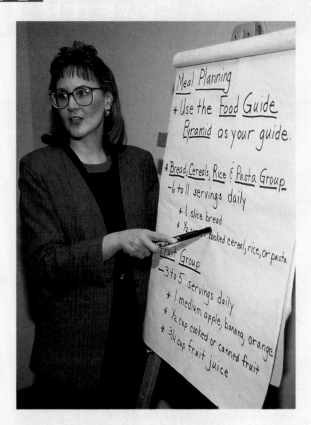

Sue Anderson
Extension Home
Economist

Current position:

"I'm one of two home economists working for the Cooperative Extension Service in a small rural county."

Responsibilities:

"My job is multi-faceted, but my basic duties are to educate the public about home economics. I do this through phone calls that come in to my office, through video programs that I plan and prepare, and through articles that I write for the media."

Skills:

"Because the majority of my time is spent talking to people about home economics, communication skills are very important for this job. Flexibility and creativity are also valued skills."

Education:

"I have a four-year college degree in home economics with a minor in communications."

Work environment:

"Every day is different. Some days are spent in the office writing press releases or answering telephone calls from the public. Other days are spent out in the community, delivering programs and speeches to groups of people. My hours can vary greatly, including evening and weekend work."

Favorite part of the job:

"Most enjoyable for me is being able to provide people with the kind of information they need in their everyday lives, whether it be food preparation or managing a household budget. I also like the variety that goes with this job."

- Do you think you'd like a job in which every day is different? Why or why not?
- What are the advantages of having hours that vary? What are the disadvantages?

135

Summary

Section 4.1
Daily Meals and Snacks: People follow many different eating patterns, from three traditional meals a day to "grazing." No matter what eating pattern you follow, be sure your daily food choices provide the right amount of calories and nutrients. It's also important to eat regularly, start the day with a nutritious breakfast, and choose snacks wisely

Section 4.2
Improving Your Eating Habits: Keeping a food record is a good way to identify your current eating habits. Then you can evaluate your habits and decide whether you want to change them. Work at improving your eating habits gradually and set specific, realistic goals.

Section 4.3
Eating Out Nutritiously: Different types of restaurants have pros and cons when it comes to nutrition. Learn to identify the healthful choices on a restaurant menu, a salad bar, or a buffet. Wise food choices are also important when eating at school or eating on the go.

Section 4.4
Vegetarian Food Choices: Some vegetarians eat only foods from plants, while others also eat dairy products or eggs. People become vegetarians for many reasons. The vegetarian way of eating can be healthful as long as wise food choices are made. To plan vegetarian meals, modify the basic guidelines for good nutrition.

REVIEWING FACTS

1. Identify two ways to judge whether an eating pattern is nutritionally sound. (4.1)
2. Name two negative consequences of skipping breakfast. (4.1)
3. What is meant by "grazing"? (4.1)
4. Briefly describe how to keep a food record. (4.2)
5. When planning to improve your food habits, why is it important to decide on specific changes? (4.2)
6. Name three clues that a food on a restaurant menu may be high in fat. (4.3)
7. What does ordering "a la carte" mean? How can it help you choose healthier foods when eating out? (4.3)
8. Name four types of vegetarians and the foods eaten by each. (4.4)
9. Why do some vegetarians need to be careful about eating too much fat? (4.4)
10. Why is calcium a concern for some vegetarians? Name two foods that can help meet their calcium needs. (4.4)

LEARNING BY DOING

1. **Foods lab:** Using recipe books or magazines, find three ideas for quick and easy foods that would make a nutritious breakfast. Prepare the foods in class. (4.1)
2. **Computer lab:** Using a word processing program or other software, produce a form that could be used when keeping a food record. Include spaces for recording the food eaten, amount, time of day, and situation. (4.2)

3. *Taste test:* Taste samples of vegetarian dishes provided by your teacher. Judge them on taste and appearance. (4.4)

THINKING CRITICALLY

1. *Analyzing a statement:* Your friend tells you that snacking is bad for you. Do you agree or disagree? Why? (4.1)

2. *Analyzing behavior:* Alyssa was reviewing her food record. She noticed that when she ate alone or with her family, she usually made healthful food choices. However, her choices were less wise when she ate out with friends. Why might this be so? (4.2)

3. *Predicting consequences:* How might consumer complaints or suggestions affect menu items offered by a restaurant? What might happen if restaurant owners ignore consumer complaints and suggestions? (4.3, 4.4)

4. *Recognizing stereotypes:* Suppose you and a friend are eating out. You hear a person at the next table asking if there are any vegetarian dishes on the menu. Your friend says, "How dumb. People who don't eat meat are weird. I'll bet he's a real weakling." Is this a reasonable judgment? What can you say to help your friend better understand vegetarians and their way of eating? (4.4)

MAKING DECISIONS AND SOLVING PROBLEMS

What Would You Do?

1. Your dad routinely fixes breakfast for the family. Most mornings he prepares eggs, bacon or sausage, buttered biscuits, and whole milk. You appreciate his willingness to see that you have a hot breakfast each morning. However, you are concerned about the fat and cholesterol in the foods he prepares. (4.1)

2. Analyzing your food record, you find that you are most likely to make poor food choices late in the day, a few hours after the evening meal. You also find you eat very few fruits. (4.2)

3. You would like to eat in your school cafeteria each day. However, you have noticed that many of the foods served seem high in fat. (4.3)

4. One of your cousins is coming to stay with you for a week while his parents are out of town. He has just reminded you that he is a lacto-vegetarian. Your family routinely serves meat at every meal. (4.4)

LINKING YOUR STUDIES

1. *Social studies:* Using library resources, research the eating patterns in two other cultures. Present your findings to the class. Discuss why eating patterns vary from one culture to another. (4.1)

2. *Math:* Use a calorie-counting guide and a one-day food record. Determine approximately how many calories were in each meal and snack. Express the calories for each meal or snack as a percentage of the total calories for the day. (4.1, 4.2)

3. *Math:* At a popular fast-food restaurant chain, a cheeseburger has 305 calories, 9 grams of fat, 50 milligrams of cholesterol, and 725 milligrams of sodium. A small order of fries has 220 calories, 12 grams of fat, no cholesterol, and 110 milligrams of sodium. What is the total amount of calories, fat, cholesterol, and sodium for this meal? If one gram of fat has 9 calories, how many calories does the fat in this meal provide? (4.3)

4. *Writing:* Write a dialogue in which a vegetarian explains his or her food choices to a non-vegetarian. (4.4)

CHAPTER 5
Food and Fitness

Section 5.1
A Healthy Weight

Objectives

After studying this section, you should be able to:

- Explain why there is no one ideal body shape.
- Describe methods used to determine whether a person's weight is at a healthy level.

Look for This Term

waist-to-hip ratio

Margo was confused. According to the weight charts, she was at least five pounds too heavy for her height. Yet she knew that she ate sensibly and exercised regularly. She also knew that she wasn't as slender as some of her friends. Maybe the weight charts were right.

The Myth of the "Ideal" Body

Like Margo, many people are concerned or dissatisfied with their weight. One reason is a lack of realistic goals.

About half the people trying to lose weight today are not really overweight. Instead, they are trying to reduce to a body size or weight that's impossible for them to reach. Movies and television shows, along with advertisers, set up a slim body as the ideal for everyone.

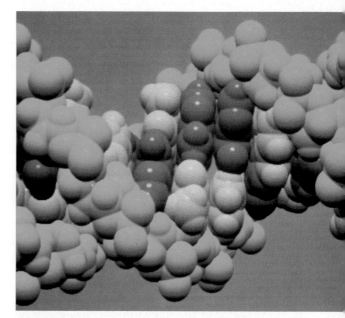

Inherited characteristics play a major role in determining body shape. DNA molecules, like this one, are located in the nucleus of each cell. They carry the genetic code of characteristics unique to you.

In reality, the human body comes in many different shapes and sizes. These differences have nothing to do with being "too fat" or "too thin." They are simply part of each person's inherited traits.

Through the genes, children inherit characteristics from their parents, grandparents, and other ancestors. Some people have inherited wider shoulders or hips than others. Legs may be short, long, or in-between. When you look around, you see many different combinations, from tall, thin bodies to short, stocky ones. How do you judge body shapes? Does shape make one person more worthy than another one?

Most people are much more critical of their own body shape than other people's bodies. In their minds, they have an image of an "ideal" body and try desperately to reach that ideal. In most cases, it's a losing battle. The slim model or movie star inherited that shape, just as you did yours. Unless their genetic makeup allows it, most people cannot possibly change their body shape to match the ideal image.

Successful weight management starts with accepting the body you were born with. Then you can take steps to achieve a healthy weight within your body limits. You may never look like a model or star athlete. However, it's far more important to be fit and healthy, whatever your shape and size.

What Is a Healthy Weight?

The Dietary Guidelines urge people to maintain a healthy weight. That means a weight that will help you stay healthy throughout your life, within the framework of your own inherited shape.

Health professionals use a variety of methods to evaluate whether a person is overweight or underweight. These include weight charts, body fat tests, and waist-to-hip ratio.

Weight Charts

A weight chart, such as the one below, gives recommendations for heights (without shoes) and weights (without clothes) for adults. The table suggests that, as people age, a slight increase in weight is acceptable.

Suggested Weights for Adults		
Height[1]	Weight in pounds[2]	
	19 to 34 years	35 years and over
5'0"	[3]97-128	108-138
5'1"	101-132	111-143
5'2"	104-137	115-148
5'3"	107-141	119-152
5'4"	111-146	122-157
5'5"	114-150	126-162
5'6"	118-155	130-167
5'7"	121-160	134-172
5'8"	125-164	138-178
5'9"	129-169	142-183
5'10"	132-174	146-188
5'11"	136-179	151-194
6'0"	140-184	155-199
6'1"	144-189	159-205
6'2"	148-195	164-210
6'3"	152-200	168-216
6'4"	156-205	173-222
6'5"	160-211	177-228
6'6"	164-216	182-234

[1]Without shoes.
[2]Without clothes.
[3]The higher weights in the ranges generally apply to men, who tend to have more muscle and bone; the lower weights more often apply to women, who have less muscle and bone.

Source: Dietary Guidelines for Americans

Weight charts are not available for children and teens. That's because they are growing rapidly and at different rates.

Body-Fat Tests

Instead of weight, some health professionals prefer to check the amount of body fat in relation to muscle. In many cases, this gives a truer picture than a number on a scale does.

When Margo saw that she weighed more than the charts recommended, she became concerned. However, body-fat tests showed that the extra pounds were from muscle, not fat. Margo actually had less body fat than average. Her physician reassured her that she did not need to lose weight.

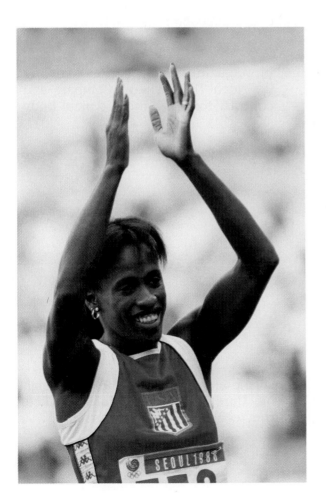

Waist-to-Hip Ratio

Health professionals also look at how fat is distributed in the body. Researchers have divided people into two groups, according to where fat is located. Adults with a pear-like shape carry most of the fat on the thighs and hips. Those with an apple-like shape carry most of it over the abdomen. Research shows that "apples" may have a greater risk of health problems than the "pears." "Apples," however, seem to be able to lose excess weight more easily than "pears."

Adults can check their body shape very easily. They should stand relaxed and measure their waist without pulling in their stomach. Then they should measure their hips where they are the largest. Divide the waist measurement by the hip measurement. This will give the **waist-to-hip ratio.**

Adult women should have a ratio no higher than 0.80, while men should have no more than 0.95. Ratios above these limits may increase the risk of health problems, even if the scale shows that weight is at a healthy level.

Successful athletes pay careful attention to the ratio of fat to muscle. They understand the vital role nutrition plays in a training program.

The Right Weight for You

As you can see, there's more to evaluating a person's weight than meets the eye. If you're wondering about your weight, don't compare yourself to your friends or to a picture in a magazine. Instead, talk to a health professional. He or she can use reliable methods to judge whether your weight is right for you.

No matter what your shape or size, a sound weight management program can benefit you. In the next section, you'll learn some basic guidelines to help you maintain a healthy weight throughout your life.

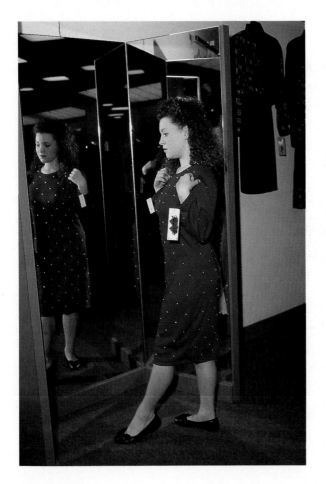

Be realistic about what is a healthy weight for you. Unrealistic expectations can keep you from feeling good about yourself.

Section 5.2
Weight Management

Look for These Terms

fad diets
"yo-yo" dieting
behavior modification

A weight management program can help you achieve a healthy weight and maintain it throughout your life. Beginning weight management now can lead to a lifetime of better health. Whether you need to lose weight, gain weight, or keep your weight about where it is now, you'll find tips in this section to help you.

Losing Excess Weight

As you have learned, excess weight can be a health risk. Studies show that overweight is a risk factor in heart disease, diabetes, cancer, and high blood pressure. For many people, losing weight is a positive step toward better health.

By eating right and staying active, you can maintain a healthy weight.

A woman should never go on a weight-loss diet during pregnancy. Weight gain is very important for expectant mothers. Their own health, and that of the baby, depends on getting enough nutritious food. You can read more about this subject in Section 6.1.

Evaluating Weight-Loss Methods

These days, with so much attention focused on health and appearance, weight loss is big business. Everywhere you turn you can find books, articles, and advertisements that claim to provide the answers to weight loss.

Popular types of weight-loss methods include:

- *Weight-loss diets*—eating plans that restrict calorie intake.
- *Weight-control centers*—organizations that provide a diet and psychological support.
- *Weight-control products*—anything from pills to candies, crackers, milkshakes, and even prepared meals, all sold with the promise of helping people lose weight.

Some of the weight-loss methods that are promoted are based on sound nutrition principles. Many, however, are not. **Fad diets** are current, popular weight-loss methods that ignore good nutrition. Some, as you will see, can even be dangerous to health.

Dangers to Avoid

Many weight-loss plans rely on unsafe methods. Avoid the following:

- ❖ Very low-calorie diets (800 calories or less per day). These may not provide enough energy or enough of the nutrients needed for good health.
- ❖ Diets based on a single food, such as grapefruit. As you know, your body needs a variety of foods every day.
- ❖ Fasting—going without food. This can be extremely damaging to your health.
- ❖ Diet pills. Some contain drugs that could create serious health problems.
- ❖ Plans that promise quick weight loss (over 2 pounds, or 1 kg, per week).

Even a weight-loss plan that would be acceptable for an adult may pose a problem for teens. At this point in your life, you are probably still growing. If you follow a weight-loss plan now, you might not get enough nutrients to grow into a healthy adult. If you are overweight now, see a health professional before you begin a weight-loss plan.

There are no magic ways to lose weight. The advertisements for diet pills, for example, don't tell you they can cause serious health problems.

People who lose weight too quickly may develop the following symptoms due to lack of nutrients:

❖ Constant fatigue.
❖ Large, dark circles under the eyes.
❖ Sagging, flaking, or dry skin.
❖ Brittle or soft fingernails.
❖ Dull or thinning hair.

Disadvantages to Consider

Not all weight-loss methods are dangerous to health. However, many have other disadvantages.

Some methods are simply frauds. For instance, some products that claim to suppress appetite may use ingredients that actually have no effect.

Cost is another consideration. Weight control centers and special diet products can be expensive. Think carefully about what you are getting for your money.

Some weight-loss plans offer very limited food choices. Favorite foods are denied and the diet becomes monotonous. As a result, people find it difficult to stay on the plan long enough to get the results they want.

Of those who do manage to lose weight by dieting, at least 95 percent gain it back. The most likely reason is that weight-loss diets are seen as a temporary way of eating. Instead of learning to make healthful food choices, dieters often rely on printed menus or prepackaged meals. As soon as they have lost the weight, they tend to go back to their old eating habits.

Many dieters get caught up in the cycle of **"yo-yo" dieting.** They lose weight when dieting and gain weight when the diet stops. Then they go back on a diet and repeat the same cycle.

People who are overweight are more likely to suffer from heart disease. Many heart attacks are brought on by atherosclerosis. Fatty deposits—linked to a high-fat diet—build up in the blood vessels. When a vessel becomes completely blocked, the heart is deprived of oxygen. This causes a heart attack.

Research shows the yo-yo dieting is a risk factor in diseases such as high blood pressure and heart disease. What's more, with each diet, more weight is gained back than was lost. The weight becomes harder and harder to lose. Thus, people who practice yo-yo dieting often end up weighing more than when they started the process. They also have a greater risk of health problems.

Successful Weight Loss

If so many weight-loss methods don't work, what does work? The most successful way to manage weight is by making gradual, permanent changes in eating and exercise habits. This is known as **behavior modification.** It is the key to keeping your weight at a healthy level throughout your life.

It's wise to have a medical checkup before beginning any weight-loss program. A health professional can help you judge whether you truly have a weight problem that needs attention. You may have to consider other health factors besides excess weight. In addition, a health professional can give you expert advice that will help you succeed.

Set Reasonable Goals

Setting specific goals for weight loss can help motivate you and give you a way to see your progress. However, make sure your goals are reasonable.

First, be realistic about the size and shape of your body. Don't try to reach a weight or clothing size that's not right for you.

If you have a large amount of weight to lose, divide the task into a series of smaller goals. For instance, Deanna needed to lose 40 pounds (18 kg), but her first goal was to lose just 10 pounds (4.5 kg). The smaller goal was easier to reach and gave her the encouragement she needed to stick with her program.

Give yourself plenty of time to reach your goal. Remember, it's taken you a lifetime to develop your eating and exercise habits. You cannot expect to change them in a matter of a few days or weeks.

Aim for a weight loss of no more than 1/2 to 2 pounds (0.25 to 1 kg) a week. The more slowly you lose weight, the better your body can adjust to it. Your weight loss has a greater chance of being permanent.

Get More Exercise

Lack of exercise is one of the basic causes of overweight. Just increasing your physical activity, even without cutting down on food, can often result in a leaner body.

Remember, the balance between energy in food and the energy you use for activities affects your weight. If you use up about the same number of calories as you get from food, your weight should stay at about the same level. If the food you eat provides more calories than you need for your activities, your body stores the extra as fat. Therefore, you gain weight. If you use up more calories in activities than you take in from food, you should lose weight.

In theory, you could change your energy balance just by eating less. In reality, however, it's better to increase your activity level as well. Why? Studies show that exercise not only burns calories during the activity, but also increases metabolism for some time

Exercise is a key element in successful weight loss. Besides using up calories, moderate exercise often seems to reduce appetite.

Calories Burned in Activities
The more strenuous an activity, the more calories you burn. The following chart shows the approximate number of calories used during one minute of activity. These figures are for someone who weighs 140 pounds (63 kg). Someone who weighs more would burn slightly more calories. Someone who weighs less would burn slightly fewer.
Sitting or standing quietly ....1 to 2 calories per minute *Light activity:* cleaning house, playing baseball ....4 calories per minute *Moderate activity:* brisk walking, gardening, ...6 calories per minute cycling, dancing, playing basketball *Strenuous activity:* jogging, playing football, ...9 to 10 calories per minute swimming *Very strenuous activity:* running fast,...............................12 calories per minute racquetball, skiing

afterward. In other words, it increases the amount of energy used for basic body processes. Regular exercise also helps ensure that the weight you lose comes from body fat, not muscle.

Whatever your level of physical activity when you start a weight-loss plan, try to increase it. Without the added physical activity, you probably will not lose much weight. Section 5.3 discusses different types of exercise and gives guidelines for planning an exercise program.

Change Your Eating Habits

Establishing new, more healthful eating habits will also help you reach and maintain a healthy weight. Be sure to follow a sensible eating plan that you enjoy and that allows you to eat a reasonable number of calories a day. You can get a reliable plan from a physician, nutritionist, or dietitian.

One of the keys to successful weight loss is to eat less fat. Remember, fat supplies more than twice as many calories as carbohydrates or proteins. Therefore, foods high in fat will make you gain weight much faster than other foods. In addition, studies suggest that fats in food are turned into body fat more easily than excess carbohydrates and proteins.

Avoiding high-fat foods can help you lose weight faster. A baked or broiled skinless chicken breast would be a better choice than fried chicken.

TIPS for Success

Losing Weight

❖ Weigh yourself no more than once a week. That way the weight loss will be more noticeable. You won't be discouraged by the natural ups and downs in weight that occur from day to day.

❖ Don't give up if you don't show a weight loss for the first three or four weeks. It takes time for your body to adjust.

❖ After you have lost a little weight, you may suddenly stop losing. This is common and is called a "plateau." To continue losing weight, you may have to eat less fat and fewer calories or just increase your daily activity slightly.

❖ Eat slowly. Take time to relax and enjoy the taste of the food. Wait awhile to let your body tell you if it is full before deciding to take a second helping.

❖ If you eat a high-fat, high-calorie favorite, don't feel guilty or give up. Just enjoy the food, then go back to your plan.

❖ About once a month, keep a food record (as explained in Section 4.2). See whether your eating habits are changing as planned.

❖ If possible, find others who are trying to lose weight by changing their eating habits. Give each other moral support.

❖ Reward yourself when you reach a goal. Don't celebrate by going back to old eating habits. Instead, go to a concert or buy a special poster you've wanted.

As you learn to make more sensible food choices, become aware of nutrient-dense foods. They give you the most nutrients for the least number of calories. Select foods carefully from the five food groups. Be sure to choose lean meats and low-fat dairy products. Eat plenty of grain products and fresh fruits and vegetables. By eating less fat and sugar, you may find that you can eat more food instead of less and still lose weight.

If you've read Section 4.2, then you have already found good advice for improving your eating habits. Remember, most people make both sound and poor food choices. The focus is to keep the sensible choices and improve the poor ones. At the same time, the food choices must be enjoyable ones.

Gaining Needed Weight

Although many people are concerned with weight loss, some need to gain weight. For instance, male teens, who have very high energy needs, may find it a challenge to get enough calories each day. Teens who are going through a growth spurt may appear thin until weight catches up with height.

If you're concerned about being too thin, discuss the matter with a physician. There may be a medical reason for inability to put on weight.

Here are some hints to help you gain weight without adding fat to your food choices:

❖ Have larger portions of nutritious foods from the five food groups.

❖ Eat regular meals.

❖ Enjoy healthful snacks between meals.

❖ Avoid high-sugar and high-fat snacks such as candy, chips, and french fries. Instead, rely on snacks with more nutrients, such as yogurt and fresh or dried fruit.

People with eating disorders can become dangerously thin. Overcoming the problem is not a simple matter, since the causes are complex and not well understood. Section 6.3 discusses eating disorders in more detail.

Whatever your weight goals, make your food choices nutritious ones.

Maintaining a Healthy Weight

Todd has finally filled out. Now he wants to hold his weight steady at this level. His father, who has successfully lost 20 pounds, also wants to keep the healthy weight he has reached. Todd's mother has always been at a healthy weight. However, she is concerned about staying that way as she gets older.

Once a healthy weight has been reached, the next goal is to maintain it. If you continue to follow good eating and exercise habits, you should have no problem maintaining a healthy weight. Still, if your weight starts to change, here are some suggestions:

❖ Keep track of the food you eat for a few days and analyze the results. You may be slipping into poor eating patterns.
❖ If you find your weight going up, be sure you're getting plenty of exercise.
❖ If you find you're eating too much or too little because of stress, look for healthy ways to cope with your problems.

Section 5.2 Review

RECALL THE FACTS

1. What are the health risks associated with overweight?

2. Name three signs that a weight-loss plan is unsafe.

3. What is behavior modification? How does it relate to weight loss?

4. Give two tips for gaining weight and two tips for maintaining weight.

DISCUSS YOUR IDEAS

5. Why are fad diets popular? What could be done to educate people about the problems associated with them?

APPLY YOUR LEARNING

6. In newspapers and magazines, find ads for weight-loss methods. Evaluate them based on the information you have read in this section.

Section 5.3
Exercise Basics

Objectives

After studying this section, you should be able to:

❖ Explain the benefits of exercise.
❖ Describe the basic types of exercise.
❖ Make a plan for an exercise program.

Look for This Term

aerobic

Almost everywhere you look, you can see people enjoying physical activity—walking in the park, shooting baskets in a school yard, digging in the garden. These people have discovered the physical and emotional benefits provided by regular, enjoyable exercise.

Benefits of Exercise

Exercise does have many benefits:

❖ It helps keep the body mobile. If muscles are not used regularly, they tend to stiffen and movement eventually becomes painful and difficult. Regular exercise can keep the muscles strong and flexible throughout life.
❖ It helps improve psychological health. Regular exercise helps people feel better by reducing stress and anxiety. Studies show that regular exercisers have a brighter outlook on life.

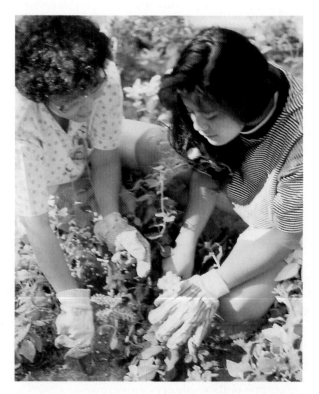

Exercise includes more than running or lifting weights. Hobbies like gardening can reduce stress and increase physical activity.

- It helps improve physical health. Exercise speeds up the metabolism and increases the flow of energy in the body. It can help people lose and keep off excess weight. Exercise reduces the risk of osteoporosis, the condition marked by weak and brittle bones. It can also lower blood pressure and blood cholesterol levels and reduce the risk of heart disease.
- Just as important, exercise can be fun. Many people of all ages enjoy sports and other physical activities.

Types of Exercise

The many forms of exercise can be divided into three basic kinds. A well-rounded exercise program includes all three.

- Stretching exercises gently stretch the muscles. Performing these exercises correctly will keep the body flexible and can help prevent injury.
- **Aerobic** (uh-ROW-bick) exercises give your heart and lungs a workout. Aerobic means "using oxygen." During the exercise, your body needs more oxygen, so you breathe more deeply. Your heart pumps faster and harder to send blood through your body. As a result, the heart and lungs are exercised. This helps lower the risk of heart disease. Aerobic exercises include walking, jogging, climbing stairs, bicycling, aerobic dance, and swimming.
- Strengthening exercises build strong muscles in the arms, legs, and torso. Having strong muscles aids in everyday activities and helps prevent injury. Strengthening exercises include push-ups and sit-ups. Another way to strengthen muscles is by lifting weights. People generally start with light weights and gradually increase to heavier ones. However, weightlifting exercises are not recommended until the body has reached full adult development. Seek advice from a health professional before starting to lift weights.

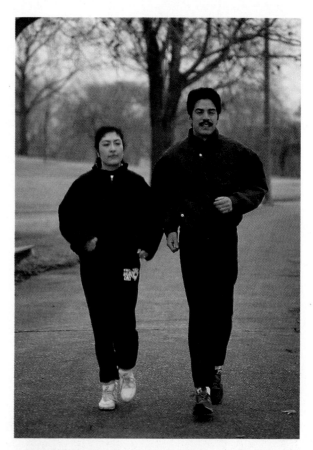

Aerobic exercise raises your heart rate. Experts recommend regular aerobic exercise—at least three times per week for 20 to 30 minutes at a time.

Safety Check

Exercise can improve health, but it can also result in injury if you're not careful. Use the proper equipment and follow the correct techniques for each activity. Learn how to warm up and cool down properly. If you feel pain while exercising, stop at once. Following these guidelines will help keep your workouts safe and enjoyable.

Getting the Exercise Habit

If you do not exercise regularly, think about starting now. Begin with a medical checkup. Then experiment with different kinds of exercise and choose several that interest you. That way, you won't be bored and will be more likely to exercise regularly. If possible, get other members of the family involved or exercise with friends.

There are exercise options to suit every taste and budget. Depending on the activity, you can exercise outdoors, at school or a fitness center, or at home. You might enjoy playing sports or using fitness equipment such as a stationary bicycle or treadmill. Exercise classes and videotapes offer still more options. Many activities, such as walking or jumping rope, require little more than a comfortable pair of shoes.

Technology Tidbit

You may have seen or used exercise equipment that has computer readouts. For instance, some stationary bicycles have a display that keeps track of your pulse rate, the time and "distance" you have pedaled, and the number of calories you have burned.

If you exercise at home, try listening to music or watching your favorite program. You'll find the time goes faster and you will enjoy it more.

You don't have to exercise strenuously. Research is beginning to show that even moderate exercise has health benefits. Begin your program by exercising five or ten minutes a day, every other day. Gradually increase the time to about 30 minutes. Exercise at least three times a week, although every day is preferable.

Many people don't exercise because they think they don't have time. When you make out your schedule, allow time for exercise. Don't think of it as one more chore to cram into an already busy day, but as your fun time, a time to enjoy yourself.

The benefits of exercise are well worth the time spent. Like good nutrition, regular exercise is a habit that gives a lifetime of physical and emotional rewards.

Try out a variety of activities to find the ones you enjoy most. Many people prefer sports because they can spend time with friends while they work out.

Healthy Attitudes

You can easily work exercise into everyday activities. You might try:
- Walking to school or work.
- Taking the stairs instead of the elevator.
- Getting up to change the channel instead of using the remote control.
- Playing upbeat music while doing household chores.
- Planning social activities around physical ones. For example, turn a birthday party into a roller skating party.

Section 5.3 Review

RECALL THE FACTS

1. Name three benefits of exercise.

2. What are the basic types of exercise? Why is each important?

3. What are the steps for beginning a new exercise program?

DISCUSS YOUR IDEAS

4. Why do you think people are advised to get a medical checkup before beginning a new exercise program?

5. What is your favorite form of exercise? Which of the three basic types of exercise does it involve?

APPLY YOUR LEARNING

6. Make a chart which outlines an exercise plan for the next week. Include at least three exercise sessions and at least two different types of activities. Be prepared to explain the benefits of your plan.

Objectives

After studying this section, you should be able to:

❖ Explain how an athlete's nutrient needs can be met.
❖ Give suggestions for pre-game meals.
❖ Point out the dangers of using steroids to build muscles.

Look for These Terms

dehydration
anabolic steroids

When you think of "athlete," what comes to mind? Perhaps it's a superstar whose career depends on building the physical strength, skill, and stamina needed for success. However, an athlete may also be a high school swimmer or a 50-year-old who enjoys her morning run. Regardless of how seriously they are involved, all athletes' performance can benefit from good nutrition.

Eating right can't improve an athlete's skills—only practice can do that. An athlete's daily food choices, however, can make a difference between a good performance and a poor one.

Nutrient Needs of Athletes

Generally, an athlete's nutrition needs can be met by following the Food Guide Pyramid's recommendations. However, the athlete does have two nutritional needs that far exceed those of the average person: the need for energy and for water.

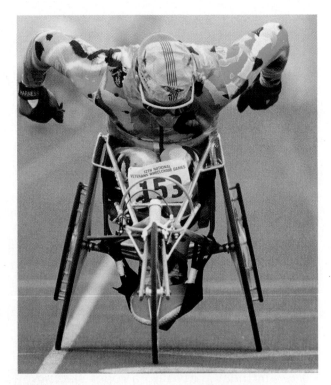

Successful athletes know that performing their best requires good nutrition.

Energy Needs

As you have learned, during digestion carbohydrates are broken down into the simple sugar glucose, which is used for energy. Extra carbohydrates are turned into a storage form of glucose known as glycogen (GLIE-kuh-juhn). Glycogen is stored in the liver and muscles.

During vigorous and extended periods of exercise, the body uses glycogen for fuel. When the glycogen is used up, the athlete runs out of energy. Therefore, it's essential for athletes to eat plenty of carbohydrates to build up their glycogen stores.

During training and competition, athletes may need two or three times as much energy as the average person. To supply this additional energy, complex carbohydrates are the best choice. These include foods such as dry beans and peas, breads, cereal, pasta, rice, and potatoes. About 60 percent of an athlete's calories should come from carbohydrates, about 25 percent from fat, and about 15 percent from protein.

Healthy Attitudes

"Carbohydrate loading" refers to techniques designed to increase the amount of glycogen stored in the muscles. There are many myths about carbohydrate loading. Here are the facts:

- For the average athlete, carbohydrate loading is not necessary. It can, however, be helpful when training for a long, intense event, such as a marathon.
- The proper way to practice carbohydrate loading is simple. Just continue to eat healthfully with an emphasis on complex carbohydrates. A few days before the event, cut back on exercise. This gives the muscles a chance to rest and store glycogen.

Pasta and other complex carbohydrates are an excellent source of the extra energy athletes need.

Liquid Needs

Athletes lose a great deal of water through perspiration—as much as 3 to 5 quarts (3 to 5 L) during a strenuous workout. If the water is not replaced right away, **dehydration** (dee-high-DRAY-shun), or lack of adequate fluids in the body, can result. This can lead to serious health problems.

An athlete who is dehydrated may become weak and confused. The body can become overheated, especially when exercising in hot weather. Heat exhaustion or heat stroke can result. These are serious conditions requiring first aid.

To prevent dehydration, athletes should drink water before, during, and after an event. They should drink water even if they do not feel thirsty. Thirst is a sign that dehydration has already begun.

One good way to gauge the amount of water to drink is to weigh in before and after the event. Loss of water usually shows up as a loss in body weight. For each pound (500 g) lost during exercise, athletes should drink 2 cups (500 mL) of fluid.

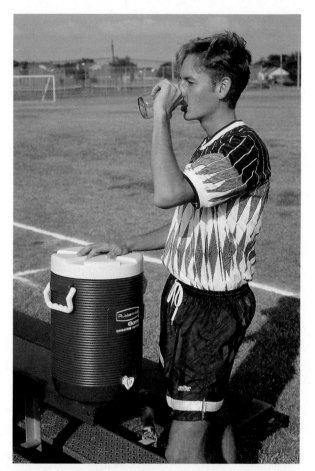

Be sure to drink additional water whenever you exercise vigorously. Even if you don't feel thirsty, you need to replace water lost through perspiration.

Safety Check

Heat stroke is a medical emergency. Signs of heat stroke include very high body temperature; hot, red, dry skin; and rapid pulse. The person may become unconscious. Immediate medical attention is needed.

Heat exhaustion usually results in pale, clammy skin. The person may sweat heavily; feel tired, dizzy, and nauseated; and have a headache. A person with heat exhaustion should lie down (in a cool place, if possible) and sip water.

In addition to water, juices and fruit drinks can be used. However, because they are high in sugar, the body absorbs them more slowly. To cut down on sugar, dilute juices and fruit drinks by one-half with water.

Sports drinks are also available. They are valuable mainly to athletes involved in exercise lasting more than two hours.

Common Myths

Some athletes believe they need extra protein to build muscles. It's true that dietary protein is needed to build body protein. Remember, however, that most Americans eat far more protein than they need. An athlete's protein requirements can be met easily through normal eating. Excess protein does nothing to build up muscles—only physical training can do that.

Likewise, athletes who eat nutritious meals do not need vitamin or mineral supplements. These supplements do not supply anything of special value to an athlete.

Athletes generally do not need salt tablets. It's true that salt and potassium are lost through perspiration. However, these minerals can be easily replaced in well-chosen daily meals.

Timing of Meals

If you eat just before an athletic event, the digestive process competes with your muscles for energy. Instead, eat three to four hours prior to the event to allow for proper digestion.

Follow these suggestions to get the most from your pre-event meal:

❖ Choose a meal that is low in fat and protein and high in complex carbohydrates. As you may recall, fat and protein take the longest to digest.

❖ Eat foods you enjoy and have eaten before. A pre-game meal is no time to experiment with a new food.

❖ Choose foods that you know you can digest easily.

❖ Have a reasonably sized meal, not too large, so the stomach is relatively empty by event time.

❖ Drink large amounts of fluids with the meal.

❖ Avoid sugary foods, such as candy, within an hour before the event. These will give you quick bursts of energy that don't last. This can lead to feelings of fatigue or shakiness during the event.

After an athletic event or a hard workout, you need to refuel your body. In addition to replacing the water you have lost, be sure to eat nutritious food within one to four hours after the event.

Anabolic Steroids

All athletes want to perform well in sports and to have well-developed muscles. Many, however, are in a hurry to build up their muscles. Instead of depending on training alone, they use drugs called **anabolic steroids** (AN-uh-boll-ick STEER-oyds).

Steroid drugs were developed years ago for medical purposes and can be obtained only by prescription. Today, they are rarely prescribed by physicians.

To perform your best, eat a pre-game meal three to four hours before the event starts.

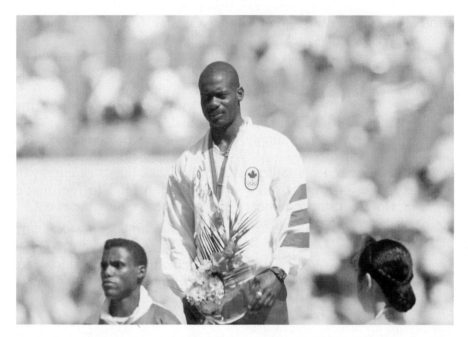

Canadian sprinter Ben Johnson was stripped of his Olympic medal, and eventually of the right to compete, for illegal use of steroids. Steroids can cause serious permanent damage to the body.

Besides their medical effect, steroids can increase strength when they are combined with muscle-building exercises. As a result, illegal steroid use is increasing among teenage athletes, who manage to get the drug without a prescription.

Many athletes do not realize that steroids have dangerous side effects which create serious health risks. Steroids interfere with fertility, a person's ability to have children. In teens they can impair bone growth, even though muscles get large. Taken over a period of time, steroids damage the liver, heart, and stomach and cause high blood pressure. Other physical side effects of steroid use include trembling, breath odor, and acne.

Steroids also have psychological side effects. Users become aggressive, irritable, and hyperactive. Some experience hallucinations. Studies suggest that some steroid users suffer from even more serious psychological problems.

Remember that there are no "quick fixes" to improving athletic performance. Careful training and sound nutrition, practiced every day, are the surest ways to long-lasting top athletic performance.

Section 5.4 Review

RECALL THE FACTS

1. How do the nutritional needs of athletes differ from those of nonathletes?

2. Do athletes need more protein than other people? Why or why not?

3. Give three suggestions for planning meals before an athletic event.

4. What are five major negative side effects of steroids?

DISCUSS YOUR IDEAS

5. How could you convince a friend or teammate to avoid using anabolic steroids?

APPLY YOUR LEARNING

6. Use the Food Guide Pyramid and recipe books to plan three meals for an athlete who is in training for a sport of your choice.

CAREER PROFILE

Mel Logsdon
Health Club
Trainer

Current position:

"I work as a personal trainer at a medium-sized health club."

Responsibilities:

"I teach several exercise classes each day. I also work with individual members, designing fitness programs that suit their needs and goals."

Skills:

"In addition to knowledge of exercise and weight management, the ability to relate to and work with people is a must."

Education:

"I've taken college courses in nutrition, and I'm also a certified fitness instructor."

Future plans:

"I'm working toward a degree in sports sciences. A degree is not necessarily required for this job, but I may pursue a job as an athletic trainer in the future."

Biggest challenge:

"Believe me, this job requires a lot of energy! That's why it's so important that I pay attention to my own nutrition and health."

Favorite part of the job:

"I like being able to see that I can help make a difference in people's lives when they start shaping up."

- How might good nutrition help Mel, or anyone, perform better on the job?
- What aspects of Mel's job do you think you might enjoy? Why?

Summary

Section 5.1
A Healthy Weight: Instead of trying to achieve the "ideal body," it's best to accept your inherited body shape and focus on being fit and healthy. Health professionals use several methods to evaluate whether an individual is at a healthy weight. These include weight charts, body-fat tests, and waist-to-hip ratio.

Section 5.2
Weight Management: A weight management program can help you achieve and maintain a healthy weight. Many popular weight-loss methods are ineffective, and some are dangerous to health. The best way to lose weight is through gradual, permanent changes in eating and exercise habits. Those who need to gain weight or maintain their present weight can also benefit from a weight-management program.

Section 5.3
Exercise Basics: Regular exercise has many physical and psychological benefits. Each of the three basic types of exercise—stretching, aerobic, and strengthening—is important to good health. An exercise program that includes a variety of enjoyable physical activities is more likely to be successful.

Section 5.4
Nutrition for Sports and Fitness: Athletes should emphasize complex carbohydrates and drink plenty of fluids. They generally do not need extra protein, nutrient supplements, or salt tablets. Pre-event meals should be planned carefully to avoid digestive problems. Using anabolic steroids to build muscles is not only illegal, but has dangerous side effects.

REVIEWING FACTS

1. Why are children and teens excluded from most weight charts? (5.1)

2. In terms of health, what is the difference between having an "apple"-shaped figure and a "pear"-shaped figure? (5.1)

3. What is yo-yo dieting? What are the possible consequences of it? (5.2)

4. List three guidelines for setting a reasonable weight-loss goal. (5.2)

5. Give two suggestions for gaining weight healthfully. (5.2)

6. Name three specific physical benefits of exercise. (5.3)

7. What is meant by aerobic exercise? Give two examples. (5.3)

8. About what percentage of an athlete's calories should come from complex carbohydrates? (5.4)

9. What can happen if an athlete doesn't replace water lost through perspiration? (5.4)

10. About how long before an athletic event should the pre-event meal be eaten? Why? (5.4)

LEARNING BY DOING

1. **Foods lab:** Make a list of simple snacks that would be suitable for a person who is changing eating habits to lose weight. The snacks should be easy to prepare, low in fat and calories, and nutritious. Work in groups to prepare the snacks. (5.2)

2. **Demonstration:** Working in groups, prepare a demonstration of safe exercises for stretching or strengthening muscles. Use books, tapes, magazines, or other references to learn the proper form for each exercise. Demonstrate the exercises to other class members. (5.3)

3. **Foods lab:** Plan and prepare a pre-event meal for a group of athletes in your school. Prepare a handout giving facts about nutrition and athletic performance to give each participant. Interview members of the team after their performance to find out how they felt during the event. (5.4)

THINKING CRITICALLY

1. **Determining credibility:** Suppose you are interested in losing weight. Several of your friends are following the plan described in a best-selling diet book. Before you decide whether to join them, what information would you want to know about the author? About the diet plan? How will you find the information? How will it influence your decision? (5.2)

2. **Recognizing bias:** Why do you think some children receive more encouragement to participate in exercise and sports than others? How do you think children are affected by such encouragement (or lack of it)? (5.3)

3. **Recognizing fallacies:** A basketball coach recommends a special "power supplement," claiming it will improve performance. After using the supplement for a week, several members of the team say that it helped them shoot more accurately. Do you think they are right? Why or why not? (5.4)

MAKING DECISIONS AND SOLVING PROBLEMS

What Would You Do?

1. Your friend is seriously overweight. It doesn't seem to bother him, but you are concerned about his health. On the other hand, you're also worried about hurting his feelings. (5.1, 5.2)

2. You strain your leg muscle while jogging one day. The doctor tells you to try to stay off your feet for a few weeks. However, you want to continue with some type of exercise during that time. (5.3)

3. A friend of yours is a star player on the football team and counting on a football scholarship to get into college. He tells you that he has begun taking steroids to improve his performance. He asks you not to tell anyone else. (5.4)

LINKING YOUR STUDIES

1. **Math:** Find the waist-to-hip ratio for each of the following adults. (Round off to two decimal places.) Which of the ratios indicate a health risk? (5.1)

   A. Female, waist 27 in., hips 36 in.

   B. Female, waist 33 in., hips 40 in.

   C. Female, waist 35 in., hips 45 in.

   D. Male, waist 36 in., hips 35 in.

   E. Male, waist 34 in., hips 36 in.

2. **Writing:** Write an article for a newspaper or newsletter on one of the following subjects: safe weight loss, planning an exercise program, or nutrition for athletes. (5.2, 5.3, 5.4)

3. **Health:** Conduct library research to find out more about the dangers of anabolic steroids. (5.4)

CHAPTER 6

Special Topics in Nutrition

Objectives

After studying this section, you should be able to:

❖ Identify the varying nutritional needs for each stage of the life cycle.

❖ Explain how to encourage healthful eating habits for people in every stage of the life cycle.

Look for These Terms

life cycle
fetus
obstetrician
colostrum
pediatrician

A person's movement from one stage of development to the next is called the **life cycle.** The stages of the life cycle include prenatal development, infancy, childhood, adolescence, and adulthood. At each stage, people experience changes in growth and nutrition needs.

To stay healthy throughout your life, you must be aware of the stage of the life cycle you're experiencing. That way, you can make any necessary changes in your wellness program to help you live a long and active life.

Prenatal Development

During the nine months of a normal pregnancy, a single cell grows and develops into a baby able to survive in the outside world. Proper development depends on the right nutrients. However, the unborn baby—called a **fetus** (FEE-tus)—cannot control its own nutrition. That is the most important responsibility of a pregnant woman.

While eating right is essential throughout life, nutritional needs vary at different stages of the life cycle.

Nutrition During Pregnancy

Concern about good nutrition should begin before pregnancy. A healthy woman who has good eating habits before her pregnancy begins is more likely to have a safe pregnancy and healthy baby. A woman usually does not learn of her pregnancy until a month or more after she has become pregnant. Meanwhile, the food she has been eating has been the only nourishment for the unborn baby. If the expectant mother has been making poor food choices, she runs the risk of health problems for herself and the baby.

Poor nutrition during pregnancy can lead to babies with low birth weight (under 5½ pounds or 2.5 kg). Such babies often have serious physical problems and may have learning problems as well.

Teen Pregnancy

Pregnant teens are at special risk, because they need added nutrients for themselves and the fetus. Poor eating habits can increase the risk of having a baby with health problems. Because most teens are not fully developed, they are also more likely to have difficult pregnancies.

Guidelines for Pregnant Women

As soon as a woman suspects she is pregnant, she should see a health professional, such as a physician or nurse practitioner. Some women see an **obstetrician** (ahb-stuh-TRISH-un), a physician who specializes in pregnancy.

An expectant mother should follow her health professional's recommendations for the kind and amount of food to be eaten.

Low birth weight significantly increases the risk a baby will die or have long-term health or learning problems.

During pregnancy, six to eight glasses of liquid are needed daily.

mal. Most of the added weight comes from the fetus, its surrounding fluids, and body changes in the mother. Little of it is fat. Those who have made nutritious food choices should return to their prepregnancy weight within a few months after childbirth.

Pregnant women should avoid using any drugs, medicines, or nutrient supplements unless directed by a physician. Smoking and drinking alcoholic beverages can be especially dangerous to the physical and mental development of the fetus. Smoking often results in low birth weight. Drinking alcoholic beverages may result in severe mental and physical problems known as "fetal alcohol syndrome." The baby is abnormally small at birth with a small brain. Such babies never catch up to normal growth, either physically or mentally. Many have heart defects.

These recommendations may include:
* Choose low-fat, nutrient-dense foods from the Food Guide Pyramid. (See pages 97-102.
* Increase calories slightly to supply enough energy for both mother and fetus.
* Choose at least four daily servings of high-protein foods, such as fish, poultry, meat, eggs, and dry beans.
* Have at least three servings of milk or low-fat cheese or yogurt a day (at least four for pregnant teens).
* Eat foods rich in iron, such as meat, poultry, fish, dry beans, and leafy green vegetables, to help build red blood cells. Foods that contain vitamin C, such as fruits and vegetables, help the body use iron from plant sources more efficiently.
* Eat foods rich in folate, such as whole-grain breads and cereals, fruits, and dark green vegetables.
* Drink at least six to eight glasses of liquid daily, including water, juices, and milk.

Women should not go on a weight-loss diet during pregnancy. Dieting deprives the fetus of much-needed nutrients and can seriously affect the baby's health. A weight gain of about 25 to 35 pounds (11 to 16 kg) is nor-

Infancy

The first years of life are a time of exceptional growth and development. Good nutrition plays a key role. The harmful effects of poor nutrition during infancy can last a lifetime.

Feeding Newborns

There are two choices for feeding newborn infants—breast-feeding or bottle-feeding infant formula. Both provide all the nutrients the baby needs for the first four to six months.

Breast milk has the right amount and kind of fat for a baby. The protein is more easily digested and absorbed than the protein in cow's milk.

During about the first three days after the birth, the mother's breasts give **colostrum** (kuh-LAW-strum), a thick, yellowish fluid. It is easily digested, highly nutritious, and contains antibodies that protect the baby from infection. Later, the colostrum changes to true breast milk.

A woman who is breast-feeding should eat the same kinds of foods recommended

What would be the advantages and disadvantages of bottle-feeding?

during pregnancy and drink plenty of liquids. The right food choices will insure that she produces enough milk to keep the baby well fed and healthy. She should not diet while she is breast-feeding.

Bottle-feeding infant formula can also provide good nutrition. Infant formula is usually made of a nonfat cow's milk base. Vegetable oils and carbohydrates are added to make it more similar to breast milk. Other types of formula are also available. For infants allergic to cow's milk, formulas with a soybean base are often used.

Do not give a baby sugar water, soft drinks, diet beverages, coffee, or tea. Also, do not give a baby honey during the first year of life. The honey may contain microorganisms that are harmful to the baby.

Adding Solid Foods

After the first four to six months, the baby will be ready for solid food. The **pediatrician,** a physician who cares for infants and children, can make recommendations.

A baby's first "solid" foods are actually strained foods that are easy to swallow and digest. They should be introduced one at a time. That way the cause of any food allergies can be identified. The first solid food is usually iron-fortified rice cereal, followed by strained vegetables and fruits. Other foods can be added later.

During the last half of the first year, infants' eating skills improve. They can be given foods that need some chewing. They begin to learn to pick up solid food with their fingers. Good "finger foods" include pieces of fruit, cooked vegetables, cheese, and crackers. They also begin to learn to use a spoon for self-feeding.

Do not add salt, sugar, fat, or spices to the baby's food. Babies do not need them because their taste buds are more sensitive than an adult's. Added salt, sugar, or fat may also start babies on poor eating habits.

Certain foods should not be fed to infants and small children because they can cause choking. These include nuts, seeds, raw carrots, hot dogs, candy, grapes, popcorn, and peanut butter.

By the end of the first year, a baby usually can eat the same foods as the rest of the

TIPS for Success

Feeding Solid Food to Infants

❖ Offer new foods at the beginning of the meal, when the baby is the most hungry.

❖ Keep mealtime quiet, relaxed, and enjoyable for you and the baby.

❖ When the baby is ready for table foods, cut them into very small pieces for easier handling and safe eating.

❖ Have patience. Until the baby learns to chew and swallow properly, much of the food will end up on the baby and the surroundings. Do not become angry or scold—the baby is doing the best he or she can.

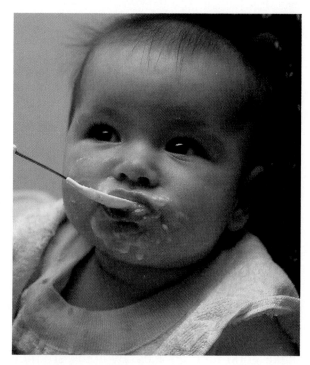

Introducing solid foods one at a time makes it easier to pinpoint any food allergies. Which solid food is usually introduced first?

family, but in smaller amounts. Parents and caregivers should not try to limit the amount of fat that children under age two eat. Babies and toddlers have high energy requirements. They need more fat in their diet than older children and adults do.

Childhood

Young children are active and growing. It is essential that they receive a wide selection of nutritious foods from the five food groups in the Food Guide Pyramid. However, children have small stomachs that cannot hold very much food at one time.

When serving food at meals, keep portions small. Many experts recommend beginning with 1 tablespoon (15 mL) of a food for each year of the child's life. If the child is still hungry, he or she can be given more. The amount of food needed varies from child to child and week to week. During periods of very rapid growth, called growth spurts, children may eat more than usual. At other times, they may want less food.

Young children need 2 cups (500 mL) of milk each day. It can be served in three or four smaller portions.

Children also need between-meal snacks to help supply them with enough energy and nutrients. Good snacks include juice, yogurt, milk, pieces of fruit or vegetables, cooked meat or poultry, unsweetened cereal, and whole-grain crackers. Avoid foods that are high in fat, sugar, or salt.

Promoting Good Eating Habits

Most children go through phases of strong food likes and dislikes. Usually this is no cause for concern. Eventually they will try new foods.

Young children need nutritious food served attractively. Simply varying the colors and shapes of foods makes meals more inviting.

Here are some tips to encourage children to develop good eating habits:

- ❖ Teach children how to prepare several simple, nutritious foods by themselves.
- ❖ Let children help prepare a simple part of a meal.
- ❖ Serve colorful foods with different textures and flavors. If foods are attractive, children will be more likely to eat them.
- ❖ Eat meals with children. Model good eating habits and acceptable mealtime behavior. Mealtime companionship may encourage children to try new foods.
- ❖ Avoid using food to reward or punish children. This gives them the wrong impression about the purpose of food and can lead to poor eating habits.
- ❖ Do not force children to eat more than they want or insist that they clean their plates. Doing so only creates negative feelings and makes mealtime unpleasant.
- ❖ Let children decide what foods they want to eat for some meals, when possible.

Adolescence

As adolescents move from childhood to adulthood, dramatic physical and psychological changes occur. The growth rate is rapid and varies widely. As a result, teens have an increased need for almost all nutrients.

Many teens choose foods that often do not provide enough calcium, zinc, iron, or vitamins A and C. Be sure to eat at least the minimum number of servings suggested in the Food Guide Pyramid for adolescents. Teens who are growing or have a high activity level may need the maximum number of servings.

As a teen, you are assuming more responsibility for your life, including food choices. Developing good food and fitness habits at this stage gives you a foundation for a healthy adult life. How sensible are your food choices?

Adulthood

Adults, in general, have lower calorie needs than teens. They are no longer growing and may be less active than they were as teens. If adults continue to eat as much food as when they were younger, they may put on weight.

Although adults may need fewer calories, they still need their full share of nutrients. They should choose a variety of low-fat, low-calorie foods from the Food Guide Pyramid. Continuing to get regular exercise throughout adulthood is important as well.

Most adults have many demands on their time—work, family, community activities, and perhaps additional schooling. They may feel too busy to give time and thought to their eating and exercise habits. However, even under such hectic conditions, adults can still make good food choices. By doing so, they can help insure good health in the future.

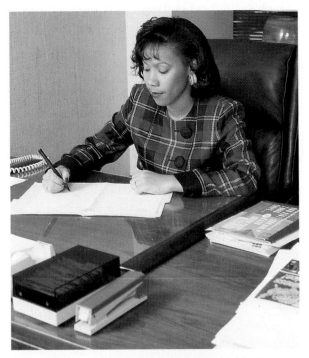

During adulthood, many people become less active. What effects might this have on their nutrition and health?

Many adults don't realize that they have slipped into poor eating and exercise habits until they develop a health problem. Developing healthy habits in your teen years may help eliminate future health problems. It will also be easier to continue these habits throughout life.

Older Adults

As people age, they continue to need the same nutrients. However, the amounts needed may change. Older adults may also need fewer calories. If they're physically active, they can eat as much as younger adults.

With maturity, the body's thirst signal often declines and people don't drink as much water as needed. Older people, like all adults, need to drink six to eight cups (1.5 to 2 liters) of liquid daily.

Special Problems of the Elderly

Some elderly people face special challenges in meeting their nutritional needs. Many live on fixed incomes that are too low to provide enough nutritious food. Those who live alone may not feel like preparing a meal just for one. Some elderly persons have health problems that create nutrition risks.

Many communities have social service programs to help elderly people in these situations. Senior and community centers often offer meals at reduced rates for the elderly. They provide nutritious meals and an opportunity for socializing.

Living alone or on a limited income can make meal planning challenging for people of any age, not just the elderly. Chapter 11 provides helpful suggestions. In addition, people of any age may have to cope with medical problems or physical impairments. You will learn more about these in the next section.

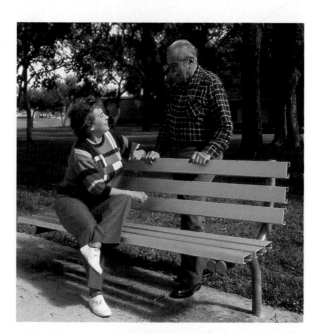

With proper nutrition, exercise, and good health, many older adults remain very active.

■ Section 6.1 Review ■

RECALL THE FACTS

1. Why are good nutrition habits important for a woman even before she knows she is pregnant?

2. What is colostrum?

3. Identify three good "finger foods" for infants and three good snack foods for young children.

4. How can adults get their full share of nutrients without getting too many calories?

DISCUSS YOUR IDEAS

5. Why do you suppose the text recommends getting children involved in meal preparation? How might this promote good eating habits?

APPLY YOUR LEARNING

6. Think of a simple food that children can prepare for themselves. Write down directions for preparing the food as you would explain it to a child.

Managing Health Conditions

Objectives

After studying this section, you should be able to:

❖ Explain the relationship between stress and nutrition.

❖ Identify the role of nutrition in recovery from illness or injury.

❖ Give examples of how those with medical conditions or physical impairments can meet their nutritional needs.

Look for These Terms

stress
convalescence
diabetes
food allergy

As you have learned, good nutrition is essential for anyone's health. However, certain situations result in special nutrition needs or challenges.

Nutrition and Stress

Have you ever lost sleep the night before a big exam or had butterflies in your stomach when meeting someone new? If so, you were experiencing stress. **Stress** is physical or mental tension triggered by an event or situation in your life.

Not everyone finds the same situations stressful. Some people experience "test anxiety," while others don't. A person who works in an office will experience different kinds of job stress than a police officer. Even positive events, such as going on a date or receiving an award, can be stressful.

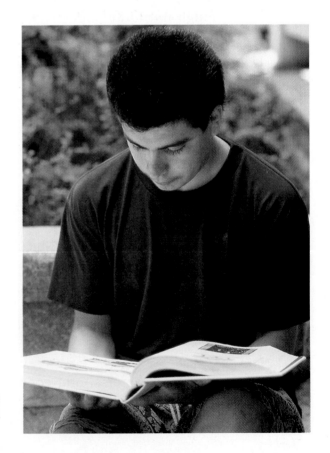

No two people react in quite the same way to a situation. How does your response to an upcoming test compare with your friends'?

Taking time to relax can help you manage the stress in your life.

Stressful situations are part of life and can't be avoided. The key is in learning how to react to these situations positively. Your reaction makes a big difference in whether stress becomes a problem for you. For healthy ways to cope with stressful situations, see the "Tips for Success" on this page.

When stress is not handled effectively, the body and mind may react in various ways. For some people, stress often brings feelings of worry, fear, or anger. A person may become depressed and lack energy. Stress may also cause physical symptoms, such as a headache, stiff neck, or sore back. Stress even plays a role in serious illnesses such as high blood pressure and heart disease.

Stress and nutrition are related in a number of ways. For example, negative emotions can cause some people to experience digestive problems such as heartburn, diarrhea, or constipation. Others react to stress by changing their eating habits. They may overeat or choose too many foods high in fat, sugar, or salt. On the other hand, stress causes some people to lose their appetite.

TIPS for Success

Managing Stress

❖ Take care of your health. You'll be better able to handle challenges if you eat right, get enough rest, and exercise regularly.

❖ Learn to manage your time. Allow time each day to relax and enjoy yourself.

❖ Take positive action to solve a problem if you can. If the problem is beyond your control, learn to accept it for the time being. Perhaps later you may be able to change it.

❖ Develop your sense of humor. Laughter can relieve tension and help you think more clearly.

❖ Try physical activity when you feel upset. Run, walk, ride a bike, or clean out a closet.

❖ Share your feelings and problems with someone you trust.

Making poor food choices is not a positive way to deal with stress. It does nothing to help you cope with what is causing your stress. Poor eating habits can make you feel worse in the long run—often leading to poor nutrition, an unhealthy weight, and perhaps serious health problems.

In contrast, good nutrition can help reduce stress. Eating right is one way to help prevent stress-related illnesses or manage their symptoms. By reacting to stressful situations in a positive way, people can take control of their lives and reduce the risk of illness.

Illness and Convalescence

Any illness puts an additional strain on the body. Whether fighting off a sore throat or the measles, a healthy, well-nourished body is better equipped to handle the problem. Even though a person who is ill may lose interest in eating, the body needs the nutrients found in good food.

Convalescence is the period of recovery after a serious illness or injury. While the patient is recovering, nutritious food and extra rest aid the healing process.

During illness or convalescence, a physician or a dietitian may give special directions about the patient's diet. For example, the patient may be restricted to liquids or soft foods for a time.

If you are helping to care for someone who is ill or recovering from an illness, here are some guidelines:

❖ Ask the physician or pharmacist whether the patient's medication affects the appetite or the way the body uses nutrients.
❖ Encourage the patient to get enough rest so healing can take place.
❖ Be sure the patient gets enough liquids. The physician may specify how much is needed.
❖ Serve nutritious food attractively. A meal that includes foods of various colors, shapes, textures, and temperatures is more appealing.

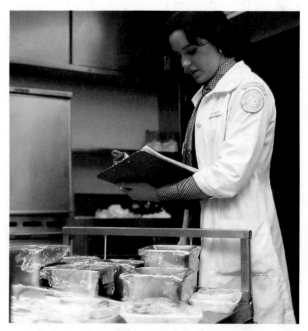

Hospitals know that good nutrition is essential to the healing process. Dietitians make sure that patients receive a diet that meets their particular needs.

❖ Use disposable paper or plastic plates and cups if the patient has an illness that can spread to others.

Special Diets for Medical Conditions

Some people, because of long-term medical conditions, must be especially aware of their food choices. Their physician may prescribe a special diet to keep the medical condition under control. Some common examples of such special diets are:

❖ **_Low-cholesterol, low-fat diets._** People with heart problems or high blood cholesterol may need to follow a special diet to reduce the amount of cholesterol in the blood. Their choices include low-fat, low-cholesterol foods. For instance, someone who has always enjoyed fried food must learn to adjust to foods that are baked or broiled instead.

CHOL 173 mg/dl

Reflotron®

Low-cholesterol, low-fat diets can help lower cholesterol levels in the blood. This can reduce the risk of heart problems. Even children and teens can have elevated cholesterol levels.

❖ **Low-sodium diets.** With certain medical conditions, such as kidney disease, too much sodium in the diet can cause serious problems. In such cases, people must not add salt when preparing and eating food. They must also limit foods high in sodium, such as processed foods.

❖ **Diabetic diets. Diabetes** is a condition in which the body cannot control blood sugar properly, resulting in high blood sugar levels. Diabetes may cause serious damage to the kidneys, the eyes, and other parts of the body. Eating the right balance of food plays a role in controlling the blood sugar level. Like most people, those with diabetes need to eat foods high in complex carbohydrates and fiber and low in fats, cholesterol, sodium, and sugar. Eating all foods in moderation also helps control weight, which is very important for diabetics. Diets for people with diabetes are individually prescribed for each patient and must be closely followed.

❖ **Food allergy diets.** Some people have an unpleasant reaction after eating even a small amount of a certain food. This condition is called a **food allergy.** Symptoms may include itching, rash, hives, abdominal pain, nausea, or difficulty in breathing. Some of the more common allergy-causing foods are cow's milk, eggs, fish, shellfish, nuts, and peanuts. Special tests are used to determine which foods are responsible for the allergy.

It takes time for people who have been put on a special diet to adjust to a new way of eating. If you know of anyone in this situation, offer your support and encouragement. Try to help them look upon the special diet as an opportunity to try new foods.

When shopping for foods to fit a special diet, read labels carefully. Check for fats, sodium, or other ingredients that must be limited. You may be able to find substitute products, such as no-cholesterol egg substitutes.

You might be surprised at the variety of flavorful foods that can be prepared within the limitations of special diets. For instance, you could learn to use different herbs and spices and to make low-fat or low-sodium sauces and gravies. Many hospitals and clinics offer classes on cooking for special diets. Cookbooks focusing on special diets are also available.

Physical Impairments

Sometimes a physical impairment requires that a person make adaptations in order to meet his or her nutritional needs. This can be true of some elderly people or some people with physical handicaps. However, it can also be true in a number of other situations. Generally the person's nutrition needs are no different from those of anyone else who is similar in age, gender, and activity level. However, physical limitations may affect how those needs are met.

For instance, some people have dental problems. Hard breads and rolls, raw fruits and vegetables, and certain meats may be difficult for them to eat. Try substituting softer foods that are also nutritious, such as:

❖ High-fiber cereal softened with milk.
❖ Ground meat, ground poultry, or fish.
❖ Soft, enriched breads and rolls.
❖ Canned, unsweetened fruits.

Other examples of physical impairments might include limited mobility, limited use of the hands, or vision problems. Physical limitations such as these might make it difficult to use standard kitchen equipment. In this case, the solution is to adapt the kitchen and its equipment. In Chapters 7 and 14 you will read about adaptations to help those with physical impairments be self-sufficient.

A physical impairment sometimes makes it difficult to prepare food in a standard kitchen. Adapting the kitchen for easier use encourages independence and good nutrition.

Section 6.2 Review

RECALL THE FACTS

1. What is stress? Give three examples of how a negative reaction to stress can affect nutrition.

2. What is convalescence? How does nutrition play a part in it?

3. Give three suggestions for planning and preparing meals to fit a medically prescribed special diet.

4. In general, how do physical impairments relate to nutrition needs?

DISCUSS YOUR IDEAS

5. Discuss ways that good nutrition might help you handle stress more effectively.

APPLY YOUR LEARNING

6. Imagine that you are caring for someone who is convalescing from surgery. Identify at least six ways that you could make meals more enjoyable for this person.

Objectives

After studying this section, you should be able to:

❖ Identify the characteristics of anorexia nervosa and bulimia nervosa.

❖ Describe the effects of eating disorders on health.

❖ Explain what can be done to help someone with an eating disorder.

Look for These Terms

eating disorder
anorexia nervosa
bulimia nervosa

When Charlene began to lose excess weight, her friends supported her efforts. As the weeks passed, Charlene reached a weight considered healthy for her age and height. However, she continued her diet.

Months later, Charlene had lost so much weight that she almost looked like a skeleton. She was lightheaded, had stopped menstruating, and felt tired all the time. Concerned, her family scheduled a medical checkup. After a thorough evaluation, Dr. Cho diagnosed Charlene's problem as an eating disorder.

What Are Eating Disorders?

The term **eating disorder** describes extreme, unhealthy behavior relating to food, eating, and weight. The causes of eating disorders are not clearly understood, although research continues.

People with eating disorders are unable to view their weight and eating habits realistically. Without treatment, eating disorders can cause serious health problems or even death.

Eating disorders generally occur among teens and young adults, especially females. It's estimated that from 1 to 10 percent of all teens suffer from an eating disorder.

The term "eating disorder" usually refers to two specific problems called *anorexia nervosa* and *bulimia nervosa.* Both are related to an overwhelming desire to gain control in life through controlling weight.

Anorexia Nervosa

Anorexia nervosa (an-uh-RECK-see-yuh ner-VOH-suh) involves an irresistible urge to lose weight through self-starvation. It is often described as "dieting out of control." No matter how thin anorexics become, they "feel fat." They see themselves as being overweight and show an obsessive fear of gaining weight.

Anorexics will do anything to lose as much weight as possible. They refuse to eat or eat very little. They may use laxatives and diet aids or force themselves to vomit after a meal. In spite of feeling tired, some exercise strenuously every day for long periods of time. Still, most deny that they have any problem and believe that their behavior is normal.

Bulimia Nervosa

Bulimia nervosa (byou-LIM-ee-yuh ner-VOH-suh) involves episodes of binge eating, or rapidly consuming very large amounts of food. The binge is followed by purging—using self-induced vomiting, laxatives, or vigorous exercise to prevent weight gain. Unlike anorexics, most bulimics are usually within 10 to 15 pounds (5 to 8 kg) of a healthy weight.

Bulimics use secret eating binges in an attempt to cope with problems such as anger, loneliness, boredom, and frustration. Usually they binge on high-fat, high-calorie foods which they might normally consider "forbidden," such as pastries, candy, chips, and ice cream. The foods are eaten in a short time, usually within two hours. It's not unusual for bulimics to eat 3,000 to 5,000 calories at a time. During a day of repeated bingeing, some can eat as many as 20,000 calories. They stop eating only when their stomach hurts, they fall asleep, they run out of food, or someone interrupts them.

After bingeing, bulimics feel guilty and depressed. Because they don't want to gain weight, they follow the binge with purging. A typical bulimic has two or more eating binges a week. The binge-purge cycle becomes a way of life.

People with bulimia nervosa have frequent episodes of bingeing on foods high in calories and fat.

Effects of Eating Disorders

Eating disorders can create serious health problems. Anorexia can result in lowered heart rate and body temperature, constipation, and lowered blood pressure and breathing rate. Female anorexics stop menstruating. About 10 percent of anorexics die of starvation.

Bulimics lose fluid and potassium, which may result in fatigue, heart problems, and kidney damage. The vomiting damages their esophagus, teeth, and gums. Their salivary glands, located on each side of the neck, enlarge. Many bulimics have a sore throat almost all the time.

What steps might you take if a friend shows several signs that might indicate an eating disorder?

What Can Be Done?

It's important to realize that anorexics and bulimics have an illness. Most can't stop their self-destructive behavior on their own. Often it's up to others to recognize the problem and encourage the person to get help.

Recognizing Eating Disorders

Anorexics often exhibit warning signs. In addition to losing large amounts of weight, eating little, and exercising for hours, they may:
❖ Show sensitivity to cold temperatures.
❖ Seem preoccupied with food and calories.
❖ Develop food-related rituals, such as always cutting food into very tiny pieces.
❖ Prepare elaborate meals, but not eat them. Some actually become gourmet cooks.
❖ Begin to avoid their friends and spend more time by themselves.

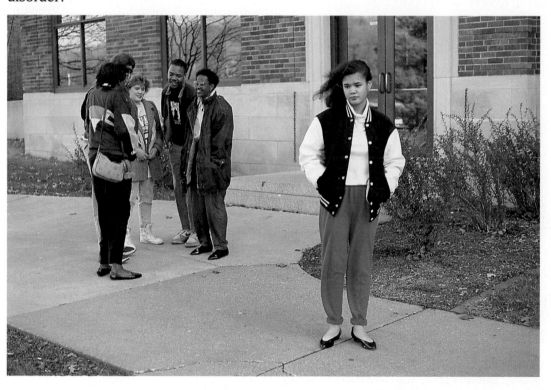

Bulimics are aware that they have no control over their unusual eating habits. They are embarrassed by their lack of self-control. As a result, they are very secretive and can hide their unusual eating habits quite successfully. For this reason, and because they generally maintain their weight, bulimics are much harder to recognize than anorexics. Warning signs include:

❖ Preoccupation with food and eating.
❖ Physical changes, such as swollen glands or tooth problems.

Getting Help

Eating disorders stem from complex problems that require professional help. Treatment usually includes nutritional and psychological counseling as well as medical help. Often the person must be hospitalized in an eating disorder clinic.

People with eating disorders can recover, but the process is very slow. It usually takes at least one or two years of treatment for full recovery to occur. As with any other illness, support from family and friends is an important part of the recovery process.

Professional help is needed to recover from an eating disorder. Some residential treatment centers are devoted solely to eating disorders.

Section 6.3 Review

RECALL THE FACTS

1. List four characteristics of anorexia nervosa.

2. Describe two key ways in which bulimia differs from anorexia.

3. Name three health problems that may occur as a result of eating disorders.

4. What help is available to persons who suffer from eating disorders?

DISCUSS YOUR IDEAS

5. In recent years, a number of celebrities have admitted having eating disorders. Do you think such publicity has a positive or negative effect? Explain.

APPLY YOUR LEARNING

6. Imagine that Charlene—the girl described at the beginning of the section—is a friend of yours. You have just learned about her eating disorder. Write a journal entry describing the signs that led you to suspect there was a problem. Close by explaining how you plan to give support to Charlene.

CAREER PROFILE

Carmen Ragusa
Hospital Volunteer

Current position:

"I volunteer three evenings a week at a community hospital."

Responsibilities:

"Basically, I go wherever I'm needed. I make sure patients have fresh water, I help serve their meal trays, and I try to make them comfortable in any way I can—sometimes just by talking with them or buying them magazines at the gift shop."

Why I chose this job:

"I was interested in working at a hospital, but I wasn't sure if I was suited for it. Volunteering has given me a chance to explore my options."

Skills:

"In this job, you have to be willing to do anything and be cheerful while you're doing it, even if you aren't feeling particularly cheerful at the moment."

Favorite part of the job:

"I really like it when I can take a tray to a person who's feeling down and leave him in a better mood by showing him genuine concern and compassion. Not everyone is receptive, though, so I do take my cues from the patient."

Favorite part of the job:

"I'm still exploring my options, but I'm leaning toward a career as a clinical dietitian. I think I would enjoy teaching people good nutrition practices."

- What are the advantages of volunteering?
- What aspects of Carmen's job do you think you might enjoy? Why?

179

Summary

Section 6.1
Food and the Life Cycle: At each stage of the life cycle, people experience changes in nutritional needs. Good nutrition during pregnancy is essential for the health of the baby. Infants and children need the right kinds of food for health and growth. Children should also be encouraged to develop good eating habits. Through adolescence and adulthood, changing energy needs are a consideration. Some elderly people face special challenges to nutrition.

Section 6.2
Managing Health Conditions: Good nutrition is essential in preventing and managing stress-related illnesses. Along with rest, nutritious food helps the body heal itself during illness and convalescence. Some people have long-term medical conditions requiring special diets. Physical impairments sometimes require that a person make adaptations in order to meet nutritional needs.

Section 6.3
Eating Disorders: Anorexia nervosa involves losing weight through self-starvation. Bulimia nervosa involves bingeing and purging. Both eating disorders can cause serious damage to health. Warning signs may indicate a problem. People with eating disorders need professional help.

REVIEWING FACTS

1. Why is nutrition of particular concern for pregnant teens? (6.1)

2. Name five foods that should not be given to infants or small children because they may cause choking. (6.1)

3. Why do people often tend to put on weight as they move from the teen years to adulthood? (6.1)

4. Name two factors that may keep some elderly people from eating nutritious meals. (6.1)

5. List four positive ways to cope with stress. (6.2)

6. What is diabetes? Give two characteristics of a diet to control diabetes. (6.2)

7. List three nutritious, easy-to-chew foods appropriate for a person with dental problems. (6.2)

8. In which groups of people do eating disorders occur most often? (6.3)

9. Describe the binge-purge cycle characteristic of bulimia. (6.3)

10. Why is it usually more difficult to recognize bulimia than anorexia? (6.3)

LEARNING BY DOING

1. ***Foods lab:*** List ideas for making nutritious foods that would appeal to young children. Consider using unusual colors, animal shapes, funny faces, etc. Prepare samples of the foods. Serve them to classmates or to a group of young children, if possible. (6.1)

2. ***Foods lab:*** Find and prepare a simple recipe designed for a special diet, such as diabetic, low-salt, or wheat-free. Rate the food for appearance, texture, and flavor. (6.2)

3. **Foods lab:** Prepare a simple meal, such as soup and a sandwich. Place it on a tray as if you were serving it to someone who was in bed recovering from an illness. Show how you would make the meal attractive as well as easy to eat. (6.2)

THINKING CRITICALLY

1. **Analyzing cause and effect:** The text states that using food to reward or punish children can lead to poor eating habits. Give some examples to show how this might happen. (6.1)

2. **Determining accuracy:** Some people believe that certain foods can help cure certain illnesses—for example, that chicken soup helps cure a cold. Do you think there is any truth to these beliefs? Why or why not? How might a scientist try to test such theories? (6.2)

3. **Predicting consequences:** How might family members be affected if a member of the family is suffering from an eating disorder? (6.3)

MAKING DECISIONS AND SOLVING PROBLEMS

What Would You Do?

1. Next week, you will start babysitting your neighbor's five-year-old after school each day. The parents want you to give the child a nutritious snack. You've been told the child is a very picky eater. (6.1)

2. Your elderly neighbor has poor vision and no longer drives a car. He does his grocery shopping only when someone is available to drive him to the supermarket. You are worried that he isn't getting regular, nutritious meals. (6.1, 6.2)

3. Each morning, your sister prepares an elaborate sack lunch. You've often seen her throw the lunch in the trash as soon as she arrives at school. She often cooks dinner for the family but seldom eats any of it, claiming she is still full from lunch. She is getting thinner and thinner. (6.3)

LINKING YOUR STUDIES

1. **Writing:** Work in groups to write, illustrate, and produce a pamphlet discussing the importance of good nutrition during pregnancy. Distribute the pamphlet in your school or community. (6.1)

2. **Science:** Using library sources, research the connection between nutrition and the healing process. Possible topics include: What effect does nutrition have on the immune system? What nutrients are important for bone and muscle repair and rebuilding? Do some diets seem to help with chronic or terminal illnesses? Report your findings to the class. (6.2)

3. **Literature:** Find a book written by or about someone with an eating disorder. (You may want to ask your teacher or a librarian for suggestions.) After reading the book, write a brief report discussing how the person's story affected you. (6.3)

Food preparation involves many tasks and many tools. This section introduces you to the equipment and work centers you will find in a kitchen, whether at home or in the school foods lab.

Types of Kitchen Equipment

Kitchens contain three basic kinds of equipment: major appliances, small appliances, and utensils.

A **major appliance** is a large device that gets its energy from electricity or gas. Most kitchens have at least two major appliances: a refrigerator-freezer for cold storage and a range for cooking. Some kitchens have a separate cooktop and oven instead of a single range unit. Many kitchens also have a microwave oven and a dishwasher.

A **small appliance** is a small electrical device used to perform tasks such as mixing, chopping, and cooking. The blender, toaster, and mixer are examples of small appliances.

The major appliances, small appliances, and utensils in a kitchen help make efficient food preparation possible. The amount and type of equipment depend on lifestyle and budget.

Utensils include kitchen tools such as measuring cups, knives, and peelers. They also include cookware, such as pots and pans.

Appliances and utensils require careful use and regular care. Before using or cleaning any appliance, read the owner's manual. Following the use and care instructions carefully can prevent injuries and save costly repair bills.

As you study basic kitchen skills, you will learn how to use and care for specific pieces of equipment. In Chapter 14, you can learn about buying equipment for the kitchen.

Kitchen Work Centers

Most home kitchens and school foods labs are organized around work centers. **Work centers** are areas designed for specific kitchen tasks. A well-designed work center includes the equipment needed for the task, enough storage space, and a safe, convenient work space.

A basic principle of kitchen organization is to store items near the place they will be used most often. As you read about the kitchen work centers, notice the types of food and equipment that would logically be kept there.

Basic Work Centers

The refrigerator-freezer, sink, and range—and the counters and cabinets around them—form the three basic kitchen centers.

❖ *Cold storage center.* The refrigerator-freezer is the focus of this center. Items that might be stored nearby include storage bags, food wraps, and containers for leftover foods.

❖ *Sink center.* This center is the main source of water. It is used for a variety of tasks—washing fresh fruits and vegetables, draining foods, washing dishes, and others. Equipment such as dishpans and other cleanup supplies should be handy.

❖ *Cooking center.* This center includes the range and related items such as cooking tools, pots and pans, and potholders. Small cooking appliances may be kept near the range. Some canned and packaged foods may also be stored here.

This kitchen has a mixing center. Note the lowered countertop and convenient placement of appliances, utensils, and supplies.

Sometimes there is more than one logical place for equipment. For instance, a microwave oven could be part of the cooking center. It could also be placed near the refrigerator-freezer for quick heating of leftovers and frozen food. José's family keeps the microwave on a sturdy rolling cart so it can be moved wherever needed.

Other Work Centers

Some kitchens include additional, separate work centers.

❖ **Mixing center.** This area is used for preparing and mixing foods. Equipment such as measuring cups, bowls, mixing spoons, and an electric mixer can be stored here, along with foods such as flour and spices. In a small kitchen, this center may be combined with one of the others.

❖ **Planning center.** Some home kitchens include a planning center with space to store cookbooks, recipes, and coupons. A desk is convenient for writing out meal plans and shopping lists. Other useful features might include a calendar, a bulletin board, a telephone, and perhaps even a computer.

A well-organized and well-equipped kitchen is a place where good food can be prepared quickly, easily, and safely.

In what ways might having a planning center in the kitchen be an advantage? Would there be any disadvantages?

RECALL THE FACTS

1. What is a major appliance? A small appliance? A utensil?

2. What is a kitchen work center?

3. Name the three major work centers of the kitchen.

DISCUSS YOUR IDEAS

4. Which of the three kinds of kitchen equipment do you think you could most easily get along without—major appliances, small appliances, or utensils? Why?

5. Why is it important to organize a kitchen around work centers?

APPLY YOUR LEARNING

6. Draw a rough floor plan of your school foods lab kitchen. Show the location of the sink, the major appliances, cabinets, and counters. Circle and label each work center. Identify the location of at least two small appliances and three different kinds of utensils.

Objectives

After studying this section, you should be able to:

* Identify ways to prevent common kitchen accidents.
* Discuss special safety needs.
* Describe what to do if a kitchen accident results in injury.

Look for These Terms

polarized plugs
Heimlich Maneuver
CPR

Cal was in a hurry and needed to fix a meal fast. As he cracked some eggs for an omelet into a bowl, some egg white fell on the floor. "I'll clean that up later," he thought. He rushed to the refrigerator to get several other omelet ingredients. He balanced them in one hand as he reached for the cutting board that hung on the wall. Just then the telephone rang. As Cal turned to answer the call, he felt something slick underfoot. "The egg white!" he thought, as his foot slid out from under him.

Safety Throughout the Kitchen

Most people think of a kitchen as a pleasant place to prepare enjoyable food. While this is true, just a few seconds of carelessness can turn the kitchen into an accident zone. Falls, electrical shocks, cuts, burns, and poisoning are all kitchen hazards. The keys to preventing kitchen accidents are careful kitchen management and safe work habits.

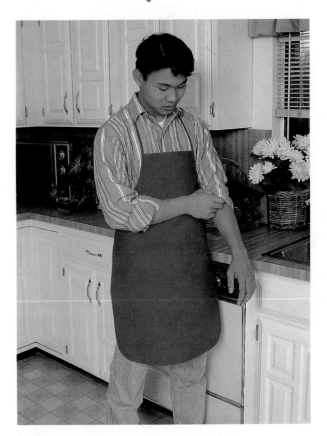

Safety in the kitchen begins with dressing appropriately.

General Safety Guidelines

Your work habits are vital to your safety in the kitchen. Here are some general guidelines:

❖ Do not let hair, jewelry, sleeves, or apron strings dangle. They could catch fire or get tangled in appliances.

❖ Keep your mind on what you're doing.

❖ Prevent clutter. Put items back where they belong as you finish with them or after you have washed them.

❖ Close drawers and doors completely after you open them. You can be seriously hurt if you bump into an open door or drawer.

❖ Use the right tool for the job. Don't use a knife to pry off a jar cover, for instance. Take the time to find the tool you need.

❖ Store heavy or bulky items, like cookware, on low shelves. That way you can reach them safely.

Safety Afoot

Many accidents occur because of what's on the floor. To prevent falls, keep the floor clean and free of clutter. Wipe up spills, spatters, and peelings so no one slips on them. Eliminate other hazards, such as slippery throw rugs and damaged or worn flooring. Don't wear untied shoes, floppy slippers, or long clothing that could cause you to trip.

To reach higher shelves, use a firm stepstool. If you use a chair or a box, you could fall and be injured.

Sharp Objects

Cuts are an everyday hazard for the cook. Here are some safety guidelines for handling knives, sharp tools, and broken glass:

❖ Keep knives sharp and use them properly. You'll learn how in Section 8.4.

❖ Use a drawer divider or knife rack for sharp cutting tools.

❖ Don't try to catch a falling knife—you might grab the blade instead of the handle.

❖ Don't soak knives or other sharp-edged utensils in a sink or dishpan of water.

Storing knives in a special drawer divider or knife rack helps prevent cuts. It also keeps the knives in better condition.

When you reach into the water, you could cut yourself.

❖ Sweep up broken glass from the floor immediately using a broom and dustpan. If you need to pick up pieces by hand, use a wet paper towel instead of bare fingers.

Electrical Safety

Electrical appliances save both time and work in the kitchen. However, they can also be a source of shocks, burns, and other injuries.

Carefully read the owner's manual that comes with each kitchen appliance. Follow the directions it gives for using the appliance safely. In addition, remember these basic guidelines:

❖ **Water and electricity don't mix.** Combined, they can give you a serious shock or even kill you. Never use an electric appliance when your hands are wet or when you are standing on a wet floor.

When you unplug an appliance, grasp the plug, not the cord. Damaged cords can cause electrical shocks and fires.

Keep small electric appliances away from water when you use them. Don't run cords around a sink. If an electric appliance falls into the water, unplug it immediately. Don't put small appliances in water for cleaning unless the owner's manual says it is safe.

❖ **Avoid damage to electrical cords.** Even a single exposed wire could start a fire or give you a shock. To keep from damaging cords, don't run them over a hot surface or try to staple or nail them in place. Never try to disconnect an appliance by tugging on the cord. Instead, grasp the plug at the electrical outlet and remove it.

❖ **Use outlets properly.** Plugging too many cords into an electrical outlet can cause a fire. Some plugs are made with one blade wider than the other. Called **polarized plugs,** they are designed to fit in the outlet in only one way. If the outlets are older, you may not be able to fit polarized plugs into them. If this happens, don't try to force the plug in or change the shape of the plug. Instead, have the outlet replaced.

❖ **Use care with any plugged-in appliance.** Never put your fingers or a kitchen tool inside an appliance that is plugged in. You might touch parts that could shock you, or you might accidentally turn the appliance on and injure yourself. Don't let cords dangle off the counter—an appliance could accidentally be pulled off while in use. Turn off and disconnect small appliances as soon as you are through with them.

❖ **Watch for problems.** Don't try to use a damaged appliance or one that gives you a shock. Have it repaired before you use it again. If an appliance starts to burn, unplug it immediately.

Hazardous Chemicals

Hazardous household chemicals include oven cleaners, lighter fluid, drain cleaners, pesticides, and polishes. Some can cause burns, breathing difficulties, and poisoning.

Look for less hazardous alternatives to household cleaners and chemicals. For example, orange peels and spices such as cinnamon can replace chemical air fresheners.

Before you buy any household chemicals, read the label carefully to be sure you are willing to follow the directions. You will find important information about adequate ventilation, protecting yourself, and disposing of any unused product. You will also learn what to do if the product is accidentally consumed. Never transfer a hazardous product to another container. You'll need the directions that appear on the original container each time you use it.

Never mix different chemical products. They could combine to give off poisonous fumes.

With spray products, make sure you're pointing the spray nozzle where the product is supposed to go. Never point it at yourself or anyone else.

Store hazardous chemical products away from food. Be sure children can't reach them. Flammable products, such as kerosene, lighter fluid, and aerosol sprays, must be stored away from any source of heat.

Avoid using hazardous chemicals unnecessarily. Whenever you can, substitute simple, safe cleaners, such as lemon juice, vinegar, soap, baking soda, washing soda, or borax.

Range and Microwave Safety

The range is the most likely place for fires and burns. The microwave oven, too, presents some hazards. Here are some rules for using these appliances safely.

❖ Use potholders or oven mitts when picking up or uncovering hot pots and pans.
❖ When uncovering a pan, lift up the far edge of the cover first. That way, the steam will flow away from you. Otherwise it could burn your face and hands.
❖ Use only pots and pans in good condition. A loose handle or warped bottom could cause an accident.
❖ Keep pan handles turned toward the back or middle of the range top to prevent accidental spills.

Oven mitts provide more protection than potholders. They are a good choice for removing large or heavy items from the oven.

❖ Keep flammable items, such as paper towels, away from the range. A draft could blow them onto the range and start a fire. For the same reason, do not put curtains on a window that is close to the range.
❖ Do not use plastic items near the range, except for ovenproof plastic. Some plastics are highly flammable and give off poisonous fumes when they burn.
❖ Arrange oven racks properly before you start the oven. You risk a burn if you have to reposition them once the oven is hot.
❖ Stand to the side when you open the oven door. Otherwise the heat rushing from the oven can burn your face.
❖ Don't reach into a hot oven. Pull out the rack first, using a potholder.
❖ Make sure cooktop and oven/broiler controls are turned off when not in use.
❖ Keep a fire extinguisher handy and make sure everyone knows how to use it.

If a Fire Starts

Kitchen fires can start suddenly. What to do depends on where the fire occurs.

❖ **Range top or electric skillet:** Turn off the heat. Put the cover on the pan or pour salt or baking soda on the flames. Never use water—the grease will spatter and burn you. Don't use baking powder—it could make the fire worse.

❖ **Oven, broiler, microwave, toaster oven:** Turn off or disconnect the appliance. Keep the oven door closed until the fire goes out.

Never attempt to carry a pan with burning contents. You could cause an injury or a bigger fire. If you can't immediately put out a fire, call the fire department and go outdoors.

Every kitchen should have a fire extinguisher. Do you know how to use one correctly?

Gas Range Safety

❖ If you smell gas, turn off all range controls and open the windows for ventilation. Alert others and leave the building immediately. Call your local gas company from another location.

❖ To relight the pilot light on an older gas range, light the match first, then turn on the burner and light it. If you turn on the burner first, gas will accumulate and could cause an explosion when you strike the match.

Special Safety Needs

As a rule, any safety precautions you take will benefit the entire family. The very young and old, however, may need special attention.

Kitchen Safety and Children

Children like to be where adults are—especially the kitchen. They want to watch you and do what you're doing. If there are children in your kitchen, follow these guidelines for their safety and yours.

❖ Never leave young children alone in the kitchen, even for a few seconds.

❖ Protect toddlers by using safety latches on drawers and cabinet doors.

❖ If children want to help you work, set up a child-size table or a safe stepstool. Provide small utensils they can use easily for simple tasks such as mixing and mashing. Don't let young children use knives or work near the range. Supervise them at all times.

❖ Model safe work habits for children. If you have safe work habits in the kitchen, they will too.

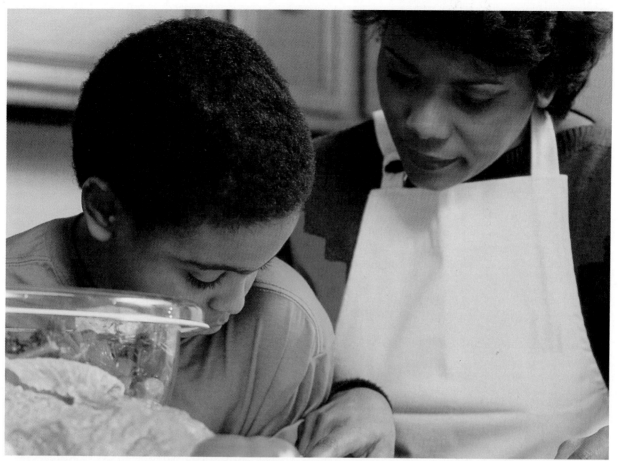

Teaching children basic food preparation skills boosts self-confidence and increases independence. Teach safety first and be sure to supervise their efforts.

Kitchen Safety for the Elderly or Handicapped

Kitchen safety is an important issue for those with physical challenges, such as poor eyesight or arthritis. Changes in the workspace or equipment may be needed so that they can use the kitchen safely. Ask for their suggestions. What kitchen tasks are hard for them? How could kitchen organization be changed to make jobs easier and safer? Here are some ideas.

❖ Keep a magnifying glass in the kitchen to aid with reading small print.

❖ Relabel items in larger letters, if needed, using stick-on labels and a marking pen.

❖ Add more or better lighting.

❖ Store frequently used equipment and foods in easy-to-reach places.

❖ Add a cart with wheels to the kitchen to make it easier to move food and equipment from place to place.

❖ Use non-breakable dishes and glassware.

❖ Replace hard-to-open cabinet hardware with U-shaped or pull handles.

❖ Provide tongs or grippers to grab items that would otherwise be out of reach.

❖ Put mixing bowls on a damp dishcloth or rubber disk jar opener to keep them from sliding on a slippery countertop during mixing.

❖ Use rubber disk jar openers for gripping appliance knobs.

❖ Provide a stool or tall chair so that the person can sit while working at the counter.

Section 14.3, "Designing a Kitchen," discusses other ways to adapt a kitchen to suit special needs.

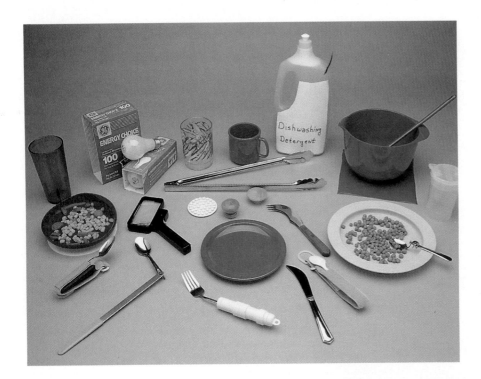

These are some of the items available to make food preparation and eating easier for people with physical challenges.

In Case of Accident

In spite of all your precautions, an accident may happen when you are working in the kitchen. To prepare for that possibility, keep a list of emergency numbers next to the phone. Also keep a first aid kit and book of instructions handy.

If you don't know first aid techniques, ask the local Red Cross about first aid training. Everyone should learn how to use the **Heimlich Maneuver,** a technique used in case of choking. Another vital technique is **CPR,** or cardiopulmonary resuscitation (KARD-ee-oh-PULL-muh-nair-ee rih-suhs-uh-TAY-shun). It is used if a person's breathing and heartbeat have stopped. Knowing these techniques can save a life.

If an accident does occur, stay calm. Panic will only keep you from thinking clearly. If necessary, take a few deep breaths to get yourself under control.

Never hesitate to call for help, whether for yourself or someone else. It's better to ask for help, even though you may not need it, than to try to handle an accident by yourself.

Section 7.2 Review

RECALL THE FACTS

1. Name three ways to prevent falls.

2. Why should you keep small appliances away from water when in use?

3. Name two safety rules for using the kitchen range.

4. Give three suggestions that might improve kitchen safety for an elderly person.

5. Name two things you should do in case of an accident in the kitchen.

DISCUSS YOUR IDEAS

6. What is the most serious kitchen accident you've ever had? Why did it happen? What safety rule did you neglect?

APPLY YOUR LEARNING

7. Make a mini-poster for the school foods lab to remind class members of one of the safety pointers discussed in this section.

Look for These Terms

sanitation
microorganism
toxins
parasites
cross-contamination
spores

James checked the chicken sizzling on the grill. "It's done!" he called to his aunt. "I'll bring it in." Looking around, he spotted the platter he had used to carry the raw chicken outside. As he started to pick up the platter, his aunt stopped him. "Don't use that! It hasn't been washed. I'll get you a clean plate."

James almost forgot an important rule of sanitation. **Sanitation** means following practices that help prevent disease. It is one of your biggest responsibilities when working with food.

Why Is Sanitation Important?

It's estimated that up to 80 million Americans suffer from food-borne illness, also known as food poisoning, every year. The illness may be mild, lasting just a day or two, or severe enough to require hospitalization. In some cases it can even result in death. Children, pregnant women, the elderly, and people with chronic illness are most at risk.

Harmful microorganisms that cause food poisoning are too small to see, but powerful enough to cause severe illness or even death. Salmonella, shown here, is one of the most common.

Most cases of food-borne illness can be traced to harmful **microorganisms**—tiny living creatures visible only through a microscope. In another sense, however, people are to blame. Poor food handling practices allow harmful microorganisms to grow and spread. It's up to you to handle food properly to prevent illness.

Types of Harmful Microorganisms

Most of the harmful microorganisms are bacteria. Bacteria are everywhere. They are carried by people, animals, insects, and objects. Many bacteria are harmless, but others can cause illness. Sometimes the illness is not caused by the bacteria themselves, but by the **toxins,** or poisons, that they produce.

Most harmful bacteria can be tolerated by the human body in small amounts. When the amounts multiply to dangerous levels, however, they create a health hazard. Bacteria reproduce quickly in the presence of food, moisture, and warmth. In just a few hours, one can multiply into thousands. You can't tell whether food contains harmful bacteria—the food generally looks, smells, and tastes normal.

In addition to bacteria and their toxins, food-borne illness can also be caused by parasites. **Parasites** (PAIR-uh-sights) are organisms that get their nutrients from other living organisms. Parasites found in food can infect people and cause illness.

The chart on pages 198-199 gives information about several common food-borne illnesses.

Cleanliness in the Kitchen

Cleanliness is one of the keys to sanitation. Whenever you work with food, be sure to keep yourself and the kitchen clean.

Personal Hygiene

Personal hygiene means keeping yourself clean so you do not introduce harmful microorganisms into food as you handle it. Here are some suggestions:

❖ Wear clean clothes and cover them with a clean apron. Spots and stains can harbor bacteria.
❖ Remove dangling jewelry, roll up long sleeves, and tie back long hair to keep them out of food.
❖ Scrub your hands for 20 seconds before you begin to handle food. Use soap and warm water. Use a brush to clean under and around your fingernails.
❖ Use rubber or plastic gloves if you have an open wound on your hands. Gloves can pick up bacteria, too. Wash gloved hands as often as you wash bare hands.
❖ Wash your hands immediately after using the toilet or blowing your nose.
❖ Do not sneeze or cough into food.
❖ Do not touch your face, hair, or any other part of your body while working with food. If you do, stop working and scrub your hands.

Good personal hygiene is essential for anyone preparing food. If you consistently practice the guidelines listed above, they will soon become good habits.

As in many other African countries, people in Morocco traditionally eat food with their hands directly from a large communal bowl. It is also customary for the host to bring a pitcher of water and a basin and pour the water as the guests wash their hands. This is done both before and after the meal. Besides being a good sanitation practice, what other meaning might this custom convey?

Pets are a common source of bacteria. Keep them out of the kitchen.

Sanitary Work Methods

In addition to keeping yourself clean, remember to follow these important guidelines:

* Make sure that work areas and equipment are clean before you start preparing food.
* Avoid **cross-contamination**—letting microorganisms from one food get into another. For example, the juices from raw meat, poultry, or fish contain microorganisms. A knife used to cut raw meat could contaminate raw vegetables. After you have handled raw meat, poultry, or fish, wash everything that came in contact with it. This includes tools, work surfaces, and your hands.
* Use plastic cutting boards, not wooden ones. Wooden cutting boards may trap harmful bacteria. Clean cutting boards carefully.
* Wash the top of a can before opening it to keep dirt from getting into the food.
* Use a clean spoon each time you taste food during preparation. That way, you won't transfer harmful bacteria from your mouth to the food you're preparing.
* Keep pets out of the kitchen.
* Keep two towels handy in your kitchen—one for wiping hands and a separate one for drying dishes.

Cleanup Time

After food has been prepared and eaten, it's time to clean up. A clean kitchen has no food particles and spills to encourage bacterial growth, insects, and rodents.

Using Cleanup Appliances

Many kitchens are equipped with a food waste disposal and a dishwasher to help speed cleanup.

A food waste disposal grinds food waste and flushes it down the drain. Always run plenty of cold water when grinding food. Do not overfill the disposal, but grind small batches at a time. To avoid clogging, do not put fibrous food in the disposal, such as onion skins or corn husks.

When using an automatic dishwasher, follow the instructions in the owner's manual. Make sure the dishwasher is full before running it. Small loads waste water and energy.

Food-Borne Illnesses

Illness and Symptoms	Type of Microorganism	Prevention
Salmonellosis (sal-muh-nell-OH-sis) Stomach pain, diarrhea, nausea, chills, fever, and headache. Begins 6 to 48 hours after eating contaminated food. May last 3 to 5 days. Infants and young children, the ill, and the elderly may be seriously affected.	Bacteria (*salmonella*). Often found in raw or undercooked foods, such as poultry, eggs, and meat. May also be found in unpasteurized milk. May spread to other foods through cross-contamination.	❖ Follow the sanitation procedures described in the text. ❖ Don't drink unpasteurized milk.
Staph Nausea, vomiting, diarrhea. Begins 30 minutes to 8 hours after eating contaminated food. May last a day or two.	Toxin from bacteria (*staphylococcus aureus*). Staph bacteria are found on human skin, in nose, and in throat. Spread by improper food handling.	❖ Follow the sanitation procedures described in the text.
E. coli poisoning Severe abdominal cramps followed by diarrhea (often bloody), nausea, vomiting, and occasionally a low-grade fever. Begins 3 to 4 days after contaminated food is eaten. Can last up to 10 days. Often requires hospitalization. Sometimes leads to urinary tract infection and kidney failure.	Toxin from a specific type of *E. coli* bacteria. Sources include contaminated water, raw or rare ground beef, and unpasteurized milk.	❖ Follow the sanitation procedures described in the text.
Listeriosis (lih-STEER-ee-OH-sis) Rare but potentially fatal. In adults: fever, chills, headache, backache, and sometimes abdominal pain and diarrhea.	Bacteria (*listeria monocytogenes*). Found frequently in the environment. Can grow slowly at refrigerator temperatures.	❖ Follow the sanitation procedures described in the text. ❖ Avoid raw milk and cheese made from unpasteurized milk.

Disease / Symptoms	Cause	Prevention
Listeriosis (continued) In newborns: respiratory distress, refusal to drink, and vomiting. Possible complications include meningitis and blood poisoning. Can cause miscarriages and stillbirths.		❖ Store food properly. Observe "sell by" and "use by" dates on processed products.
Perfringens poisoning (purr-FRIN-jens) Diarrhea and gas pains. Begins 9 to 15 hours after eating contaminated food. Usually lasts about one day. Elderly people and ulcer patients can be affected more seriously.	Toxin from bacteria (clostridium perfringens). The bacteria grow only where there is little or no oxygen. Spores can survive cooking. Called the "cafeteria germ" because it often strikes food served in quantity and left for long periods on a steam table or at room temperature.	❖ Follow the sanitation procedures described in the text.
Botulism (botch-uh-liz-um) Affects the nervous system and can be fatal if not treated. Symptoms appear 12 to 48 hours after eating contaminated food. They include double vision, droopy eyelids, trouble speaking and swallowing, and difficulty breathing. Patients who do recover may suffer nerve damage.	Toxin from bacteria (clostridium botulinum). The bacteria grow only where there is little or no oxygen. Spores may survive cooking. Associated with improperly processed canned foods; also with cooked foods held at room or warm temperatures for an extended time with limited oxygen (such as potatoes wrapped tightly in foil).	❖ Follow the sanitation procedures described in the text. ❖ Follow established guidelines for home canning. (See Section 24.5) ❖ See Section 7.4, pages 205–206, for signs of spoiled food and what to do with suspect foods.
Toxoplasmosis (tocks-oh-plaz-MOH-sis) Can cause nerve damage. If a pregnant woman is infected, the illness can affect the central nervous system of the unborn child.	A parasite (toxoplasmosa gondii) common in mammals, reptiles, and birds. People are infected through eating undercooked meat or poultry that contains the parasite or by cleaning the litter box of a cat with the parasite.	❖ Follow the sanitation procedures described in the text. ❖ Wash hands after cleaning a cat's litter box. Pregnant women should not clean litter boxes.

Adapted from Food Safety and Inspection Service, USDA

Careful dishwashing is one key to sanitation in the kitchen. Any food left on dishes or utensils allows microorganisms to multiply.

Washing Dishes by Hand

Washing dishes is faster and easier if you are well organized. Here are some suggestions.

Rinse soiled dishes and place them to one side of the sink. Group like items together and arrange in this order: glasses, flatware, dishes, kitchen tools, and cookware. Keep sharp knives separate. If food is stuck to cookware, pre-soak it. Pour a little dish detergent in, add hot water, and let the pan stand for a while.

Fill a dishpan or sink with soapy water hot enough to remove grease, but not hot enough to burn your hands. Using a sponge or dishcloth, wash the dishes in the order you grouped them. Glasses are washed first and greasy cookware last. When necessary, refill the sink or dishpan with clean, hot, soapy water.

Rinse dishes thoroughly in hot water. A safe and easy way is to put the dish rack in the sink and let hot water run over it. Be sure the insides of containers are well rinsed. Let the dishes air dry in the rack or dry them with a clean, dry towel.

Cleaning the Work and Eating Areas

When you are through washing dishes, wipe off the dining table. Clean all the work areas and appliances that were used. Don't forget to wash the can opener blade and the cutting board. Rinse the dishcloth often as you work, using hot, soapy water.

Wipe up spills on the floor. Wash the sink to remove grease and food particles, then run the disposal.

Finally, put any garbage in a plastic bag, close it tightly, and put it in the garbage can outside. Wash garbage cans regularly to avoid attracting insects and rodents.

Be sure to wrap garbage tightly and store it outside the home.

Proper Food Temperatures

Besides cleanliness, another important aspect of sanitation is keeping food at safe temperatures.

How Temperatures Affect Microorganisms

Bacteria multiply rapidly at temperatures between 60°F and 125°F (16°C to 52°C). Note that this range includes room temperatures. Most food-borne illnesses are caused by bacteria that thrive in these temperatures.

High food temperatures from 165°F to 212°F (74°C to 100°C) kill most of the harmful bacteria. These temperatures are normally reached during cooking. However, some bacteria produce **spores,** cells that will develop into bacteria if conditions are right. Spores can survive cooking heat.

Cold refrigerator temperatures below 40°F (4°C) slow down the growth of some of the bacteria, but do not kill them.

If food is frozen at 0°F (-18°C), bacteria stop growing. Bacteria or spores already present in the food, however, will not be killed. When the food is thawed, bacteria will start to grow again.

The diagram on page 202 shows you the proper temperatures for storing and cooking food. Red is the danger zone where bacteria grow rapidly. Bacteria also grow in the orange zone, but more slowly.

As you have learned, food-borne illness can also be caused by toxins or parasites. Some types of toxins are destroyed by heat. Others remain unchanged even after food is cooked. Thorough cooking destroys parasites.

Food Handling Guidelines

Many foods require special care to keep them out of the danger zone. These include meat, poultry, fish, eggs, and dairy products, for example.

When cooking and serving food, follow these guidelines:

❖ Cook food to the proper internal temperature or until thoroughly cooked. Avoid partial cooking—cook the food completely at one time.

❖ Taste foods containing ingredients from animal sources only after they are fully cooked. Do not taste them when they are raw or during cooking.

❖ When microwaving, take steps to ensure even, thorough cooking, as explained in Section 9.3.

❖ Do not leave food out more than two hours at room temperature, or more than one hour if the temperature is above 90°F (32°C).

❖ Keep extra quantities of food either hot—using the range or another cooking appliance—or cold, in the refrigerator.

❖ Do not add more food to a serving dish of food that has been out for a while. Instead, use a clean dish.

250°F 120°C

240°F 116°C

212°F 100°C

**High Temperatures Destroy
Most Bacteria**

165°F 74°C

**No Bacterial Growth
Some Bacteria Live**

140°F 60°C

Many Bacteria Survive

125°F 52°C

**DANGER
Rapid Bacterial Growth**

60°F 15°C

Some Bacterial Growth

40°F 4°C

**Refrigerator Temperatures
Slow Bacterial Growth**

32°F 0°C

**Freezing Temperatures
No Bacterial Growth**

0°F -18°C

Temperature is one of the most important factors in food safety. Bacteria multiply very rapidly in the danger zone—60°F to 125°F (15°C to 52°C). What kinds of foods are most at risk?

❖ Discard foods that have been held at room temperature for more than two hours.

❖ Refrigerate food in shallow containers. Large, deep containers keep the food from cooling rapidly and evenly.

❖ When reheating food that has been refrigerated, bring it to an internal temperature of 165°F (74°C) or higher to kill any bacteria. Keep in mind that if the food has not been properly stored, it cannot be made safe just by reheating. You will learn more about storing food in the next section.

Tall containers work well for dry foods that are stored at room temperature. Choose shallow containers for foods to be refrigerated or frozen. The food will cool to safe temperatures more quickly.

Thawing Food Safely

Do not thaw food at room temperature. If you do, the outside may contain millions of harmful bacteria by the time the inside is thawed. To thaw food safely, use one of these methods:

❖ Place food in the refrigerator, where it will thaw slowly.

❖ For faster thawing, put the package in a water-tight plastic bag and submerge it in cold water. Change the water every 30 minutes. The cold slows down the growth of bacteria as the food thaws.

❖ Use a microwave for quick, safe defrosting. Follow the manufacturer's directions. Foods thawed this way should be cooked immediately.

By handling foods carefully and practicing cleanliness, you'll avoid food-borne illnesses.

Section 7.3 Review

RECALL THE FACTS

1. Describe two kinds of microorganisms that can cause food-borne illness.

2. Name five instances when you should wash your hands while working with food.

3. What temperature range is considered the "danger zone"? Why?

4. What is the time limit for leaving most foods at room temperature?

DISCUSS YOUR IDEAS

5. Why do you think so many Americans get food poisoning each year?

APPLY YOUR LEARNING

6. Write at least six slogans or rhymes that could help you and your classmates remember important rules of sanitation.

Objectives

After studying this section, you should be able to:

❖ Identify causes and signs of food spoilage.
❖ Give examples of foods that are stored at room temperature and in cold storage.
❖ Give guidelines for each type of storage.

Look for These Terms

shelf life
shelf-stable
perishable
freezer burn
inventory

Proper storage of food helps you in many ways. You can keep a variety of foods on hand, plan ahead, and work more efficiently. Most important, proper storage helps retain nutrients and keeps food from spoiling.

Spoilage and Nutrient Loss

Food that is not stored properly starts to lose quality and nutrients. Eventually it will spoil. Spoiled food often develops bad tastes and odors and must be thrown out. Some types of spoilage can cause food-borne illness.

What causes spoilage? Under the right conditions, harmful bacteria, yeasts, and molds can spoil food. Spoilage can also be caused by natural chemical changes within the cells of the food.

Mold on bread makes it unsuitable for eating. Controlling spoilage reduces food waste.

Science Connection

Chemistry:

Enzymes and Spoilage

The cells of living things contain *enzymes,* protein substances that cause chemical changes to occur. When a plant or animal is processed into a food, some of the enzymes remain active. Unless foods are heated to destroy the enzymes, chemical changes continue—destroying the cells and causing the food to spoil.

■ ■ ■

Conditions in the environment can also cause or speed up nutrient loss and spoilage. Controlling these conditions is a key to proper storage.

❖ *Heat* speeds up chemical reactions that cause spoilage.
❖ *Air* contains oxygen. Exposure to oxygen can destroy some nutrients, such as vitamins C and E. It can also cause oils to become rancid—they develop an unpleasant flavor.
❖ *Too little moisture* can cause fresh foods to dry out, wilt, and lose nutrients.
❖ *Too much moisture* can lead to spoilage. Bacteria thrive in moist areas.
❖ *Light* can destroy nutrients, especially vitamin C and riboflavin.
❖ *Dirt* contains harmful microorganisms.
❖ *Damage* to food or packaging makes spoilage by microorganisms more likely.

When Food Is Spoiled

How do you know when food is starting to spoil? Some fresh foods, such as apples and celery, dry out. They may wilt, get wrinkled, or turn brown. Some foods become slimy, a sign that decay has started. Spots of fuzzy

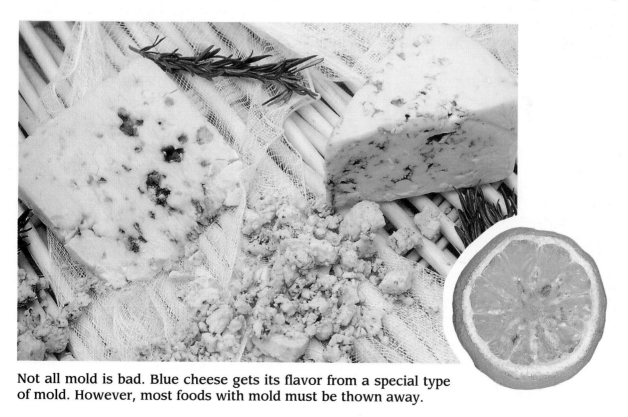

Not all mold is bad. Blue cheese gets its flavor from a special type of mold. However, most foods with mold must be thown away.

mold, damage such as holes, tears and bruises, bad flavors, and bad odors are all signs of spoilage.

Most spoiled foods should be discarded. However, spots of mold can be cut off hard cheese, hard salami, and dry cured country ham. Pare away about an inch (2.5 cm) of the food around the area where the mold spot was. Discard all other visibly moldy foods.

Mold gives off spores. To keep mold from spreading, very gently wrap the moldy food or place it in a bag before discarding. Examine other foods that may have been in contact with the moldy food. Clean the container that held the moldy food, and if necessary, wash out the refrigerator.

Basic Storage Principles

No food can be stored indefinitely. Each food has a **shelf life,** the length of time it can be stored and still retain its quality. Shelf life depends on the type of food, packaging, storage temperature, and how the food is handled.

To avoid loss of quality, follow these guidelines:

❖ Buy only what you need.
❖ Follow the principle of "first in, first out." Store new food behind the same kind of older food. Use up the older food first.
❖ Look for "sell by" or "use by" dates on food containers. If there is none, you may want to write the purchase date on the container before storing. Use canned food within a year.
❖ Clean storage areas regularly. Throw out any food that has started to spoil or containers that have been damaged. Wash and dry surfaces thoroughly.

There are two basic kinds of food storage methods: room temperature storage and cold storage.

Room Temperature Storage

Many canned, bottled, and packaged foods will last for weeks or even months at room temperatures below 85°F (29°C). Such foods are called **shelf-stable.** Examples include most canned foods, dry beans and peas, oils and shortening, and many grain products (except whole grains). In general, foods that you find on grocery shelves when shopping can be stored at room temperature when you bring them home.

Kitchen cabinets are used for most room temperature storage. They should be clean and dry with doors to keep out light and dirt. Temperatures should be no higher than 85°F (29°C) and no lower than freezing, 32°F (0°C). Do not store food on shelves near or above heat sources such as the range, refrigerator, or a radiator. Also avoid areas that may get wet, like under-sink cabinets.

After opening packages or containers, reseal them if possible. Otherwise, transfer the contents to storage containers with tight-fitting covers. Do the same with foods you buy in bulk.

Safety Check

In some cases, spoiled food can make you ill. If you aren't sure whether food is spoiled, play it safe—discard it.

Be alert for these signs of spoilage in canned and bottled foods: bulging cans, liquids that spurt when you open the container, or liquids that are cloudy when they should be clear. If you see these signs, *do not taste the food.* Wrap it and discard it where no people or animals can get to it.

Perishable foods, like those at the left, need cold storage to delay spoilage. Shelf-stable foods, like those at the right, may be stored at normal room temperature. To prevent food waste, buy only the amount of food you can use and store it properly.

Cold Storage

Perishable foods spoil quickly at room temperature. They require cold storage in the refrigerator or freezer, depending on the kind of food and how long you want to store it. The chart on pages 208-209 gives you a general timetable for foods in cold storage.

Refrigerator Storage

Foods normally refrigerated include:
- Foods that were refrigerated in the store, including dairy products, eggs, delicatessen foods, and fresh meat, poultry, and fish.
- Most fresh fruits and vegetables. Exceptions are onions, potatoes, and sweet potatoes, which should be stored in a cool, dry area.
- Whole grain products, seeds and nuts. They contain oils which can spoil and give foods an off-flavor.
- Leftover cooked foods.
- Baked goods with fruit or cream fillings.
- Any foods that, according to label directions, must be refrigerated. Some shelf-stable foods must be refrigerated after opening.

Safety Check

If you have to stack items to store them, put the lightest on the top. Boxes of dried soup mix, for example, can be stored on top of canned soups. That way you'll be less likely to accidentally knock over heavy items that could cause injury.

Some foods are very delicate and have a short shelf life. Foods with cream fillings must be refrigerated and eaten promptly.

COLD STORAGE CHART

NOTE: — — — — means food should not be stored in that area.

TYPE OF FOOD	REFRIGERATOR STORAGE 40° F (4°C)	FREEZER STORAGE 0° F (-18° C)
Meats, Poultry, Fish		
Beef roasts, steaks	3-5 days	6-12 months
Pork roasts, chops	3-5 days	4-6 months
Lamb roasts, chops	3-5 days	6-9 months
Veal roasts	3-5 days	4-8 months
Chicken or turkey, whole	1-2 days	1 year
Chicken or turkey, pieces	1-2 days	9 months
Ground meats or poultry	1-2 days	3-4 months
Lean fish (cod)	1-2 days	6 months
Fatty fish (salmon)	1-2 days	2-3 months
Shellfish (shrimp)	1-2 days	3-6 months
Dairy Products		
Fresh milk, cream	5 days	— — — —
Butter, margarine	1-2 weeks	2 months
Buttermilk	2 weeks	— — — —
Sour cream	4 weeks	— — — —
Yogurt, plain or flavored	2 weeks	— — — —
Cottage cheese	1 week	— — — —
Hard cheese (cheddar), opened	3-4 weeks	— — — —
Hard cheese, unopened	3-6 months	— — — —
Ice cream, sherbet	— — — —	1 month
Miscellaneous Foods		
Bread	— — — —	3 months
Cakes, cookies, pies (not cream-filled)	1-3 days	2-3 months
Cream pies	1-2 days	— — — —
Commercially frozen foods	— — — —	3-4 months
Fresh eggs, in shell	3 weeks	— — — —
Raw yolks, whites	2-4 days	1 year
Hard-cooked eggs	1 week	— — — —
Egg substitutes, opened	3 days	— — — —
Egg substitutes, unopened	10 days	1 year
Mayonnaise, salad dressing (Refrigerate after opening)	2 months	— — — —

COLD STORAGE CHART (Continued)

NOTE: ———— means food should not be stored in that area.

TYPE OF FOOD	REFRIGERATOR STORAGE 40° F (4°C)	FREEZER STORAGE 0° F (-18° C)
Cooked Foods, Leftovers		
Cooked meats, meat dishes	3-4 days	2-3 months
Fried chicken	3-4 days	4 months
Poultry covered in broth	1-2 days	6 months
Soups and stews (not creamed)	3-4 days	2 months
Fish stews, soups (not creamed)	1 day	1 month
Cured Meats		
Hot dogs, opened	1 week	1-2 months
Lunch meats, opened	3-5 days	1-2 months
Hot dogs, lunch meats, unopened	2 weeks	1-2 months
Bacon	7 days	1 month
Sausage (beef, pork, turkey)	1-2 days	1-2 months
Hard sausage (pepperoni)	2-3 weeks	1-2 months
Ham, canned (refrigerated, unopened)	6-9 months	————
Ham, fully cooked, whole	7 days	1-2 months
Ham, fully cooked, half	3-5 days	1-2 months
Ham, fully cooked, slices	3-4 days	1-2 months

The refrigerator should be kept at 40°F (4°C). Do not let the refrigerator temperature fall below freezing (32°F or 0°C). Foods with a high water content, such as lettuce, may freeze and be damaged.

Avoid overloading the refrigerator. The cold air will not circulate well and some areas may become too warm to store perishables safely.

Store foods tightly covered. This will keep them from drying out and will also prevent odors from being picked up by other foods. Opened canned goods may pick up an off-flavor from the can, so transfer them to another storage container.

Store meat, poultry, and fish in the store wrap unless it is damaged or leaking. If it is, put the package in a plastic bag or on a plate. Leaking foods can contaminate other stored foods.

When storing fruits and vegetables, wash them only if necessary to remove dirt. Wipe hard-skinned ones dry and drain others well.

Leftovers require special care. To ensure thorough chilling, use shallow containers. Large, deep containers keep food from cooling rapidly and evenly. Cut large pieces of meat into smaller ones so they cool quickly. Close the containers tightly and label with the current date. Be sure to use the food within a few days. (Remember that some foods can be frozen for longer storage.) You may want to keep all leftovers on the same shelf so they don't get overlooked.

Freezer Storage

Freezing allows long-term storage of many foods. At temperatures of 0°F (-18°C) or below, foods keep from one month to a year, depending on the type of food and proper packaging.

These packaging materials can help prevent freezer burn. What types of wraps and containers would not provide adequate protection?

Foods purchased frozen should be stored promptly in the home freezer. Many other foods can also be frozen to increase shelf life. These include fresh meat, poultry, and fish; baked goods such as breads and rolls; and many leftovers.

Some foods do not freeze well. These include fresh vegetables that are to be eaten raw; cooked or whole raw eggs; products made with mayonnaise; meat and poultry stuffing; cream- or egg-based sauces; custards; baked goods with cream filling; and many cheeses.

To freeze foods at home, a two-door refrigerator-freezer or a separate freezer unit is needed. Separate freezer units generally maintain food quality longer than refrigerator-freezers.

Some refrigerators have only one outside door and a small freezer compartment inside. The freezer compartment maintains a temperature of 10°F to 15°F (-12°C to -9°C). It can be used for storing already frozen food for several weeks. However, it is not cold enough to freeze fresh or leftover food satisfactorily.

A freezer functions best when fairly full. Some freezers need regular defrosting.

How to Package and Freeze Foods

Foods that are purchased already frozen can be stored in their original packaging. However, foods frozen at home must be specially packaged to avoid freezer burn. **Freezer burn** results when food is improperly packaged or stored in the freezer too long. The food dries out and loses flavor and texture.

Packaging materials for freezing must be vapor- and moisture-resistant. These include plastic containers with tight-fitting covers, heavy-duty plastic freezer bags, and wraps such as heavy-duty foil and freezer wrap. Do not use regular refrigerator storage bags or plastic tubs from foods such as margarine and yogurt. They do not provide enough protection. Fresh meat, poultry, and fish need additional wrap for freezing—the store wrapping is too lightweight.

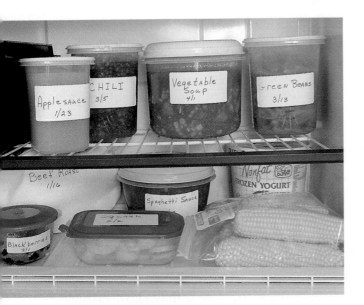

Labeling frozen foods clearly and keeping an inventory of food in the freezer can minimize food waste. Foods freeze more quickly when air circulates between packages during the freezing process.

When wrapping solid foods, such as meat, squeeze out as much air as possible to prevent freezer burn. Seal packages with freezer tape.

When filling storage containers, leave enough space for food to expand as it freezes. This is about one inch (2.5 cm) in a quart (or liter) container. Then seal the container tightly.

Label all packages and containers with the contents, amount (or number of servings), date frozen, and any special instructions.

For best quality, freeze food quickly. Spread the packages out so they all touch the coils or sides of the freezer. Leave enough air between packages for air to circulate. When the food is frozen (at least 24 hours later), you can stack it according to the kind of food.

Keep an **inventory,** or up-to-date record, of the food in the freezer. Include the food, date frozen, and quantity. This page shows a typical freezer inventory. As you remove food, change the quantity on the inventory so you know how much is left.

When the Power Goes Off

When the power goes off or the refrigerator-freezer breaks down, the food inside is in danger of spoiling. In general, avoid opening the door of the freezer or refrigerator. This will help maintain cold temperatures longer.

Keeping Frozen Foods Safe

A full freezer will keep food frozen for about two days after losing power. A half-full freezer will keep food frozen for about one day. If the freezer is not full, stack packages closely together so they will stay cold.

Separate frozen meat, poultry, and fish from other foods. That way, if they begin to thaw, juices will not get into other foods.

Date Frozen	Food (amount in package)	Number of packages
2/8	Chicken fryers (halves)	~~6~~ 5
2/11	Beef stew (1 serving)	3
2/12	Mixed vegetables (2 lb.)	~~6~~ 5
2/13	Corn on the cob (4 ears)	4 3
2/20	Eggplant Parmesan (1 serving)	4

If the power will be off longer than two days, you can put dry ice (frozen carbon dioxide) in the freezer. BE CAREFUL! Never touch dry ice with bare hands or breathe its vapors in an enclosed area. Carbon dioxide gas in high concentration is poisonous.

When the freezer is working again, here's how to decide what to do with the food:

❖ If ice crystals are still visible, or the food feels as cold as if it were refrigerated, it is safe to refreeze. Some foods may lose quality, but they can still be eaten.

❖ Discard any food that thawed or was held above 40°F (4°C) for more than two hours. Also discard food that has a strange odor.

Once the freezer is working again, wash up any food spills and wipe surfaces dry. If odors remain, wash again with a solution of 2 tablespoons (30 mL) baking soda dissolved in 1 quart (1 L) warm water. Leave an open box of baking soda inside the freezer to absorb odors.

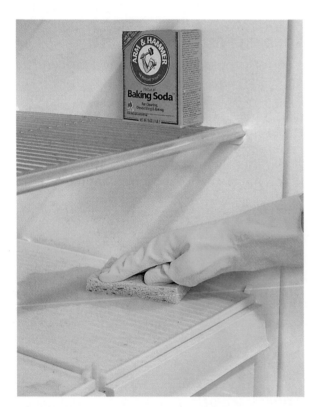

If power goes out for any period of time, discard any refrigerated or frozen food that may be unsafe to eat. Then clean the unit thoroughly to remove odors and bacteria.

Keeping Refrigerated Foods Safe

During a power outage, food will usually keep in the refrigerator for four to six hours, depending on the temperature of the room. If the power will be out for a long time, you can place a block of ice in the refrigerator.

When the refrigerator is working again, follow these guidelines to decide what to do with the food:

❖ Discard fresh meats, poultry, fish, lunch meats, hot dogs, eggs, milk, soft cheeses, and cooked foods if they have been held above 40°F (4°C) for more than two hours.

❖ Keep butter and margarine if they have not melted and do not have a rancid odor.

❖ Other foods, including fresh fruits and vegetables, are safe if they show no signs of mold, sliminess, or bad odor.

Once the refrigerator is working again, clean it the same way as described for the freezer.

■ Section 7.4 Review ■

RECALL THE FACTS

1. Name three signs that food has spoiled.

2. What is the difference between shelf-stable foods and perishable foods?

3. What is the ideal temperature range for room temperature storage? Refrigerator storage? Freezer storage?

4. Describe how you would wrap a package of fresh ground meat for freezing.

DISCUSS YOUR IDEAS

5. Most people have to throw away spoiled food now and then. What do you think is the major reason?

APPLY YOUR LEARNING

6. Use a refrigerator-freezer thermometer to check cold storage temperatures at home or in the foods lab. Are they at safe levels?

Section 7.5
Conserving Natural Resources

Look for This Term
disposable

Neil was studying in the kitchen. He could hear the kitchen radio vaguely in the background, some news about environmental problems. He had heard most of it before. Conserve natural resources...use them wisely...don't waste or pollute them. He went back to his studies and ignored the radio. "I'm just one person," he thought. "Not much I can do."

Neil, like many others, never thought about the kitchen as one of the biggest polluters and household energy-guzzlers. Gas, electricity, and water are pumped into homes and used liberally in the kitchen. The kitchen is also a major source of household trash.

Some people believe they can't do much to help solve environmental problems. Yet conservation begins with the individual. If each person does his or her share, waste and pollution can be cut down. Here are some ways to conserve natural resources in the kitchen at home or at school.

Pollution is a global problem. The decisions you make daily can increase or decrease its severity.

Conserve Energy

Neil wasn't listening to the radio. As a result, he wasted electricity by not turning it off. Every watt of electricity used in the home sends about two pounds (1 kg) of carbon dioxide, an air pollutant, into the atmosphere.

To save energy, follow these suggestions:

❖ Turn off lights and appliances when they are not in use.
❖ Cook as many foods as possible when using the oven. Freeze the extra for future meals.
❖ Use small appliances or a microwave oven when cooking small amounts of food. They use less energy than the range.
❖ Match the pan size to the size of the burner or heating unit for top-of-range cooking. Less energy will be lost.
❖ Decide what you want to eat before opening the refrigerator door. The air in the refrigerator warms up if you leave the door open. It takes more energy to cool it down.
❖ Keep the refrigerator and freezer well organized so you can find food easily.
❖ Don't run the dishwasher unless it's full.

Safety Check

Never try to save energy by letting hot food sit at room temperature before refrigerating it. Remember, harmful bacteria grow quickly at room temperature.

Conserve Water

Clean, safe water is scarce in some areas. Water use may be restricted because of a shortage. Learn more about the water situation in your area. By conserving water in your home, you can help preserve this resource for all.

Look for ways to use less water during food preparation. For example, don't let tap water run unnecessarily as you pare vegetables.

Putting aerators on faucets is an easy, inexpensive way to cut water usage.

Cleanup takes lots of water, but you can conserve. When handwashing dishes, don't keep the water running. Wash all the dishes first and then rinse them off at the same time as quickly as possible.

Be sure to repair dripping faucets immediately. Water dripping at the rate of a drop a second can waste about 700 gallons (2700 L) a year.

Reduce Trash

Picture a four-lane highway running from Boston to Los Angeles, filled with trash about 6 feet (3 m) deep. That's about the amount of trash Americans create in a year. The trash usually ends up in landfills, which pollute soil and water. Communities are running out of landfill space.

You can help minimize the trash problem. Start by remembering three key words: reduce, reuse, and recycle.

Reduce

One way to cut down on trash is to reduce the use of **disposable,** or throwaway, products. For example, use dishcloths instead of paper towels to wipe up spills. Use cloth napkins instead of paper ones. Buy or make cloth bags to carry groceries. Choose items in reusable or recyclable containers rather than disposable ones.

Reuse

Reusing gives second life to materials. Find creative ways to reuse items that might otherwise be thrown away. In the kitchen, you might:

❖ Wash plastic tubs from margarine, yogurt, and cottage cheese and use them to refrigerate leftovers. Do not use them for freezing—they are not heavy enough and food will dry out.

Most trash ends up in landfills. Reducing use of disposable items, reusing materials, and recycling whenever possible are the keys to cutting waste.

- Turn glass jars and bottles with tight-fitting covers into storage containers. Use them for foods such as rice, pasta, and dry beans. Wash the jars and covers carefully, then let them air dry for at least 24 hours to remove odors.
- Reuse plastic or paper grocery bags as trash bags.

Recycle

Cooperate with recycling programs in your community. The kinds of materials recycled vary, depending on the community. Generally, newspapers, aluminum cans and foil, glass bottles, and some plastic containers are recycled.

Some communities have curb-side pickup for recycled materials. In others, the items must be brought to collection centers. Many supermarkets collect plastic shopping bags for recycling.

Many materials can be recycled and used again. What steps has your community taken to recycle waste?

Show Your Concern

Some people blame business, industry, and government for environmental problems. Even there, individual consumers have a voice. Every time you buy a product or use a service, you "vote" for it and for the policies of the organization. If you don't buy items or services that waste energy or pollute, the producers will improve them or develop new ones. Consumer power is an effective way to conserve natural resources.

By making the right choices and cooperating with community programs, you can do your share to help conserve natural resources.

Section 7.5 Review

RECALL THE FACTS

1. Why is it important for individuals to conserve resources?

2. Name five ways to conserve energy in the home.

3. What are three ways to conserve water?

4. Name three keys to reducing trash and give an example of each.

DISCUSS YOUR IDEAS

5. How might you convince someone who doesn't recycle to start recycling?

APPLY YOUR LEARNING

6. Develop a plan to reduce, reuse, and recycle at home. Where can you start? How can you proceed? How might you convince family members to take part in your plan?

CAREER PROFILE

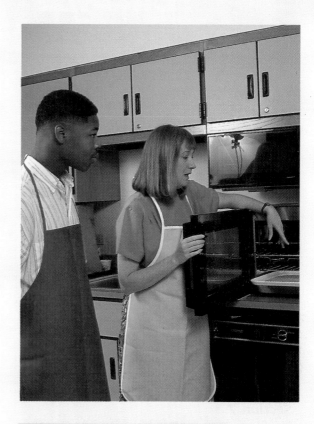

Jan Bradshaw
Home Economics
Teacher

Current position:

"I teach home economics to high school students in a medium-sized urban school district."

Responsibilities:

"I help my students develop skills that they will use throughout their life—everything from preparing nutritious meals to managing a family budget to preparing for a career."

Skills:

"Of course a teacher must be knowledgeable in his or her subject area. You also must be able to communicate with and motivate students. It helps to have a genuine enthusiasm for working with young people."

Education:

"I have a bachelor's degree in education with an emphasis on home economics, and I'm certified to teach by the State Department of Education."

Work environment:

"I work long hours both in and out of the classroom. Besides actually teaching, my job involves planning lessons, grading papers, preparing report cards, meeting with parents and school staff, and attending workshops and conferences."

Favorite part of the job:

"I love working with young people. It's very rewarding to help them learn. Often, I learn from them, too!"

- What are some advantages and disadvantages of a teacher's varied work schedule?
- What aspects of Jan's job do you think you might enjoy? Why?

Summary

Section 7.1
Introduction to the Kitchen: Kitchens are equipped with major appliances, small appliances, and utensils. They are organized around work centers, which include the sink, cold storage, and cooking centers.

Section 7.2
Safety in the Kitchen: Good management and safe work habits are the keys to kitchen safety. Common kitchen hazards include falls, sharp objects, electrical appliances, hazardous chemicals, and the range. Children, the elderly, and people with handicaps require special safety measures. Consider first aid training, including the Heimlich Maneuver and CPR.

Section 7.3
Sanitation: If food is handled improperly, microorganisms can multiply and cause food-borne illness. Prevent illness by practicing good personal hygiene, using sanitary work methods, keeping the kitchen clean, and keeping food at proper temperatures.

Section 7.4
Storing Food: Proper storage prevents spoilage and nutrient loss. Shelf-stable foods may be stored at room temperature. Store perishable foods in the freezer or in the refrigerator. Frozen and refrigerated foods require special handling after a power outage.

Section 7.5
Conserving Natural Resources: Conservation begins with the individual. Consider simple measures for saving energy and conserving water. To reduce trash, identify ways to reduce, reuse, and recyle.

REVIEWING FACTS

1. Name three items that might be found at each of the three basic kitchen work centers. (7.1)

2. List two knife safety rules. (7.2)

3. Give three guidelines for storing hazardous household chemicals. (7.2)

4. How can you help children learn safe kitchen work habits? (7.2)

5. List two personal hygiene habits that can help prevent food-borne illness. (7.3)

6. What is cross-contamination? How can you prevent it? (7.3)

7. Describe two procedures for thawing food safely. (7.3)

8. What is "shelf life"? (7.4)

9. Name two ways to keep frozen foods safe when the power goes off. (7.4)

10. Give three examples of alternatives to disposable items. (7.5)

LEARNING BY DOING

1. **Foods lab:** Prepare a food using a recipe that requires the use of three kitchen centers. Analyze how organizing a kitchen by work centers helped ease and speed this food preparation task. (7.1)

2. **Safety demonstration:** Perform a skit for your class showing how three different kinds of kitchen accidents can happen. Take suggestions from the class about how they could have been avoided. (7.2)

3. **Food science lab:** Observe spoilage in fresh fruits with this experiment. Label small samples of fresh fruits with the type of fruit and the date. Leave the samples out at room temperature (along with a sign warning "Do Not Eat"). Each day, record changes in appearance and smell. (7.4)

4. **Demonstration:** Collect items from home or school that could be recycled or reused (such as aluminum cans, newpapers, and glass jars). Give a demonstration showing how to prepare and sort items for recycling. Have your classmates offer suggestions for how to reuse some of the items. (7.5)

THINKING CRITICALLY

1. **Recognizing assumptions:** Elaine's mother uses a toaster with a damaged wire. She says that the toaster still works and refuses to have it fixed or buy a new one. What assumption is she making? Is it a correct one? (7.2)

2. **Predicting consequences:** What result might you expect if foods cooked for a picnic are left out on the table and eaten over the course of four or five hours? (7.3)

3. **Distinguishing between fact and opinion:** "I use up leftovers, even if they smell a little spoiled. After all, if I boil food long enough, it can't make people sick." Which of these sentences is a fact? Which is an opinion? Defend your answer. (7.4)

4. **Recognizing alternatives:** What alternatives can you suggest to reduce, reuse, and recycle the products your family uses? (7.5)

MAKING DECISIONS AND SOLVING PROBLEMS

What Would You Do?

1. Your family has a hard time functioning in the kitchen on weekday mornings. Some of you make bag lunches while others are preparing a quick breakfast. As family members get in each other's way, there are frequent accidents. (7.1, 7.2)

2. Your grandmother lives alone. Her vision and hearing are poor, but she insists on preparing her own meals. You are worried about her safety. (7.2)

3. You and your mother eat two heat-and-serve frozen meat pies out of the four purchased at the supermarket. Early the next morning, you are both nauseated and have severe diarrhea. Two of the meat pies remain in the freezer. You had planned to have them for supper the next night. (7.3)

4. You are preparing a tossed salad, hamburgers, and baked beans for your family when the power goes out. You are concerned about keeping the food safe to eat. (7.4)

LINKING YOUR STUDIES

1. **Health:** Using a first aid book as a reference, make a list of first aid supplies for the major kinds of kitchen accidents. Assemble a first aid kit for your kitchen at home, using a shoebox or other container. (7.2)

2. **Math:** Some species of bacteria can double their numbers every 20 minutes. At this rate, if you started with one bacterium, how many would there be after five hours? (7.3)

3. **Health:** Working with a partner, use library resources to find information about treatment for each of the foodborne illnesses in the chart on pages 198-199. (7.3)

4. **Science:** Investigate and report on the effects of water pollution on drinking water supplies. (7.5)

CHAPTER 8

Recipe Skills

Objectives

After studying this section, you should be able to:

* List the kinds of information a good recipe provides.
* Give guidelines for evaluating and collecting recipes.

Look for This Term

yield

A recipe is a set of directions for making a food or beverage. Your success in using it depends on how well the recipe is written, as well as your ability to understand and follow the directions.

Recipe Information

A well-written, complete recipe includes the following:

* *List of ingredients and amounts.* The ingredients are generally listed in the order they are used, which makes it easier for you to follow the recipe and not omit an ingredient. Amounts of ingredients are also given.
* *Number of servings or amount the recipe makes.* This is known as the **yield.**
* *Essential information about temperature, time, and equipment.* This may include pan size and type, oven temperature or power, and cooking time. The recipe will also indicate whether a conventional oven should be preheated.
* *Step-by-step directions.* The directions should be clear and easy to follow. Steps may be numbered so you won't skip any or lose your place. Some recipes include more than one set of directions, such as a conventional method and a microwave method.
* *Nutrition information.* This information is not essential, but it can be useful in helping you choose nutritious recipes. Typical nutrition information tells you the amount of calories, fat, and sodium for each serving of the food. Some recipes also include information about carbohydrates, protein, cholesterol, saturated and unsaturated fats, fiber, vitamins, and minerals.

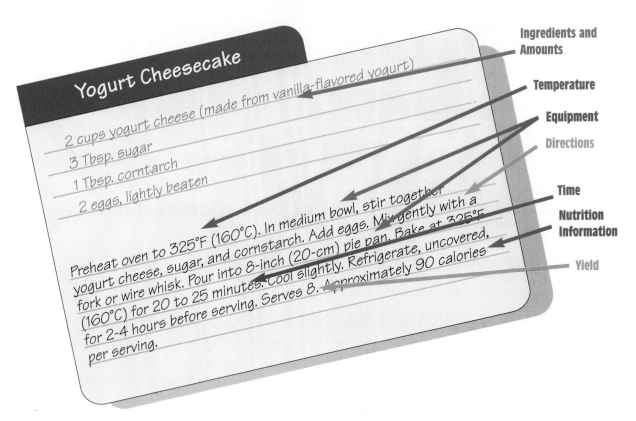

Ingredients and Amounts

Temperature

Equipment

Directions

Time

Nutrition Information

Yield

Yogurt Cheesecake

2 cups yogurt cheese (made from vanilla-flavored yogurt)

3 Tbsp. sugar

1 Tbsp. cornstarch

2 eggs, lightly beaten

Preheat oven to 325°F (160°C). In medium bowl, stir together yogurt cheese, sugar, and cornstarch. Add eggs. Mix gently with a fork or wire whisk. Pour into 8-inch (20-cm) pie pan. Bake at 325°F (160°C) for 20 to 25 minutes. Cool slightly. Refrigerate, uncovered, for 2-4 hours before serving. Serves 8. Approximately 90 calories per serving.

A well-written recipe should include all of the above information in an easy-to-follow format.

The standard, or most common, format for a recipe lists the ingredients first, in the order they are to be used. Then the assembly directions, which tell how to put the ingredients together, are given. This format, the clearest and easiest to follow, is used for the recipes in this book.

Less common recipe formats combine the ingredients and assembly directions. You may see a recipe written this way on a food package, for example. It takes less space than the standard format.

Collecting Recipes

The most reliable recipe source is a basic cookbook that gives standard recipes for common foods. You probably have several in your home economics classroom. If you don't find one you like, your teacher can make recommendations.

Once you have a basic cookbook, you can expand your recipe collection in whatever direction you choose, depending on the kinds of food you enjoy. For example, Janice collects vegetarian recipes. Recipe sources include your friends, magazines, newspapers, and the labels on many basic foods.

Recipes aren't always accurate or complete. When you first read a recipe, analyze it. Are basic ingredients missing? Are descriptions of ingredients clear? Is a direction included for each ingredient? Do you have all the information needed to prepare the recipe? If the answer to any of these questions is "no," look for another recipe.

Once you've tried a new recipe, you can decide whether to add it to your list of favorites. If you plan to use a new recipe on a special occasion, try it ahead of time first and evaluate the results.

Organizing your recipes can help you find them when you need them. You might want to paste your recipes on index cards and use a card file box or a shoe box for storage.

Healthy Attitudes

If you choose recipes wisely, you can prepare homemade meals that are lower in fat, sodium, and sugar than packaged convenience foods. Why not start a collection of recipes that are good-tasting, healthy, and easy to prepare?

What are the advantages of starting your own recipe collection?

Section 8.1 Review

RECALL THE FACTS

1. What basic information should be found in a well-written recipe?

2. What information does the yield of a recipe give?

3. Identify three things to look for when evaluating a new recipe.

DISCUSS YOUR IDEAS

4. Discuss the characteristics that make it difficult or easy to follow a recipe.

APPLY YOUR LEARNING

5. Find a recipe on a food package or in a magazine or newspaper. Analyze it to determine whether you would want to try it, using the guidelines given in this section. Write down any questions you have about the recipe. What are some ways that this recipe could be improved?

Objectives

After studying this section, you should be able to:

* Identify customary and metric units of measure.
* Identify measuring tools.
* Describe the proper procedures for measuring various types of ingredients.

Look for These Terms

volume
equivalent

Dominic bought a glass of lemonade at his little brother Carl's lemonade stand. It was so sweet he couldn't finish it. "How much sugar did you put in this?" Dominic asked. "The directions said 1 cup," Carl replied, "so I just used Mom's big coffee mug. Why?" As Dominic and his brother found out, measuring properly can be very important.

Units of Measurement

In a recipe, amounts of ingredients can be given in several ways. Most ingredients are measured by **volume,** or the amount of space they take up. For example, a salad recipe might list "1 cup cooked pasta." Some ingredients are measured by weight, or heaviness, such as a pound of fish filets. A few ingredients may be measured by the number of items, such as one medium banana or two eggs.

Would any of these items be suitable for measuring a cup of flour or a teaspoon of vanilla for a recipe? Why or why not?

In addition, there are two different systems of measurement. The customary system is the system of weights and measures used in the United States. In every other country, the metric system is used. The United States is gradually moving toward adopting the metric system, especially with increasing world trade. Most recipes use either one measuring system or the other. Some, like the recipes in this book, include both customary and metric units.

Customary Units

Following are the most common customary units found in recipes. Often they are abbreviated, as shown in parentheses.

❖ *Volume:* teaspoon (tsp.), tablespoon (Tbsp.), cup (c.), fluid ounce (fl. oz.), pint (pt.), quart (qt.), gallon (gal.)
❖ *Weight:* ounce (oz.), pound (lb.)
❖ *Temperature:* degrees Fahrenheit (˚F)
❖ *Length:* inches (in.)

Notice that weight may be measured in ounces. This kind of ounce is not the same as a fluid ounce, which is a measure of volume, not weight. Think of the difference between a cup of popcorn and a cup of water. Both take up the same amount of space—8 fluid ounces. However, they do not weigh the same. The water is heavier. To find out how much each weighs, you would use a scale, not a measuring cup.

Metric Units

The metric system is based on multiples of ten. For instance, just as there are 100 pennies in one dollar, there are 100 centimeters in one meter. Once you become familiar with it, the metric system is easier to use than the customary system.

Here are the metric units and symbols most often found in recipes:

❖ *Volume:* milliter (mL), liter (L)
❖ *Weight:* milligram (mg), gram (g), kilogram (kg)
❖ *Temperature:* degree Celsius (˚C)
❖ *Length:* centimeter (cm)

Equivalents

You can express the same amount in different ways by using different units of measure. This is called an **equivalent**. For instance, 4 tablespoons of flour is the same amount as 1/4 cup of flour, or about 50 milliliters. The chart on page 226 shows equivalents for food preparation.

Equipment for Measuring

A well-equipped kitchen includes the following measuring tools. Each has specific uses, as you will learn.

❖ *Dry measures* usually come in a set of several sizes. A typical customary set includes 1/4 cup, 1/3 cup, 1/2 cup, and 1 cup measures. A metric set includes 50 mL, 125 mL, and 250 mL measures.

Dry measuring cups are used for accurate measuring of ingredients such as the ones shown here.

Equivalents

Customary Measure	Customary Equivalent	Approximate Metric Equivalent
Volume		
1 tsp.		5 mL
1 Tbsp.	3 tsp.	15 mL
1 fl. oz.	2 Tbsp.	30 mL
1/4 cup		50 mL
1/3 cup		75 mL
1/2 cup		125 mL
2/3 cup		150 mL
3/4 cup		175 mL
1 cup	8 fl. oz. or 16 Tbsp.	250 mL
1 pt.	2 cups or 16 fl. oz.	500 mL
1 qt.	2 pt. or 4 cups or 32 fl. oz.	1000 mL or 1 L
1 gal.	4 qt.	4 L
Weight		
1 oz.		28 g
1 lb.	16 oz.	500 g
2 lb.	32 oz.	1000 g or 1 kg
Temperatures		
0°F		-18°C
32°F		0°C
350°F		180°C
400°F		200°C

- **Liquid measuring cups** are transparent and have measurement markings on the side. They are typically marked in fractions of a cup, fluid ounces, and milliliters. There is a headspace of about 1/4 inch above the top marking, which makes it easier to move a filled cup without spilling. A spout makes pouring easier. Common sizes are 1 cup (250 mL) and 2 cup (500 mL).
- **Measuring spoons** generally come in a set of four or five. Most customary sets include these sizes: 1/4 teaspoon, 1/2 teaspoon, 1 teaspoon, and 1 tablespoon. Metric sets include 1 mL, 2 mL, 5 mL, 15 mL and 25 mL measures.

Always use standard measuring cups and spoons. A standard 1-cup measuring cup, no matter how it is shaped or designed, always holds the same amount. Nonstandard items, such as cups and spoons used for serving food, vary in size.

Other helpful measuring tools include a straight-edge spatula for leveling off dry ingredients, a rubber scraper for removing ingredients from measuring cups, and a food scale for measuring ingredients by weight.

Measuring spoons come in a set of four or five spoons. You may need to use more than one spoon to measure an ingredient. How would you measure 3/4 teaspoon?

Using Combinations of Measures

When using measuring cups and spoons, you will sometimes need to use a combination of cup or spoon sizes to get the amount you need. For instance, if you need 3/4 cup flour, use the 1/2 cup and 1/4 cup measures. For 2/3 cup, measure 1/3 cup twice.

Sometimes you may need to measure unusual amounts of an ingredient, such as 5/8 cup. How would you measure such an amount?

First, measure out the closest amount you can with a standard size measure. For example, the closest measure to 5/8 cup is 1/2 cup (since 1/2 = 4/8). This leaves you with 1/8 cup left to measure. Since 1/8 cup is a small amount, you will need to use measuring spoons. This is where equivalents come in handy. Remember, there are 16 tablespoons in one cup. Therefore, 1/8 cup equals 2 tablespoons (1/8 x 16 = 16/8 = 2). You would add 2 tablespoons to 1/2 cup to get 5/8 cup.

You can also remove small amounts from a measuring cup to get the exact amount called for in a recipe. To get 7/8 cup milk, you would first measure one cup, then remove 2 tablespoons (1/8 cup). How would you measure 3/8 cup?

Techniques for Measuring

In addition to the correct tools, the proper procedures are essential to accurate measuring. The guidelines that follow will help you.

Measuring Liquids

Liquid measuring cups are used to measure all liquids, including oils and syrups. To measure liquids, follow these steps:
1. Set the cup on a level surface. If you try to hold it in your hand, you may tip it and get an inaccurate reading.

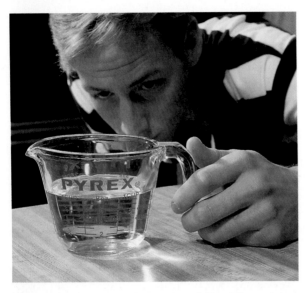

Check the measurement of liquids at eye level. What might happen if you looked down at the cup?

1. Put a piece of waxed paper under the measuring cup to catch any extra ingredient. Don't measure an ingredient while holding the cup over the bowl in which you are mixing.

2. Fill the cup with the ingredient. Some ingredients must be spooned into the cup lightly. Others can be packed down if specified in the recipe.

3. Level off the top of the cup using the straight edge of a spatula. Let the excess fall on the waxed paper. Put the excess back into the original container.

4. Pour the ingredient into the mixture. With semisolid foods, such as yogurt, use a rubber scraper to make sure all of the ingredient has been emptied out of the cup.

As a general rule, spoon flour and sugar into the measuring cup lightly. If you shake the cup or pack it down, you will measure too much of the ingredient.

2. Carefully pour the liquid into the measuring cup.

3. Bend down to check the measurement at eye level for an accurate reading.

4. Add more liquid or pour off excess, if needed, until the top of the liquid is at the desired measurement mark.

5. Pour the ingredient into the mixing container. If needed, use a rubber scraper to empty the cup completely.

For small amounts of liquids, use measuring spoons. To measure 1/8 teaspoon of a liquid ingredient, dribble it into the 1/4 teaspoon measure until it looks half full.

Measuring Dry Ingredients

Dry measures are used to measure dry ingredients such as flour, sugar, and dry beans. They can also be used for foods such as diced meat, chopped vegetables, and yogurt. Here are the steps to take when measuring dry ingredients:

When measuring dry ingredients, use waxed paper to catch spills. Carefully level off the ingredient with a straight-edge spatula.

Some recipes call for sifted flour. Put the flour through the sifter, then measure it. Never sift whole-grain flours—they are too coarse to go through the sifter. Instead, stir whole-grain flour with a spoon before measuring.

Sift powdered sugar before you measure it. Granulated sugar can be sifted to remove lumps, if needed.

Brown sugar contains moisture and tends to be fluffy, so pack it down with a spoon. When you empty the cup, the sugar should hold its shape.

For amounts smaller than 1/4 cup or 50 mL, use measuring spoons. Dry ingredients are usually measured by leveling them off evenly at the rim of the spoon. Sometimes, however, a recipe calls for a "heaping" measure. In this case, the ingredient is not leveled off. A heaping measure will give almost twice the amount you would get in a leveled-off measure.

If you need 1/8 teaspoon of a dry ingredient, fill the 1/4 teaspoon measure and level it off. Then, using the tip of a straight-edge spatula or table knife, remove half the ingredient.

Still smaller amounts of dry ingredients are measured as a dash or a pinch, the amount that can be held between the thumb and finger. These amounts are generally used for herbs and spices.

Measuring Fats

Fats, such as margarine or shortening, can be measured in several ways.

❖ **Stick method.** Use this for fat that comes in 1/4 lb. sticks, such as butter or margarine. The wrapper is marked in tablespoons and in fractions of a cup. Simply cut off the amount you need.

❖ **Dry measuring cup method.** Pack the fat down into the cup, pressing firmly to fill in all spaces. Level off the top. Using a rubber scraper, empty as much of the fat as possible. Use the same technique when using measuring spoons to measure fat.

❖ **Water displacement method.** This method involves combining fat with water in a liquid measuring cup. It requires some math. First, subtract the amount of fat to be measured from one cup. The difference is the amount of water to pour into the measuring cup. (For example, to measure 2/3 cup of shortening, use 1/3 cup of water.) Next, spoon the fat into the cup, making sure it is completely below the level of the water. When the water reaches the 1-cup level, you have the right amount of fat. Pour off the water and remove the fat with a rubber scraper.

Unless a recipe specifies a heaping spoonful, level off the measuring spoon.

The water displacement method is one way to measure solid fats accurately.

Measuring by Weight

As you have read, the amounts of some recipe ingredients may be given by weight. Sometimes you can buy the exact weight of food you need, such as an 8-oz. package of spaghetti. If that's not practical, a food scale comes in handy.

To use a food scale:

1. Decide what container you will put the food in. Place the empty container on the scale.

2. Adjust the scale until it reads zero. Usually this is done by turning a knob.

3. Add the food to the container until the scale shows the desired amount.

Remember, ounces of weight is not the same as fluid ounces. Do not use a dry or liquid measuring cup to measure an ingredient when the amount is given by weight. The measurement will not be accurate.

Section 8.2 Review

RECALL THE FACTS

1. One cup is equivalent to how many fluid ounces? How many tablespoons? About how many milliliters?

2. How does a liquid measuring cup differ from a dry measuring cup?

3. Describe the basic steps you would follow to measure 2/3 cup of sifted flour.

4. Name three ways to measure fats.

DISCUSS YOUR IDEAS

5. Why is accuracy so important when measuring ingredients?

APPLY YOUR LEARNING

6. Find a recipe with at least 10 ingredients. List all the measuring tools you would need to measure the ingredients. Describe any special techniques needed.

Some ingredients are normally measured by weight. Both customary and metric scales are available.

Thinking About the Recipe

Read the recipe for "Chocolate Citrus Shake" and answer the following questions.

1. For which ingredient(s) would you use a liquid measuring cup? Dry measuring cups? Measuring spoons?
2. What should be done to the powdered sugar before measuring it?

Chocolate Citrus Shake

Customary	Ingredients	Metric
1 cup	Orange juice	250 mL
1/3 cup	Plain nonfat yogurt	75 mL
1/2 cup	Crushed ice	125 mL
1/2 medium	Banana	1/2 medium
1/2 cup	Nonfat dry milk	125 mL
1/4 cup	Powdered sugar	50 mL
2 Tbsp.	Unsweetened cocoa	30 mL
1 tsp.	Strawberry extract	5 mL

Yield: Three 8-oz. (250-mL) servings

Directions

1. Place all ingredients in blender container.
2. Cover and blend until smooth.
3. Pour into glasses and serve immediately.

Nutrition Information

Per serving (approximate): 160 calories, 7 g protein, 31 g carbohydrate, 1 g fat, 0 mg cholesterol, 85 mg sodium

Objectives

After studying this section, you should be able to:

* Explain how to increase or decrease recipe yield.
* Give basic strategies for changing a recipe to decrease fats and sodium.
* Describe how high altitudes affect the cooking process.

Look for This Term

desired yield

Heather was in the middle of making drop biscuits when she found she didn't have any buttermilk. It didn't stop her. She substituted a mixture of skim milk and vinegar for the buttermilk and continued with the recipe.

Why Change a Recipe?

From time to time, you may find that, like Heather, you have to change a recipe. Perhaps you don't have one of the ingredients and can't take the time to go out and buy it. You might want to substitute a more healthful or less expensive ingredient for the one in the recipe. You might want to increase or decrease the recipe yield.

The success of recipe substitutions depends on choosing appropriate substitutes and measuring accurately. Chopped dates worked well as a substitute for raisins in this recipe.

Changes are more likely to be successful in some recipes than others. Mixtures such as salads, stir-fried foods, soups, and stews can usually be changed easily. On the other hand, recipes for baked products such as muffins and custards are like chemical formulas. Each ingredient does a job in the recipe. They must be used in specific amounts in relation to each other. If one amount is changed or one ingredient is omitted, you risk failure.

If you change the ingredients in mixtures, you may notice a difference in flavor and texture. For instance, Olga loves to make tacos. She sometimes substitutes cooked turkey or chicken for beef, or omits the meat and doubles the refried beans. How might each change affect the flavor and texture of tacos?

When increasing the yield of a recipe, you may also need to increase the size of the cooking container.

Changing the Yield

Recipes may need to be changed if the yield—the number of servings the recipe makes—is not what you need. With basic math skills you can increase or decrease many recipes.

Changing the recipe is part of the tradition of preparing a *paella* (pie-EL-uh). This Spanish main dish is based on rice, olive oil, and a spice called saffron. The rest of the ingredients are determined by the resourcefulness and creativity of the chef. Almost any meat or seafood can be used. Paellas also can include a great variety of legumes and vegetables, including broad beans, peas, onions, tomatoes, artichokes, and green peppers. What combination of ingredients do you think would make a good paella?

Most recipes, even those for baked goods, can be successfully doubled. Larger equipment may be needed for mixing and cooking, and cooking times often need adjustment. For most baked goods, it is best to use two baking pans of the original size rather than one larger one.

Many recipes for mixtures such as casseroles and soups can be not only doubled, but halved, tripled, and so on. The same basic process is used for both increasing and decreasing.

1. ***Decide how many servings you need.*** This amount is called the **desired yield.**

2. ***Use the formula.*** To adjust the yield of a recipe, the amount of each ingredient is multiplied by the same number. That number is determined by a simple formula:

   desired yield ÷ original yield =

   number to multiply by

   Example: Your chili recipe serves eight and you need to serve four: $4 \div 8 = 0.5$

3. ***Multiply each ingredient amount by that number.*** This keeps all the ingredients in the same proportion as in the original recipe.

4. ***As needed, convert answers to logical, measurable amounts.*** Sometimes the multiplication process gives you answers like 6/4 cups of flour or 12 tablespoons of brown sugar. Look again at the equivalents chart on page 226. Most amounts can be expressed in more than one unit of measurement. Think, too, about the equipment you will use for measuring. Then make any conversions needed.

   Examples: 6/4 cups flour = 1 ½ cups

   12 Tbsp. brown sugar = 3/4 cup

   1/6 cup oil = 2 Tbsp. + 2 tsp.

5. ***Make any necessary adjustments to equipment, temperature, and time.*** The depth of food in a pan affects how fast it cooks. Use pans that are the right size for the amount of food, not too large or small.

Making Ingredient Substitutions

If you don't have an ingredient you need for a recipe, you may be able to substitute another one. The chart on page 235 gives some common substitutions.

People who are concerned about healthy eating may have another reason to make substitutions. They want to reduce the fat and sodium in their diet.

Substitutions That Reduce Fat

Most recipes can be modified to reduce their fat content. Changes in the ingredients used or the amounts of ingredients can make a significant difference. A change in the cooking method can sometimes also reduce the amount of fat.

Tony decided to try to reduce the fat in his favorite spaghetti sauce. He tried two new versions. First, he reduced the amount of beef from 1 ½ pounds to 1 pound. He also

It may take some experimentation, but you can develop lower-fat versions of many of your favorite recipes.

Emergency Substitutions

For	Substitute
Baking chocolate, 1 oz.	3 Tbsp. cocoa + 1 Tbsp. butter or margarine
Buttermilk, 1 cup	1 Tbsp. lemon juice or vinegar + enough skim milk to measure 1 cup
Cake flour, 1 cup	7/8 cup sifted all-purpose flour
Garlic, 1 clove	1/8 tsp. garlic powder
Herbs, 1 tsp. dried, crushed	1 Tbsp. fresh chopped
Lemon juice	Equal amount vinegar
Milk, skim, 1 cup	1/4 cup nonfat dry milk powder + 7/8 cup water
Mustard, dry, 1 tsp.	1 Tbsp. prepared mustard
Onion, 1 small	1 Tbsp. minced dried onion or 1 tsp. onion powder
Rice, 1 cup cooked	1 cup cooked bulgur or millet
Spaghetti, uncooked, 6 oz. (3 cups cooked)	4 oz. (3 cups) uncooked egg noodles or 4 oz. (1 ¼ cup) uncooked macaroni
Sugar, granulated, 1 cup	2 cups sifted powdered sugar or 1cup packed brown sugar
Thickening, 1 ½ Tbsp. flour	1 Tbsp. quick-cooking tapioca or 1 Tbsp. cornstarch
Worcestershire sauce, 1 Tbsp.	1 Tbsp. soy sauce + dash red pepper sauce

chose ground round instead of ground beef because the round has less fat. Instead of cooking the onion and garlic in 2 tablespoons of oil, he used a nonstick pan and cooking spray. In the second version, he substituted 1 ¼ pounds of ground chicken meat for the ground beef. He increased the amount of seasoning because chicken has a less distinct flavor than beef. He again reduced the oil. His analysis: version one had more flavor than version two, but also more fat. He is still experimenting.

Ground turkey breast meat was substituted for ground beef in this recipe. With a spicy sauce, there is little change in flavor but significantly less fat.

Here are some suggestions for reducing fat in recipes:

❖ Compare similar recipes and choose those with the least fat. Many recipes (like those in this book) show the fat content as grams of fat per serving.
❖ Use skim or low-fat dairy products in place of all or part of high-fat dairy products. For example, a mixture of half mayonnaise and half nonfat yogurt can be used instead of mayonnaise.
❖ Choose very lean cuts of meat for any recipe that requires meat.
❖ Substitute chicken or turkey for high-fat cuts of meat. Use fresh, ground, skinless turkey breast in place of ground beef for meatloaf, for instance. For more flavor, you may want to increase the seasonings.
❖ Use lemon juice, flavored vinegar, or fat-free dressings instead of salad dressings that contain oil.
❖ Substitute two egg whites for a whole egg.
❖ Use less oil for cooking food. Many foods will cook well using just a nonstick pan and vegetable oil cooking spray.

Substitutions That Reduce Sodium

Most people take in far more sodium than the body needs. This excess can have harmful effects. Here are some ideas for reducing sodium in recipes:

❖ Replace high-sodium ingredients such as broths, soy sauce, and tamari sauce with low-sodium versions.
❖ Use herbs, spices, lemon juice, or vinegar to enhance food flavors.

High-Altitude Cooking

Unless otherwise indicated, recipes are intended to be used at altitudes of 3,000 feet (about 1000 m) or below. If used at higher altitudes, they may not turn out as desired. Why? As the altitude gets higher, the air pressure gets lower. This affects food preparation in two main ways:

If you are cooking at high altitudes, look for recipes specially designed for such areas.

❖ First, water boils at a lower temperature. Therefore foods such as pasta are cooking at a temperature lower than 212°F (100°C), even though they are boiling. Because the temperature is lower, they take longer to cook.

❖ Second, when the air pressure is low, bubbles of gas may form more readily in liquids and escape. As a result, baked goods are likely to rise less and be heavy. Sometimes reducing the amount of baking powder or soda and sugar and increasing the liquid can help.

People who live in high-altitude areas often can get helpful information about adapting recipes from their local utility company, newspapers, or nearest Cooperative Extension office. Many packaged foods include special directions for preparation at high altitudes.

Section 8.3 Review

RECALL THE FACTS

1. Name three reasons to change a recipe.

2. List the basic steps in changing recipe yield.

3. Give three suggestions for lowering the fat in a recipe.

4. Why do some foods take longer to cook at high altitudes?

DISCUSS YOUR IDEAS

5. What are some other ways Tony might modify the spaghetti sauce to make it healthful while maintaining good flavor?

APPLY YOUR LEARNING

6. Find a simple recipe that makes four servings. Show how you would change the ingredient amounts to make twelve servings or two servings.

Look for This Term
serrated

Success when preparing food depends a great deal on being able to follow recipe directions accurately. To do this, you first need to understand what recipe terms mean. You must also know what equipment to use for each task and the proper way to use it. In this section, you will learn about tools and techniques for some common recipe preparation tasks.

Cutting Foods

Food preparation often involves a variety of cutting tasks. You may need to trim unwanted parts from food or cut food to the desired size. With practice and attention to safety, you can become a cutting expert.

Equipment for Cutting

Cutting tools vary from graters and knives to small appliances such as the food chopper. Some basic cutting equipment is illustrated and described on page 239.

Note the proper hand position for holding a chef's knife (top). Whenever you cut, the hand holding the food should be kept away from the knife (bottom).

Bread knife. Has a **serrated,** or saw-tooth, edge for cutting bread.

Slicing knife. Used for cutting large foods, including meat and poultry.

Chef's knife. Also called a French knife. Has a large triangular blade, wide at the handle and narrow at the tip. Used for slicing, cutting, chopping, and dicing.

Utility knife. Used for cutting small foods.

Boning knife. Has a thin blade. Used to trim fat from meat and remove meat from bones before cooking or serving.

Paring knife. Used to clean, pare, and slice small fruits and vegetables.

Sharpening steel. A long steel rod on a handle, used to sharpen knives.

Food grinder. A hand-operated tool or small electric appliance for grinding foods.

Cutting board. Protects the kitchen counter when cutting. For proper sanitation, use a cutting board made of plastic instead of wood.

Food processor. A small electric appliance, similar to a blender but shaped differently. It comes with an assortment of blades and can do cutting jobs that a blender cannot do.

Peeler. Has a blade that swivels to cut peel thinly from fruits and vegetables.

Food chopper. Ranges in size from a small hand-operated nut chopper to a large chopper with several blades.

Blender. A small electric appliance used for a variety of cutting and mixing tasks. Has a tall, covered container with blades at the bottom. The container fits on a motor base that drives the blades. Most models have different speeds for specific tasks.

Kitchen shears. Useful for tasks such as snipping fresh herbs, trimming pastry, and cutting dried fruit.

Grater. Food is rubbed against the rough surface of the grater for grating or shredding.

Using a Sharpening Steel

Sharp knives cut more easily and safely. Regular use of a sharpening steel can keep knives in top shape. Here's how:

1. Hold the handle of the steel in your left hand. Place the point straight down, very firmly, on a cutting board. In your right hand, hold the knife by the handle, blade down. (Reverse if you are left-handed.)

2. Place the knife blade at a 20° angle against the right side of the steel. The knife blade and steel should touch near the handles.

3. Draw the blade down the steel and toward you, keeping it at a 20° angle to the steel. Use gentle pressure.

4. When the tip of the knife reaches the tip of the steel, repeat the process holding the knife against the steel on the left. Draw the blade down along the steel four or five times, alternating right and left sides.

Techniques for Cutting

Using knives is a basic kitchen skill. To use most knives, hold the food on the cutting board with one hand and hold the knife by its handle with the other. Use a back-and-forth sawing motion while pressing down gently at the same time.

Cutting tools are used for many tasks in the kitchen. Following is a list of terms you will find in recipes:

❖ **Slice.** To cut a food in large, thin pieces.
❖ **Pare.** To cut off a very thin layer of peel. A peeler or paring knife works best.
❖ **Score.** To make shallow, straight cuts in the surface of a food such as a flank

Slice

Score

Mince

Pare

Chop

Cube

Grate

steak. This helps to tenderize meat. A slicing knife is most often used to score meats.

❖ **Chop and mince.** To cut food into small, irregular pieces. Minced pieces are smaller than chopped pieces. To use a chef's knife to chop or mince, hold the knife handle with one hand, pressing the tip against the cutting board. The other hand should rest lightly on the back of the blade, near the tip. Pump the knife handle up and down, keeping the tip of the blade on the board, so the blade chops through the food.

❖ **Cube and dice.** To cube or dice food means to cut it into small, square pieces. Make the pieces about 1/2 inch (1.3 cm) on each side when cubing and 1/8 to 1/4 inch (3 to 6 cm) when dicing.

❖ **Grate.** To cut food into small pieces by pressing and rubbing the food against the rough surface of the grater.

Safety Check

Keep knives sharp. A dull knife is much more likely to slip and cut you because you will have to exert more pressure. When using a knife, keep your fingers away from the sharp edge of the blade. Never hold the food in your hand while cutting, and never cut with the blade facing your body.

Mixing Foods

Another common recipe task is combining ingredients. Different mixing tools and techniques are used, depending on the food and the desired results.

Equipment for Mixing

Many kinds of mixing tools, from small hand-held utensils to electric appliances, are used for mixing tasks. Some common ones are shown on page 243. The blender and food processor (shown on page 239) can also be used for some mixing tasks.

Techniques for Mixing

Mixing tools are used for a variety of tasks in the kitchen. Here are some mixing terms often found in recipes:

* ❖ *Mix, combine, blend.* To mix ingredients thoroughly, using a spoon, wire whisk, rotary beater, electric mixer, or electric blender.
* ❖ *Stir.* To mix by hand, using a spoon or wire whisk and a circular motion. Stirring can also be done while cooking to keep food from sticking to the pan and to distribute heat through foods.
* ❖ *Beat.* To thoroughly mix foods using a vigorous over-and-over motion. A rotary beater, electric mixer, spoon, or wire whisk can be used for the job. Ingredients may also be beaten to add air to them, as when beating egg whites.
* ❖ *Cream.* To beat together ingredients, such as shortening and sugar, until soft and creamy.
* ❖ *Whip.* To incorporate air into a mixture by beating it vigorously, making it light and fluffy.
* ❖ *Fold.* A gentle mixing method used for delicate or whipped ingredients. Usually a rubber scraper or wooden spoon is used. Cut down through the mixture, move the utensil across the bottom of the bowl, and bring it back up to the surface along with some of the mixture from the bottom of the bowl. The utensil itself is never lifted out of the mixture.
* ❖ *Sift.* To put dry ingredients, such as flour, through a sifter or strainer. This is done to add air, remove small lumps, or mix dry ingredients.

Mix, blend, combine

Stir

Beat

Fold

Sift

Mixing bowls. Come in many different sizes. May be of stainless steel, glass, pottery, or plastic.

Wooden spoon. Used for many mixing tasks.

Sifter. A container with a fine wire screen at the bottom and a blade that forces dry ingredients through the screen.

Wire whisk. Made of wire loops held together by a handle. Used for mixing, stirring, beating, and whipping.

Rotary beater. Used to mix and whip foods more quickly and easily than can be done with a spoon or whisk. Often used to beat egg whites.

Electric mixer. Used to blend, beat, and whip ingredients. Lightweight, hand-held models are convenient. There are also heavy-duty models that are attached permanently to a stand.

Rubber scraper. Used to scrape food from bowls, pans, and other containers. Helpful in moving thick ingredients from the sides of the bowl to the middle while mixing. Also used for folding.

Other Tasks

A variety of other tools and techniques are used in food preparation. Here are some additional terms you may find in recipes:

- ❖ **Strain.** To separate solid particles from a liquid, such as broth or juice. The liquid is poured through a bowl-shaped fine screen called a strainer or sieve.
- ❖ **Drain.** To allow liquids to drain from a solid food, such as fruits, vegetables, or cooked pasta. This is done by putting the food in a colander—a bowl with small holes in the bottom—or a large strainer.
- ❖ **Puree** (pure-RAY or pure-REE). To make food smooth and thick by putting it through a strainer, blender, or food processer.
- ❖ **Baste.** To brush or pour liquid over food as it cooks.
- ❖ **Dredge.** To coat a food with a dry ingredient, such as flour or crumbs.

Of course, many heating and cooking tasks are also involved in food preparation. You will learn about cooking terms, equipment, and techniques in Chapter 9, "Cooking Methods."

■ Section 8.4 Review ■

RECALL THE FACTS

1. Describe the differences between a paring knife, boning knife, and chef's knife.

2. How is chopping different from mincing? From cubing or dicing?

3. What is meant by "beating" ingredients? Name three tools that could be used to beat a mixture.

4. Name two small electric appliances that are useful for both cutting and mixing tasks.

DISCUSS YOUR IDEAS

5. What might happen if you tried to follow a recipe without understanding the meaning of food preparation terms?

APPLY YOUR LEARNING

6. Find a salad recipe that requires the use of at least two cutting techniques and one mixing technique. Describe the tools and techniques needed.

A colander (left) and strainer (right) are useful for straining and draining foods.

Thinking About the Recipe

Read the recipe for "Pineapple-Pistachio Delight" and answer the following questions.

1. If you didn't have an electric mixer, what equipment could you use to beat the pineapple and pudding?
2. Why does this recipe tell you to "fold in" the whipped topping?

Pineapple-Pistachio Delight

Customary	Ingredients	Metric
20 oz. can	Crushed pineapple in juice	567-gram can
3-oz. package	Instant pistachio pudding and pie filling mix	95-gram package
4-oz. carton	Light, non-dairy whipped topping, thawed	112-gram carton
1/3 cup	Pistachios or walnuts, chopped	75 mL

Yield: 8 servings

Directions

Equipment: 2 qt. (2 L) mixing bowl
1. Pour pineapple and juice into mixing bowl. Add pudding mix.
2. Beat at lowest speed with an electric mixer until well blended, about 1 to 2 minutes.
3. Fold in whipped topping and nuts.
4. Spoon into dessert dishes. Pudding will set and be ready to eat in 5 minutes.

Nutrition Information

Per serving (approximate): 151 calories, 1 g protein, 27 g carbohydrate, 7 g fat, trace of cholesterol, 181 mg sodium

Note: To reduce fat, omit nuts.

Look for These Terms

work plan
pre-preparation
dovetail

Whenever you are preparing food, time is likely to be a concern. Whether it's a recipe you are preparing for a foods lab or your family's dinner, there are deadlines to meet. Good planning can help you meet your deadlines. So can learning the tricks of efficient food preparation and effective teamwork.

Time Management in the Kitchen

Winning a race takes strategy, speed, and skill. Those are also the keys to time management in the kitchen. The examples here are based on preparing a recipe, but the same process is used for preparing an entire meal. You will read more about meal management in Section 11.1.

Strategy: Making a Work Plan

Food preparation involves more than choosing a recipe and starting to work. Think it through first. Do you have the ingredient and equipment you need? Do you have th skills? Can you complete the food preparatio and cleanup in the time available?

A smart strategy is to start with a **work plan.** Basically, this is a list of all the tasks required to complete the recipe and an estimate of how long each task will take.

Recipes and package directions often provide help in estimating time. A spaghetti package, for example, may say to cook the spaghetti for 9 minutes. However, you will have to draw on your experience to estimate the time for other tasks, such as chopping vegetables or cleaning salad greens. As you improve your skills, you will be able to work faster (and make more accurate time estimates). It's wise to allow a bit more time than you think you will need.

Look at the recipe for "Pizza Snacks" below and the work plan on page 248 Naomi made for it. Note that some of the first steps on the work plan come from the list of ingredients, not the recipe directions. Naomi saw that the ingredients included:

❖ *Halved* English muffins.
❖ *Shredded* cheese.
❖ *Chopped* and *sliced* toppings.

Before beginning Step 1 of the recipe directions, Naomi would need to complete tasks such as washing and chopping the green pepper. Such tasks are called **pre-preparation** because they are done before actual recipe preparation. Measuring the ingredients is also part of pre-preparation.

A work plan often includes important tasks like washing your hands and setting the oven temperature. Including such steps insures they won't be forgotten.

Speed: Making a Schedule

Once you have a work plan, you can use it to make a schedule that shows when each task must be started. First, refer to your work plan to find the time you estimated it will take to complete each task. Add up these times to find the total preparation time. Next, subtract the total preparation time from the time you want the food to be ready. That

Pizza Snacks

2 English muffins, split in halves

1/2 cup prepared pizza sauce

1 Tbsp. chopped green pepper

1 Tbsp. sliced mushrooms

1 Tbsp. chopped onions

1/2 cup shredded low-fat mozzarella cheese

1. Place English muffin halves, crust-side down, on broiler pan.

2. Spread each muffin half with 2 Tbsp. pizza sauce.

3. Top with green pepper, mushrooms, and onion.

4. Sprinkle each muffin half with 2 Tbsp. cheese.

5. Position broiler pan so the tops of the muffins are about 4 inches from the heat. Turn on broiler.

6. Broil until cheese is bubbly, about 2 to 4 minutes. Remove immediately and serve hot.

NOTE: Broiling time may vary.

Yield: 4 small pizzas

Work Plan—Pizza Snacks

Task	Approx. Time
Gather ingredients and equipment. Scrub hands.	8 min.
Split English muffins in half.	2 min.
Chop green pepper and onion. Slice mushrooms.	7 min.
Shred cheese.	3 min.
Put muffins on broiler pan and put on toppings.	3 min.
Broil until cheese is bubbly.	6 min.
Prepare to serve.	1 min.
	Total: 30 min.

tells you what time to start. Naomi's estimated total preparation time is 30 minutes. She plans to serve the pizzas at 6:30, so she needs to start at 6:00.

To make her schedule, Naomi decides to chop and slice the vegetables first, shred the cheese next, and then split the English muffins. For this recipe, the remaining tasks match the order of the recipe directions.

When you are learning to prepare food, it's a good idea to make a work plan and schedule every time. Eventually, you may need to do so only when you prepare a new dish or plan a special meal.

Schedule—Pizza Snacks

6:00	Get ready.
6:08	Split English muffins.
6:10	Chop and slice vegetables.
6:17	Shred cheese.
6:20	Assemble pizzas.
6:23	Broil pizzas.
6:29	Prepare to serve.
6:30	Serve pizzas.

Skill: Working Efficiently

As you gain food preparation experience, you will notice an obvious improvement in your skills. You'll be able to complete many tasks more quickly than before.

However, there's more to efficiency than experience. Even a beginner can be efficient by identifying ways to save time and energy. Here are some keys to efficiency:

❖ *Organize the kitchen.* Always store items in the same place so you won't waste time looking for them.

❖ *Learn to use equipment properly.* Take the time to read the owner's manuals for the small and large appliances in the kitchen. Besides learning to use them safely, you may find they can be helpful in ways you didn't realize. Practice using your tools until you are comfortable with them.

❖ *Look for ways to simplify.* Could a different piece of equipment complete a task more quickly? Would a different cooking method be more efficient? Thinking through your options can help you save time and energy.

❖ *Gather all equipment and ingredients first.* Assembling everything you will need before you start has several advantages. You won't discover, halfway through a recipe, that you are out of an ingredient you need. It will be easier to check whether you used every ingredient. Most important, you will be able to work efficiently because everything is at your fingertips.

❖ *Dovetail tasks.* To **dovetail** means to fit different tasks together smoothly. Not every preparation step needs your undivided attention. You could, for example, make a tossed salad while chicken pieces are baking. Checking the chicken from time to time is all that's needed. Dovetailing is especially important when you are preparing a whole meal. If you plan to dovetail tasks, be sure to adjust your time schedule.

❖ *Clean up as you work.* It's discouraging to finish the preparation and face dirty dishes and a messy kitchen. There is a more efficient way. Before you start work, fill the sink or a dishpan with hot, sudsy water. Whenever you have a few free moments, wash the equipment you have finished using. Also keep a clean, wet dishcloth handy to wipe up spills as they happen. Put away ingredients as you finish with them. Your final cleanup will take much less time.

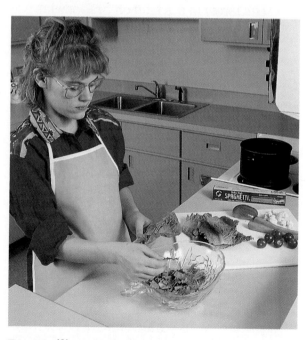

Dovetailing tasks can help you prepare a meal quickly. For example, you could prepare a tossed salad while cooking spaghetti.

Remember, there's a difference between efficiency and carelessness. Don't be in such a hurry that you ignore safety guidelines. Keep your mind on what you're doing at all times.

Teamwork in the Kitchen

In the foods lab at school, you will be working as part of a team. You will also be working against the clock. Every lab activity will need to be completed—including cleanup and evaluation—within a limited period of time. Success depends on organization and cooperation.

❖ *Organizing the job.* Start with a basic work plan. When you plan your schedule, decide not only when each task should start, but also who will do it. With every team member working, several tasks can be accomplished at the same time. You may want to use a schedule that has five-minute blocks of time down the left and columns with each person's name across the top. That way you can show what each person should be doing throughout the lab period. Be sure to consider work space and equipment as you plan your schedule.

❖ *Working together.* Foods labs, like many school and work situations, depend on everyone working together well. Be responsible for the tasks you have agreed to do. Work quickly and efficiently. Remember that accuracy is essential. If you have a question or a problem, ask another team member for help. You, too, need to be willing to help out when someone else falls behind or makes a mistake. Keeping a sense of humor will help the work go more smoothly.

- ❖ **Cleaning up.** Cleaning as you go will make end-of-class cleanup easier and faster. Be sure all equipment is clean and dry. Most important, return everything to its proper place. Otherwise, you will slow down the next team using the kitchen. Be sure all work surfaces and appliances are also clean. Dispose of garbage properly.
- ❖ **Evaluating the results.** Labs usually involve evaluating both the finished product and the preparation process. Thoughtfulness and honesty are important for both. This is especially true if the food did not turn out as expected, you experienced preparation problems, or your team did not work together well. Think about what you learned from the experience and what you might do differently the next time.

In many ways, teamwork in your kitchen at home is similar to working in the foods lab. Organization, cooperation, and cleanup are just as important. However, the atmosphere is usually much more informal. "Evaluation" may be a compliment on what you have made or simply the satisfaction of knowing you have done a good job.

Whether you are responsible for helping prepare family meals on a regular basis or just occasionally, remember that these times can be fun. You might help a younger brother or sister learn a new cooking skill or just take time to talk to a family member. When you have more time, try out a new recipe together. Daily food preparation can be a chore or an opportunity for togetherness. It all depends on your attitude.

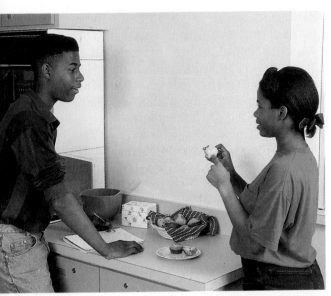

Evaluation is one of the most important parts of the foods lab experience. You can learn from your mistakes as well as your successes.

Section 8.5 Review

RECALL THE FACTS

1. What is a work plan? How can it help you manage time when preparing food?

2. Give three examples of ways to work efficiently in the kitchen or foods lab.

3. What should you think about when evaluating a completed foods lab?

DISCUSS YOUR IDEAS

4. What other ideas for working efficiently can you think of?

APPLY YOUR LEARNING

5. Design a work plan and schedule form that could be used when planning school foods labs.

CAREER PROFILE

Beth Lane
Food Researcher

Current position:

"I'm a researcher in a food processing lab for a large food manufacturer."

Responsibilities:

"I work as part of a team that develops prototypes for new products. It's our job to find the right formulation of ingredients to make the product as good as it can be."

Skills:

"A background in nutrition and food science is important, as well as the ability to work well with a team. It's also important to be able to communicate well, both orally and in writing."

Education:

"I have a bachelor's degree in nutrition and a master's degree in chemistry."

Work environment:

"Even though I work as part of a team, I spend a lot of time alone in the lab. After doing my part of the research, I get together with others to compile our findings and work out a finished product."

Favorite part of the job:

"It's exciting to me to try to come up with the best-tasting and most attractive product I can. I enjoy seeing the product on the supermarket shelf and being able to say that I had a major part in putting it there."

- Why is teamwork essential to a job like Beth's?
- Do you think you might enjoy Beth's job? Why or why not?

251

Summary

Section 8.1
Recipe Basics: Before using a recipe, check to be sure it includes certain basic information and is clearly written. Recipes are available from many sources. A well-organized recipe collection is easier to use.

Section 8.2
Measuring Ingredients: Recipes include weight and volume measurements in customary or metric units. For accurate measurements, be sure to select the right measuring tools and follow the correct procedures.

Section 8.3
Changing a Recipe: You can alter the yield of a recipe by changing the amounts of ingredients. You might substitute different ingredients to reduce the amount of fat or sodium. High-altitude cooking may require changes in cooking time or ingredients.

Section 8.4
Preparation Tasks: Food preparation may involve a number of different tasks. To follow a recipe, you need to understand the meaning of the terms used. You also need to know which utensil or appliance to use and the correct technique.

Section 8.5
Time Management and Teamwork: A work plan can help you identify the tasks that must be done when preparing food. A schedule tells you when to do them. Look for ways to make the job easier and more efficient. Teamwork is essential when several people are working in the kitchen at once.

REVIEWING FACTS

1. List four kinds of information included in a well-written recipe. (8.1)

2. In measuring, what is an "equivalent"? Give an example. (8.2)

3. Describe how to measure liquids accurately. (8.2)

4. What type of recipe is more difficult to alter? Why? (8.3)

5. When changing the yield of a recipe, how do you determine the number to multiply each ingredient amount by? (8.3)

6. Define: score, pare, mince, grate. (8.4)

7. Name two small electric appliances that can be used for cutting or mixing tasks. (8.4)

8. Describe the technique for folding one ingredient into another. (8.4)

9. Give four suggestions for working efficiently in the kitchen or foods lab. (8.5)

10. Describe how a work plan for a team differs from a work plan for an individual. (8.5)

LEARNING BY DOING

1. **Measurement lab:** Working in groups, make a list of five amounts to be measured. Exchange lists with another group. Measure the amounts once using a dry ingredient (such as flour) and again using water. Check each other's measurements for accuracy. (8.2)

2. **Foods lab:** Choose a recipe from a cookbook or use one provided by your teacher. Make at least one ingredient substitution to lower the fat. Evaluate the results. (8.3)

3. **Foods lab:** Pare a raw potato. Cut it into slices 1/2 inch (1.3 cm) thick. Set two slices aside, then cube the rest. Set some of the cubed pieces aside and dice the rest. Have your teacher check your work. (8.4)

4. **Computer lab:** Design and print out a form that could be used for a foods lab work plan and schedule. (8.5)

THINKING CRITICALLY

1. **Analyzing decisions:** Peggy looked through several cookbooks trying to find a recipe for a special meal. Finally, she decided to make a dish she had prepared many times before. What are some possible reasons for Peggy's decision? (8.1)

2. **Predicting consequences:** Dana didn't want to bother to calculate how to reduce a muffin recipe by half. He decided instead to measure out the whole amount of each ingredient and use a large spoon to put about half back. What is likely to happen when he bakes the muffins? (8.3)

3. **Recognizing alternatives:** Suppose a recipe called for sifted flour, but you didn't have a sifter. What might you use instead? (8.4)

4. **Recognizing points of view:** Some people may believe that it's not worth spending the time to make a work plan and schedule. Why might they feel this way? What could you say to change their opinion? (8.5)

MAKING DECISIONS AND SOLVING PROBLEMS

What Would You Do?

1. You've found a recipe for a casserole that you want to try. The ingredients list includes shredded cheese, but the directions do not tell you what to do with it. (8.1)

2. You and your sister are both working in the kitchen, each preparing a different recipe. You have the measuring spoons, but your sister is using the 1/4 cup dry measuring cup that you need. (8.2)

3. In the last two foods labs, your group has been unable to finish on time. You think the work would get done faster if you did it all yourself. However, part of your grade is based on how well you work as a team. (8.5)

LINKING YOUR STUDIES

1. **Writing:** Choose a recipe to put into story form. From the first person point of view ("I"), tell how you collected the ingredients and followed the directions to prepare the food. Tell how the recipe turned out. (8.1)

2. **Science:** Using references from the library, prepare a report telling how the metric system of measurement originated. (8.2)

3. **Math:** Find a recipe that makes twelve or more servings. Change the recipe so that it yields four servings. (8.3)

4. **History:** Using the library or other resources, find information about food preparation in colonial America or another historical period. Describe at least three tools that were used for common food preparation tasks. How did the tools differ from what is used today? (8.4)

5. **Math:** Make a work plan for a recipe you might use in the foods lab or at home. Estimate the time needed for each of the following: getting ready to cook, assembling the recipe, cooking or baking time, and cleanup. Express each of these as a percentage of the total time needed for the work plan. Show your findings in a chart. (8.5)

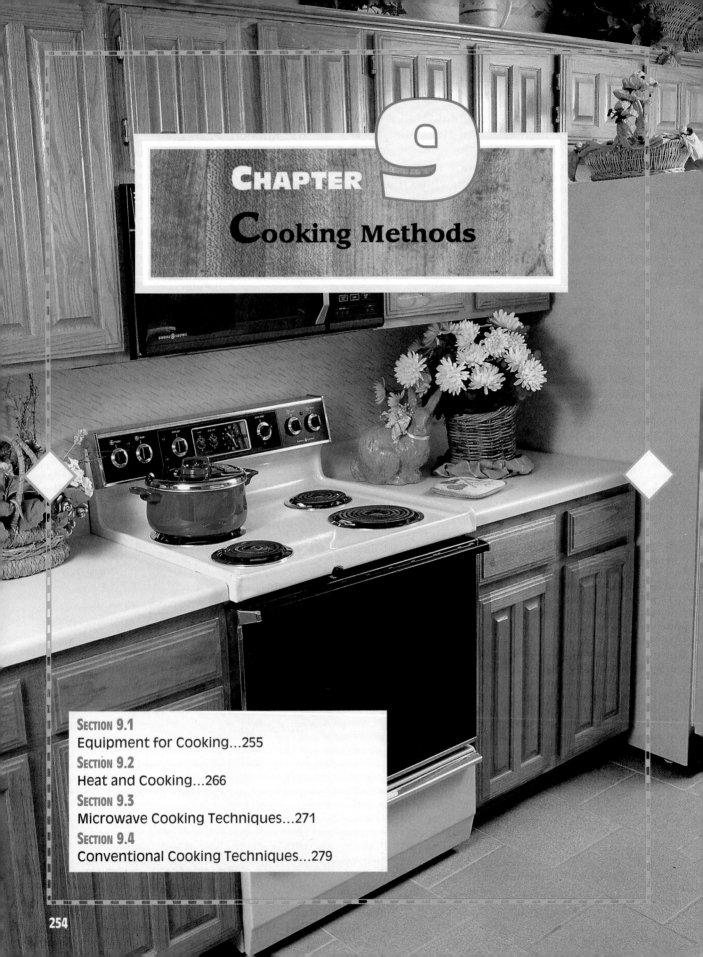

CHAPTER 9

Cooking Methods

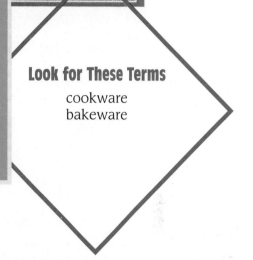

Objectives

After studying this section, you should be able to:

* Describe how cooktops and conventional, convection, and microwave ovens work.
* Identify small cooking appliances and describe their uses.
* Identify cookware, bakeware, and cooking tools.

Look for These Terms

cookware
bakeware

Look around any kitchen and you'll find many kinds of equipment designed for cooking. These include major appliances, small appliances, and a variety of utensils.

Major Cooking Appliances

The major appliances used for cooking are the conventional range, the convection oven, and the microwave oven.

The Range

A range usually consists of a cooktop with four burners, elements, or surface units, an oven, and a broiler. The cooktop has either dials or push buttons to control the heat. Ovens have thermostatic controls so that you can set the exact temperature you need. Oven temperature settings vary from "warm," or below 200°F (93°C), to "broil," or about 500°F (260°C). The broiler cooks food by direct heat from a burner or electrical element located in the top of the compartment.

Instead of a freestanding range, some kitchens have separate cooktop and oven units built into cabinets. Another alternative is a portable oven that can be placed on a countertop or cart.

Ranges use either gas or electricity for fuel. The two types of ranges have slightly different features.

Ranges use either gas or electricity for fuel. Both freestanding and built-in models are available.

Gas Range

In a gas range, the oven and broiler are usually in separate compartments. The broiler is generally located below the oven.

The heating units in gas ranges are called burners. The burners in gas cooktops heat with a flame that is easily regulated. The change in heat level is immediate. (Some gas ranges have sealed burners without a visible flame.)

In most newer ranges, when a burner is turned on, gas flows through and is ignited by an electronic spark (pilotless ignition). Older ranges contain pilot lights—small gas flames that burn continuously. When the burner is turned on, the pilot lights ignite the gas. Sometimes, however, the pilot lights go out and must be relighted. (See page 192 for information about relighting a pilot light.)

Air flow is needed for burning gas, so take care not to block the vents in a gas range. The burner bowls should not be lined with foil for this reason. If air flow is blocked, the gas will not burn properly and will give off carbon monoxide, a deadly gas.

Electric Range

An electric range heats with heating units or elements. Electricity passes through the element or unit, causing it to heat up.

The oven and broiler in an electric range are in the same compartment. The compartment has two heating elements, one at the top and one at the bottom. The bottom element heats the oven for all cooking purposes except broiling. When broiling in the oven, only the top element comes on. When broiling in an electric range, leave the door open slightly.

Several types of cooktops are available in electric ranges. Each has its own unique characteristics.

❖ **Coil elements.** Elements heat up and cool down relatively quickly (although

Science Connection

Physics

Electrical Resistance and Heat

As electricity passes through a material, its flow is impeded by a characteristic of the material called *resistance*. The result is that the material heats up. The greater the current flow and the higher the resistance of the material, the greater the heat produced. Cooktop elements have high resistance to produce the heat needed for cooking.

■ ■ ■

more slowly than gas burners). Coils may vary in size to fit smaller and larger pans.

❖ **Solid disk elements.** New technology has made it possible to eliminate cleanup problems with this enclosed element. However, solid disks take much longer to heat up and cool down. They require special cookware with extra-flat bottoms for even cooking.

❖ **Induction cooktops.** A glass-ceramic top covers the heating elements, making this cooktop very easy to keep clean. With induction cooktops, heat is produced when a ferrous metal pan (such as stainless steel or cast iron) is placed on the element. The magnetic attraction between the pan and the heating element produces heat. This cooktop stays cool, except for any heat transferred from the pan.

New technology has simplified cleanup problems on cooktops. Both induction cooktops (left) and solid disk cooktops (below) are totally enclosed.

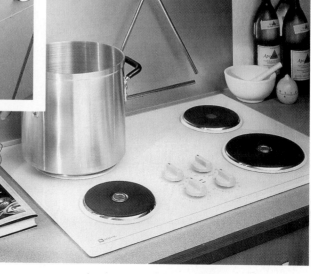

The Convection Oven

A convection oven is like a conventional oven except that a fan circulates the heated air. This speeds up cooking time and keeps temperatures even throughout the oven. As a result, foods brown more evenly than in a conventional oven. A convection oven cooks more quickly than a conventional oven, but not as quickly as a microwave oven.

A convection oven can be combined with either a conventional or a microwave oven. The combination oven has more advantages than any single type.

The Microwave Oven

Microwaves are a form of energy that travels like radio waves. In a microwave oven, a magnetron (MAG-nuh-trawn) tube turns electricity into microwaves. The microwaves are distributed through the oven by a "stirrer blade," a fan-like device. The microwaves bounce off the oven's walls and floor until they are absorbed by food. Microwave energy is reflected from metal but passes through glass, paper, and plastic to get to food.

Microwaves make food molecules vibrate against each other, producing friction. This friction produces heat which cooks the food. Microwave ovens cook many foods in one-fourth the time that it takes to cook them conventionally, making this an energy-efficient way to cook.

Small Cooking Appliances

Many different small appliances are available for making cooking tasks faster and easier. Here are some basic ones.

* **Toaster.** Browns bread products on both sides at the same time. You set the controls for the degree of browning. Two- and four-slice models are available.
* **Toaster oven.** Toasts bread, heats up foods, and bakes small amounts of many foods. Some toaster ovens can broil food.
* **Electric skillet.** A thermostat controls the temperature on the skillet. Useful for frying, roasting, steaming, and baking.
* **Portable electric burner.** A small appliance that works like the cooktop on a range.
* **Slow cooker.** A deep pot with a heating element in the base that allows food to cook slowly over many hours. It's a convenient way to cook one-dish meals like stews.
* **Broiler/grill.** A small, portable electric grill used to broil or grill food indoors.
* **Rice cooker/steamer.** Used to cook large quantities of rice or steam vegetables. The controlled heat cooks all types of rice perfectly.

Convection ovens use a built-in fan to circulate hot air in the oven compartment. This speeds cooking and browns foods more evenly.

Toaster

Toaster oven

Electric skillet

Slow cooker

Rice cooker/steamer

Broiler/grill

Cookware and Bakeware

Cookware is used for cooking food on top of the range. **Bakeware** is used to cook food in an oven. Both cookware and bakeware are made from many different materials, as shown in the chart on pages 260-261. Microwave ovens have special requirements for cooking containers.

Safety Check

Don't use copper cookware if it's unlined or the lining wears out. Acidic foods can release copper into food. Too much copper in food can cause nausea, vomiting, and diarrhea.

Materials for Cookware

Material	Advantages	Disadvantages	Use and Care
Aluminum	❖ Conducts heat quickly, evenly. ❖ Lightweight. ❖ Durable. ❖ Comes in a variety of finishes.	❖ Warps, dents, and scratches easily. ❖ Darkens and stains, especially in dishwasher. ❖ Pits if used to store salty or acid foods.	❖ Cool before washing to prevent warping. ❖ Avoid sharp tools like knives and beaters. ❖ Do not use to store salty or acid foods.
Stainless Steel	❖ Durable, tough, hard. ❖ Will not dent easily. ❖ Attractive.	❖ Conducts heat unevenly. ❖ Stains when overheated or from starchy foods. ❖ Can develop hot spots. ❖ Pits if used to store salty or acid foods.	❖ Use nonabrasive cleaners and nylon scrubbers. ❖ Use stainless steel cleaner to remove stains. ❖ Do not use to store salty or acid foods.
Copper	❖ Excellent heat conductor. ❖ Attractive.	❖ Discolors easily. ❖ Discolors food and may create toxic compounds. Inside must be lined with tin or stainless steel.	❖ Dry after washing. ❖ Do not scour inside—the thin lining may be worn away. ❖ Polish with copper cleaner or mixture of flour and vinegar.
Cast Iron	❖ Distributes heat evenly. ❖ Retains heat well.	❖ Heavy. ❖ Rusts if not wiped dry after washing.	❖ Store in a dry place. ❖ Store cover separately—pan may rust if stored covered.
Glass	❖ Attractive. Can be used for cooking and serving. ❖ Easy to clean.	❖ Breaks easily, especially if extreme temperature change. ❖ Some can be used only on the cooktop; others just in the oven. ❖ Holds heat, but does not conduct heat well.	❖ May need a wire grid if used on an electric cooktop. ❖ Use nonabrasive cleaners and nylon scrubbers. ❖ Do not plunge hot pan into cold water or put into the refrigerator.

Material	Characteristics	Cautions	Care
Glass-Ceramic	❖ Goes from freezer to oven or cooktop. ❖ Durable, heat-resistant, attractive. ❖ Used for roasting, broiling, and baking in conventional or microwave ovens.	❖ May break if dropped. ❖ Holds heat well—reduce oven temperatures by 25°F (14°C) for baked goods.	❖ Use nonabrasive cleaners and nylon scrubbers. ❖ Dishwasher safe. ❖ Use manufacturer's care instructions.
Stoneware	❖ Attractive. ❖ Use for cooking and serving. ❖ Retains heat.	❖ Breaks easily.	❖ Dishwasher safe. ❖ Use nonabrasive cleaners and nylon scrubbers.
Enamel (glass baked on metal)	❖ Attractive. Can be used to cook and serve.	❖ Chips easily.	❖ Dishwasher safe. ❖ Use nonabrasive cleaners and nylon scrubbers.
Microwave-safe plastic	❖ Durable. ❖ Stain-resistant. ❖ Easy to clean.	❖ Some cannot be used in conventional ovens. ❖ Can be scratched by sharp kitchen tools.	❖ Dishwasher safe. ❖ Use nonabrasive cleaners and nylon scrubbers.
Nonstick Finishes	❖ Keeps foods from sticking to pans—fat may not be necessary for browning, sautéing, or frying.	❖ Easily scratched by metal kitchen tools or abrasive cleaners. ❖ High heat may stain finish or warp pan.	❖ Follow manufacturer's directions for use and care. Some cannot be washed in dishwasher. ❖ Use non-metal tools to prevent scratching.

- As a general rule, all types of cookware should be washed in hot water with detergent.
- To remove baked-on food, soak pans in hot water with a little detergent prior to washing.

Cookware

Many kinds of cookware are available for cooktop use.

❖ **Saucepans.** The most common type of cookware. They have one long handle and often come with a cover. Sizes range from 1/2 qt. to 4 qt. (500 mL to 4 L). Usually made of metal or heatproof glass.

❖ **Pots.** Larger and heavier than saucepans, ranging in size from 3 to 20 qt. (3 to 20 L). Pots have two small handles, one on either side, making it easier to lift a heavy pot. Most pots come with covers.

❖ **Skillets** (sometimes called frypans). Used for browning and frying foods. They vary in size and often have matching covers.

❖ **Double boiler.** Consists of two saucepans—a smaller one fitting into a larger one—and a cover. Boiling water in the bottom pan gently heats the food in the upper pan. Used for cooking foods that scorch easily, such as milk, chocolate, sauces, and cereal.

❖ **Dutch oven.** A pot with a close-fitting cover. Some come with a rack to keep meat and poultry from sticking to the bottom. The Dutch oven is used on top of the range or in the oven.

❖ **Steamer.** A basketlike container that holds food. It is placed inside a saucepan containing a small amount of boiling water. Small holes in the steamer allow steam to pass through to cook food.

❖ **Pressure cooker.** A heavy pan with a locked-on cover and a steam gauge. Steam builds up inside the pan, causing very high cooking temperatures that cook food more quickly.

Dutch oven

Skillet

Saucepans

Steamer

Stockpot

Double boiler

Pressure cooker

Bakeware

Most bakeware consists of pans of different sizes and shapes. Light-colored pans transfer oven heat to food quickly and give baked products a light, delicate crust. Darker pans absorb more heat from the oven and can produce thick brown crusts in baked products, though not in other foods.

Glass pans absorb more heat than metal bakeware. If you use a glass pan for baking, reduce the oven temperature by 25°F (14°C).

Here are some basic types of bakeware:

- **Loaf pan.** A deep, narrow, rectangular pan used for baking breads and meatloaf.
- **Cookie sheet.** A flat, rectangular pan designed for baking cookies and biscuits. A cookie sheet has two or three open sides.
- **Baking sheet.** Similar to a cookie sheet, except it has four shallow sides about 1 inch (2.5 cm) deep. Used for baking sheet cakes, pizza, chicken pieces, and fish.
- **Cake pans.** Come in assorted sizes and shapes.
- **Tube pan.** A cake pan with a tube in the center. Used for baking angel food cakes.
- **Pie pans.** Shallow round pans with slanted sides. Used for pies, tarts, and quiches.
- **Muffin pans.** Used for baking muffins, rolls, and cupcakes. Available with six or twelve cups.
- **Roasting pans.** Large, heavy pans, oval or rectangular in shape. They may be covered or uncovered. Used for roasting meat and poultry.
- **Casserole.** A covered or uncovered pan used for baking and serving main dishes and desserts. Various sizes are available.

A variety of bakeware is available. Shiny metal pans give a light, delicate crust. Darker metal pans give a darker, thicker crust.

One traditional method of cooking food in India is with a *tandoor.* This is a clay oven shaped like a bucket or a beehive. Food is placed in the tandoor and cooked over a charcoal fire.

Cooking Tools

A variety of tools are available for the many different cooking tasks. Here are some you might find helpful:

* **Turner.** Used to lift and turn flat foods such as hamburgers and pancakes.
* **Tongs.** Used to grip and lift hot, bulky foods, such as broccoli spears.
* **Basting spoon.** Used to stir and baste foods during cooking.
* **Baster.** A long tube with a bulb on the end used for suctioning up juices for basting.
* **Ladle.** Has a small bowl and a long handle for dipping hot liquids from a pan.
* **Pastry brush.** Used to brush hot foods with sauce or pastry with a glaze.
* **Skewers.** Long rods made of metal or bamboo, with one pointed end. Pieces of food are threaded onto them for cooking or serving.
* **Meat thermometer.** Used to measure the internal temperature of meat and poultry. Different types are used for conventional and microwave cooking.
* **Wire cooling racks.** Used for holding baked goods during cooling or hot pans when they are removed from the heat.
* **Potholders, oven mitts.** Thick cloth pads used to protect hands while handling hot containers.
* **Wooden spoon.** Used to stir hot food. Does not retain heat.
* **Candy thermometer.** Measures the temperature of sugar syrup. or candy cooked to high temperatures.

Turner

Tongs

Basting spoon

Baster

Ladle

Pastry brush

Skewers

Meat thermometer

Section 9.1 Review

RECALL THE FACTS

1. How are the conventional, convection, and microwave ovens alike? How are they different?

2. Name four small appliances for cooking foods.

3. What are the key differences between a saucepan and a pot? Between a cookie sheet and a baking sheet?

DISCUSS YOUR IDEAS

4. What small cooking appliances might you find most useful in a kitchen? Why?

APPLY YOUR LEARNING

5. Working in groups, identify the cooking equipment found in the foods lab kitchen and where it is located. Be prepared to report orally to your teacher.

Wire cooling rack

Wooden spoon

Potholders, oven mitts

Candy thermometer

Objectives

After studying this section, you should be able to:

❖ Explain how heat is transferred by conduction, convection, and radiation.
❖ Describe some changes in food brought about by cooking.
❖ Explain basic differences between moist heat cooking, dry heat cooking, and frying.

Look for These Terms

conduction
convection
convection current
radiation
moist heat
dry heat
frying

Wonderful things happen in the kitchen. A mixture of vegetables, meat, and water becomes a savory stew. A turkey browning in the oven or soup simmering on top of the range creates delectable aromas. All these delightful changes—and many, many more—are the result of applying heat to food. Learning more about heat and its effects can help you better understand basic cooking procedures.

Methods of Heat Transfer

When any material—metal, glass, or a food—is heated, its molecules vibrate. The greater the heat, the higher the vibration.

As you learned in Section 9.1, there are many different cooking appliances. They use a variety of methods to create heat for cooking. For example, the heat may come from:

❖ Combustion, or burning, as in the flame on a gas burner.
❖ Electrical resistance, as in an electric range or a toaster oven.
❖ A magnetic field in an induction cooktop.
❖ Vibrations caused by microwave energy.

Heat affects the appearance, flavor, and texture of foods.

No matter how the heat is generated, it must travel to the food or within the food. Heat always flows from warmer areas to cooler areas. This can happen in three ways.

❖ **Conduction.** In **conduction,** heat travels by direct contact. As molecules are heated, they pass the heat on to neighboring molecules. In this way, heat can travel within an object and to other objects in direct contact. Think of a pancake cooking in a skillet. Heat from the cooktop element is conducted to the skillet. The heat from the skillet is conducted to the bottom of the pancake, and from there to the inside. To cook the top of the pancake, you flip it over. Can you see why?

❖ **Convection.** Heat can also be transferred by the movement of air or liquid. This process is called **convection.** As air or liquid is heated, the hotter portions rise above the cold. This creates a **convection current**—a circular flow of air or liquid resulting from uneven heating. Imagine a saucepan of water heating on the cooktop. The water nearest the bottom of the saucepan gets warm and rises through the colder water to the surface. The colder

Conduction

In conduction, heat is transferred to food through direct contact with a heated surface.

water on the surface is forced down to the saucepan bottom. As the cold water on the bottom of the saucepan warms up, it again rises to the surface. This process continually repeats, creating a convection current. This same process also occurs with heated air in an oven.

Convection— Heated Air

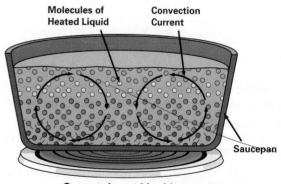
Convection— Liquids

Convection currents result from the flow of warm and cool air or liquid.

❖ *Radiation.* Heat can travel through space in the form of waves of energy called *infrared rays.* When these rays strike an object, the object is warmed. This heat transfer method is called **radiation.** The sun radiates heat to warm the Earth. In a similar way, radiant heat from a broiler strikes the food in the pan below.

Most cooking techniques use a combination of some or all of these heat transfer processes. For example, a broiler heats the surface of a food by radiation. The heat travels through the food by conduction.

Waves of Radiant Energy

Thermal Radiation

Heat can also be transferred through infrared rays, as in a broiler or charcoal grill.

How Heat Affects Food

Heat affects food in many ways. For instance, it changes the color of foods. Some foods become darker and some lighter when cooked.

Heat also releases flavor and aroma from food. Cooking different foods together allows flavors to mingle, creating a pleasing combination.

Heat changes the texture of foods, too. Some foods become harder, some softer, some crispy, and some tender. Too much heat can dry food out, scorch or burn it, and boil away liquids. Heat also has an effect on nutrients, as you will see.

The exact effect of heat on food depends on the food and the cooking method.

Differences in Cooking Methods

Most cooking methods fall into three basic categories: moist heat, dry heat, and frying. Each has different characteristics.

Moist heat cooking involves either liquid or steam. Examples range from rice cooked in a saucepan of water to stew made in a slow cooker.

Moist heat cooking can produce tender, flavorful one-dish meals. What other types of foods are best cooked with moist heat?

Moist heat may be used for a number of reasons. Long, slow moist heat cooking can help tenderize meat. Some foods, like rice or dry beans, must absorb liquid as they cook. Sometimes cooking foods together in broth or a sauce helps to blend their flavors.

Foods cooked in moist heat (or in the microwave) do not brown. They also do not develop a crisp or tender crust.

Cooking in **dry heat** means cooking food uncovered without added moisture. It requires a conventional range or similar appliance, such as a toaster oven. A microwave oven will not give the same results.

Food cooked in dry heat browns and develops a crisp or tender crust, yet stays moist and tender inside. A rack may be used under foods to help drain away fats and liquids.

Frying—cooking in fat—is a third basic method. Fat can be heated to a higher temperature than water. This high cooking temperature gives the food a brown, crisp surface and distinct flavor. A disadvantage of frying is that it adds fat to food.

As you continue your studies, you will learn more about different cooking methods and their effects on specific foods.

Dry heat cooking is used for tender meat, poultry, and fish and for baked products. The food develops a brown crust.

Science Connection

Chemistry

The Maillard Reaction

Food cooked in dry heat or in fat goes through a browning process. As food browns, the color, flavor, and texture change due to complex chemical changes. One of these changes is called the *Maillard reaction.* It occurs when carbohydrates (either sugar or starch) and amino acids combine on the surface of a food such as roasting meat. The reaction occurs only at temperatures over 300°F (150°C). The surface of food cooked in dry heat or in fat reaches that temperature. With moist heat, the cooking temperature is limited to the boiling point of water, 212°F (100°C). That is why foods cooked in moist heat do not brown.

How Cooking Affects Nutrients

One of the goals of food preparation is to retain nutrients such as vitamins and minerals. You have already learned that proper storage helps retain nutrients. Another key is to choose cooking methods that minimize nutrient loss and use them properly.

Some nutrients can be destroyed by cooking heat. These include vitamin C, thiamin, and folate.

When foods are cooked in liquid, water-soluble vitamins and some minerals dissolve into the liquid. Unless the cooking liquid is eaten, the nutrients are lost. Some minerals and fat-soluble vitamins may be lost as fats and juices drip from meat, poultry, and fish.

Very little protein is lost during cooking. However, animal proteins are sensitive to high temperatures. Overcooking in dry heat toughens them, making them hard to eat.

As you study different foods and cooking methods, you will learn more about specific ways to retain vitamins and minerals and reduce fat.

■ Section 9.2 Review ■

RECALL THE FACTS

1. Briefly describe the three ways heat can be transferred to food during cooking.

2. Name three general ways cooking can change food.

3. What are three basic categories of cooking methods? Which could you use to make meat more tender? Which could you use to brown meat?

DISCUSS YOUR IDEAS

4. How might understanding heat transfer processes help you in using appliances to cook food?

APPLY YOUR LEARNING

5. Find a simple recipe for a cooked vegetable. Compare the taste, aroma, texture, and color of the vegetable before and after cooking. Describe your findings to the class.

Learning more about cooking methods will help you minimize nutrient loss in the foods you prepare.

Objectives

After studying this section, you should be able to:

❖ Explain why the choice of power setting, foods for cooking, and cookware are important in microwave cooking.

❖ Describe the techniques necessary for successful microwaving.

❖ Identify safety precautions for microwave oven use.

Look for These Terms

watts
hot spots
arcing
vent
standing time

Microwaving is a fast, healthful way to cook. Food cooks quickly with less fat and liquid than most conventional methods. That means more of the water-soluble vitamins are retained and fewer vitamins are destroyed by heat.

Microwave Oven Basics

Microwave cooking is not complicated, but it is different from conventional methods. For success, start by reading the owner's manual. It will give specific directions for using your microwave oven. It will also help you understand how the microwave power settings work, the kinds of foods that can be microwaved, and the proper equipment to use.

Power Settings

To cook in a microwave oven, you choose a power setting. The higher the power setting, the more microwaves produced and the faster the cooking. The power setting may be identified as a percentage, such as 50 or 100 percent power, or a description, such as low, medium, or high. The chart below gives typical equivalents for these two kinds of power settings. Microwave ovens do differ, so be sure to check the owner's manual.

Microwave Power Levels	
Description	Percentage of Power
High	100%
Medium-High	70%
Medium	50%
Medium-Low	30%
Low	10%

Microwave ovens vary in the amount of microwaves they produce at each setting because they have different power ratings. Electrical power is measured in units called **watts.** The higher the oven wattage, the more microwaves are produced at various settings. Ovens range in wattage from about 400 to 700 watts. You'll usually find the watt rating on the back of the oven, along with the serial and model numbers.

Foods to Microwave

Microwaves cook by making food molecules vibrate. The microwaves penetrate food to a depth of about 1 ½ inches (3.8 cm). There they agitate food molecules and produce heat. If the food is thicker, conduction moves the heat deeper into the food and eventually cooks it throughout.

Microwave ovens vary in size, wattage, and types of controls. What is the wattage shown on this label?

Standards for microwave ovens require at least two independent interlock systems. Each of these systems stops the production of microwaves the moment the latch is released or the door is opened. If an interlock system fails, a monitoring system stops the oven. Don't operate the oven if the door is bent, the latches or hinges are broken or loosened, or the door seals are damaged.

Microwaves produced by the magnetron tube are distributed throughout the oven by the stirrer blade. Those that hit the walls bounce off and back to the food.

Microwave cooking is a better choice for some foods than others. Generally, the best choices are foods that are moist to begin with or can be cooked in moist heat.

Food Composition

What a food is made up of—its composition—affects the way it cooks in the microwave. Understanding a few basic principles will help you microwave successfully.

Water, fat, and sugar are heated most quickly by microwaves. Foods high in water, such as vegetables, will cook faster than foods with a lower water content, such as meat.

Foods like pasta or rice need time to absorb liquids as they cook. As a result, there is no real time savings from cooking such foods in the microwave.

Concentrations of fat and sugar become much hotter than the rest of the food, creating **hot spots**—areas of intense heat. These hot spots can burn your skin and mouth. With a jelly doughnut, for example, the jelly may be superheated when the doughnut is only warm.

Before microwaving, use a fork to pierce foods that have a protective skin. This will keep the food from bursting as steam develops during cooking.

Salt also attracts microwaves. The food under the salt will cook faster. Wait until after cooking to sprinkle salt on food.

Foods like potatoes and winter squash have a skin that keeps moisture from evaporating. Steam can build up inside the skin and cause the food to burst. Pierce foods like these with a fork to allow steam to escape. For the same reason, do not cook eggs in the shell in the microwave—they will burst.

Other Factors

Here are some additional principles to guide you in microwave cooking.

* ❖ **Food density.** The more dense the food, the longer the cooking time. The heavier a food feels for its size, the more dense it is. For example, a slice of bread is less dense than a slice of meat of the same size.
* ❖ **Shape and size of food.** Foods of a uniform thickness cook most evenly. If foods are unevenly shaped, the thinner parts will cook through before the thicker parts. Smaller pieces cook faster than large ones.
* ❖ **Starting temperature of food.** The colder the food is to start with, the longer it will take to cook. Thaw most frozen foods, except vegetables, before microwaving. For commercially frozen foods, follow package directions.
* ❖ **Amount of food.** The more food you're cooking, the longer it will take. The same number of microwaves are produced no matter how much food you put in. One potato cooks quickly, but four potatoes take longer because they must share the microwaves.

Microwave Cookware

Microwaves are reflected by metal but pass through glass, plastic, and paper materials. These characteristics are important to remember when choosing and using containers for cooking.

Metal and foil are not generally used in microwave ovens. They can cause **arcing,** electrical sparks that can damage the oven or start a fire. Use metal and foil only *if* and *how* your owner's manual specifies. Never leave metal tools, such as a spoon, in food being microwaved.

Some general guidelines are given here for choosing containers for microwave cooking. Some containers that cannot withstand the high temperatures of cooking are safe for heating foods to low temperatures.

❖ *Glass and glass-ceramic.* Use ovenproof glass and glass-ceramic for cooking. Regular glass may be suitable for heating.

❖ *Stoneware, china, and pottery.* Most items are suitable for cooking unless they have metal trim. Avoid pottery with metallic glazes.

❖ *Plastic.* For cooking, use only plastic items that are marked "microwave-safe." Some special plastic can be used both in the microwave and at low to moderate temperatures in conventional ovens.

❖ *Paper.* Use paper plates only if they are firm enough to hold food. Choose paper towels labeled "microwave-safe." Avoid products containing recycled paper. They may contain metal fragments or chemicals that could catch fire.

When you use the microwave oven, consider the shape of the container. Round containers cook food more evenly than square or rectangular ones.

The size and shape of microwave cookware also affects the way food cooks and the cooking time. Pans should be shallow with straight sides. Ring-shaped and round pans allow for even cooking. Square and rectangular pans should have rounded corners.

Be sure to choose cookware that can be used safely in a microwave oven. What are some types that would not be suitable?

Microwaving Successfully

A few special techniques are needed in microwave cooking. They involve food placement in the oven and in the pan, covering, stirring, rotating, turning, and timing.

Food Placement

The best arrangement of food for microwaving is a ring shape. This allows the microwaves to enter food from as many sides as possible. A meatloaf, for example, can be shaped into a ring in a pan or cooked in a ring mold.

When possible, leave space between pieces of food. This, too, allows better microwave penetration.

When cooking foods of uneven thickness, use the characteristics of microwave patterns to your advantage. Food in the center of the oven cooks more slowly. Arrange food like the spokes of a wheel, with the thickest or toughest parts toward the outside and the thinnest or most tender parts toward the center. With broccoli spears, for example, place the tops toward the center and the stalks toward the outside.

Covering Food

A cover holds in steam, keeps food moist, and shortens cooking time. It also keeps food from spattering in the oven.

Foods you would cover for conventional cooking are usually covered for microwave cooking. If you want foods to steam, cover them tightly. For drier foods, cover loosely.

Foods may be covered with microwave-safe glass or plastic covers. Plastic wrap, waxed paper, and paper toweling are also useful.

❖ **Plastic wrap.** Microwave-safe plastic wrap holds in steam and heat. Too much steam may build up during cooking and split the plastic. To prevent splitting, **vent** the plastic: after covering the dish, roll back one edge slightly to allow steam to escape.

❖ **Waxed paper.** Waxed paper prevents spatters and allows some steam and moisture to escape. Use it on foods such as casseroles.

❖ **Paper towels.** Paper towels absorb excess moisture and prevent spatters. Wrap rolls, breads, and sandwiches in paper towels before microwaving to keep them from becoming soggy.

When you remove covers or plastic wrap, use a potholder and tilt the cover away from you. Escaping steam can burn.

For even cooking, arrange foods for microwaving with the thickest or toughest parts toward the outside.

Choose the method of covering food that will give the results you want.

Stirring, Rotating, and Turning

Microwaves may not be distributed evenly throughout the oven, especially in older models. To make sure that food cooks as evenly as possible, it must be stirred, rotated, or turned. Unless directed otherwise, stir or turn foods after half the cooking time.

Stirring helps foods cook evenly. If the food cannot be stirred, rotate the pan. To rotate, use a potholder to grasp the pan and give it a quarter or half turn. Dense foods such as meat and poultry also have to be turned over. Use a pair of tongs and turn the food over in the pan.

Determining Cooking Time

Microwave cooking has two parts. Cooking occurs when microwaves are being produced while the food is in the oven and the oven is on. When the oven turns off, the heat inside the food continues cooking the food as it stands. This is called **standing time.**

Recipes give directions for cooking and for standing time. If the food was cooked uncovered, cover it during standing time to retain heat.

Foods continue to cook after they are removed from the microwave oven. Recipes should indicate the standing time.

Check the progress the food makes as it cooks, just as you do with conventional methods. Test food for doneness after the standing time, not before. Avoid overcooking. Foods overcooked in the microwave oven become hard and tough.

Microwave Recipes

Most microwave recipes are written for 650-watt ovens—the most common kind sold. Foods will cook slightly faster in higher wattage ovens and a bit slower in lower wattage ovens.

To adapt a standard recipe for the microwave oven, it's best to find a similar microwave recipe. A basic microwave cookbook can help you ease into microwave cooking successfully. With experience, you can begin experimenting.

A well-written microwave recipe has the same features as conventional recipes. In addition, it specifies:
❖ The size and shape of the cooking container.
❖ How to arrange food for even cooking.
❖ Whether or not to cover the dish.
❖ A range of cooking and standing times.

One Half Turn

Some foods should be rotated during the cooking time so they cook more evenly. When you give a dish a half turn, the end that was at the left side of the oven is switched to the right side.

Microwave Safety and Care

Safety rules for conventional cooking also apply to microwave cooking. Review Section 7.2. Here are some additional microwave safety rules:

❖ Never turn on the oven unless there's food in it. You could damage the oven.
❖ Follow the manufacturer's directions for preparing commercially frozen foods in the microwave oven. Don't eat the food if the package turns brown. Don't reuse containers.
❖ Loosen tight-fitting covers or caps before microwaving. Otherwise, a buildup of steam pressure could cause the container to explode.
❖ Never attach kitchen magnets to the microwave oven. They can affect the electronic controls.
❖ Have your microwave oven tested by an authorized repairperson if you are concerned about microwaves leaking from the oven. Microwave leakage meters available for home use are often not reliable.

Always use potholders when removing hot foods from the microwave oven. Heat from the food can make the container too hot to handle.

Cleaning the Microwave Oven

Clean spots and spills after every use. If allowed to build up, they will absorb microwaves and cut down on the cooking power. Keep the door seal clean. Spilled food also allows bacteria to grow.

To clean the interior of the oven, wipe it with a clean, wet dishcloth. Dry it thoroughly. Do not use abrasive cleaners.

Section 9.3 Review

RECALL THE FACTS

1. What does the power setting on a microwave oven do?
2. Why are metal pans not suitable for microwave cooking?
3. What is the purpose of stirring, rotating, and turning food during cooking?
4. Give three guidelines for safe use of the microwave.

DISCUSS YOUR IDEAS

5. Many American families use their microwave ovens mainly for thawing frozen foods and for heating leftovers, commercially frozen convenience foods, and water. Why do you think more people do not use the microwave oven for other types of cooking?

APPLY YOUR LEARNING

6. Check plastic containers, tools, and cookware in the foods lab. Which items are marked microwave-safe?

Thinking About the Recipe

Read the recipe for "Microwave Baked Potatoes" and answer the following questions.

1. What would be the best arrangement of the potatoes for microwave cooking?
2. Why are the potatoes turned and rearranged after half the cooking time?

Microwave Baked Potatoes

Customary	Ingredients	Metric
4	Potatoes for baking	4

Yield: 4 servings

Directions

Pan: Microwave-safe dish
Power level: 100%

1. Pierce potatoes with a cooking fork.
2. Place one inch apart in microwave-safe dish. Place dish in oven.
3. Cook for 6 to 8 minutes, using 100% power.
4. Turn the potatoes over and rearrange.
5. Cook for an additional 6 to 8 minutes until done. Potatoes may still feel firm.
6. Wrap each potato in foil or paper towel. Let stand about 5 minutes to finish cooking.

Nutrition Information

Per serving (approximate): 145 calories, 3 g protein, 34 g carbohydrate, trace of fat, 0 mg cholesterol, 8 mg sodium

Objectives

After studying this section, you should be able to:

❖ Identify specific types of moist heat cooking, dry heat cooking, frying, and combination methods.

❖ Give guidelines for conventional cooking.

Look for These Terms

stew
poach
preheating
sauté
wok

Kristie wanted to try something new, so she bought and cooked a chuck roast for her family. She cooked it the way her mother always cooked roasts—in an open pan in the oven. The roast was so tough and dry that it was hard to eat. Kristie didn't know that it was a different kind of roast than her mother usually bought and required a different cooking method.

Cooking methods vary depending on the kind of food being cooked and the results desired. In this section, you will learn about several basic methods of conventional cooking.

Moist Heat Methods

As you learned earlier, moist heat cooking methods are those in which food is cooked in a hot liquid, steam, or a combination of both. Many cooking appliances, including the microwave and slow cooker, use moist heat. When using the conventional range, you can choose between several moist heat methods. These include boiling, simmering, steaming, and pressure cooking.

Liquids bubble vigorously at boiling temperatures. The large bubbles rise quickly to the surface and break.

Boiling

When a liquid reaches boiling temperature, it forms large bubbles that rise to the surface and break. Water boils at 212°F (100°C).

Boiling is suitable for only a few foods. Corn-on-the-cob and pasta are cooked in boiling water. Boiling is also useful when you want liquid to evaporate quickly. For instance, you might boil a sauce to thicken it or boil a soup to concentrate the flavor.

Many foods may overcook easily or break apart if boiled. Nutrient loss is higher than with other methods. Boiling also toughens foods high in protein, such as eggs.

When boiling foods, be sure to use a saucepan or pot large enough to hold the food and the boiling liquid. Bring the liquid to the boiling point, then add the food. Be sure the liquid continues boiling as the food cooks.

Simmering

Simmering differs from boiling in that bubbles in the liquid rise gently and just begin to break the surface. Water simmers at about 186°F to 210°F (86°C to 99°C).

Foods that would break apart or toughen if boiled can be simmered instead. Simmering is used to cook many types of food, including fruits, vegetables, and less tender cuts of meat and poultry.

To **stew** food means to cover small pieces of food with liquid, then simmer until done. To **poach** food means to simmer whole foods in a small amount of liquid until done. Eggs, fish, and whole fruits can be poached.

To simmer food, bring the liquid to a boil and then add the food. After the liquid returns to a boil, reduce the heat so the food simmers. A slow cooker can also be used to simmer some foods, such as meats and dry beans.

As with boiling, some nutrients are lost, especially water-soluble vitamins. Whenever possible, use the cooking liquid from foods such as vegetables and dry beans.

Steaming

Steaming is a method of cooking food over, but not in, boiling water. The food is usually placed in a steamer basket that fits inside a saucepan. Steam is created by a

Stewing uses simmering liquid to cook food.

Steaming foods helps them retain nutrients. Can you explain why?

small amount of boiling water in the bottom of the pan. The boiling water does not come in contact with the food. The pan is covered during cooking to trap the steam. You can also use an electric steamer to cook food.

Many foods can be cooked in steam, including vegetables and fish. Foods retain their color, shape, and flavor well when steamed. Few nutrients are lost. Cooking time is longer with steaming than with boiling or simmering.

Pressure Cooking

A pressure cooker cooks food in steam under pressure. Because the pressure makes temperatures above 212°F (100°C) possible, the food cooks three to ten times faster than with other methods.

Use the pressure cooker for foods that take a long time to cook, such as less tender cuts of meat and poultry, dry beans, soups, one-dish meals, and vegetables. This method

has all the advantages of steaming plus faster cooking times. Follow the manufacturer's directions and safety guidelines carefully. The food in a pressure cooker is superheated and under high pressure.

Dry Heat Methods

As you have learned, cooking in dry heat means cooking food uncovered without adding any liquid or fat. Dry heat methods include roasting and baking, broiling, and pan-broiling.

Roasting and Baking

Roasting and baking both mean cooking food uncovered in a conventional or convection oven. "Roasting" generally refers to cooking large, tender cuts of meat or poultry.

Roasting and baking both refer to a dry heat cooking method used for tender foods.

Pan Placement in the Oven

When baking, placement and spacing of pans are important. The pans must be placed so the hot air in the oven can circulate freely. If pans touch each other or the oven walls, they create a hot spot—an area of concentrated heat. The food overcooks in these areas. When baking several pans of food at one time, place them diagonally opposite one another, as shown here.

One Pan

Two Pans

Three Pans

Four Pans

"Baking" is the term used with foods such as breads, cookies, vegetables, and casseroles. However, meat, poultry, and fish may be "baked," too. (Examples include baked ham and baked chicken.)

Roasting gives tender meat and poultry a flavorful, crispy, brown crust. Use a shallow, uncovered roasting pan with a rack. The roasting rack allows fat to drain away from the food—a real benefit to those trying to reduce their fat intake.

For baked goods such as breads and cakes, preheating is important. **Preheating** means to turn the oven on about 10 minutes before using it so it will be at the desired temperature when the food is put in.

Broiling

Broiling refers to cooking food under direct heat. The broiler pan is placed below a burner or heating element. The heat radiates down onto the food, cooking it.

Broiling is suitable for cooking tender foods such as fish, fruits, some vegetables, and tender cuts of meat and poultry. The foods cook quickly and brown well. Foods that are already cooked may be broiled for a short time to brown them or to melt cheese toppings.

A broiler pan has two parts. A slotted grid holds the food. The grid fits on the top of a shallow pan that catches drippings. This allows fat to drain away during cooking.

For broiling in most ranges, set the oven control on "broil." You cannot control the exact broiling temperature. To control the cooking, you can vary the distance of the pan from the heat and the cooking time. For thicker foods, the pan is positioned farther from the heat and the cooking time is increased. This allows the food to cook all the way through without burning on the outside. Check a cookbook for guidelines about positioning specific foods for broiling.

Cooking on an outdoor or indoor grill is similar to broiling except the heat source is below the food. The food is placed on a wire grid.

Broiler Grid

Broiler Pan

A broiler pan consists of two parts that fit together. The slots in the grid allow melted fat from the food to drain into the pan below. That makes broiling a low-fat cooking method.

TIPS for Success

Broiling Food
* To prevent foods from sticking, always start with a cold broiler pan.
* Before broiling, pat meat and poultry dry. Moisture can keep food from becoming brown and crisp.
* Do not salt foods before broiling. Salt draws moisture from foods, causing them to dry out.
* Brush fish, fruit, and vegetables lightly with oil or melted butter or margarine to keep them from charring.
* To turn food during broiling, use tongs instead of a fork. The fork pierces holes which allow juices to escape.

Pan-Broiling

Pan-broiling is a top-of-the-range method of dry heat cooking. Foods such as hamburgers, tender cuts of steak, and some cuts of pork may be pan-broiled. The food cooks quickly and retains a minimum amount of fat.

To pan-broil, cook the food in a heavy skillet over medium heat. Do not add fat. As fat accumulates in the pan during cooking, pour it off\or remove it with a baster.

Frying

Frying involves cooking food in oil or melted fat. There are several different methods:

❖ *Sautéing.* To **sauté** (saw-TAY) means to brown or cook foods in a skillet with a small amount of fat. Low to medium heat is used. This method is often used for chopped vegetables, such as onions and peppers, and small pieces of meat and fish.

❖ *Pan-frying.* Pan-frying is similar to sautéing but usually involves larger pieces of meat, poultry, or fish. The food may need to be turned several times during the cooking process for complete, even cooking. Pan-frying is often used to brown meat before cooking it in moist heat.

Sautéing is a form of frying. Small pieces of food, such as chopped onions, are cooked in a small amount of fat.

In pan-broiling, fat is removed from the skillet as it accumulates.

❖ **Deep-fat frying.** This method is also called french frying. Food is immersed in hot fat and fried until done. It is used for tender foods, such as vegetables, and some breads, such as doughnuts. For best deep-fat frying results, use a deep-fat or candy thermometer to keep the fat at the correct temperature.

Combination Methods

Sometimes the best way to cook a food is by using a combination of methods. Braising and stir-frying are two popular cooking methods that combine dry heat and moist heat cooking.

Braising

Braising combines browning food (frying) with a long period of simmering to tenderize the food and enhance the flavor. It is often used for large, less tender cuts of meat and poultry.

Use a Dutch oven or other heavy pot with a tight-fitting cover. The food is pan-fried or browned on all sides. Then seasonings and a small amount of liquid are added to the food and the pot is covered. The cooking may be completed in the oven (usually at 350°F or 180°C) or on top of the range. Vegetables are sometimes added to braised meat or poultry near the end of the cooking time.

Braising combines frying and moist heat cooking. A pot roast with vegetables is prepared by braising.

Stir-Frying

Stir-frying also combines frying and moist heat cooking. Small pieces of food are fried quickly in a small amount of oil at high heat. The food is stirred constantly to keep it from sticking to the pan. During the last few minutes of cooking, a small amount of liquid is usually added to the food and the pan is covered, allowing the food to steam.

Stir-frying, which began in Asia, is most often used for cooking mixtures of vegetables and other foods. A special pan called a **wok** is traditionally used, but a skillet also works well.

Stir-frying is a quick way to cook foods.

Science Connection

Chemistry
Smoking Points of Fats

All fats have a *smoking point*—a temperature at which they begin to give off irritating smoke and break down chemically. Oil that has reached its smoking point is no longer good for cooking. Animal fats, such as butter and lard, have low smoking points. Safflower, soybean, corn, and peanut oils have relatively high smoking points. They make the best choices for frying.

Section 9.4 Review

RECALL THE FACTS

1. Explain the difference between simmering and boiling.

2. What equipment is needed for steaming?

3. List the methods of dry heat cooking.

4. Name and describe three methods of frying.

DISCUSS YOUR IDEAS

5. Discuss some possible reasons why more people are using steamers and woks in cooking meals.

APPLY YOUR LEARNING

6. Find several recipes for each of the following: eggs for breakfast; a vegetable side dish; a ground beef dish; soup; and chicken. Which basic cooking method does each recipe use?

CAREER PROFILE

Robert Ridgeway
Chef

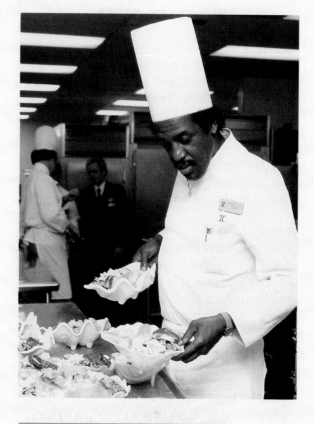

Current position:

"I'm an executive chef for a large upscale hotel."

Responsibilities:

"I'm responsible for preparing traditional meals that are both tasty and attractively presented, as well as creating new and interesting offerings."

Skills:

"A keen sense of taste and smell is very helpful in this career. You also need creativity and an understanding of design."

Education:

"I've taken vocational courses in commercial food preparation and have completed an extensive training program sponsored by the hotel chain that employs me."

Why I chose this career:

"Even as a little boy I could always be found hanging around my mom in the kitchen, watching her cook. I've always enjoyed working with food."

Favorite part of the job:

"What's most satisfying for me is when customers take the time to send their 'compliments to the chef.'"

- Why would a sense of design be helpful in Robert's career?
- What aspects of Robert's job do you think you might find interesting? Why?

Summary

Section 9.1
Equipment for Cooking: Major cooking appliances include gas and electric ranges, convection ovens, and microwave ovens. Each has different characteristics. Small cooking appliances are useful for specialized tasks. Cookware and bakeware pieces have specific uses and are available in a wide range of materials. Several small tools are also used in cooking.

Section 9.2
Heat and Cooking: Heat travels by conduction, convection, or radiation. When food is heated, the color, flavor, aroma, and texture are affected. The three basic types of cooking methods—moist heat, dry heat, and frying—affect food differently. Take steps to minimize nutrient losses during cooking.

Section 9.3
Microwave Cooking Techniques: Microwave cooking requires a basic understanding of the oven's power settings and the way microwaves affect different foods and materials. Be sure to follow instructions for arranging, covering, stirring, rotating, turning, and timing foods. Use the oven safely and care for it properly.

Section 9.4
Conventional Cooking Techniques: Moist heat cooking methods include boiling, simmering, steaming, and pressure cooking. Roasting or baking, broiling, and pan-broiling are methods of cooking in dry heat. Frying methods include sautéing, pan-frying, and deep-fat frying. Braising and stir-frying are cooking techniques that combine two basic methods.

REVIEWING FACTS

1. Where is the broiler in a gas range? In an electric range? (9.1)

2. What is a double boiler used for? (9.1)

3. List four cooking tools and tell what they are used for. (9.1)

4. What is convection? How is it different from conduction? (9.2)

5. Name three possible reasons for using moist heat cooking in certain situations. (9.2)

6. What happens when you change the power setting of a microwave oven from high to medium? How does this affect the cooking time? (9.3)

7. Name four specific materials suitable for microwave cooking. (9.3)

8. What is the difference between stewing and poaching? (9.4)

9. What kinds of foods can you roast successfully? (9.4)

10. How is pan-broiling different from broiling? (9.4)

LEARNING BY DOING

1. **Cookware demonstration:** Collect several cookware and bakeware items. Give a presentation explaining how the differences in size, shape, materials, and handle placement make each item helpful for particular kinds of cooking tasks. (9.1)

2. **Foods lab:** Cook potato slices by baking, simmering, boiling, and frying. Compare the flavors and textures. (9.2, 9.4)

3. ***Foods lab:*** Work in groups to compare conventional and microwave methods of sautéing. To sauté chopped green pepper in the microwave, use a 2-qt. (2-L) casserole. Add 1 Tbsp. (15 mL) margarine and 1 cup (250 mL) chopped green pepper. Cover. Microwave at 100% power for 3 to 4 minutes until softened. Meanwhile, sauté an equal amount of green pepper on the conventional range. Compare the results, time required, and cleanup for the two methods. (9.3, 9.4)

THINKING CRITICALLY

1. ***Identifying cause and effect:*** Many more kinds of cookware, bakeware, and kitchen tools are available now than 50 or even 20 years ago. What are possible reasons? (9.1)

2. ***Recognizing values:*** The popularity of the microwave oven is the result of what trends in American values? (9.1, 9.3)

3. ***Recognizing competency:*** Cookbooks usually have a page describing the author or panel of authors who wrote the book. What would you expect to find in a description of the author of a microwave cookbook? (9.3)

4. ***Drawing conclusions:*** Joyce used a recipe to braise a mixture of meat and vegetables. When the cooking time ended, she was dismayed to find the food dried out and charred on the bottom. What might have caused this? What recommendations do you have for Joyce in the future? (9.4)

MAKING DECISIONS AND SOLVING PROBLEMS

What Would You Do?

1. Your family is packing for a week's vacation at a lakeside cabin that has a small gas range. Your parents have asked you to choose what cookware, bakeware, and kitchen tools to pack. You can only take as much as you can fit in a small cardboard box. (9.1)

2. You sometimes help an elderly neighbor prepare meals. He has purchased an inexpensive cut of meat and asks you to broil it. He tells you to be sure and broil it a long time to make it tender. (9.2, 9.4)

3. You have a favorite recipe for chicken with a sauce, but it takes so long to prepare that you seldom use it. You've been looking for a microwave version of the recipe without success. (9.3)

LINKING YOUR STUDIES

1. ***Science:*** Place a long all-metal kitchen tool, such as a ladle, in a saucepan of boiling water. Using a watch with a second hand, time how long it takes for the handle to become hot to the touch at the midpoint and at the end. What kind of heat transfer is involved in the movement of heat through the metal handle? (9.2)

2. ***Art:*** Develop a diagram that shows how to arrange fresh broccoli in a casserole for microwaving. Indicate how the microwaves will be absorbed by the food. (9.3)

3. ***Reading and study skills:*** Summarize Section 9.4 in outline form. Include what you feel are the most important points to remember about each cooking method discussed. (9.4)

CHAPTER 10
Mealtime Customs

Section 10.1
Serving Family Meals

Objectives

After studying this section, you should be able to:

❖ Explain why meals together can be important to a family.
❖ Demonstrate how to arrange tableware for a simple family meal.
❖ Describe family service and plate service.

Look for These Terms

place setting
serving pieces
cover

Family meals, a time when the whole family eats together, are an important part of family life. They are a time when family members can relax, enjoy food, talk with each other, and have fun. In today's fast-paced society, it may not be easy to find time to sit down and enjoy a family meal. Many families, however, make time because they know these meals strengthen the family bond.

Both of Lynette's parents work. In addition, one goes to school in the evenings. The other is a volunteer reading teacher two nights a week. Lynette and her sisters have their own after-school activities. Morning is the only time the family can get together, so breakfast is the family meal. Everyone gets up a little early and pitches in to help with the meal. Sharing news about their activities and plans for the day is part of the family routine. They know that they can depend on each other, even with their busy schedules.

Busy families may not have as much time to spend together as they'd like. When they do share a meal, it's worth a little extra effort to make the experience pleasant and enjoyable.

Mealtime Atmosphere

A pleasant mealtime atmosphere is just as essential to your health as nutritious food. It helps you enjoy your meal more. Studies also show that relaxation while eating helps digestion.

The place to start is with making the eating area attractive. Take time to put a simple decoration on the table. Try a vase with a single garden flower or a few interesting seashells.

Keep family meals fun. Mealtime is not the time to complain, criticize, or air the day's problems. Focus on the pleasure of eating and each other's company. What interesting topics can you think of to discuss?

If you're eating alone, sit down and take time to eat, relax, and enjoy yourself. People who read or watch television as they eat pay little attention to what and how much they eat. They often eat more than they would if they relaxed, concentrated on the food, and enjoyed the meal.

For a simple meal, the cover for each person needs to include only the basic items.

Setting the Table for Family Meals

Tableware includes dinnerware, flatware, glassware, and linens. "Linens" can mean anything from a cloth tablecloth and napkins to wipe-clean placemats.

The pieces of tableware used by one person to eat a meal are called a **place setting**. Platters, large bowls, and other tableware used for serving food are called **serving pieces.**

The arrangement of a place setting for one person is called a **cover.** The rules of an arrangement are based on both tradition and practicality. Knowing how to set a cover will help you serve family meals, entertain guests, and feel comfortable when you eat out.

Most families choose simple table settings for everyday meals. For most meals, you need at least a dinner plate, fork, knife, teaspoon, and beverage glass. At home, the fork

For a more elaborate or formal meal, more dinnerware, flatware, and glassware are used. Note the placement of the salad plate and cup and saucer.

can be used to eat a salad as well as the main dish. It may also be used for dessert, if one is served. (When eating a formal meal, separate salad and dessert forks would be used.) Add a cup and saucer or a mug if a hot beverage is being served. If salad is on the menu, add a salad plate or bowl. For soup, you will need a bowl and soup spoon.

The cover is arranged for the convenience of the diner and is usually on the table before people sit down to eat. The plate is placed in the center of the cover, about one inch (2.5 cm) from the edge of the table.

Flatware is arranged in the order in which it is used, starting at the outside and working in toward the center. All forks are to the left of the plate and knives to the right. Spoons are placed to the right of the knives. If you have a soup spoon and a teaspoon, the soup spoon would probably be used first. Place it to the right of the teaspoon.

A beverage glass is placed just above the tip of the dinner knife. The cup and saucer or mug are to the right of the spoon, about one inch (2.5 cm) from the edge of the table. The napkin is usually placed to the left of the fork.

Serving Family Meals

Meals can be served in several ways. The most common styles for family meals are plate service and family service.

Plate Service

Plate service is generally used only for family meals or in restaurants. The table is set without dinner plates, but space is left on each cover for the plate. Food is placed on the plates directly from the pans in which it was cooked, and the plates are placed on the table.

The advantage of plate service is that food remaining in the pans can be kept warm in the kitchen. If people want more food, they can ask for second helpings. It also saves time because serving dishes are not used and therefore do not have to be washed.

Many families use plate service at home. When setting the table, space is left for the plates. The food is put on the plates in the kitchen and the filled plates are brought to the table.

Family Service

In family service, the cover is set with the necessary tableware. The food is placed in serving dishes and passed around the table, with people helping themselves. It's less confusing if all the foods are passed in the same direction, generally to the right.

Sometimes, if a serving plate is too hot or a roast or ham is sliced at the table, that food is served at the table by a family member. In that case, the dinner plates are stacked in front of the server. The food is placed on a plate and passed along to the diners, who then help themselves to other foods in the meal.

The main advantage of family service is that people can serve themselves the amount they want. The main disadvantage, however, is that hot food left on the table in serving bowls may cool quickly.

General Guidelines

Breads and rolls are placed on a plate or in a basket and passed around the table. If a basket is used, line it with a napkin. Diners can place bread or rolls on the edge of their dinner plates. In more formal meals, a small bread-and-butter plate may be provided above the forks.

Salads may be served in individual bowls at each place setting or passed around the table in a serving bowl. If possible, serve salad dressing separately, so people can use the amount they want.

Dessert is served after the dinner plates, salad bowls, and serving dishes have been cleared from the table. If forks or spoons are needed, they are brought to the table with the dessert.

In a restaurant, dessert is brought to the table on individual plates after the other dishes have been cleared away. The same method is used when dessert is served at home.

Section 10.1 Review

RECALL THE FACTS

1. Identify two benefits of a pleasant mealtime atmosphere.

2. Name the items included in a simple, everyday table setting.

3. How does family service differ from plate service?

DISCUSS YOUR IDEAS

4. What obstacles do many families face in planning meals together? How might they be overcome?

APPLY YOUR LEARNING

5. Set a cover incorrectly. Have a classmate identify the error in the setting and correct it.

Objectives

After studying this section, you should be able to:

❖ Explain the importance of knowing simple table etiquette.
❖ Describe basic etiquette guidelines.

Look for These Terms

table etiquette
reservations
tip

While you may enjoy a casual approach to dining, it's also important to know basic table etiquette. **Table etiquette** is simply the courtesy shown by good manners at meals. Table manners have one purpose—to make eating a pleasant experience for everyone at the table. Most rules of etiquette involve common sense and consideration of other people.

Good manners help you be more comfortable in social situations. Showing you have good table etiquette can be an asset in the working world as well. Many business transactions take place at mealtime. Often, when companies consider an applicant for a job, the interview may include a meal. This gives the interviewer a chance to find out how the applicant would act under similar business situations.

Knowing proper table etiquette is an advantage in both social and business situations.

Basic Etiquette

Here are some general etiquette guidelines:

❖ Place the napkin on your lap before you start eating. Don't tuck it into a belt or under your chin.

❖ If there are six or fewer people at the table, wait until everyone is served before you begin to eat. If there are more, wait until two or three have been served.

❖ You may reach for serving dishes as long as you don't have to lean across your neighbor. If you can't reach the food easily, ask the person nearest the food to please pass it to you.

❖ If you're having problems getting foods (such as peas) on your fork, push them on with a piece of bread. If you have none, use the tip of the dinner knife to push the food onto the fork.

❖ Break bread into smaller pieces before buttering or eating it.

❖ If you're dining at someone's home and aren't sure what to do, follow the actions of the host or hostess as a guide.

❖ Don't talk with your mouth full. Finish chewing, swallow the food, and then talk.

❖ Cut food into small pieces for eating. If you try to eat large pieces, you may have difficulty chewing and might choke.

❖ Sit up straight when you eat and don't lean on your elbows.

❖ If you must cough or sneeze, cover your mouth and nose with a handkerchief or a napkin. If your coughing continues, excuse yourself and leave the table.

❖ Don't leave a spoon in your cup. You might knock the cup over if your hand accidentally hits the spoon.

❖ At home and in fast food restaurants, you can eat fried chicken with your fingers. When dining in someone else's home, use the actions of the host or hostess as a guide. In fine restaurants, eat all meat except crisp bacon with a knife and fork.

❖ Some foods are normally eaten with the fingers, regardless of where you are eating. These include breads, celery, olives, carrot sticks, pickles, crisp bacon, and most sandwiches.

The acts of offering and accepting food make up interesting etiquette rituals that vary among cultures. In the Fiji Islands, for example, it is considered polite to accept all food offered and eat as much as desired. In Colombia, on the other hand, it may be considered impolite to accept a second helping. Meanwhile, a polite guest in Syria will refuse the first two offers of food, accepting only when it is offered a third time.

❖ When you have finished eating, place your fork and knife on your plate, pointing toward the center.

❖ Never comb your hair or apply makeup while at the table.

❖ Remember, people from different countries and cultures have table manners that may be different from yours. Respect and accept people with other customs.

At the end of the meal, place your knife and fork pointing toward the center of your plate and loosely fold your napkin on the table.

Restaurant Etiquette

Restaurant etiquette involves the same good manners that you use anywhere else. Still, there are a few basic guidelines that deal with situations found only in restaurants.

When You Enter a Restaurant

A few restaurants may require **reservations.** That means you call ahead of time to reserve a table. Give your name, the number of people in your group, and the time you plan to arrive. If you will be late or decide not to go, call and cancel the reservation.

When you arrive, you may see a coat check room, where you leave coats, umbrellas, packages, and briefcases. You are expected to tip the attendant.

Unless a sign states otherwise, never seat yourself. A restaurant employee will direct you and your group to a table.

The Meal

If you have any questions regarding the menu, ask the server. Be sure you understand the prices so you will know exactly what you must pay. Sometimes the price of the entree (or main dish) includes side dishes such as vegetables and salad. Other restaurants price each food individually.

Often, each person in a group wants to pay for his or her own meal. The bill for the food you order is called a check. If the group is small, ask the server for separate checks before you order the food. In some restaurants, however, only one check is made out for each table. Then you might ask the server to figure out the cost for each person, or have each person keep track of the cost of his or her meal.

If you want to call your server, try to catch his or her attention by raising your hand. If necessary, ask one of the other servers to get your server. Never call out or disturb other diners.

Be polite to servers, whether in a fast food or elegant restaurant. Remember, they are

If each person in a group is paying separately, be sure to tell the server before you order.

working hard to serve you and a number of other people at the same time. Be considerate and patient, especially during rush hours.

Restaurants may serve more food than some people can eat. If you have leftover food, such as part of a steak or chicken, ask to have it wrapped so you can take it home. Most restaurants have special containers and supply them to diners. However, this does not apply to all-you-can-eat buffets or salad bars.

In fast food restaurants, delicatessens, and some cafeterias, customers are expected to clear their table after they have eaten. Trays and disposables are deposited in containers provided for the purpose.

Paying the Check and Tipping

The check for the meal will be brought to you by the server. Look over the check carefully and add up the items. If there is a mistake, quietly point it out to the server. The server should correct any mistake or explain why the amount shown is right.

Sometimes the check is brought to you inside a small folder. If so, place your money or credit card inside the folder after you have looked over the check. Your server will take the payment and return your change or credit slip.

In some restaurants you pay your server. In others you take the check to the cashier for payment. If you're not sure, ask the server.

A **tip** is extra money given to the server in appreciation for good service. Servers rely on tips as an important part of their pay. If you are paying for your meal in cash, leave the tip on the table or on the tray on which the check was presented.

If you use a credit card, the server or cashier will process the card and hand you the credit card slip. Again, go over the math and make sure the totals are correct. The slip has a space for the tip. Fill in the amount, add the final total, sign the slip, and hand it back to the server or cashier. Be sure to get your copy of the credit card slip for your records, and don't forget the credit card.

People often wonder how much to tip.The average amount for a tip is 15 percent of the total check. However, in more elegant restaurants, a tip of up to 20 percent may be expected. Also, people often tip more than 15 percent if the service has been exceptionally good. Tips may be higher in some areas of the country than in others.

In a buffet-type restaurant, servers usually fill water glasses, bring beverages, and clear the table. For this service, tip 10 percent of the bill.

In a coffee shop, the smallest tip for just a beverage should be no less than 25 cents. If food is ordered, the tip should be 15 percent of the bill or at least 50 cents, whichever is greater.

In fast food restaurants, delicatessens, and cafeterias, you usually pay for the food when you order it. Tipping is not necessary unless an employee brings the food to you.

Complaints and Compliments

If you have any complaints about the food, tell the server. If nothing is done, complain to the manager. You can also complain to the manager if the service was poor.

While people do not hesitate to voice their complaints, few remember to express their appreciation for exceptional food and service. This is just as important to the management as complaints.

Section 10.2 Review

RECALL THE FACTS

1. What is the importance of using good table manners?

2. Explain two ways of solving the problem of getting food on your fork.

3. Describe two polite ways of calling your waiter or waitress to the table.

4. What is the average percentage of tip?

DISCUSS YOUR IDEAS

5. Describe some ways that knowing dining etiquette benefits you now and in the future.

APPLY YOUR LEARNING

6. With one or two classmates, write and perform a skit demonstrating at least three dining etiquette errors. Have the rest of the class identify the errors and offer suggestions to correct them.

CAREER PROFILE

Joanne Hanson
Etiquette Consultant

Current position:

"I'm a self-employed etiquette consultant who specializes in working with business people."

Responsibilities:

"Businesses hire me to conduct classes and workshops for their employees on etiquette and proper table manners. I also teach foreign table customs for those who travel."

Skills:

"You must be able to communicate with people in a tactful way, so that you can teach proper manners without offending anyone. It also helps to be friendly and self-motivated, and of course you must know proper etiquette!"

Education:

"I have a college degree in communications. I also received training from a school that specializes in basic and international etiquette."

How I got started:

"I worked for six years in the personnel department of a large firm. When the company was sold, I was laid off. My former supervisor suggested I start my own business."

Favorite part of the job:

"I put a lot of enthusiasm into my job. It's fun for me to know that I am helping others get ahead in their careers."

- In what ways might Joanne's former job have helped prepare her for this one?
- What do you think would be the most interesting part of Joanne's job? Why?

Summary

Section 10.1

Serving Family Meals: Family meals are important for strengthening family bonds. Creating a pleasant mealtime atmosphere, including the table setting, helps make meals more enjoyable. A basic cover includes a dinner plate, fork, knife, teaspoon, and a beverage glass. The items are arranged in a specific way based on tradition and convenience. Meals may be served using either family service or plate service.

Section 10.2

Mealtime Etiquette: The purpose of table manners is to make eating a pleasant experience for everyone at the table. Rules of etiquette involve common sense and consideration for others. When dining in a restaurant, follow the accepted etiquette for making reservations, ordering and paying for the meal, and leaving a tip. Be courteous to food servers and offer your compliments for good food and service.

REVIEWING FACTS

1. Give three general guidelines for creating a pleasant mealtime atmosphere. (10.1)

2. Describe how to arrange the flatware in a cover. (10.1)

3. Name one advantage and one disadvantage of family service. (10.1)

4. When dining with others, when may you begin to eat? (10.2)

5. Give five examples of acceptable finger foods. (10.2)

6. Explain the procedure for paying the bill and leaving a tip when paying with cash and by credit card. (10.2)

7. How much should you tip food servers in an elegant restaurant? A buffet-style restaurant? A coffee shop? (10.2)

8. If your food or service was poor, how should you register your complaint? (10.2)

LEARNING BY DOING

1. **Demonstration:** Design and carry out a table setting, using items available in the foods lab or brought from home. Choose a specific meal and theme. Include table linens and decorations as well as all necessary tableware items in their proper places. (10.1)

2. **Simulation:** Simulate a family meal using either family service or plate service. Include the proper arrangement of tableware, the rules of mealtime etiquette, and conversation that would contribute to a pleasant dining atmosphere. (10.1, 10.2)

3. **Demonstration:** Demonstrate rules of restaurant etiquette for one of the following situations: arriving at the restaurant and being seated; ordering and eating the meal; paying the bill and leaving the tip; registering a complaint or compliment with the manager. (10.2)

THINKING CRITICALLY

1. **Identifying cause and effect:** How might eating family meals together affect family members' attitudes toward food and nutrition? (10.1)

2. **Analyzing behavior:** Why do you think a meal is part of many job interviews? What might an employer learn about a job applicant by his or her dining etiquette? (10.2)

3. **Forming hypotheses:** How do you think some rules of mealtime etiquette developed? What might be the practical basis for some of these rules? (10.2)

4. **Recognizing stereotypes:** Suppose you and a friend are at a restaurant and see someone eating food in a manner that seems strange to you. Your friend thinks the person is either stupid or deliberately rude. Is this a fair judgment? What are some possible explanations for the person's behavior? (10.2)

MAKING DECISIONS AND SOLVING PROBLEMS

What Would You Do?

1. Your family would like to eat more meals together. However, conflicting schedules make it difficult to find a time that is convenient for everyone. (10.1)

2. Although your family often eats meals together, there is little conversation. You would like to encourage family members to be more open and sharing at mealtime. (10.1)

3. You are being considered for a job that you want very much. Your potential employer has asked you to lunch at an elegant restaurant. You are worried about making a good impression. (10.2)

4. A friend is eating dinner with your family. She has been making some etiquette mistakes that are embarrassing her and your family. You try to think of a way to put everyone at ease. (10.2)

LINKING YOUR STUDIES

1. **Social studies:** Visit a restaurant that serves ethnic cuisine to find information about table settings in other cultures. Share your findings with the class. If possible, bring the tableware to class and demonstrate its proper arrangement.(10.1)

2. **Reading and study skills:** Using library resources, gather information about tableware from different time periods and cultures. What materials were used for tableware and why? What serving and flatware pieces were used in previous ages? How and why have they changed? Prepare your information in outline form. (10.1)

3. **Social studies:** Use library resources to find information about mealtime etiquette in another culture. How are meals served? What is the proper way to eat the meal? Prepare a brief presentation for the class in which you act out a typical meal in that culture. (10.1, 10.2)

4. **Literature:** Many short stories and novels contain memorable scenes involving meals. Choose one and read the description of the meal. (Ask a librarian for suggestions if needed.) Be prepared to discuss the following in class: What details of the meal does the author give? What impression or mood is conveyed to the reader? Would you find this meal enjoyable? Why or why not? (10.1, 10.2)

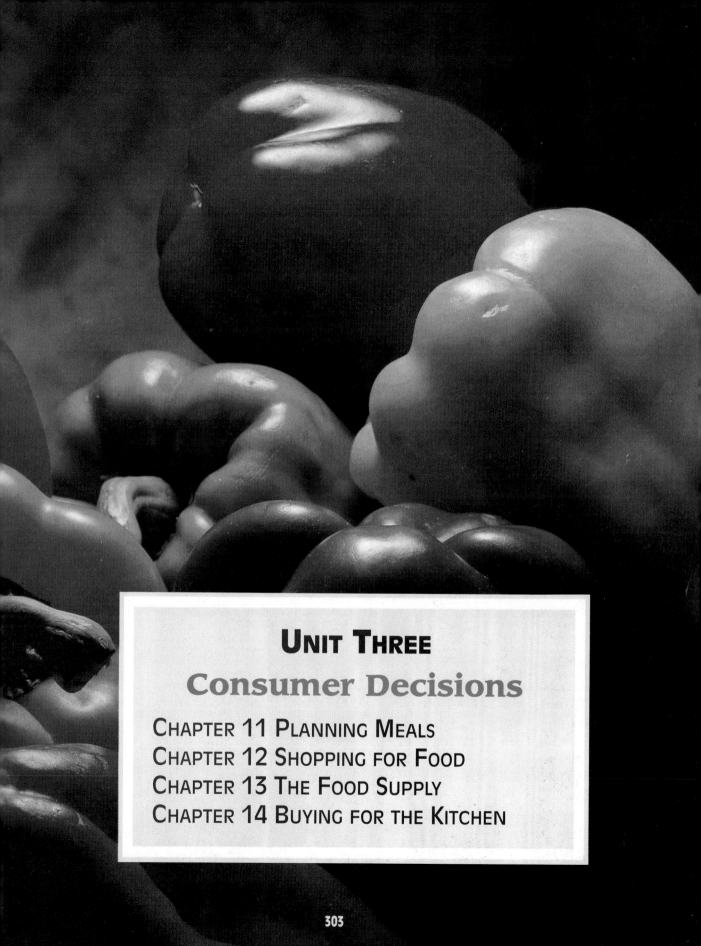

UNIT THREE
Consumer Decisions

CHAPTER 11

Planning Meals

Look for These Terms

meal appeal
texture

In earlier chapters, you have learned how to make nutritious food choices and plan a schedule for a simple recipe. Planning an entire meal draws on the same skills, plus a few others. With creativity and good management, you can plan nutritious meals that are a pleasure to prepare and a pleasure to eat.

Factors to Consider

Planning a meal involves decisions about what foods to include and how to prepare them. As you begin to plan, there are a number of points to keep in mind.

Nutrition is an important goal in meal planning. Use what you have learned about the Dietary Guidelines and Food Guide Pyramid to create healthful menus. (If you need to review these guidelines, see Chapter 3.)

Think about how the meal fits in with the day's eating pattern. You might choose different foods for the main meal of the day than you would for a light lunch or supper.

Also consider those who will be eating the meal. What are their individual nutrition needs? What foods do they like and dislike? Are there certain foods that must be avoided for medical or other reasons?

Finally, consider your resources. It's an essential step in making any decision.

With a little experience, you can plan simple, delicious, attractive meals.

Resources for Meals

Everyone works within limited resources, but you can use your creativity to make the most of what you have. Some of the resources related to meal preparation include:

❖ **Time and energy.** If there won't be much time or energy for meal preparation, plan a meal that's simple to fix. You might look for a quick and easy recipe or think about using convenience foods along with fresh ones.

❖ **Food choices and availability.** Local supermarkets offer an amazing variety of food. Still, your choices may be limited. Some foods are seasonal, especially fresh fruits. Your supermarket may not carry the items needed to prepare an unusual recipe. You might have to substitute a different ingredient or choose another recipe.

How do you use your resources when meal planning? What tradeoffs are you willing to make?

Meal planning can help you make wise use of not only personal resources, but also natural resources. For example:

• By planning meals at least a day ahead, you can remember to put frozen meat in the refrigerator to thaw. Otherwise, you might need to defrost the meat in the microwave or cook it while still frozen. Both use extra energy.

• Planning lets you make the best use of cooking appliances. Cooking several foods in the oven at one time conserves energy, as does using small appliances.

❖ **Money.** Most people have a limited amount of money to spend on food. With careful planning, however, you can stretch your food dollars. You'll find useful suggestions in Sections 11.3 and 12.3.

❖ **Your preparation skills.** If you are just learning to cook, choose simple recipes that you can prepare with confidence. As you develop your skills, you can choose more complex recipes.

❖ **Equipment.** When you find a recipe you like, consider whether you have the necessary appliances, tools, and cookware. If not, what other items might be substituted? For example, a chicken and rice one-dish meal could be cooked in a casserole dish in the oven instead of an electric skillet.

Using resources wisely often means making tradeoffs. For instance, a microwave oven lets you use one resource (equipment) to save another (time). Convenience foods also save time, but generally cost more than preparing a meal from scratch. You must decide which is more important to you, time or money.

Making Meals Appealing

Usually, meal planning begins with choosing a main course. Then you add side dishes that will complement it. As you do, consider **meal appeal**—the characteristics that make a meal appetizing and enjoyable. Nutritious foods that look, smell, and taste good have the most appeal. In addition, the different foods in the meal should work together to create a pleasing whole. To enhance meal appeal, pay attention to:

❖ **Color.** Plan meals that include a variety of colors. Colorful fruits and vegetables can help brighten any meal.

❖ **Shape and size.** Food is most appealing when the shapes and sizes vary. For example, carrots could be cut into strips and tomatoes into quarters. To vary the shape, food can also be chopped, diced, cubed, served whole, or shaped with molds and decorative cutters.

❖ **Texture.** The way food feels when you chew it, such as soft, hard, crisp, or chewy, is called **texture.** A meal should include a variety of textures. For example, with a soft main dish, such as pasta, you might serve toasted garlic bread and a crispy tossed salad.

❖ **Flavor.** Avoid using foods with similar flavors in one meal. If all the foods have a strong flavor, the combination can be unpleasant. Instead, serve both strong-flavored and mild foods for a meal. For example, which would you choose to eat with a spicy chili—corn bread or garlic bread? Why?

❖ **Temperature.** If you were planning lunch for a cold winter day, steaming hot soup would be more appealing than a chilled salad. Keep meal appeal in mind when you serve the food, too. Hot foods should be piping hot and cold foods crisply chilled. To make sure they stay that way, serve hot and cold foods on separate plates.

Here's an example of a well-planned menu. Notice the pleasing variety of nutritious, appetizing foods:

Barbecued chicken

Baked potatoes   Broccoli spears

Tossed salad

Whole-wheat rolls

Lemon sherbet

Milk   Coffee

Which of these meals looks more inviting to you? Why?

Making a Schedule for the Meal

As stated earlier, time is an important resource to consider when planning a meal. You need to think about not only how long each food will take to prepare, but how all the preparation tasks will fit together. You want to be sure you can comfortably prepare the meal in the time available and have all the foods ready to eat at the same time.

The best way to ensure successful meal preparation is to use a work plan and schedule. Section 8.5 explained the basics of putting together a work plan and schedule for a recipe. As you recall, a work plan lists all the tasks needed to prepare the food in the order they need to be done. A schedule shows what time you need to start each task.

As soon as you have a tentative menu in mind, think about the work plan and schedule. That way, if you find the menu presents a schedule problem, you can change it.

To make a work plan for an entire meal, start by listing the basic steps in preparing each dish that will be served. Estimate the preparation time or cooking time needed for each step. Also estimate the time needed for general tasks, such as getting ready to cook and setting the table.

Next, look for the best way to combine the separate tasks for each food into one work plan for the meal. To do this, you will need to think about which tasks take the most time and how you might dovetail tasks.

A basic principle is start with the food that takes the longest to prepare. Suppose you plan to bake chicken pieces in the oven for an hour. If the other foods will take less time, plan to get the chicken ready to bake first. Then you can work on other parts of the meal while the chicken is in the oven.

To cut down on last-minute tasks, consider whether any foods can safely be prepared early. For instance, a tossed salad could be assembled (except for the dressing) and then put in the refrigerator. Setting the table can also be done ahead of time, or you might plan on asking a helper to do it for you.

Safety Check

As you make your work plan, remember to allow time for:

❖ Washing utensils and work surfaces to prevent cross-contamination.
❖ Returning perishable foods to the refrigerator or freezer.
❖ Cooking or chilling food thoroughly.

TIPS for Success

Using Dovetailing in Your Work Plan

Dovetailing—fitting different tasks together smoothly—is a key to successfully preparing several foods at once. Here are some tips:

❖ Plan on no more than one complicated recipe per meal.
❖ Look for the "free time" in each recipe—the time it takes for water to boil, vegetables to drain, or foods to cook unattended, for instance. Think of ways to use this time for other tasks.
❖ Consider how to use equipment efficiently. If two different foods can be baked at the same temperature, they might share the oven. If the main dish will be prepared in the microwave, perhaps a side dish could be simmering on the range at the same time.

A tossed salad can be made ahead and refrigerated until you're ready to serve the meal. What other types of foods might you be able to prepare ahead of time?

After you've decided on the sequence of steps in your work plan, figure out the total time needed. If the meal will take too long to prepare, think about changes that would help. For example, would chicken pieces cook faster than a whole chicken? What about changing to a different cooking method?

When you're satisfied with the work plan, you can use it to make a schedule for meal preparation. Decide what time you want to serve the meal. Count backwards from that time to determine when you need to start preparation.

The examples that follow show how the planning process works for a simple breakfast. Notice how the list of tasks for each food in the meal (below) were combined into a work plan and schedule (page 310).

Task	Preparation Time	Cooking Time
General tasks:		
Get ready to cook	10 min.	
Set table	10 min.	
Oven French Toast:		
Preheat oven		15 min.
Grease baking dish	5 min.	
Mix egg batter; dip bread slices in batter; put in baking pan	10 min.	
Bake on first side		8 min.
Turn and bake on other side		8 min.
Glazed Cherry Topping:		
Open canned cherries; put in saucepan; mix cornstarch and water and add to cherries	5 min.	
Cook cherry mixture as directed in recipe		4-6 min.
Orange juice:		
Mix frozen concentrate in pitcher; refrigerate	5 min.	
Coffee:		
Prepare in coffee maker	5 min.	15 min.
Serving tasks:		
Put food in serving dishes	2 min.	
Pour beverages	2 min.	

Work Plan and Schedule

7:00	Get ready to cook
7:10	Set table
7:20	Mix juice and refrigerate
7:25	Turn on oven to preheat Grease baking dish
7:30	Mix batter; dip bread slices; put in baking dish
7:40	Put French toast in oven; set timer for 8 min. Start coffee
7:45	Start preparing cherry mixture
7:48	Turn French toast; set timer for 8 min. Continue preparing cherry mixture
7:56	Remove French toast from oven; put on platter; put cherry topping in serving dish
7:58	Pour juice and milk
8:00	Serve coffee; breakfast is ready!

Weekly Meal Planning

Most people find it helpful to plan meals for a week or more at a time. Long-range planning has several advantages. It cuts down on the time and anxiety spent in deciding what to serve every day. It means a greater variety in meals. It helps you get the most for your food dollar and avoid extra trips to the supermarket for forgotten items. It also makes food preparation more organized and efficient.

When planning a week's worth of meals, use what you have already learned about planning menus. Here are some additional suggestions:

❖ Set aside a regular time and place for meal planning.
❖ Ask family members about their plans for the week. Knowing when family members need to eat early, late, or away from home can affect the menus and recipes you choose.
❖ Check the refrigerator, freezer, and kitchen cabinets to see what you already have on hand. Think of ways to use these foods (especially perishables such as leftovers and fresh fruits and vegetables).
❖ Check newspaper ads to see what foods are on sale.
❖ Aim for balanced nutrition. Include a wide variety of nutritious foods. Check to see that the meals for each day provide enough servings from the five food groups.
❖ Plan nutritious snacks as well as meals.

A sample weekly meal plan is shown on page 311. Once you have the menus for the week, you can use them to make your shopping list. As you will learn in Chapter 12, a shopping list can help you manage money as well as time.

When you first try it, planning a week's worth of meals may seem time-consuming. However, it becomes easier with practice. Once you have planned menus for several months, you can use them over and over again. In the long run, weekly planning is well worth the initial investment of time.

SAMPLE WEEKLY MENU PLAN

	Breakfast	Lunch	Dinner	Snacks	Memos

MONDAY	Bran Cereal
	Sliced Bananas
	Rye Toast
	Milk/Coffee
		(Packed)
		Turkey Sandwich
		Carrot/Celery
		  Sticks
		Apple
		Milk (buy)
			Spaghetti and
			  Meatballs
			Tossed Salad
			Garlic Bread
			Milk/Coffee
				Fresh Fruits or
				  Vegetables
				Trail Mix
				Cranberry Juice
					Steve late for
					dinner.

TUESDAY	French Toast
	Sliced Kiwi
	Milk/Coffee
		(Packed)
		Peanut Butter-
		  Whole Wheat
		  Sandwich
		Broccoli/Carrots
		Pear
		Milk (buy)
			Beans and Rice
			Corn Tortillas
			Spinach Salad
			Milk/Coffee
			Sliced Fruit
				Fresh Fruits or
				  Vegetables
				Popcorn
				Vegetable Juice
					Everyone home
					for dinner.

WEDNESDAY	Bagels with Nonfat
	  Cream Cheese
	Orange Slices
	Milk/Coffee
		Parents-lunch out
		Kids-school lunch
			Baked Chicken
			Brown Rice
			Broccoli Spears
			Whole Wheat Rolls
			Coleslaw
			Milk/Coffee
				Fresh Fruits or
				  Vegetables
				Pretzels
					Mom late for
					dinner—picking
					up dry cleaning.

THURSDAY	Oatmeal with
	  Raisins
	Whole Wheat
	  Toast
	Orange Juice
	Milk/Coffee
		(Packed)
		Leftover Chicken
		  Sandwiches
		Carrot/Celery
		  Sticks
		Banana
		Milk (buy)
			Spicy Chili with
			  Beans
			Cornbread
			Tossed Salad
			Milk
				Popcorn
				Strawberry Frozen
				  Yogurt
					Mike's basketball
					game—eat
					early.

FRIDAY	Assorted Cereals
	Banana
	Whole Wheat Toast
	Milk/Coffee
		(Packed)
		Leftover Chili
		Red and Green
		  Pepper Sticks
		Mixed Fruit Cup
		Milk (buy)
			**Pick up take-out
			Pizza
			Tossed Salad
			Mixed Fruit Juice
				Fresh Fruit with
				  Plain Yogurt
				Bran Muffin
					Everyone's home
					—rent a movie.

SATURDAY	Scrambled Eggs
	Bacon
	Whole Wheat Toast
	Orange Juice
	Milk/Coffee
		Hearty Vegetable
		  Soup
		Corn Muffin
		Fruit
		Milk
			Grilled Burgers
			  with Buns
			Potato Salad
			Sliced Tomatoes
			Milk/Coffee
				Popcorn
				Flavored Yogurt
				Mixed Fruit Juice	

SUNDAY	Bran Muffins
	Grapefruit
	Milk/Coffee
		Baked Ham
		Sweet Potatoes
		Broccoli
		Fruit Salad
		Milk
		Angel Food Cake
			Sandwiches or
			  Leftover Pizza
			Cole Slaw
			Milk/Coffee
				Fresh Fruits or
				  Vegetables
				Rice Cakes
					Relax.
					Check homework.

Taking a few minutes to plan meal preparation is good management. Planning makes it possible to serve nutritious, appealing homemade meals.

Section 11.1 Review

RECALL THE FACTS

1. Identify six factors that affect your decisions when planning meals.

2. What is meal appeal?

3. What is the first step in making a work plan for a meal?

4. Name three benefits of planning a week's worth of meals at a time.

DISCUSS YOUR IDEAS

5. Do you think that it is necessary to make a work plan and schedule for every meal? What are the pros and cons?

6. How are energy, time, and money management related in meal planning?

APPLY YOUR LEARNING

7. Plan a basic meal for you and your family. Develop a work plan and schedule for preparing this meal.

Section 11.2
Challenges in Meal Planning

Objectives

After studying this section, you should be able to:

❖ Identify meal-planning strategies for families with busy schedules.
❖ Give suggestions for planning meals for one.
❖ Discuss ways to handle unexpected changes in mealtime plans.

Look for This Term

cooking style

Trends in lifestyles have made meal planning a challenge for many people today. Busy personal and family schedules may leave little time to shop, cook, or even eat. People living on their own sometimes find that cooking for one has its drawbacks.

People in these situations do face real challenges to meal planning. However, they don't have to give up nutrition, taste, or pleasurable meals. There are many possible solutions.

Each individual or family must choose the strategies that are right for them. It all depends on individual needs and wants, including cooking style. Your **cooking style** reflects how you feel about food preparation and how much time you're willing to spend on it. Some people want to spend as little time as possible in the kitchen. Others love to cook, though they may not have the opportunity as often as they'd like. No matter what your cooking style, you may find ideas in this section to help you meet the challenges of meal planning.

Your busy lifestyle may influence your cooking style. How do you and your family work together in preparing meals?

Busy Schedules

"There's no time to cook—but I'm tired of frozen dinners and take-out food!" Does this sound like your family? When everyone is busy with work, school, and other activities, finding time for home-prepared meals may seem difficult. With planning and ingenuity, however, you can find ways around this dilemma.

Start by holding a family conference to decide who will be responsible for different food tasks such as planning, shopping, cooking, and cleaning up. You may want to rotate these responsibilities from week to week.

Planning at least a week's worth of meals at a time, as explained in Section 11.1, can help. Keep your meal plans and shopping lists to use again. After you've planned menus for two or three months, rotate them. Here are some additional suggestions for time-saving meals:

- ❖ Start a collection of nutritious recipes that fit your busy lifestyle. File them where they are easy to find quickly.
- ❖ Get acquainted with your microwave oven. It can be used for much more than heating leftovers and convenience foods.
- ❖ Make use of one-dish meals. They're often easier to prepare than a main dish with separate side dishes.
- ❖ Look for ways to combine convenience foods with fresh foods in recipes and meals.
- ❖ Cook for the freezer. When preparing a recipe, double it and freeze the extra.
- ❖ Look for recipes with versatility. For instance, Janice has a recipe for a basic seasoned meat-and-bean mixture. Once the mixture is prepared, it can be used in a number of different recipes such as chili, burritos, and taco salad. She prepares a large amount and freezes it in recipe-size quantities to use in different ways.

When family members have varied schedules, it's not always possible for everyone to sit down to a meal together. Here are some ideas for flexible meals.

- ❖ Plan meals that can be cooked early and refrigerated or frozen with instructions on how to assemble or reheat.
- ❖ Prepare one-dish meals in a slow cooker. Family members can help themselves any time.
- ❖ Set up a breakfast bar near the refrigerator with assorted cereals, bowls, spoons, and glasses for a quick, nutritious breakfast. Keep milk, juice, and fresh fruit on one refrigerator shelf within easy reach.

You can often save time by choosing a simple one-dish meal recipe.

Meals for One

Shopping and preparing food for one person requires thought, planning, and creativity. One common problem faced by singles is simply a matter of quantity. Most recipes provide four, six, or even eight servings, and not all can be decreased easily. Small sizes of packaged foods may be hard to find or more expensive. Yet buying and preparing large quantities of food can mean the monotony of eating the same food day after day. Here are some suggestions for getting around this problem:

❖ Buy bulk foods in just the quantity needed.
❖ Share large food packages with a friend.
❖ Ask meat and produce managers for smaller packages of fresh foods, such as two pork chops instead of six.
❖ Store as many foods as possible in single-serving packages. For example, divide a pound of ground meat into four patties, wrap them separately, and freeze.

❖ Consider buying small portions of salad ingredients at the supermarket salad bar if one is available. It may be more costly, but you'll have less waste.

Some singles slip into poor eating habits because they neglect to plan for and prepare nutritious meals. Cooking and cleaning up a meal may not seem worth the effort for just one person. Here again, management skills can help. The suggestions already given for busy lifestyles can help make meal preparation easier for singles.

Another possibility is to share mealtimes with other singles. For instance, Jorge started a weekly meal club with three friends. Once a week, the group gets together at the home of one of the members. Each person brings a dish to share. They take turns preparing different parts of the meal.

Even when dining alone, make mealtime special. Setting the table attractively and having a relaxing meal can be an enjoyable end to a busy day.

Larger packages of meat may be more economical. Singles can avoid waste by dividing the meat into single-serving portions to store in the freezer.

When Plans Must Change

Even with the best plans, unexpected emergencies may arise. You may not get home in time to prepare the meal you had planned. Illness or last-minute schedule changes can also disrupt meals.

To prepare for these times, keep a small supply of "emergency" foods on hand. Stock up on nutritious, quick-to-prepare foods that can be kept on a shelf or in the freezer. Some basic items to consider are nonfat dry milk; canned chicken, tuna, and salmon; canned beans; and frozen portions of cooked dry beans, rice, and pasta. Set aside a few recipes or menus planned around your "emergency" foods. When the unexpected happens, you'll be prepared.

Section 11.2 Review

RECALL THE FACTS

1. What is meant by "cooking style"? How does it affect meal planning?

2. Identify five ways to make home-prepared meals fit a busy schedule.

3. Give three suggestions for helping singles plan and prepare meals.

DISCUSS YOUR IDEAS

4. Suppose you are living on your own. Which of the suggestions in this section might be most helpful to you? Why?

APPLY YOUR LEARNING

5. Plan an "emergency" meal for you and your family using foods that can be kept on hand. Evaluate it for nutrition and appeal.

Keeping foods such as these on hand makes it possible to serve nutritious "emergency" meals in minutes.

Objectives

After studying this section, you should be able to:

❖ Identify reasons why food spending varies from family to family.

❖ Describe how using a food budget can help control spending on food.

❖ Identify programs that offer food assistance to persons and families in need.

Look for This Term

budget

One day at the supermarket, Myra overheard a couple talking about the price of food. "Food has gotten so expensive. Many of the foods our family likes just don't fit in the budget anymore." Myra started to wonder about the food budget for her own family. "I wonder what Mom thinks about the cost of food?"

income on food simply because there is less income to work with. The challenge is in meeting nutrient needs without spending more than the budget allows. (The chart below shows how a typical family spends its income.)

Why Budget?

A **budget** is a valuable management tool for handling money. It's a way of planning your spending so you can pay for the necessities of life, save for the future, and still have some money for other activities. Budgeting involves looking at your income and deciding how much money to set aside for different uses, such as housing, food, clothing, transportation, health care, and savings.

Food expenses make up a significant portion of most family and personal budgets. For example, an average middle-income family spends about 15 percent of the family income on food. A lower-income family will spend a greater percentage of the family

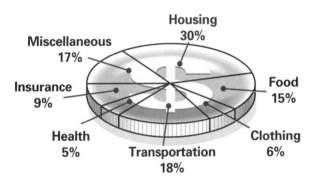

According to surveys, about 15 percent of consumer spending goes to buy food.

Factors Affecting Food Expenditures

The amount of money spent on food varies depending on your personal or family resources, goals, and priorities. Here are some factors you might consider when thinking about the amount of money you spend on food:

❖ Size of family income.
❖ Number of family members.
❖ Age of family members. (It costs the most to feed teens.)
❖ Food prices in your area at different times of year.
❖ How much food is eaten away from home.
❖ Time and skills available for food preparation.

If someone in your family enjoys cooking, you might spend less money by eating more home-prepared meals. However, if busy schedules make convenience a family priority, you may spend more money on convenience foods. Every family has different priorities, so food budgets will vary.

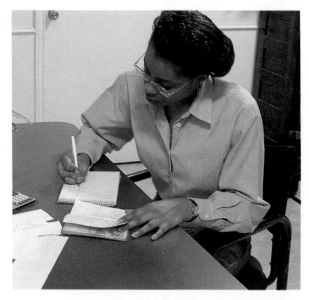

Keeping track of your food spending for a period of time helps you decide on a realistic amount for your food budget.

Using a Food Budget

Whether you spend a little or a lot, you can benefit from keeping a food budget. It can show you where you may be wasting money. It can also help you think about your food choices and decide if they are wise ones.

Keeping a Spending Record

Setting up a food budget is not difficult. To begin, analyze how much you spend on food now. Keep a record of all the food you buy for two typical weeks. Divide your record into food bought at the supermarket and food eaten out. Eating out includes takeout food, snacks, and foods bought from vending machines. Do not include non-food supplies in your list, such as paper products, even if you buy them at the supermarket.

Add up the expenses for groceries and eating out for the two weeks. Divide the total by two to get the average you spend per week.

TIPS for Success

Figuring Percentages

To find the percentage of monthly income that is spent on food:

❖ Total the amount spent on food per month.
❖ Divide by the monthly income.
❖ Multiply by 100 to convert the decimal to a percentage.

Setting a Budget Amount

Use the information from your spending record when you plan your budget. What percentage of your income are you spending on food? Are you comfortable with the amount you are currently spending? If so, plan to spend a similar amount in future weeks. If you want to plan on spending less, set an amount that's slightly lower. Don't set an amount that's unrealistically low—you'll find it hard to stick with your budget.

Sticking With Your Budget

Once you've set an amount for your food budget, make up your mind to stick with it. Continue keeping regular records of how much you spend on groceries and eating out. You will likely spend more some weeks than others, such as when you buy staples or special items. If you have any money left over, keep it as a reserve in your food budget for emergencies.

Evaluating the Food Budget

After you have used your budget for several weeks, take a look at what you've spent. On the average, were you able to stay within your budget?

If you regularly spend more than the budget allows, don't give up. Basically, you have two choices: increase the amount budgeted or reduce your spending.

Use your spending record to evaluate your food purchases. If you made only basic purchases (with no frills) and you haven't eaten out, you may not be allowing enough money for food to begin with. Take a look at your budget again. Perhaps you can cut back in some other spending category to allow more money for food.

On the other hand, you may decide that you are spending more than you would like on food. If so, planning and money management can help you reduce your spending.

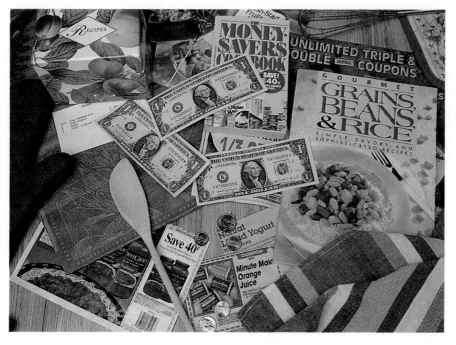

Through careful planning, many people are able to cut down on food spending. The money they save can be used to meet other goals.

Reducing Your Spending

You can save money even before you begin spending it by planning your meals with your budget in mind. Here are some helpful tips to guide you:

❖ **Look for supermarket advertisements.** Newspaper ads can tell you about special prices on nutritious foods that your family can enjoy. Compare prices among different stores.

❖ **Choose economical main dishes.** Meat is generally the most expensive part of a meal. You can save money by serving more protein foods from plant sources, such as beans and grains. If you want to include meat, fish, or poultry in meals, use a smaller amount in combination with other nutritious foods.

❖ **Trim your food budget by reducing waste.** As you plan meals, think about how much your family eats. Prepare amounts that can be safely stored and served.

❖ **Prepare simple meals at home more often.** In general, homemade meals cost less than convenience meals or food eaten out. Your family may find it worthwhile to take the extra time needed to prepare meals at home. Sharing meal preparation tasks can cut down on preparation time and bring family members closer together.

❖ **Allow some flexibility in meal planning.** Be ready to take advantage of good prices on certain items such as seasonal fresh fruits and vegetables. Fresh produce in season is often less expensive.

❖ **Choose less expensive forms of food.** Compare prices between different forms (fresh, frozen, canned, dried) to find the best buy.

There are many other ways to save money when you go shopping for food. Careful shoppers find ways of getting more for less. You will learn more about shopping practices and techniques in Chapter 12.

Many fresh fruits and vegetables cost less at certain times of the year. You can save by learning to recognize bargains.

Food Assistance Programs

Some people may not have enough money to pay for the necessities of life, including food. They may be retired, living on a low or limited income. They may be too ill to work or unable to find a job.

Help is available from a variety of sources. Federal, state, and local governments, along with many private organizations, have food assistance programs for those who cannot afford to buy food.

❖ **Food stamps.** Low-income households that qualify receive a certain number of food stamps, depending on income and family size. The stamps are used in place of money when buying food. They cannot be used for nonfood items, such as tobacco and alcohol. They also can't be used for restaurant meals, takeout foods, and pet foods.

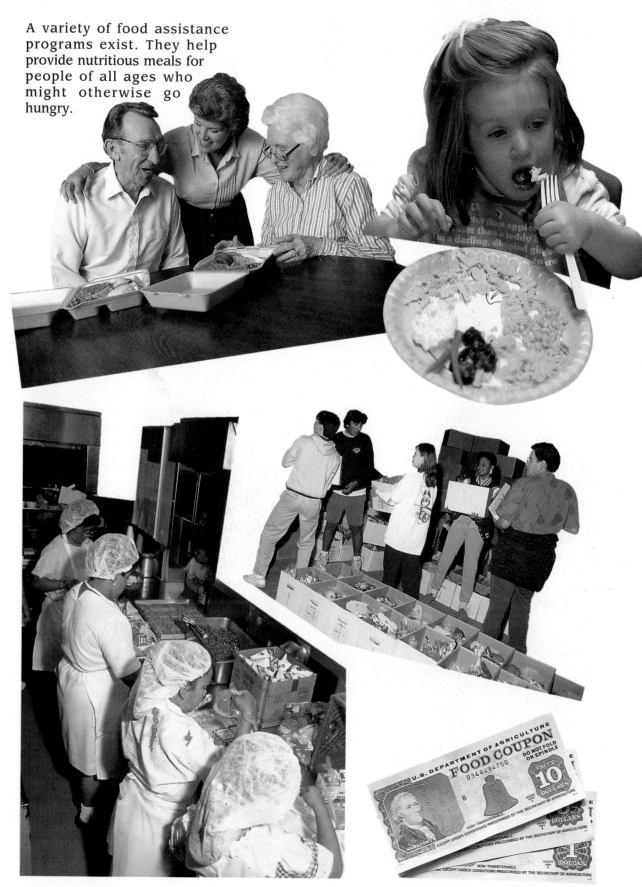

A variety of food assistance programs exist. They help provide nutritious meals for people of all ages who might otherwise go hungry.

* **National School Lunch Program**. Low-income students may qualify to receive free or reduced-price meals. Some schools also offer school breakfast programs. Nonprofit food services in elementary schools, secondary schools, and residential child care centers receive government surplus foods and some cash to provide for children in need. In some areas, the Summer Food Service Program provides breakfast and lunch during summer vacation.

* **Child and Adult Care Food Program.** Cash and food assistance are provided to child and adult care centers and family day care homes. The program operates similarly to the National School Lunch Program.

* **WIC (Women, Infants, and Children) Program.** This program works to improve the health of low-income pregnant and breast-feeding women, infants, and children up to five years of age. Supplemental foods, nutrition education, and access to health services are provided. Participants receive vouchers that can be used at retail food stores for specified nutritious foods.

* **Nutrition Program for the Elderly.** This program provides cash and food for meals served in senior citizen centers or delivered by meals-on-wheels programs.

* **Soup kitchens and food banks.** These provide food for people in need of meals or food assistance. Many are run by churches, synagogues, mosques, and temples as well as by private nonprofit organizations.

If you know of anyone in need of food assistance, let him or her know of the food programs available in your area. You can get details by calling local government agencies such as social services and public health nursing services.

What organizations in your community provide assistance for people in need?

Section 11.3 Review

RECALL THE FACTS

1. Identify four factors that affect how much families spend on food.

2. What is the benefit of keeping a food budget?

3. Give five suggestions for reducing food spending through wise meal planning.

4. Give two examples of food assistance programs for those in need.

DISCUSS YOUR IDEAS

5. Why do you think many people often spend more for food than they would like?

APPLY YOUR LEARNING

6. Imagine that you have only $4.00 to spend on a meal for a family of four. Plan the meal and figure the cost by choosing foods from newspaper ads and store flyers, or by taking a trip to the store.

CAREER PROFILE

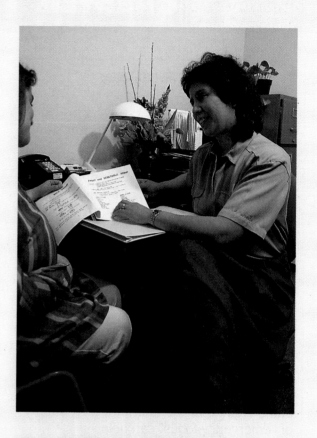

Anita Jaggard
WIC Manager

Current position:

"I manage the Women, Infants, and Children (WIC) program for an urban county health department. The program provides food assistance and education to pregnant women, nursing mothers, infants, and children."

Responsibilities:

"I am responsible for seeing that the program is run properly and meets state and federal funding guidelines."

Skills:

"For this job you must have a strong desire to help people. A background in nutrition also is required, and patience and compassion definitely help."

Education and experience:

"I have a four-year college degree in nutrition and human services. I also have a background in working for government agencies."

Work environment:

"I spend much of my time in my office, where I supervise staff and meet with clients. I also teach classes on proper nutrition for women and children."

Favorite part of the job:

"I genuinely like helping people. It's particularly satisfying to me to know I can help a baby get a better start in life by teaching the mother about proper nutrition."

- In what ways has Anita's education and work experience prepared her for this job?
- What aspects of Anita's job do you think you might enjoy? Why?

Summary

Section 11.1
Basic Meal Planning: When you plan meals, consider nutrition, eating patterns, individual needs and preferences, and your resources. Meals should appeal to all the senses. Timing a meal so that all the foods are done at once requires good management skills. Weekly meal planning can help you use your resources wisely.

Section 11.2
Challenges in Meal Planning: Today, many individuals and families face challenges to meal planning. Whether the challenge is busy schedules or preparing meals for one, there are many possible solutions. Which you choose depends on your own cooking style. On days when plans change at the last minute, a supply of "emergency foods" can help.

Section 11.3
Food Costs and Budgeting: Food expenses make up a significant portion of most family and personal budgets. The amount of money spent on food depends on the family's own situation. A spending record and food budget can help you decide if you are making wise food-buying choices. If you want to reduce your food spending, planning and money management can help. A number of food assistance programs are available to help those in need.

REVIEWING FACTS

1. How do food choices and availability affect meal planning? (11.1)

2. Name five elements of meal appeal. (11.1)

3. Give two suggestions for deciding the sequence in which to prepare the foods in a meal. (11.1)

4. Name three things you should find out before writing a weekly meal plan. (11.1)

5. Give three suggestions to help families with busy schedules plan meals. (11.2)

6. List two suggestions to help single people avoid buying larger quantities than they need. (11.2)

7. Give three examples of foods to keep on hand for meal emergencies. (11.2)

8. What is the first step in setting up a food budget? (11.3)

9. How can flexibility in meal planning help you save money? (11.3)

10. What services are provided by the WIC Program? To whom are they provided? (11.3)

LEARNING BY DOING

1. **Foods lab:** Write out a work plan and schedule for a simple meal. Use them when preparing the meal in the foods lab. Evaluate how well your schedule worked. What would you change before preparing the same meal again? (11.1)

2. **Computer lab:** If menu planning software is available, use it to help you make a weekly meal plan. Or use other software, such as a word processing program. Be sure to take into consideration the factors you read about in this chapter. (11.2)

3. **Foods lab:** Write out the menu for a meal that you might purchase from a restaurant or supermarket deli. Find or create recipes to prepare these foods yourself. Estimate the price difference between the purchased meal and the homemade meal. If possible, prepare the meal and compare it to the purchased version. (11.3)

THINKING CRITICALLY

1. **Predicting consequences:** What might be the consequences of not allowing yourself plenty of time to complete each meal preparation task? (11.1)

2. **Recognizing values:** How does a family's use of its different resources in meal planning reveal its values? (11.2)

3. **Recognizing stereotypes:** You hear a friend say that people who use food assistance programs are simply too lazy or unintelligent to get decent jobs to support themselves. How do you respond? (11.3)

MAKING DECISIONS AND SOLVING PROBLEMS

What Would You Do?

1. The main ingredients of your family's favorite chicken-rice casserole are cooked rice, diced chicken, cream soup, and shredded Swiss cheese. Usually it is served with dinner rolls and pie for dessert. You want to increase the meal's nutrition and appeal. (11.1)

2. You and your parents do most of your family's meal planning. You would like to get your seven-year-old brother and ten-year-old sister interested and involved as well. (11.2)

3. You know that one family in your neighborhood is on a very strict budget and has been skimping on food to make ends meet. You would like to help, but you don't want to offend them. (11.3)

LINKING YOUR STUDIES

1. **Writing:** Make a list of words and phrases that could be used to describe an appealing meal. Include words that describe the color, shape and size, texture, flavor, and temperature of food. Choose from your list to write a descriptive essay or poem that paints a mental picture of an appealing meal. (11.1)

2. **Social studies:** Using library resources, prepare a report on meal planning in other cultures, such as Asian and Middle Eastern. How do cultural differences (family structure, tradition, foods that are available, etc.) affect how and when meals are prepared and served? (11.2)

3. **Math:** Keep a record of your own spending for one week. Figure what percentage of your weekly spending goes toward food. Combine your findings with those of your classmates to find the average percentage for the class. (11.3)

CHAPTER 12

Shopping for Food

201

Look for These Terms

impulse buying
staples
rebate

Food shopping is one of the most important activities related to food preparation. The food you buy is the foundation for the meals you prepare. Wise food shopping can save time and money and insure nutritious meals.

Planning Where and When to Shop

Like many other activities, food shopping begins with planning.

Where to Shop

You can buy food at any one of several kinds of food stores. Each has its pluses and minuses. Your choice will depend on your own needs and wants.

❖ **Supermarkets** are large stores that sell not only food, but also many other items and services. Some have as many as 20,000 different food items. Most supermarkets offer a variety of customer services. In a large, busy supermarket, you may find it difficult to buy just a few items in a hurry.

❖ **Warehouse stores** offer basic items with few customer services. As a result, prices are lower than in most supermarkets. Most warehouse stores are large, but have a limited variety of items. Items are usually displayed in cartons rather than on shelves. Shoppers must bag their own groceries and carry them out.

❖ **Food cooperatives** are associations owned by a group of people. Members buy food in quantity and do some work, such as sorting and unloading, themselves. This reduces the cost of the food. Some cooperatives sell to the public as well as to their members.

❖ **Specialty stores** are limited to specific items, such as fish, meat, baked goods, or delicatessen foods. Prices are usually higher than in supermarkets. In return, customers may get personal attention and fast service.

❖ **Convenience stores** give fast service and are usually open early and late. Their small size makes it easy to shop quickly, but they do not carry a full line of groceries. Prices are generally higher than in supermarkets.

Health Food Store

Food Cooperative

Farmer's Market

Convenience Store

Supermarket

Specialty Store

Food can be purchased at a number of different types of stores. Choose a store that meets your needs.

- **Health food stores** may offer a wide range of food, including items seldom found elsewhere. However, the foods may be more expensive than those in other stores.
- **Farmer's markets** sell fresh fruits and vegetables. The selection depends on the area and the season. You may find locally grown foods that are fresher and less expensive than what you find in the supermarket. Some markets are closed during cold-weather months.

What should you consider when choosing a place to shop? First of all, make sure the store is clean. Check whether the food appears to be in good condition and is stored at safe temperatures. Beyond that, consider your own priorities. What kinds of food do you shop for most often? How far will you travel to shop? Are you willing to give up some services in exchange for lower prices?

If time is a priority, you may want to do most of your shopping at one store. That way you can become familiar with the location of the items and spend less time shopping.

Technology Tidbit

Some food stores offer a shop-at-home service. Customers place their orders over the telephone, and the store delivers the items for an extra charge. In some cases, orders can be placed using a fax machine. Another option is ordering groceries by computer. Using a modem (a device that allows computers to "talk" to one another over telephone lines), shoppers can connect to a computer information service. They can then enter their grocery order and make an appointment for delivery.

Some stores use special promotions to attract customers. These can range from prize giveaways to discount clubs for frequent shoppers. When choosing a place to shop, consider whether these promotions will actually save you money. You may find you can save as much or more by shopping at a store with low everyday prices.

When to Shop

Over half of American families do their shopping once a week. How often you shop depends on the storage space you have, including the size of your refrigerator-freezer.

Try not to shop when you are hungry. Studies show that people may spend 15 percent more if they do.

Stores often advertise in newspapers on Wednesdays. Special prices may start on Thursdays and be valid through the weekend. The days may vary, depending on the area. Choose a day when sale prices will be in effect.

If possible, avoid shopping when stores are crowded. The busiest times are usually early evenings and weekends. If you avoid the crowds, you can save time and make better choices.

When a supermarket is less crowded, employees may have more time to answer questions and fulfill special requests.

Making a Shopping List

A shopping list that is well thought out can save you time and money. It speeds your shopping and saves you from making special trips for forgotten items. A list also helps prevent **impulse buying**—buying items you did not plan on and don't really need. Impulse buying can ruin any food budget.

Once you get in the habit of making a shopping list, you'll find it can be done quickly and easily. The first step is to plan the meals you will serve for that shopping period. Follow the suggestions in Chapter 11. Be sure to check newspaper ads to see what's on sale—perhaps you can include those items in your meals.

After you've planned the meals, check your menus and recipes to see what foods and ingredients are needed. If you don't have them on hand, write them on your shopping list. Be sure to include the amount you'll need to buy. Increase the amount if you plan to prepare and freeze extra portions of a recipe.

Also check your supply of basic items, including:

❖ **Staples,** or items that you use on a regular basis, such as flour, honey, and nonfat dry milk.
❖ Foods you keep on hand for emergencies, such as frozen dinners.
❖ Cleaning supplies and paper products.

If you're running low on any of these items, add them to the shopping list. Many people keep a reminder list handy in the kitchen. Whenever they notice that items are running low, they jot down a reminder. Then it's easy to remember to add the items to the shopping list.

A well-organized shopping list will make it easier to find needed items when you get to the store.

Produce
Onions
Potatoes
2 butternut squash
Carrots
Kiwi
Bananas
Lettuce
Green peppers

Dairy
1 gal. skim milk
Nonfat yogurt—flavored
Margarine (stick)

Grocery aisles
3 cans tomatoes
1 can crushed pineapple
2 cans vegetable juice
1 package navy beans
1 package brown rice
Whole wheat bread
Ginger snaps
Paper towels
Dish soap

Meat
2 lb. lean ground chuck
6 lb. broiler chickens
1 lb. stew meat
4 lb. fish fillets

Frozen
3 small cans orange juice
Large bags:
    french cut green beans
    stew vegetables
    broccoli
    corn

Organizing your shopping list will help you shop more efficiently. When writing out your list, group together items that are found in the same area of the store, such as dairy foods, meats, and frozen foods. This will help you avoid making several trips to the same area.

If you shop at one store regularly, you can make out your shopping list according to the way the store is arranged. Some stores provide a map or directory sheet showing what items are found in each aisle.

Some people keep copies of a basic shopping list that has the items they usually buy arranged in order. Each week, they just circle or check off the basic items they need and add any others. Alicia has her mother's basic shopping list in her computer. When her mother finishes the week's menus, Alicia adds the needed foods to the basic list and prints out the final one.

Using Coupons

Another consideration before you go shopping is whether you will use coupons. Coupons offer you a certain amount of savings when you buy a specific product. There are two basic ways to save with coupons.

- ❖ **Cents-off coupons.** These offer a reduced price on a specific item. You present the coupon to the cashier when you make the purchase. The coupon amount is subtracted from the total price of your purchases. Some stores will double or triple the amount of some coupons.
- ❖ **Rebate coupons.** A rebate is a partial refund given after you have purchased an item. You pay the regular price at the store. Later, you fill out the rebate coupon and mail it, along with the required proof of purchase, to a specified address. The proof of purchase might be a part of the package or a cash register receipt. A refund of part of the purchase price is sent to you by mail.

You can get coupons from many places, including newspapers, magazines, product packages, and mailed advertisements. In some stores, a checkout computer automatically prints out coupons for future use based on the purchases you have made.

32-oz. size   **Limit 1 Coupon**

PINEAPPLE JUICE .... **50¢OFF**

Subject to Applicable Taxes. Valid for limited time only.

Cents-off coupons and rebate coupons can save you money if used wisely.

Whole Wheat Cereal
$1.00 Rebate Offer
Just send us three proof-of-purchase panels from 32-oz. size boxes of Whole Wheat brand cereal.

Name_____

Street_____

City_____ State_____ Zip_____

Mail To: Whole Wheat Products, Inc.
5222 Grainery Avenue, Great Plains, Nebraska 32343

Void where prohibited. Valid for a limited time only.

Coupons can give you real savings, but it depends on what foods you usually buy. Clipping and sorting coupons takes time. For some people, the savings are well worth the effort. Others may find they can save just as much by buying less expensive products without coupons.

Here are some suggestions for using coupons:

❖ Be choosy. Collect coupons only for items you usually buy or want to try. Otherwise, you'll be tempted to buy an unnecessary item just because you have a coupon.

❖ Read coupons carefully. Some are good only on a certain size of product or only in a specific store. Most coupons have a time limit. Stores cannot accept coupons after the expiration date printed on them.

❖ Organize coupons so they are easy to find and use. For example, you might sort them alphabetically or by store aisle.

❖ Go through your coupon collection regularly. Pull out ones that expire soon so you'll remember to use them. Throw away outdated ones.

Ready to Shop

Now that you've planned your shopping, you're ready to go. Remember to take along your shopping list and your coupons. If you use cloth shopping bags, or have paper or plastic bags to return to the store, bring those too.

Consider any errands you might want to do during your shopping trip. Do them before you shop for food. That way, you can bring food home immediately so it can be properly stored.

Cloth shopping bags conserve resources because they are reusable. What items should you take to the store with you?

Section 12.1 Review

RECALL THE FACTS

1. What is an advantage of shopping in a warehouse store? Name two drawbacks.

2. Give two guidelines for choosing a time of day to shop.

3. How can a shopping list help you save money?

4. List three guidelines for using coupons.

DISCUSS YOUR IDEAS

5. Is it always wrong to buy on impulse? When is it most likely to be a problem?

APPLY YOUR LEARNING

6. List three to five places to buy food in or near your community. Identify the type of store for each. Include examples of as many different types of stores as possible.

Objectives

After studying this section, you should be able to:

❖ Identify types of information found on food labels.
❖ Explain how to interpret nutrition information and product dates found on food labels.

Look for These Terms

net weight
daily values
open dating
code dating
UPC symbol

Imagine going to the supermarket and discovering that none of the packaged foods had labels. What kinds of important information would you be missing?

Food labels are valuable tools for making wise food choices. This section will help you learn what to look for on labels.

Basic Information

Certain basic information is found on all food labels. The label tells you:

❖ The type of food in the package, such as "baked beans" or "chicken pot pie."
❖ The amount of food. This may be given as a volume measurement, such as 2 liters, or a net weight. **Net weight** means the weight of the food itself, not including the package. It includes the liquid in canned food.
❖ The name and place of business of the manufacturer, packer, or distributor.
❖ A list of ingredients (unless the food has only one ingredient). They are listed in order from largest amount to smallest by weight. If you want to avoid certain ingredients, such as a food substance you are allergic to, read the ingredients list carefully.

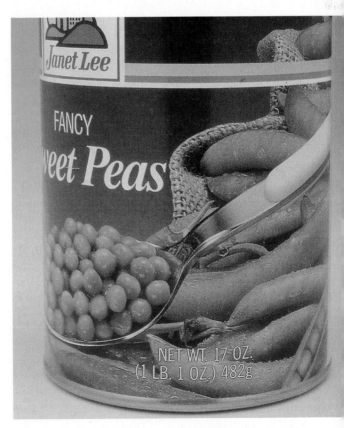

Food labels provide a variety of helpful information, such as the net weight of a package.

Nutrition Information

Grocery stores are turning into sources of greater nutrition information, thanks to food labels. In 1993, the Food and Drug Administration (FDA) issued new food label rules. As a result, food labels offer more complete, useful, and accurate nutrition information than ever before. The format makes it easy to find the information you need. That means you can use food labels to make more healthful food choices.

Nutrition Panel

Under the 1993 rules, almost all processed foods must include a "Nutrition Facts" panel similar to the one shown on this page. Here are some guidelines for understanding and using the nutrition panel.

Serving Size Information

Near the top of the panel, you will see "Serving Size" and "Servings per Container." The serving size is the amount of food customarily eaten at one time. The FDA has established standard amounts for different types of food.

The rest of the label information, including amounts of calories and nutrients, is based on the listed serving size. When reading food labels, make sure the serving size is realistic for you. If you eat a smaller or larger serving, you will need to take this into account when reading the rest of the nutrition panel. For example, if you normally eat twice as much as the serving size shown on the container, you would need to double the amounts shown for calories and nutrients.

Calorie Information

The label lists total calories per serving. It also shows the number of calories per serving from fat. You can use this information to keep track of the number of total calories and calories from fat you eat throughout the day.

Nutrition Facts

Serving Size 1/2 cup (114g)
Servings Per Container 4

Amount Per Serving

Calories 90   Calories from Fat 27

                        % Daily Value*

Total Fat 3g	**5%**
Saturated Fat 0g	**0%**
Cholesterol 0mg	**0%**
Sodium 300mg	**13%**
Total Carbohydrate 13g	**4%**
Dietary Fiber 3g	**12%**
Sugars 3g	
Protein 3g	

Vitamin A	80%	•	Vitamin C	60%
Calcium	4%	•	Iron	4%

* Percent Daily Values are based on a 2,000 calorie diet. Your daily values may be higher or lower depending on your calorie needs:

		Calories	2,000	2,500
Total Fat	Less than		65g	80g
Sat Fat	Less than		20g	25g
Cholesterol	Less than		300mg	300mg
Sodium	Less than		2,400mg	2,400mg
Total Carbohydrate			300g	375g
Fiber			25g	30g

Calories per gram:
Fat 9   •   Carbohydrates 4   •   Protein 4

The nutrition panel provides information to help you choose nutritious foods and follow a healthful eating plan.

Nutrient Amounts and Daily Values

The nutrition panel gives information about some of the nutrients that are most important to the health of today's consumers. Amounts (in grams or milligrams) are given for total fat, saturated fat, cholesterol, sodium, total carbohydrate, dietary fiber, sugars, and protein.

For most of these nutrients, the label also gives a percent of daily value. **Daily values** are reference amounts based on the recommendations of health experts. They are designed to help you put information about nutrient content into perspective.

Here's how daily values work. Look again at the sample nutrition panel on page 334. It lists 300 milligrams of sodium per serving. Unless you know health guidelines about sodium, that information may not mean anything to you. However, the "% Daily Value" column tells you that one serving of the food provides 13 percent of the daily value for sodium. In this case, the daily value is the maximum amount of sodium recommended per day—2,400 milligrams.

The daily values for cholesterol and sodium are the same for everyone. However, recommended daily amounts for fat, saturated fat, total carbohydrate, and fiber depend on how many calories you need. (Remember, calorie needs differ depending on body size, level of activity, and so on.) A chart near the bottom of the nutrition panel shows two sets of typical daily values—one for a person who needs 2,000 calories a day, the other for a person who needs 2,500 calories a day. The daily values that are right for you may be higher or lower, depending on how many calories you need.

Look again at the numbers in the "% Daily Value" column. They are based on daily values for a 2,000 calorie diet. For instance, 3 grams of fat is 5 percent of the daily value for fat—*if* you need 2,000 calories a day. If you need more than 2,000 calories, then 3 grams of fat is *less* than 5 percent of your daily value. If you need fewer than 2,000 calories a day, then 3 grams of fat is *more* than 5 percent of your daily value.

The nutrition panel also gives information about vitamins A and C, calcium, and iron. These, too, are given in percents of daily values.

Reading labels is part of being an informed consumer.

Healthy Attitudes

The nutrition panel information can be very useful to you. For instance, you can use it to keep track of how many grams of fat you eat. When shopping, you can compare nutrients in different foods. If you're looking for foods that are especially low in fat, cholesterol, sugars, or sodium, the label can help you find them easily.

For fat, saturated fat, cholesterol, and sodium, the daily value is an upper limit. In other words, the goal is to take in no more than that amount each day. For total carbohydrate, fiber, vitamin A, vitamin C, calcium, and iron, the daily value is a minimum. The goal is to take in at least that amount each day.

Label Language

You may see food packages with phrases such as "reduced calorie" or "good source of carbohydrates." These terms, and many others used to describe the level of nutrients in products, have specific meanings defined by law. Here are a few examples:

❖ **"Low in..."** The label can say "low in ..." (fat, saturated fat, cholesterol, sodium, or calories) if the food could be eaten frequently without exceeding recommended amounts. For instance, "Low in fat" means that one serving has no more than 3 grams of fat.

❖ **"Reduced..." "Less ..." or "Fewer ..."** These terms are used on products that have been nutritionally altered. The product must contain at least 25 percent less of a nutrient or calories than the regular product. For instance, "reduced fat cheddar cheese" has at least 25 percent less fat than regular cheddar cheese. Look for a specific comparison of the two products on the label.

Nutrition Facts
Serving Size 5oz (142g)
Servings Per Container 3

Amount Per Serving		
Calories 160	Calories from Fat 9	
		% Daily Value
Total Fat less than 1g		0.5%
Saturated Fat 0g		0%
Cholesterol 0mg		0%
Sodium 440mg		19%
Total Carbohydrate 32g		11%
Dietary Fiber 5g		20%
Sugars 5g		
Protein 7g		

Vitamin A	10%	•	Vitamin C	10%
Calcium	15%	•	Iron	25%

* Percent Daily Values are based on a 2,000 calorie diet. Your daily values may be higer or lower depending on your calorie needs:

		Calories	2,000	2,500
Total Fat	Less than		65g	80g
Sat Fat	Less than		20g	25g
Cholesterol	Less than		300mg	300mg
Sodium	Less than		2,400mg	2,400mg
Total Carbohydrate			300g	375g
Fiber			25g	30g

Calories per gram:
Fat 9 • Carbohydrates 4 • Protein 4

Send for:
Free copy of "Bean Basics" – 12 basic recipes using Baked Beans

Lead-free recyclable can

Ingredients: Pinto beans (soaked in water), water, tomato paste, maple syrup, applecider vinegar, salt, dehydrated onion, spices, garlic powder.

ACME FOODS
Little Town, Ca 9000

Many label claims, such as "High in Fiber," cannot be used unless the product meets specific guidelines. What other types of information are found on this can of beans?

- **"High in..."** This term means that one serving of the food provides at least 20 percent of the daily value for the specified nutrient. For instance, an orange juice label could say "high in vitamin C."
- **"Good source of..."** This means one serving of the food contains 10 to 19 percent of the daily value for a particular nutrient.

With these and other definitions, the law ensures that food labels do not use terms in ways that are misleading to consumers. Remember, if you're not sure what is meant by a term such as "low in sodium" or "reduced fat," read the nutrition panel. It will give you the specific amounts of nutrients and calories.

Two terms that have not yet been defined by the federal government are "organic" and "natural." Some states, and some associations of organic food growers, have set standards for organic foods. Foods labeled "certified organic" are guaranteed by that particular group to have been produced and handled without the use of synthetic chemicals. In addition, the food is produced on land to which prohibited chemicals have not been applied for at least three years immediately before the harvest. The term "natural," however, can mean whatever the food processor wants it to mean.

Health Claims

If foods meet certain specific requirements, they may make health claims. The claims are limited to relationships between the food or nutrient and the risk of osteoporosis, cancer, coronary heart disease, and high blood pressure.

The claims must use "may" or "might" in discussing the nutrient or food-disease relationship. They must state that other factors also play a role in that disease. For instance, the label may claim, "While many factors affect heart disease, diets low in saturated fat and cholesterol may reduce the risk of this disease."

Product Dating

Some food packages are stamped with a date. **Open dating** means the date can be understood by consumers. The exact meaning of the date varies, depending on the product and the wording.

- **Sell date.** This type of date indicates the last day the product should remain on the store shelf. It allows a reasonable amount of time for home storage and use after that date. Dairy products and cold cuts are among the foods that often carry a sell date. The package may say "Sell by (date)" or "Best if purchased by (date)."
- **"Use by" date.** Some packages say "Best if used by (date)." The product may still be safe to eat after the date has passed. However, the quality will start to go down. If a date alone appears on baked goods, such as breads and rolls, it is usually a "use by" date.

Open dating gives consumers an idea of how long a product can remain wholesome and safe. However, a package date does not guarantee quality. That depends on how the product was handled.

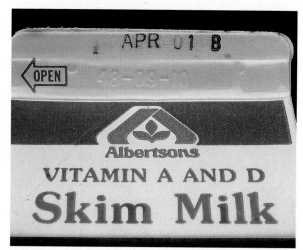

On dairy foods, package dates usually indicate the last date the product can be sold. If stored properly, the product will be safe to use for a reasonable amount of time after that date.

Code dating is used by manufacturers on products that have a long shelf life. The code is a series of numbers and letters that indicate where and when the product was packaged. If a recall is necessary, the products can be tracked down quickly and removed from the marketplace. Federal law requires code dating on most canned foods.

Other Information

You will find many other types of helpful information on food labels. For example, some products carry grades on their packaging, such as "U.S. Grade A." Grading is a system for identifying the quality of foods. You will learn more about food grades as you study specific foods in Unit Four.

Some label information is required only for certain products. For example, beverages that contain juice must list the percentages of juices.

The label often includes a picture of the product. If the product is not shown exactly as it appears in the package, the photo must be labeled "serving suggestion."

The label may give directions for using the product. If the product requires special handling, the label will give instructions, such as "Refrigerate after opening" or "Keep frozen."

Most products carry a **UPC symbol,** which stands for Universal Product Code. This is a bar code that can be read by a scanner. It gives the computer at the store's checkout counter the correct price for the product. It is also used to keep an automatic inventory of the product.

You may also find recipes, coupons and other special offers, or proof-of-purchase symbols on labels. There may be a toll-free number to call for consumer information.

Read the small print on the label or any information that has an asterisk (*). Such information may give exceptions to what is stated in larger type.

Whenever you shop, remember to read food labels carefully. They are the key to knowing what you are buying.

UPC symbols on packages help both the consumer and the food store. They speed checkout and make it easier to keep a record of the store's stock.

Section 12.2 Review

RECALL THE FACTS

1. List four types of information found on all food labels.

2. Why is it important to consider serving size when reading a nutrition panel?

3. What is the purpose of the "daily values" information on a nutrition panel?

4. What is the difference between a sell date and a "use by" date?

DISCUSS YOUR IDEAS

5. Why do you think it is difficult to define "natural" as a label term?

APPLY YOUR LEARNING

6. Bring to class a food label that includes nutrition information. Use the label information to identify the food's nutritional pluses and minuses. Do you think the label gives enough information to determine the food's healthfulness? Why or why not?

Objectives

After studying this section, you should be able to:
- Describe ways of getting the most for your money when food shopping.
- Explain how to choose and handle food to preserve nutrition, quality, and safety.
- Give guidelines for courteous shopping.

Look for These Terms

bulk foods
comparison shopping
unit price
store brands
generic

When you walk into a supermarket, you are faced with thousands of items attractively displayed to catch your eye. Consumer skills can help you find good nutrition and quality at the best price. You have already learned how to plan your shopping trip and how to read food labels. This section will show you some additional shopping skills that can help you make wise food-buying decisions.

How Stores are Organized

Supermarkets are generally organized into specific departments. Here are the basic areas of the store and what you will find in them:
- Produce (PROH-doos)—fresh fruits and vegetables.
- Fresh meat, poultry, and fish.
- Dairy—milk, yogurt, cheeses. Other refrigerated items, such as eggs, cured luncheon meats, and fresh pasta, may be found with the dairy foods or in sections of their own.
- Grocery section—shelf-stable foods in cans, jars, bottles, boxes, and packages.
- Frozen foods.

Many stores have other departments. For instance, there may be a delicatessen, salad bar, or bakery where you can buy freshly prepared foods.

Some stores have a bulk foods department. **Bulk foods** are shelf-stable foods that are sold loose and displayed in covered bins or barrels. Consumers place as much food as they want into a plastic bag, tie it, and stick a name tag on the bag so the checkout clerk can identify the contents. Foods that may be sold this way include grain products, nuts, dried fruits, dry beans and peas, snack foods, flour, sugar, herbs, and spices.

Each department of the supermarket carries specific types of foods.

Saving Money with Comparison Shopping

No matter what the size of your food budget, getting the most for your money is one of your main goals when shopping. Yet when faced with so many choices—different types of products, different brands and sizes—how can you spot the best bargain? Learning how to comparison shop can help. **Comparison shopping** means comparing the prices of similar items to see which offers the best value. Here are some guidelines to make comparison shopping easier.

Unit Prices

Which is a better buy, a 12-ounce package for $1.32 or a 16-ounce package for $1.52? To find out, you need to know the unit price of each item. The **unit price** is the price per ounce, quart, pound, or other unit.

In many stores, the unit price is shown on the shelf tab just below the item, next to the total price. This gives you a quick and easy way to compare prices. If the unit price is not shown, you can calculate it for yourself:

total price ÷ number of units = unit price

In the example given above, the smaller package costs 11 cents per ounce ($1.32 ÷ 12). The larger package costs 9.5 cents per ounce ($1.52 ÷ 16), so it is a better value.

Some stores provide the unit price on a shelf tab for the convenience of customers.

Cost Per Serving

Sometimes the unit price is not the best basis for comparison. You may have to consider the cost per serving as well. This is especially true when shopping for fresh meat, poultry, or fish.

Stan was trying to decide between fish fillets on sale at $1.80 per pound (500 g) and whole broiling chickens at 94 cents per pound. At first, the chickens seemed like a better bargain. Then Stan realized that with the chickens, he would be getting less usable meat because the package included bones, skin, and fat. Even though the unit price of the chicken was lower, he would have to buy more to feed the same number of people. He needed to know the cost per serving to make a fair comparison.

To find the cost per serving, you must first decide how many servings a given amount will provide. (The chart on this page gives general guidelines for meat, poultry, and fish.) Then divide the price for that amount by the number of servings it will provide. The result is the price for one serving.

When Stan figured the cost per serving, he made a surprising discovery. A pound of fillets gives four servings, so the cost per serving would be 45 cents ($1.80 ÷ 4). A pound of chicken with bones makes only two serv-

Servings per Pound of Meat, Poultry, and Fish

Meat

Lean, boneless	3 to 4 servings per pound
Some bone or fat	2 to 3 servings per pound
Large amount of bone or fat	1 to 2 servings per pound

Poultry

Boneless	4 servings per pound
With bones	2 servings per pound

Fish

Fillets or steaks	4 servings per pound
Dressed	2 servings per pound
Whole or drawn	1 serving per pound

ings. The cost per serving would be 47 cents ($0.94 ÷ 2). Stan chose the fish.

You can use cost per serving to help you in meal planning and budgeting. For instance, you could find the cost per serving of a homemade recipe by adding the cost of the ingredients and dividing by the recipe yield. You could find the cost per serving of a packaged food by dividing the total price by the number of servings indicated on the label.

Store Brands and Generics

You can often save money by buying store brand or generic products instead of name-brand items. **Store brands** (also called "private labels") are specially produced for the store. They are generally equal in quality to name brands, but less expensive. This is

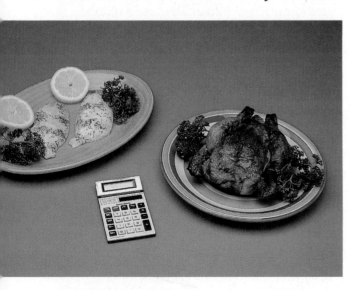

Figuring the cost per serving can help you recognize good buys.

In many stores, you have a choice between name brands and store brands or generics. What factors do you consider when deciding which to buy?

because stores do not spend as much in advertising as food manufacturers do. **Generic** items are less expensive still. Their labels are very plain and not as eye-catching as name brands, but their quality may be similar. Finding out which store brands and generics are good quality may take some experimenting, but the savings will make it worthwhile.

Other Money-Saving Ideas

Here are some additional suggestions for saving money at the supermarket.

❖ Use your shopping list, but be flexible. Look for sale items that you could substitute for the ones on your list.

❖ When using coupons, make sure you are really getting the best buy. Another brand may be less expensive, even without a coupon.

❖ Continue to check the unit price of products you buy regularly. Manufacturers sometimes keep the same price but reduce the amount in the package.

❖ Consider bulk foods. They cost less because they are not prepackaged. In addition, you can buy just the amount you want.

❖ Don't buy more food than you can store properly, or more than can be used before spoiling.

❖ Beware of strategies designed to encourage impulse buying. For instance, the most popular or profitable items are often put on shelves at eye level to catch your attention. Some foods, such as high-sugar cereals, are put on lower shelves where children can see and reach them easily. Small, high-profit items such as candy and magazines are placed next to checkout lines.

❖ Take advantage of the many customer services provided by the store. You may find a coupon rack, for example, or brochures with tips on meal planning, food budgets, and shopping.

Nutrition, Quality, and Safety

There's more to shopping than looking for low prices. To get the most value for your money, you must also pay attention to nutrition, quality, and food safety.

Remember to read labels carefully. Make sure you're getting the product and amount you want. Check the date on the package. Use the nutrition information as explained in Section 12.2. Also look for nutrition information on shelf tabs or signs.

Avoid packages that are dirty, bulging, dented, rusty, leaking, or damaged in any way. Harmful bacteria may have gotten into the food. If packages of meat, poultry, and fish leak, the juices can contaminate other foods with harmful bacteria. To be safe, put meat, poultry, and fish packages in a plastic bag so they won't drip on other foods in your cart.

When buying frozen foods, avoid packages that are frosted with ice. The frost means the package may have thawed a little and was then refrozen. This can affect food safety and quality. Choose another package.

Keep fragile items in one part of your cart. As you add heavier items, move the fragile ones up so they are always on top and won't be crushed.

What warning signs do each of these packages show? Why should you avoid buying them?

Plan your route through the store. The frozen food department should be your last stop so the food does not begin to thaw.

Courtesy When Shopping

Be considerate of other shoppers. Keep your cart on the right side of the aisle, just like driving a car on the right side of the street. Excuse yourself if you bump into someone or have to pass them. Avoid blocking the aisle or other busy areas.

Any food that is damaged by shoppers is wasted. Consumers pay for the damage in the long run—the cost is added to the price of food. Remember:

❖ Do not open containers to look at or sample the contents.

❖ Return a product to its proper place if you decide not to buy it.

❖ Handle produce gently. Do not squeeze it or throw it back into a bin.

❖ When you buy bulk foods, use the scoop or tongs provided. Do not taste the food or touch it with your hands. Close the bin or barrel when you are through.

Finishing Your Shopping

When you've selected all your items, it's time to head for the checkout line. If you choose an express line, be sure you have the right number of items. Don't choose a cash-only line if you intend to pay by check.

Many stores have computerized checkouts. The checkout clerk passes items over a scanner, which is the "eye" of the computer. The computer reads the UPC symbol on the package and searches its memory for the price. For fresh produce, the clerk usually enters a code into the computer.

Watch the display as the prices are rung up. The clerk could make a mistake or the incorrect price might be stored in the computer. If you think you are being charged incorrectly, politely ask the clerk to check it for you.

You may pay for the groceries by cash or check. If by check, you may need a store check cashing card. Some supermarkets also accept credit cards. However, using a credit card can tempt you to go over your food budget.

Take your purchases home right away and store them properly. (You may want to review the storage guidelines in Section 7.4). Put frozen foods away immediately so they don't thaw. Store refrigerated foods next, and finally shelf-stable ones. Remember to repackage bulk foods into airtight, durable containers.

If you come home and find a food you selected is spoiled or of poor quality, return it to the store as soon as possible. Do the same if you have any other problems with your purchase. Take the store receipt with you. Stores are interested in keeping their customers and will do their best to satisfy you.

Have your money or your checkbook ready when it's time to pay for your purchases.

Section 12.3 Review

RECALL THE FACTS

1. What is the formula for calculating unit price?

2. Give three examples of ways to save money when shopping.

3. Why is it important to avoid buying food in damaged containers?

4. In what way does handling food carelessly when shopping hurt other consumers?

DISCUSS YOUR IDEAS

5. Do you think some people are biased against buying store brands or generic items? If so, why? Is this bias justified?

APPLY YOUR LEARNING

6. Working in pairs, write and perform a skit demonstrating at least three poor shopping strategies. Have the rest of the class identify them.

Earth Watch

"Green shopping" means shopping with the environment in mind. You can make choices that help reduce waste and pollution and preserve natural resources. Here are some suggestions:

- Bring your own shopping bags. Consider using cloth ones, or reuse paper or plastic bags you received earlier. Some stores collect used bags for recycling.
- Choose products with the least amount of packaging.
- Buy products in containers that are recyclable in your area.

CAREER PROFILE

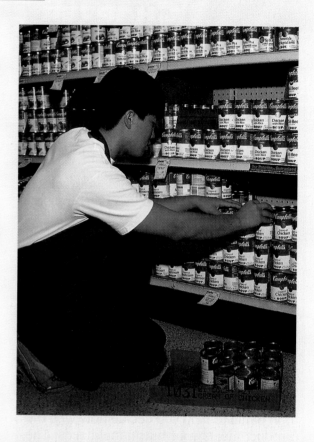

Todd Lang
Stock Clerk

Current position:

"I work part-time after school as a stock clerk for a large supermarket."

Responsibilities:

"My main responsibility is to keep the shelves stocked. I also unpack and check merchandise when it is delivered, help keep a record of items in the storeroom, and make sure shelf prices are up to date."

Why I chose this job:

"I'm interested in food retailing and took this job to learn more about how a store operates."

Skills:

"It helps to have a basic knowledge of business math in this job because it involves keeping track of inventory. Physically, you need a certain amount of strength for heavy lifting."

Favorite part of the job:

"I like being given some responsibility. It's not the most glamorous job in the world, but it's an important one. I know the store manager and the customers are all depending on me, so I try to be efficient and accurate."

Future plans:

"After I graduate from high school this spring, I'm planning to take business classes at a local community college. I'll probably also continue to work at the store. I think I'd like to become a supermarket manager or advertising director someday."

- How does Todd's positive attitude about his job affect his chances of promotion?
- What aspects of Todd's job do you think you might enjoy? Why?

Summary

Section 12.1
Before You Shop: A well-planned shopping trip begins with deciding where and when to shop. You can buy food from a number of different types of stores, which differ in items offered, services, and price. Which you choose depends on your priorities. You can save money and time by carefully choosing when to shop. Preparing a shopping list helps prevent impulse buying. Collecting coupons is another money-saving strategy.

Section 12.2
Food Labels: Food labels are valuable tools in making wise food choices. All labels must include certain basic information. Most food labels also include a nutrition panel to help you decide how well the product meets your nutritional needs. The use of certain terms and health claims on food labels is regulated by law. Open dating can help consumers judge how long products will remain safe.

Section 12.3
In the Supermarket: Shopping skills can help you find good nutrition and quality at the best price. Comparison shopping is easier if you know how to find the unit price and the price per serving. Store brand and generic items can save you money. Choose quality foods and handle them carefully to preserve their nutritional value and safety. Foods damaged or spoiled by careless handling result in higher prices for all consumers.

REVIEWING FACTS

1. How do supermarkets and specialty stores compare in terms of foods sold, services, and price? (12.1)

2. List four basic steps in making a shopping list. (12.1)

3. What is the difference between a cents-off coupon and a rebate coupon? (12.1)

4. What does "net weight" mean? (12.2)

5. On a nutrition panel, in what way is the daily value for sodium different from that for vitamin C? (12.2)

6. What does the phrase "low in fat" on a food label tell you about the specific fat content of the food? (12.2)

7. Does a package date that has not expired guarantee product quality? Explain. (12.2)

8. Describe the procedure for buying bulk foods. (12.3)

9. Why is it helpful to calculate the cost per serving when buying fresh meat, poultry, or fish? (12.3)

10. Name five signs that tell you a package of food may be unsafe. (12.3)

LEARNING BY DOING

1. **Computer lab:** Make up a basic shopping list that could be stored on the computer. Explain how you would use the list. (12.1)

2. **Foods lab:** Prepare two variations of a recipe. For the first, use the regular ingredients as called for. For the second, replace some of the ingredients with similar products labeled "light," "low-sodium," "low-fat," or "reduced cholesterol." Use the nutrition panels on the food labels to compare the nutritional value of the two versions. Also compare them for taste, texture, and appearance. (12.2)

3. **Taste test:** Compare the taste, texture, and appearance of store brand or generic items to their identical name-brand equivalents. Compare a variety of types of foods, such as canned vegetables, breakfast cereals, and frozen juices. What conclusions can you draw? (12.3)

THINKING CRITICALLY

1. **Analyzing behavior:** Why do you think people buy items on impulse? (12.1)

2. **Comparing and contrasting:** Make a chart listing at least three food stores in your community, each from a different category (convenience store, warehouse store, etc.). Describe the advantages and disadvantages of each. (12.1)

3. **Identifying ambiguous statements:** A children's breakfast cereal claims to have "less sugar per serving than one apple." What conclusion does the manufacturer want you to reach? Is it a valid one? Explain your answer. (12.2)

4. **Predicting consequences:** What might be the consequences of buying frozen food that shows signs of having been thawed and then refrozen? (12.3)

MAKING DECISIONS AND SOLVING PROBLEMS

What Would You Do?

1. You are looking over your coupons as you wait in the checkout line. You discover that two of your coupons are not good for the size of the items you are buying. It is almost your turn to check out. If you go back to exchange the items, you will have to give up your place in line. (12.1, 12.3)

2. While buying milk, you notice some cartons marked "Reduced for quick sale." You see the "sell by" date is the day after tomorrow. You wonder whether you should buy one of the reduced-price cartons. (12.2)

3. You have bought a type of cheese that you've never tried before. When you open the package, you notice it has a powerful smell. You aren't sure if this is normal or if the cheese is spoiled. (12.3)

LINKING YOUR STUDIES

1. **Social studies:** Using library resources, find information about how people in other cultures do their food shopping. How are their shopping practices similar to, and different from, those in your own culture? (12.1, 12.3)

2. **Consumer economics:** Select four regular food items and their nutritionally altered equivalents (those labeled "low-fat," "low-sodium," etc.). Compare the prices of the two different types of items. Give a short report to the class telling your findings and giving possible reasons for the price differences. (12.2, 12.3)

3. **Math:** Suppose you need chicken for a dinner party of eight people. Check the prices and selections of different forms of chicken at a supermarket. Use the "Servings Per Pound of Meat, Poultry, and Fish" chart on page 341 to determine which offers the most value. What other factors would affect your decision? (12.3)

CHAPTER 13

The Food Supply

Objectives

After studying this section, you should be able to:

❖ Trace the route food takes from farm to marketplace.
❖ Describe innovative farming, processing, and packaging techniques.
❖ Identify influences on food prices.

Look for These Terms

sustainable farming
hydroponic farming
aquaculture

Andre leaned back from his homework. Looking out the window, he could see huge snowflakes falling. He reached across the kitchen table for a favorite snack—an orange and corn chips. As Andre peeled the orange, he read on the chip bag that the chips were processed in Arkansas. He knew the orange had come from California. He chuckled to himself as he realized his food had traveled farther than he had in his entire life.

From Farm to Marketplace

North America has the advantage of an abundant food supply. A complicated network, involving the farmer, processor, distributor, and retailer, keeps shelves stocked with a wide variety of foods.

The Farmer

Most food begins its journey on farms where it is grown. Farmers in the United States and Canada produce enough food for their own countries and to sell elsewhere.

Farmers continually look for ways to produce more and better-quality food.

Farmers are continually looking for ways to produce quality food less expensively. Environmental issues have also had an impact on farming methods. Traditional methods rely on the use of chemical fertilizers and pesticides. However, there is growing concern about these chemicals contaminating the water supply and food.

One alternative is **sustainable farming.** It means cutting back on chemicals or not using them at all. Animal manure replaces chemicals as a fertilizer. Various means are used to get rid of pests and weeds without chemicals. Some farmers are turning to *integrated pest management,* which uses "good" bugs to destroy "bad" bugs. A California strawberry grower uses a huge vacuum mounted on a tractor to suck bugs from the tops of plants.

Hydroponic farming (high-druh-PAH-nik) is a method of growing plants without soil. Various materials, such as water, gravel, or sand, can be used to hold the plants. Nutrient-enriched water provides food for the plants. Look for hydroponic lettuce, cucumbers, and tomatoes in supermarkets.

Aquaculture is a method of growing fish or seafood in enclosed areas of water. Fish farms may be located near the shore and closed off with special nets, or they may be special ponds. Aquaculture is one of the fastest growing industries in the world. For example, shrimp farmers supply about 25 percent of the world shrimp market.

Because North America has so many different climate areas, different crops are grown in various places. For example, more than 60 percent of fresh vegetables used in the U.S. are grown in California, Florida, and Texas.

At harvest, the food is shipped to processors. Depending on the kind of food, it may travel by truck, train, barge, ship, or plane.

The Processor

Processing ranges from very simple to complex, depending on the food and its final use. Fresh produce, for instance, needs minimum processing. It may just be cleaned, packaged, and shipped to the marketplace.

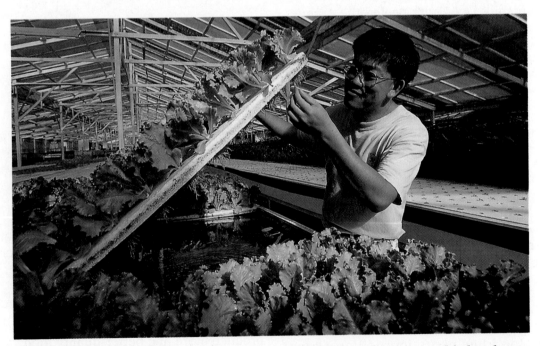

With hydroponic farming, plants can be grown indoors. Why would that be an advantage?

Foods go through various amounts and types of processing, depending on what finished product is desired.

As a part of processing, many perishable foods are preserved to prevent spoilage and lengthen their shelf life. Some commercial preservation methods include:

* **Canning.** Foods are sealed in airtight metal or glass containers and heated to destroy harmful microorganisms.
* **Freezing.** Foods are quickly frozen to slow down the growth of harmful bacteria.
* **Curing.** Ingredients such as salt, spices, sugar, sodium nitrate, and sodium nitrite are added to the food. This method is widely used in processing meats such as ham, bacon, and corned beef. It is also used to preserve fish, pickles, and some vegetables.
* **Drying.** Moisture, needed by harmful microorganisms, is removed from food. Drying is used for foods such as grains, dry beans, milk, and fruit.
* **Freeze-drying.** Food is first frozen and then dried. More flavor, texture, and nutrients are retained than with drying. Freeze-drying is used for foods such as instant coffee, dried soup mixes, strawberries, and mushrooms.
* **Controlled atmosphere storage.** Food is held in a cold area where the amounts of nitrogen, oxygen, and carbon dioxide in the atmosphere are controlled. This helps extend the shelf life of some foods, especially fruits.

Packaging Technology

Several recent developments in packaging have enabled food manufacturers and processors to expand the kinds of products they offer. Here are some examples.

- ❖ *Aseptic packages,* commonly called "juice boxes," are made of layers of plastics, paperboard, and aluminum foil. Food and the package are sterilized separately and the package is filled under sterile conditions.
- ❖ *Plastic cans and trays* are used for shelf-stable foods that can be heated in a microwave oven. Some trays also can be used in a conventional oven.
- ❖ *Modified atmosphere packaging* inserts a mixture of carbon dioxide, oxygen, and nitrogen into the package before sealing. The gas mixture slows down bacterial growth. With this method, foods such as fresh pasta, prepared salads, and cooked meats can be kept, refrigerated, up to four weeks.

Packaging methods are continually changing to keep up with new technology and the needs and wants of consumers.

The Distributor

Once food is processed and packaged, it is shipped to the distributor.

Distributors are the link between food processors and retailers (the places where you buy food). There are many different kinds of distributors, depending on the food involved. Generally, the food is shipped to large warehouses. There it is stored before being sent to the retailer.

The Retailer

From the distributor, food is shipped to the many different kinds of retailers. In Section 12.1, you read of the different kinds of stores available for shopping. Supermarkets, which offer a wide selection of products, are the most popular.

A primary job of the retailer is to present food to the consumer. In an effort to satisfy consumers, food processors and manufacturers constantly develop new products. Some stores review as many as 100 new products a week. Because shelf space is limited, they cannot accept every new product. If new products are accepted but do not sell well, they are removed.

The Ups and Downs of Food Prices

For every dollar a consumer spends on food, between 3 and 25 cents goes to the farmer. The rest of the money covers processing, packaging, advertising, and distribution. The more a food is processed, the more it will generally cost the consumer. Food prices tend to go up and down for other reasons as well.

❖ **Supply and demand.** If consumer demand for a food is greater than the supply, the price will go up. Many crops reach a peak at certain times of the year. Quantities are so large that prices are lower. Other foods, offered in limited supply, are high-priced.

❖ **Natural disasters.** Storms, earthquakes, floods, and droughts affect the price of food. A severe freeze in California or Florida can damage orange trees, reducing the supply for a whole season. In 1992, Hurricane Andrew wiped out many vegetable farms in southern Florida. Vegetable prices around the country were affected.

❖ **Consumer damage.** Careless consumers sometimes damage food when they shop. The damaged items may have to be thrown out by the store. Such losses are added to the prices consumers pay.

Natural disasters, such as floods, can destroy crops and cause food prices to go up.

Section 13.1 Review

RECALL THE FACTS

1. Name the four parts of the food supply network.

2. Identify three alternatives to traditional farming methods.

3. How and why is food cured?

4. List three factors that affect food prices.

DISCUSS YOUR IDEAS

5. What trends or concerns in society are affecting how food is produced, processed, and packaged?

APPLY YOUR LEARNING

6. Find a recipe with at least three ingredients that are processed using different commercial preservation methods. Identify the methods used.

Objectives

After studying this section, you should be able to:

❖ Explain how the government helps insure the safety of the food supply.
❖ Identify and discuss food safety issues.

Look for These Terms

additives
irradiation
biotechnology
tolerance levels
contaminants

When Ramona was choosing cucumbers at the store, she noticed they all were shiny but felt a bit sticky. She asked the produce clerk why. He explained that they were coated with a wax to prevent loss of moisture and improve their appearance. He assured her that this process met government regulations for food safety.

Safeguarding the Food Supply

Government and industry make every effort to provide a safe food supply. In doing so, they face a number of challenges. Foods must be handled properly on their way to the marketplace in order to prevent harmful microorganisms from reaching dangerous levels. **Additives**—chemicals added to food for specific reasons—must be tested and approved to be sure they will cause no harm. Questions about the safety of new food technology must be addressed. Steps must be taken to insure that harmful chemicals do not get into food accidentally.

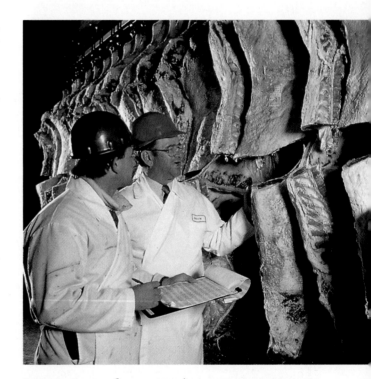

Inspectors from various government agencies work to protect the food supply.

The government usually plays a major role in monitoring the safety of a country's food supply. In the U.S., several federal agencies are responsible for food safety:

- **Food and Drug Administration** (FDA). The FDA is responsible for the general safety of food, except for meat, poultry, and eggs. It enforces laws that regulate additives, food purity, packaging, labeling, and new foods and processing methods.
- **Food Safety and Inspection Service (FSIS).** This part of the Department of Agriculture is responsible for the inspection and safety of meat, poultry, and eggs.
- **National Marine Fisheries Services.** This part of the Department of Commerce offers a voluntary inspection program to fish processors.
- **Environmental Protection Agency (EPA).** The EPA registers pesticides and sets legal limits for pesticides in food. It also regulates disposal of hazardous wastes.

What happens if tests or consumer complaints show that a food is unsafe? The FDA may first ask the manufacturer to withdraw the product voluntarily. If the manufacturer refuses, or if the situation is a life-threatening one, the FDA issues a recall. The product is removed from store shelves immediately and the public is alerted through the media. The brand name and package code numbers are announced. Consumers who have purchased any of this food are asked to return it to the store.

Food Safety Issues

Many issues related to food safety are controversial. It's important to understand the facts as well as the opinions on both sides of the issue.

Food Additives

Originally, additives were ingredients used to help preserve food or flavor it. They included basic foods such as salt and spices. As the food processing industry grew, chemicals were developed to keep foods safer or make them more appealing. By 1991, about 2,800 additives were being used. The chart on page 356 lists some common types of additives.

Hundreds of additives with a long history of use and safety are classified by the FDA as "Generally Recognized As Safe" (GRAS).

INGREDIENTS: ENRICHED FLOUR (NIACIN, REDUCED IRON, THIAMINE MONONITRATE, RIBOFLAVIN), WATER, HIGH FRUCTROSE CORN SYRUP, CONTAINS 2% OR LESS OF WHEY, SOYBEAN OIL, YEAST, SALT, CULTURED WHEY, SOY FLOUR, DOUGH CONDITIONERS (SODIUM STEAROYL LACTYLATE, AMMONIUM SULFATE, CALCIUM SULFATE, CALCIUM PEROXIDE AND/OR ASCORBIC ACID, PROTEASE), MONOCALCIUM PHOSPHATE.

Additives are used in many foods to improve the quality of the product or to lengthen shelf life.

Common Food Additives

Type of Additive	Examples
Nutritional supplements: Replace nutrients lost in processing or make food more nutritious.	• Vitamin C (often added to fruit drinks) • Vitamin D (added to milk)
Preservatives: Help extend shelf life of foods.	• BHT
Acids and alkalies: Help maintain the chemical balance in some foods. Some also help preserve food or add flavor.	• Sodium nitrite • Citric acid • Calcium propionate
Emulsifiers, stabilizers, thickeners, and texturizers: Improve the texture and "body" of foods such as baked goods.	• Vegetable gums • Modified food starch • Carrageenan
Flavoring agents: Help make foods taste more appealing.	• Natural fruit flavors • Artificial flavors • Natural and artificial sweeteners • Monosodium glutamate (MSG)
Coloring agents: Help give food a more attractive appearance.	• Caramel coloring • Artificial colors

Additives on the GRAS list can be used by food processors without further approval from the FDA. However, even these substances are undergoing additional testing to make certain they meet today's standards.

FDA approval for other additives can be a lengthy process. An additive is first tested extensively. If it proves to be safe, the FDA approves it and sets regulations for its use.

Even though additives are approved by the FDA, consumers sometimes raise questions about their safety. In some cases, the FDA undertakes a process of study and review. Consumers who are concerned about particular additives can avoid foods that contain them by reading ingredients lists carefully.

Sugar Substitutes

Sugar substitutes sweeten food, but add few or no calories. They can benefit people who must restrict the amount of sugar they eat, such as diabetics. Critics are not certain how helpful they may be for weight loss.

Artificial sweeteners currently in use include aspartame (AS-puhr-tame), acesulfame-K (ay-see-SULL-fame kay), and saccharin.

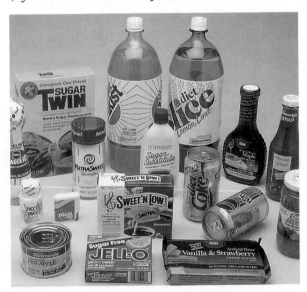

Sugar substitutes can be found in many different types of products. How many have you seen?

Sugar substitutes have sometimes proved controversial. For example, saccharin is a no-calorie artificial sweetener that was first used in the early 1900s. It was banned in 1977 after studies linked it with cancer in laboratory animals. By public demand, the rule was later changed. The new rule allowed products containing saccharin to be sold if a warning appeared on the label and in the store.

Fat Substitutes

Fat substitutes are natural or artificial substances that replace fat in processed foods such as baked goods and ice cream. They are also used in reduced-fat foods, such as low-fat cheeses.

Some natural fat substitutes are based on proteins from ingredients such as skim milk or egg whites. Others are based on carbohydrates from sources such as cornstarch and oat bran. Natural substitutes are considered safe.

Artificial fat substitutes are also being developed. Since they do not break down during digestion, they add no fat or calories to the diet. They also can be heated to high temperatures for frying. Specific FDA approval is required for artificial substitutes.

Some experts are concerned that fat substitutes will not help people learn healthy eating habits. Fat-free treats such as baked goods and frozen desserts are no substitute for more nutritious low-fat foods, such as fruits and vegetables.

Irradiation

Irradiation is the process of exposing food to gamma rays to increase its shelf life and kill harmful microorganisms. Irradiation does not make foods radioactive. It can, however, cause minor changes in flavor and texture and slight vitamin loss.

The irradiation symbol (right) identifies foods that have gone through the irradiation process (below).

Main chamber has thick concrete walls.

Food is exposed to gamma rays.

Rods of cobalt-60

Food after irradiation

Computer controls conveyor speed and amount of radiation.

Packaged food is loaded on conveyor belt.

Those in favor of irradiation cite its potential to improve food safety. It could reduce food-borne illness and eliminate the need for dangerous pesticides.

Critics of irradiation point to other concerns. They claim that irradiation produces harmful by-products that can cause cancer and birth defects. They also fear that the radioactive chemicals used in irradiation plants pose a danger to workers and the community.

The FDA approved the use of irradiation for spices years ago. It has also approved the process for fruits, vegetables, poultry, and seafood. Irradiated foods must be identified with the symbol that appears on page 357.

Biotechnology

Biotechnology, or genetic engineering, is based on a knowledge of genetics. Genes carry specific, hereditary traits from one generation to the next. Through biotechnology, scientists work to improve the characteristics of plants by modifying the genes for specific traits. Like traditional plant breeding, these new techniques are aimed at producing improved varieties. Animal biotechnology research is also underway.

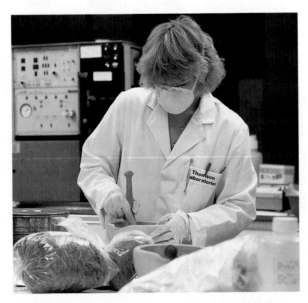

Through biotechnology, scientists work to improve the food supply.

Scientists have used biotechnology to produce a tomato that ripens but does not get soft during shipping. Other research focuses on developing more nutritious plant foods, more insect-resistant plants, and plants better able to survive harsh weather.

Some critics question the safety of foods that have been genetically altered. The FDA has developed guidelines for assessing the safety of such foods before they become available to consumers.

An even greater threat, critics feel, is loss of biodiversity. Biodiversity refers to the wide variety of plant species that occur naturally. Biotechnology could result in a food supply that is dependent on a few specifically designed plants. If so, unforeseen problems, such as a sudden change in climate, could endanger the entire food supply.

One thing is certain—biotechnology raises issues that have never had to be dealt with before. They will probably be debated for years to come.

Illegal Chemical Residues

In recent years, concern about chemical residues in food have increased. These residues are substances left behind in food after processing. Chemical residues have the potential to cause health problems, some serious.

Chemical residues can come from a variety of sources. In meat and poultry, they are usually from drugs used to improve animal health or from pesticides in animal feed. Residues gather in animal tissues. In plant foods, including grains, fruits, and vegetables, pesticides are usually the main residues.

Government agencies establish **tolerance levels**—maximum safe levels for certain chemicals in the human body. It is illegal for foods to contain more of a chemical than the tolerance level set for it. Government agencies test food samples regularly for illegal residue levels.

Pesticides serve a purpose, but they may also contribute to the problem of chemical residues and contaminants. Government agencies monitor the levels of chemicals in food and take action if problems are suspected.

Contaminants

Contaminants are substances that accidentally get into food as it moves from the farm to the table. One type of contaminant is chemical pollutants. Hazardous chemicals from industries, farms, or careless consumers can easily get into water supplies. Plants drawing on polluted water can become contaminated. Fish and animals are also affected.

Microorganisms are another source of contamination. Salmonella bacteria, for example, can contaminate eggs and chickens, causing food-borne illness. Aflatoxins (af-luh-TOCK-suns) are poisonous substances produced by certain types of mold. They can sometimes be found in grains, milk, cheese, and peanuts.

As with illegal residues, various government agencies test food for contaminants to insure the safety of the food supply.

Earth Watch

Never dump household chemicals down the drain or on the ground. The chemicals could contaminate the water and food supply. Follow package directions for proper disposal or call your local waste disposal department.

What Consumers Can Do

Contradictory reports regarding the safety of the food supply can be confusing to consumers. For reliable information, turn to a reputable consumer group concerned with food safety. Many such groups serve as watchdogs of both government and industry. Before you accept facts presented by a consumer group, however, be sure you know how it is funded. Some are merely agents for food and chemical industries.

If you are concerned about residues and contaminants, here are some suggestions.

- Wash produce with water before eating it.
- Consider buying organic fruits and vegetables—those grown without chemicals.
- Choose lean cuts of meat and remove visible fat from meat and poultry. If harmful residues are present, they are concentrated in fat and organs.

Here are some additional suggestions for promoting a safe food supply:

- ❖ Support consumer groups that reflect your views.
- ❖ Avoid buying products from companies whose policies you do not support.
- ❖ Keep track of any laws that are being introduced relating to food. Write to your representatives. Tell them how you feel about any aspect of food safety.

Consumers have the right to be informed about issues affecting food safety, such as laws about disposing of hazardous chemicals. What can consumers do to make their voices heard?

Section 13.2 Review

RECALL THE FACTS

1. Name four government agencies responsible for food safety.

2. What is a food additive? Give two examples.

3. How might irradiation improve food safety?

4. Name one benefit and one concern associated with biotechnology.

DISCUSS YOUR IDEAS

5. How large a role do you think government should play in maintaining a safe food supply?

6. What role should consumers play in food safety?

APPLY YOUR LEARNING

7. Select a food safety issue you are concerned about. Write a letter to the appropriate government agency. Identify your concern and ask for information on the government's role in this issue.

Section 13.3
The Global Food Supply

Objectives

After studying this section, you should be able to:

❖ Explain why staple foods differ around the world.
❖ Identify causes of food shortages.
❖ Discuss possible ways to remedy global food problems.

Look for These Terms

industrialized nations
developing nations
staple foods
famine
subsistence farming

Imagine 100 people eating at an unusual banquet. Fifteen of the guests sit at tables set with fine china. They eat an elegant meal prepared by world-famous chefs. Twenty-five others have a simple meal of cooked grain, flavorful sauce, and water. Meanwhile, sixty of the banquet guests sit on the floor with a meal of plain cooked grain and water.

A similar scene occurs at the annual Hunger Banquet served by an international nonprofit organization. The different groups at the banquet represent the percentage of the world's people who live in high, middle, and low income countries. The banquet dramatizes the differences in food supplies that exist around the world. How would you feel if you were one of the 60 percent who had little to eat?

The Global View

Differing economic conditions are one reason for differences in the food supply around the world. Countries are often categorized according to their economic progress. The **industrialized nations,** also called "developed" countries, are the richest. People in these countries rely on a sophisticated, organized food industry to supply them with food.

Developing nations are not yet industrialized or are just beginning to become so. People often cannot afford to buy food and must grow their own.

Many countries rank between industrial and developing countries. As they progress economically, they are able to provide more food for their people.

Staple Foods

The food supply in any region also depends on what foods can be grown there. Only certain foods can be grown in each region. They make up the basic food supply, or **staple foods.**

Geography is one factor that determines the staple foods in an area. Food is most easily grown in areas where the soil is rich, such as in valleys or on plains. In mountainous areas, farming is more difficult. Animals that can live on rocky slopes, such as goats, may be raised.

Climate is another factor. Moderate temperatures make it possible to grow a wide variety of food. In some climates, temperatures vary and food can be grown only during the warm months. Extreme temperatures, either high or low, limit the kinds of food that can be grown. Staple foods also vary depending on the amount of rainfall an area typically receives. Some crops thrive in wet areas, while others require moderate rainfall. Little, if any, food can be grown in dry areas such as deserts.

In industrialized nations, most people buy their food from supermarkets and other stores. In developing nations, most people grow their own food. The specific foods that can be grown depend on geography and climate.

In many parts of the world, grains are the main staple foods. This is especially true in developing countries. Each type of grain, such as wheat, rice, corn, and rye, is best suited to a particular climate. For example, rice grows in warm, wet climates.

Grain is also fed to animals used for food. However, animals are inefficient in converting grain to meat. With cattle, for example, it takes about 8 to 10 pounds (3.6 to 4.5 kg) of grain to produce 1 pound (500 g) of meat.

Around the world, people include a variety of protein foods in their diet. Their choices depend on availability and resources. Members of the Libinza tribe in Zaire cook and eat grubs (immature insects). Some people in South America, Africa, Australia, and Japan enjoy fried grasshoppers—a convenient, inexpensive source of protein.

What Causes Food Shortages?

It's estimated that about 700 million of the world's people don't have enough to eat. For some, it means going hungry for several days at a time. The severest form of hunger is **famine**—food shortages that continue for months or years. Many die of starvation.

The problem of world hunger is a complex one. Some of the basic causes include economics, inefficient farming methods, fuel shortages, overpopulation, wars and politics, and natural disasters. These factors may affect food production, or they may cause problems in distributing and using the food.

Economics

In many developing countries, most people have small plots of land where they must grow their own food. This is known as **subsistence farming.** They are too poor to buy food and they live on very meager meals.

Some farmers have enough land to grow crops they can sell, known as cash crops. However, when cash crops are exported, local food shortages often occur. Also, world food prices change so frequently that cash crop farmers cannot depend on a steady income.

In developing countries, good roads are rare. Villages are separated, with no modern transportation to connect them. As a result, it's difficult to distribute food. One area may have a surplus of food while a few miles away people have nothing to eat. During famine, poor distribution keeps food aid from reaching starving people.

Subsistence farming relies on simple tools powered by people or animals. Modern machinery is more efficient, but may be too expensive to be practical.

Inefficient Farming Methods

Subsistence farming makes use of ancient methods. Animals supply the power instead of gas-powered machinery. Farm tools are simple; the designs date back hundreds of years. With such tools and methods, food production is low. However, modern farming equipment and methods are costly and not always suited to the crops and conditions in developing countries.

Fuel Shortages

Most food must be cooked before eating. That means fuel for cooking is essential. In developing countries, wood is the most common cooking fuel. However, many areas are experiencing serious shortages of wood. Without fuel for cooking, people may go hungry.

Overpopulation

The world population, which now stands at more than 5.5 billion people, could increase to 6.2 billion by the year 2000. The population is increasing most quickly in developing countries. As population increases, there is a demand for more food. At the same time, more land is taken for housing, leaving less land for farming. When people clear forests to get more farmland, they destroy their source of fuel.

Will the food supply keep up with the increase in population? Some experts think not.

Wars and Politics

Wars can have a devastating effect on food supplies. Animals are killed and crops destroyed. People are forced to abandon their farms. Fighting disrupts food distribution systems.

Food is also used as a political weapon. Opposing parties may interfere with food distribution or manipulate supplies. Food aid may never reach the needy because it is stolen and sold on the black market.

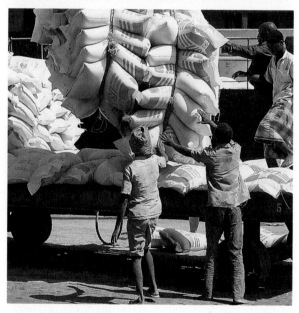

Wars can result in famine. Political problems sometimes keep food aid from reaching those who need it.

Natural Disasters

Natural disasters such as floods and earthquakes can destroy a region's food supply. Crops may be damaged and animals killed. If soil erosion occurs or roads are destroyed, food supplies can be affected for years. Prolonged drought, especially in developing countries, can result in famine and starvation.

What Can Be Done?

Many efforts are being made to increase the global food supply. The most common goal is to educate people in developing countries to help themselves. They are too poor to use modern farming machinery and methods. Therefore, programs help people work within the means available to them.

The United Nations, government agencies such as the Peace Corps, and private non-profit organizations such as the American Friends Service Committee and Oxfam International are involved in the education process. They show farmers how to improve farming methods and equipment and how to increase water supplies. In Ethiopia, for instance, food production increased just by broadening the tiny steel blade on the crude wooden plows used by farmers.

Food technology also has an important role in increasing the world's food supply. Through biotechnology (see Section 13.2), scientists hope to produce varieties of grains and other plant foods that are resistant to drought and other environmental problems.

Nutritious products are also being developed. For instance, people in some developing countries cannot easily digest milk or milk products. A nutritious product is being obtained from leaf curd made by grinding leaves into a paste. It is made into a highly nutritious crumbly cake, which is being introduced in developing countries around the world.

Solar energy offers much hope as a solution to the problem of fuel shortages. It has great potential in the tropics because the sun shines almost constantly. Several solar ovens are already being used successfully in developing countries. One type can be made inexpensively from cardboard and aluminum foil.

Solar-powered ovens like this one provide a means of cooking food in areas where fuel is scarce.

Section 13.3 Review

RECALL THE FACTS

1. What is meant by "staple foods"? Name two reasons why different regions may have different staple foods.

2. Identify five causes of food shortages.

3. What are two ways of helping to increase the global food supply?

DISCUSS YOUR IDEAS

4. Is hunger a problem in industrialized nations? Explain.

5. What problems could result from trying to introduce modern farming machinery and methods in developing nations?

APPLY YOUR LEARNING

6. In magazines and newspapers, find articles about regions that are experiencing famine. Identify the causes of the food shortage and any relief efforts being undertaken.

CAREER PROFILE

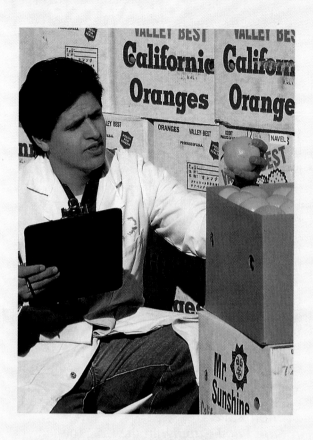

Juan Gloria
Food Safety
Inspector

Current position:

"I'm a consumer safety inspector specializing in food for the U.S. Food and Drug Administration."

Responsibilities:

"I inspect firms that deal with food, checking for violations such as inaccurate product labeling or possible contamination. I also meet with plant managers and write reports on my findings."

Skills:

"To be successful in this line of work, it helps to be detail-minded. It's also necessary to be able to communicate well with people, both orally and in writing."

Education:

"I have a college degree in agriculture and previous experience in the food industry. I also passed a required government examination to qualify for my current job."

Work environment:

"I'm on the road quite a bit, traveling from one inspection site to another. Sometimes my hours can be long and irregular. However, I enjoy traveling and meeting a lot of different people."

Favorite part of the job:

"It's satisfying to me to know that I take part in helping to make sure our country's food supply is safe to eat."

- What are the advantages and disadvantages of working irregular hours?
- What aspects of Juan's job do you think you might find interesting? Why?

Summary

Section 13.1
Where Does Food Come From?: Most food eaten in North America begins its journey to the consumer as a farm product. It is then sent to a processor, where it is prepared for its final use. Processing may include one of several preservation methods used to prevent spoilage and lengthen shelf life. The processor sends the food to the distributor, who stores it until it is purchased by the retailer. The retailer then sells the food to the consumer. The price consumers pay for the food depends on many factors, such as the amount of processing, supply and demand, natural disasters, and consumer damage.

Section 13.2
A Safe Food Supply: In the U.S., the federal government plays a major role in monitoring the safety of the nation's food supply. Various government agencies inspect food for contamination and regulate food processing, packaging, and labeling. However, some food safety issues remain controversial. As a consumer, you can affect food-related policies through your buying decisions and by staying informed, supporting consumer groups, and contacting lawmakers.

Section 13.3
The Global Food Supply: The basic food supply, or staple foods, in a region depends on geography and climate. Food shortages are caused by a number of factors that affect food production and distribution. International agencies and scientists are working to increase the food supply in developing countries.

REVIEWING FACTS

1. Give two examples of sustainable farming practices. (13.1)

2. List four commercial preservation methods. (13.1)

3. How does supply and demand affect food prices? (13.1)

4. Identify what FDA and FSIS stand for. What types of food is each agency responsible for keeping safe? (13.2)

5. What types of food additives are found on the GRAS list? (13.2)

6. What are chemical residues? How do they get into food? (13.2)

7. How does food production differ in industrialized nations and developing nations? (13.3)

8. Explain two problems associated with growing cash crops in developing countries. (13.3)

9. Explain the relationship between the growing population, food supplies, and fuel supplies. (13.3)

10. How does biotechnology play a role in increasing the world's food supply? (13.3)

LEARNING BY DOING

1. **Foods lab:** Cook or heat equal amounts of the same kind of vegetable, one fresh, the other canned or frozen. Compare the two for taste, texture, appearance, price per serving, and convenience. (13.1)

2. **Food science lab:** Conduct an experiment using two different loaves of bread—one homemade and one a commercial brand containing preservatives. Place one slice of each loaf on a plate,

uncovered. Wrap another slice from each loaf in plastic wrap. Leave the slices out at room temperature. After two, five, and seven days, compare the slices for mold and other signs of spoilage. Record your findings. What conclusions can you draw? (13.2)

3. **Foods lab:** Prepare and serve a "World Hunger Banquet," similar to the one described in this chapter, for the class. Base the menus and the percentage of students in each group on the information given in the chapter. (13.3)

THINKING CRITICALLY

1. **Recognizing alternatives:** What are some ways of obtaining food besides the network of food production and distribution described in this chapter? What are the advantages and disadvantages of each? (13.1)

2. **Determining credibility:** A respected scientist testifies before the FDA that a certain pesticide is safe and effective. Later it is discovered that the university where the scientist teaches receives large donations from the company that makes the pesticide. How does this affect your opinion of the scientist's findings? (13.2)

3. **Predicting consequences:** What might be some long-term effects of several consecutive poor growing seasons in a region? (13.3)

MAKING DECISIONS AND SOLVING PROBLEMS

What Would You Do?

1. When you go grocery shopping, you are disturbed by the amount of bruised, wilted, and otherwise damaged fruits and vegetables in the produce section. You know this drives prices up, and wonder how to solve the problem. (13.1)

2. Your friend wants to lose weight. She tells you that her weight-loss plan is based mainly on low-calorie foods and beverages made with artificial sweeteners and fat substitutes. She asks for your opinion. (13.2)

3. A friend tells you that, unless you are a scientist or politician, there is nothing you can do to increase the world's food supply. You want to prove him wrong by reducing food waste and helping the hungry in your own community. (13.3)

LINKING YOUR STUDIES

1. **Science:** Using library resources, write a brief report about one of the commercial methods used to preserve food. Describe the process and tell what foods it is usually used for. Also identify the advantages and disadvantages of this preservation method. (13.1)

2. **Social studies:** Using library sources, investigate the history of a food additive that has been in use for at least 100 years. What was the original purpose of the additive? What foods was it used in? Is it still in use today? What are its advantages and disadvantages? (13.2)

3. **Social studies:** Using library sources, locate five farming regions on at least three different continents. For each region, identify the main crops, describe the geography and climate conditions that make the crops successful, and tell what products they are used in. (13.3)

CHAPTER 14

Buying for the Kitchen

Objectives

After studying this section, you should be able to:

❖ Describe the decisions that must be made before shopping for kitchen equipment.
❖ List four important steps of shopping that can help you make wise kitchen purchases.

Look for These Terms

principal
interest
annual percentage rate
finance charge
warranty
EnergyGuide label
service contract

Shopping for a new refrigerator took Shasta's family to several different appliance stores. While her parents talked to salespeople, Shasta compared the features of the various models. The family finally chose one that fit their budget and had most of the features they wanted.

Buying equipment for a kitchen can vary from shopping for a mixing spoon to spending thousands of dollars for major appliances. No matter what you plan to buy, be a smart consumer.

Before You Shop

Before you begin, think about your reasons for buying. Decide how much you can pay and how you will pay.

Kitchen equipment can be purchased at appliance stores, department stores, discount stores, and other places. Planning your purchase makes it easier to sort out the many choices you have.

Why Buy?

Start by asking yourself why you want the item. If you are updating something you already have, will the replacement be enough of an improvement to justify its cost? If you are buying a new item, will you use it? John's mother bought an electric skillet to save energy. She uses it instead of the range for many main dishes. She also bought an electric chopper, but soon decided that she prefers using a knife. Make sure that what you plan to buy is an item you need and will use.

Paying for Your Purchase

Most people pay cash for small items. Some save so they can pay cash for larger purchases, too. However, many people use credit for at least part of the cost of major purchases.

Buying on Credit

Buying on credit means paying for a product with money you borrow from a lender. This method is more expensive than paying cash, but it allows you to use the item while you pay for it.

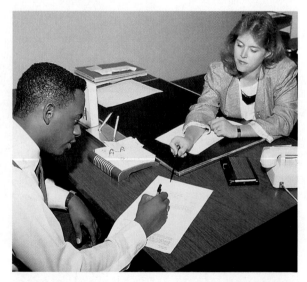

Before you sign a credit agreement, read it carefully. Ask questions about any points you don't understand.

Credit has a vocabulary of its own. The money you borrow is the **principal.** The lender charges you a fee for the loan, called **interest.** Interest is a percentage of the amount you borrow, such as 15 or 20 percent.

Interest rates vary. By law, they must be stated in terms of **annual percentage rate** (APR), which gives you the yearly cost of the loan.

When considering credit, look carefully at the **finance charge**—the total amount you will pay for borrowing. It includes interest and other costs, such as service charges and credit-related insurance premiums. Monthly payments are usually calculated by dividing the total cost (principal + finance charge) by the number of months of the loan.

For major purchases, you may have several financing options. Many stores offer financing. Loans are available from institutions such as banks and finance companies. Credit cards can also be used.

Shop for credit as carefully as for your purchase. Ask each lender for the APR and finance charges, so you can compare the cost of borrowing. The differences in total cost may surprise you.

One problem with using credit is that you may be tempted to spend more than you can afford. Failure to make monthly payments on time can cause significant problems. The item you purchased may be taken away from you, and you may find it difficult to get credit in the future. You can avoid these problems by deciding on a price range you are comfortable with and sticking to it.

Buying Guidelines

Following a few simple shopping guidelines can help you make wise choices in buying for the kitchen. Any item you plan to keep a long time should be chosen with special care.

Consider Your Needs and Wants

Begin by identifying the characteristics and features most important in the item you plan to buy. For instance, if you're buying a new appliance, write down the measurements of the space it must fit. If your new dishes must be microwave-safe, note that.

Also write down the features you would like the item to have. Rank your "wants" from most to least important. You may not be able to find an item with all these features within your price range, so it is helpful to set priorities.

Gather Information

Well-informed shoppers usually are happier with the items they purchase and often get a better price. Many sources of information are available. Look at advertisements and articles in magazines and newspapers. Some consumer magazines conduct unbiased tests to compare similar items from different manufacturers. You can also contact manufacturers directly for up-to-date information.

The reliability of the store is also important, especially for major purchases. Check with the closest Better Business Bureau to see if the business has satisfactorily settled any complaints.

Look for Consumer Safeguards

As you shop, look for consumer safeguards. Government agencies, manufacturers, and dealers have provided means for ensuring the quality of products.

Seals of Approval

Seals of approval are given by nonprofit testing agencies to show that a product meets certain standards for safety and performance.

❖ On gas appliances, look for the *American Gas Association* seal. It indicates that a gas appliance's design, performance, and reliability have been tested and certified.

❖ On electrical appliances, look for the *Underwriters Laboratories* seal. It indicates that an electrical appliance's design is reasonably free from the risk of fire, electric shock, and other hazards.

Underwriters Laboratories, Inc.

Testing agencies work to make sure that products meet standards of safety and performance. The American Gas Association has different seals for appliances (above left) and accessories (above right). The UL seal (right) is found on electrical appliances tested by Underwriters Laboratories.

Other seals of approval may be found on a product or package. Find out more about who issued the seal and what it means. Don't assume that every seal comes from a reliable product-testing agency.

Warranties

A **warranty** is a manufacturer's guarantee that a product will perform as advertised. If you have problems with the product, the manufacturer promises to replace or repair it. A warranty often has limits on the length of time it is in effect and what is covered.

EnergyGuide Labels

An **EnergyGuide label** gives information to help you estimate the energy costs of an appliance. Such labels are required for most major appliances. A dollar figure tells the average yearly energy costs for that model. You can compare the costs for different models. You can also project your own energy expenses based on the cost of gas or electricity in your area.

Service Contracts

A **service contract** is repair and maintenance insurance purchased to cover a product for a specific length of time. It is usually sold by the store that sells you the product. Service contracts often don't cover the total costs of repairs and parts. They may duplicate the protection received free with the warranty. Service contracts are often expensive and are only as good as the company that issues them.

Ten percent of the electricity used in the average home is used for refrigeration. Here are some energy-saving tips:
- Vacuum the condenser coils on the back or bottom of the refrigerator frequently.
- Keep the seals (gaskets) around the doors clean. Dirt and spills can keep them from sealing tightly.

Look for other energy-saving suggestions in the owner's manuals for your appliances.

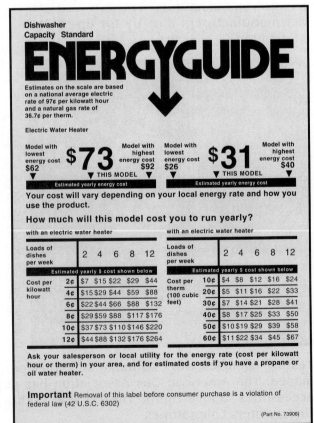

The EnergyGuide label gives the appliance's estimated energy cost. Why is this information important?

Be an Active Shopper

While shopping, don't just look. Think about how the product will perform and last.

❖ Keep written notes. Making a list of your likes and dislikes as you shop can help you make a final decision.

❖ Consider safety. Look for a seal of approval. Check carefully for safety features and potential hazards.

❖ Handle tools, cookware, and appliances. Do they seem comfortable to use and durable?

❖ Look at the warranty and owner's manual. What exactly does the warranty cover? Will the item be easy to use and care for?

❖ Compare prices. More features and better quality usually mean a higher price. Some brands are generally more expensive than others.

❖ Ask the dealer about additional costs. Are there separate charges for delivery and installation?

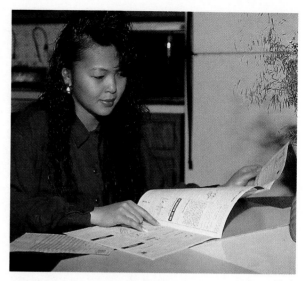

The owner's manual will tell you how to use the product safely and care for it properly. It may also provide tips to help you get the most out of your purchase.

When You Get Your Purchase Home

You will probably bring home some important documents with your purchase, especially if it's an appliance. You may have your receipt, a warranty, and an owner's manual. Keep these documents together in a safe place. If the warranty has a registration card, fill it out and send it in. Even if you don't have problems with the product, the manufacturer may need to notify you about a safety problem.

Read the owner's manual before you use the product. Then test the product to make certain it works. If it doesn't, return it to the store or call the dealer.

Section 14.1 Review

RECALL THE FACTS

1. What decisions should you make before shopping for kitchen equipment?

2. What costs should you consider when buying on credit?

3. List the four steps to follow while shopping for the kitchen.

4. What should you do when you get your purchase home?

DISCUSS YOUR IDEAS

5. What are some ways the choice of kitchen equipment affects the way a family plans and prepares meals?

APPLY YOUR LEARNING

6. Collect magazine and newspaper advertisements for different brands of a major kitchen appliance. Make a chart showing the different features.

Choosing Kitchen Equipment

Objectives

After studying this section, you should be able to:

❖ Give examples of choices available in appliances, small equipment, and tableware.
❖ Discuss features to look for when buying items for the kitchen.

Look for These Terms

self-cleaning oven
continuous cleaning oven
patterns
open stock

Just what equipment is included in a kitchen depends on budget, space, and personal preference. Equipping any kitchen is an expensive process. Most people start with the basics and add equipment over the years.

Section 14.1 gave basic strategies for making good buying decisions. In this section, you will learn more about what to look for when choosing major and small appliances, cookware, tools, and tableware.

Buying Appliances

Appliances can take up a major portion of your equipment budget. To save money, some people choose used, rather than new, appliances. Whatever the choice, it pays to shop carefully.

Underwriters Laboratories, Inc.

Both large and small appliances come in a wide range of models. Careful shopping can help you find one that meets your needs and fits your budget.

Refrigerator-Freezers

Today, there are more options than ever in refrigerator-freezers. The freezer may be placed at the top, side, or bottom. Some models defrost the freezer automatically. Manual defrost models must be emptied, thawed, and cleaned regularly.

Special features add to convenience, but also to cost. Decide which are most important and within your budget. In the refrigerator, choices include adjustable shelves, temperature- and humidity-controlled compartments for vegetables and meat, and special areas for tall or large items such as milk and soda. You will also find automatic ice makers and doors with ice and chilled water dispensers on the outside.

Consumer Checklist: Refrigerator-Freezers

✓ Fits available kitchen space. Door opens in correct direction.

✓ Size and features meet needs.

✓ Energy efficiency compares well with other models.

✓ Has separate temperature controls for refrigerator and freezer.

✓ Has good warranty and UL seal of approval.

✓ Dealer is reputable and service is available.

Some refrigerator-freezers have adjustable shelves for more efficient use of space. What are the advantages and disadvantages of other special features?

Ranges, Cooktops, and Ovens

When buying a major cooking appliance, some basic decisions must be made first. Are you looking for an all-in-one range, a countertop oven, or separate built-in cooktop and oven units? Do you want a gas or electric model? If you are replacing appliances in an existing kitchen, these decisions may already be determined. If you are remodeling or planning a new kitchen, your options are probably more open.

Cooktops

While the traditional gas burners or electric coils are still most typical, there are many new choices in cooktops. For example:

- **Sealed gas burners** have no visible flame and no pilot light. This adds safety and aids cleanup.
- **Solid cast-iron disks** are very energy efficient, though slow to heat.
- **Smooth cooktops** are easy to clean. They include induction cooktops, which use electromagnetic energy. Heat is generated when a pan made of a magnetic metal is placed on the induction cooktop.
- **Modules** are units that allow greater flexibility. A grill, griddle, or other accessory can be substituted for standard surface units.

Consumer Checklist: Ranges

- ✓ Fits available space and matches available energy source.
- ✓ Size and features meet needs.
- ✓ Design and features promote easy cleaning.
- ✓ Controls are convenient and readable.
- ✓ Good warranty coverage. Has UL or AGA seal of approval.
- ✓ Dealer is reputable and service is available.

Ovens

Shopping for an oven—as a separate unit or part of a range—begins with the choice of conventional, convection, or microwave models. You may prefer a range with two ovens—one below the cooktop and a smaller one at eye level. Another option is an oven that combines two or more cooking methods in a single unit, such as a microwave-convection oven. (As you have learned, convection ovens use a fan to circulate the heated air and reduce cooking time.)

Heat Only in Pan

Iron or Steel Pan

Ceramic Cooktop

Magnetic Field

Electric Induction Coil

An induction cooktop uses electromagnetic energy. A magnetic field forms when cookware made of iron or steel comes in contact with the cooktop. The magnetic field causes the cookware to heat up. The heat is transferred to the food inside.

Conventional and convection ovens are available with easy-clean options. A **self-cleaning oven** has a special cleaning cycle using high heat to burn off food stains. A **continuous cleaning oven** has special rough interior walls that absorb spills and spatters. Soil residue can be easily wiped off.

Microwave ovens have many feature options. Some come equipped with a turntable. Others have a rack which increases the capacity of the oven. Electronic programming can cook food automatically. Browning units improve the appearance of microwaved foods. Temperature probes allow heating to a specific temperature.

Small Appliances

The list of small appliances available seems endless, from sandwich makers to automatic bread machines. Small electric appliances can save time, money, and energy. However, having too many can cause storage problems. Before you buy, consider whether the appliance will be helpful enough to justify the cost and space required.

Many small appliances serve just one specific purpose, such as making toasted sandwiches or baking bread automatically. Consider how often you would use the appliance before you decide to purchase one.

As with any kitchen equipment, look for safety, comfort, ease of use and care, and the features you want and need. Doing research ahead of time will help you learn what to look for. For example, important safety features on a food processor include a safety lock, food pusher, and overload switch.

Buying Other Equipment

Equipment needs don't end with major and small appliances. Kitchens also need cookware and tools.

Cookware

Cookware includes the utensils used for cooking and baking. They can be made from a variety of materials, ranging from metal and glass to special plastics, depending on their intended use. Each material has advantages and disadvantages. (See Section 9.1 for more information on cookware items and materials.)

Both rangetop and oven cookware are available as sets or by the individual piece. Keep in mind that cookware is a major investment that should last for years. Consider these purchasing guidelines:

❖ Look for materials and finishes that are strong and durable enough to withstand daily use. Edges should be smooth. Handles should be heat-resistant.
❖ Choose quality. Look for seamless construction. Metal should be heavy enough to resist warping.
❖ Check the balance of each piece. Look for flat bottoms and secure lids.

Tools

As you learned in Chapters 8 and 9, dozens of different hand tools are available to make the process of preparing food faster and more convenient. Many of these tools

Cookware and kitchen tools range from everyday necessities to unusual items. What are some signs of quality to look for?

are designed for specific tasks. Others can be used for several different jobs. Follow these guidelines when selecting kitchen tools:

❖ Choose tools that fill a real need. Avoid buying ones you will seldom use.
❖ Well-designed, quality tools are easier to use and last longer. Knives, for example, should have a sturdy handle that is firmly attached to the blade. Look for at least two rivets (fasteners) through the handle and blade. Higher quality knives have three.
❖ Tools used for hot foods should be heat-resistant.
❖ Keep storage in mind. Unless you can store the tool in a convenient place, you won't use it often.

Many people in Asian cultures use chopsticks not only to eat their food, but also for food preparation. They might use a single chopstick for stirring. A person skilled in handling chopsticks can use a pair to add, remove, or turn pieces of food. Chopsticks used in preparing food are longer than those used as eating utensils.

The tools used for eating and food preparation may vary in different cultures.

Buying Tableware

Tableware refers to the items used for serving and eating food—dinnerware, flatware, glassware, and table linens. The amount, type, and formality of tableware people choose varies. Some people have one set, others two or more.

Dinnerware, flatware, and glassware are available with many different designs on them. These designs are called **patterns.** Remember, however, that patterns in tableware do not have to match. You can mix and match pieces that complement one another.

Most tableware is priced and sold by the place setting—the pieces used by one person to eat a meal. Sometimes you can buy sets for a certain number of people. Serving pieces may be sold individually or grouped as a set. Some tableware is also sold **open stock.** That means you can buy each piece separately.

Prices for tableware vary widely, depending on quality and brand name. Look for quality at a reasonable price. Fine china, crystal glassware, and silver flatware are the most formal and most expensive choices. Most people who have them use them only for special occasions. For everyday use, there are many less costly, easy-care, yet attractive options. These include stainless steel flatware, informal glassware, and dishes made of stoneware, glass-ceramic, or plastic.

Expensive, fine-quality tableware usually needs special care and handling. For everyday use, choose tableware that is durable as well as attractive.

Safety Check

Lead is a toxic metal that can travel from a container into food. It may be in tableware and cookware made from pottery. Lead crystal glassware also contains lead. Do not use lead crystal regularly or store beverages in lead crystal for more than a few hours.

Section 14.2 Review

RECALL THE FACTS

1. Give four examples of options available in ranges.

2. List three things to look for when buying cookware.

3. What does buying tableware "open stock" mean? What are two other ways tableware may be sold?

DISCUSS YOUR IDEAS

4. Suppose you and a friend decided to share an apartment while in college. How might you go about equipping a kitchen effectively on a limited budget?

APPLY YOUR LEARNING

5. Choose a large or small kitchen appliance. Using magazines or other resources, make a list of the special features that are available.

Objectives

After studying this section, you should be able to:

❖ Discuss considerations in kitchen design.
❖ Explain how the floor plan and other elements of a kitchen can affect safety and convenience.
❖ Give examples of barrier-free kitchen design.

Look for These Terms

work flow
peninsula
island
grounding
task lighting
life-span design

Understanding the basics of kitchen design and planning has several advantages. When choosing housing, you can evaluate how convenient and safe a kitchen might be. You may someday have an opportunity to plan a totally new kitchen or remodel an existing one. Even without remodeling, you can find low-cost ways to improve your kitchen. Kitchen design also offers excellent career opportunities.

Thoughtful planning can make any kitchen convenient, safe, and easy to clean. The key is a good design, not necessarily an unlimited budget or large space.

Planning a successful kitchen depends on understanding the lifestyle of those who will use it. Following well-researched principles of kitchen design helps ensure efficiency.

Considering Lifestyle

A single person who rarely cooks has different kitchen needs than a family that uses cooking as a form of entertainment. Kitchen design must take into account how the kitchen will be used. Think about:

❖ What activities, besides cooking, will take place in the kitchen?
❖ How much kitchen equipment and food must be stored?
❖ Will more than one person generally work in the kitchen at one time?
❖ What are the needs and preferences of those who will use the space?

Designing for Efficiency

An efficient kitchen starts with a well-designed floor plan. It should provide enough space for working but also keep walking to a minimum.

Any kind of work routine is known as the **work flow.** In food preparation, food is removed from storage, washed if necessary, prepared, and served. This involves moving from one area of the kitchen to another. The design of the room affects the work flow.

As you learned in Section 7.1, the sink, cooking, and cold storage centers are the three major kitchen work centers. They make up the primary path of work called the work triangle. Each work center is located at a point in the triangle. For an efficient work flow, the legs of the triangle should total between 12 and 22 feet (about 3 and 7 m).

When only one person works in the kitchen, the work triangle is an efficient arrangement. However, today's kitchens are often used by several people at one time. Additional work space and duplicate work centers help avoid traffic jams. For example, a second sink or a separate microwave oven can give space for two cooks. The kitchen may have adjacent or overlapping work triangles.

The kitchen should be arranged so that people going from one room to another do not pass through the work triangle. Such traffic can cut efficiency and may cause accidents.

A kitchen design that would work well for one family might not be right for another. It all depends on how the kitchen will be used.

The sink, cooking, and cold storage centers form the three points of the work triangle.

Basic Kitchen Plans

Kitchens are often categorized by the shape or pattern formed by the cabinets and major appliances. These common shapes have certain characteristics.

❖ *One-wall.* All three work centers are on one wall. One-wall kitchens tend to be small with limited storage and counter space.

❖ *Corridor.* The work centers are located on two parallel walls. This is efficient for one cook. However, efficiency is lessened if the corridor is a traffic lane through the kitchen.

❖ *L-shaped.* The work centers are on two connecting walls. There is no through traffic to interrupt work.

❖ *U-shaped.* This efficient plan has work centers on three connecting walls, forming a U.

These basic kitchen plans may be modified by the addition of a peninsula or an island. A **peninsula** is an extension of a kitchen counter. An **island** is a freestanding unit, often in the center of the kitchen. Both can include storage space below the countertop. They can be equipped with a sink or cooktop or may serve as an eating area.

Kitchen plans can be identified by their basic shape. What are the four basic shapes shown here?

This U-shaped kitchen has been modified by the addition of a peninsula, where the cooktop is located.

Storage and Work Space

The amount of storage and counter space in a kitchen also affects how pleasant and efficient it is to work in.

Storage

Many kitchens lack adequate storage. As you learned in Section 7.1, items should be stored near the area where they are used. For new or remodeled kitchens, the key is to identify storage needs and develop a plan to meet them. In existing kitchens, storage can often be improved inexpensively.

Kitchen cabinets include base cabinets, which rest on the floor, and wall cabinets. Base cabinets are generally 36 inches high (about 3 m) and about 24 inches (61 cm) deep. Wall cabinets, placed on the wall above the countertop, vary in size. Kitchens may also include some floor-to-ceiling cabinets for additional storage.

Many storage aids can be ordered as part of new cabinets. Some of these can also be added to existing cabinets. They include:

❖ Roll-out shelves.
❖ Cabinets with vertical dividers for cookie sheets and trays.
❖ Pull-out, ventilated baskets for produce such as potatoes and dry onions.
❖ Pop-up shelves in base cabinets for appliances such as mixers.

Cabinets can be made of a variety of materials, including wood and plastic laminate. Look for well-made units with durable hardware. Cabinets receive more use than most other furniture in a home.

Special storage aids, such as turntables and vertical tray compartments, make kitchens more efficient. The cabinet shown at left includes an area for storing small appliances behind a sliding door.

Counter Space

Each work center needs its own counter space. Additional counter areas are needed for preparing and mixing food.

Work space often can be improved in an existing kitchen without remodeling. Adding a cart, table, or island can give more work space. So can a flip-down shelf, pull-out breadboard, or an adjustable cutting board that fits over the sink.

Countertops should be durable and easy to clean. Plastic laminates are the most common. Solid surfacing is seamless and easier to clean than laminates. It is also more expensive. Ceramic tile is attractive but requires more care.

The Kitchen Environment

Cabinets and major appliances are the obvious elements of a kitchen. There are other components, however, that make up the kitchen environment. Some of these are essential but work behind the scenes. Others make the kitchen comfortable and attractive.

On plugs with three prongs, the rounded prong provides grounding for the appliance. If outlets have three holes, the home's wiring is probably grounded. However, the outlets should be tested to be certain.

Adapters are available that allow plugs with three prongs to be inserted in outlets that have only two holes.

The Electrical System

Much of the electric usage in a home comes from the kitchen. Small appliances, many large appliances, and lighting all depend on electric power.

In planning a new kitchen or remodeling an old one, providing adequate electricity should be a priority. This means having enough electric power coming into the kitchen, sufficient outlets, and a grounded electrical system.

Electricity follows the path of least resistance to the ground. If there is a problem in the wiring, **grounding** provides a path for the electrical current to travel back through the electrical system to the ground, rather than through your body.

The National Electrical Code requires that new homes have a grounding wire as part of their wiring system. Outlets with three holes usually indicate the wiring is grounded. (Check with an electrician to be certain.) These outlets accept plugs from grounded appliances, which have three prongs. For a grounded system with two-hole outlets, special adapters can be used to plug in grounded appliances.

To provide grounding, the wire or metal clip on the adapter plug must be fastened to the outlet screw. However, you should check with an electrician to be sure this will properly ground appliances. It depends on how the house wiring was installed.

Many kitchens have inadequate wiring that can cause fires. Have a qualified electrician check out the electrical system if:

❖ Lights dim when an appliance goes on.
❖ Appliances take a long time to heat.
❖ Mixers and motors slow down.
❖ The power frequently goes out due to a blown fuse or tripped circuit breaker.
❖ Extension cords are used regularly with appliances.

Lighting

Good lighting is essential in a kitchen for both comfort and safety. General lighting, usually from lighted ceiling panels or a ceiling light fixture, provides overall light. During the day, natural light from windows may also help light the room. However, **task lighting** is also needed to provide brighter, shadow-free light over specific work areas.

Task lighting is usually used over the counters, sink, and range. Spotlights or fluorescent fixtures are often mounted beneath overhead cabinets to light countertop areas. Recessed spotlights or track lights on the ceiling can also be positioned to light specific locations. Dimmer switches allow adjustment of the light to any brightness.

Ventilation

Cooking produces moisture, heat, grease, and odors. Good ventilation is needed to clear these from the kitchen. Windows, exhaust fans, and range hoods can all provide ventilation. Some cooktops and grills are available with built-in ventilation systems called downdraft systems.

Plumbing

The plumbing system brings water to the kitchen and takes away waste water. With the addition of a garbage disposal, most food waste can also be carried away.

Sinks are the most visible parts of the system. Today, there are alternatives to traditional sinks, including ones mounted without rims and others that are part of the countertop itself. In addition, there are many bowl shapes, sizes, and combinations.

Walls and Floors

Wall coverings and flooring must look good and be durable and easy to clean. There are options available at different price levels.

❖ **Wall covering** may be paint or wallpaper. Look for "scrubbable" types. Kitchen walls have to be cleaned frequently, especially areas near the sink and range.
❖ **Flooring** should be durable and easy to clean, but also comfortable to stand on. Ceramic tile has excellent durability but can be uncomfortable during long periods of standing. Vinyl or hardwood floors are resilient and easier on the feet. Choose flooring that does not have to be waxed or polished.

No-wax vinyl flooring is a popular choice for kitchens. It is durable, comfortable, and easy to care for.

Barrier-free kitchen design makes it easier for everyone to use the kitchen. What specific features make this kitchen convenient for someone in a wheelchair to use?

Designing Barrier-Free Kitchens

Food preparation is a basic activity. Kitchen designers are working to make it easier for everyone. This movement, called **life-span design,** emphasizes kitchens adaptable to people of various ages and degrees of physical ability. Life-span designs incorporate wider doorways and aisles in the kitchen to accommodate wheelchairs or walkers. Work surfaces are placed at various heights so preparation can be done sitting or standing. Open shelving and drawers, rather than closed cabinets, provide easier access.

Kitchens can also be designed, remodeled, or adapted to meet specific physical challenges. For example, cabinet knobs can be replaced with easy-to-grasp handles. Braille controls can be added to appliances. Kitchen designers, appliance manufacturers, and support organizations are good sources of information.

Section 14.3 Review

RECALL THE FACTS

1. List three questions to consider when planning the design of a kitchen.

2. Give two guidelines for evaluating the efficiency of a kitchen floor plan.

3. Name a material suitable for each of the following: countertops, kitchen wall coverings, kitchen flooring.

4. What is meant by "life-span design"? Give an example.

DISCUSS YOUR IDEAS

5. Imagine the kitchen in which you'll be preparing food 20 years from now. How will it be different from the kitchen of today?

APPLY YOUR LEARNING

6. Describe how you could reorganize one work center in your kitchen at home. List tasks done at the center and food and tools located there. Tell what should be added and what should be moved elsewhere.

CAREER PROFILE

Denise Chambers
Appliance
Salesperson

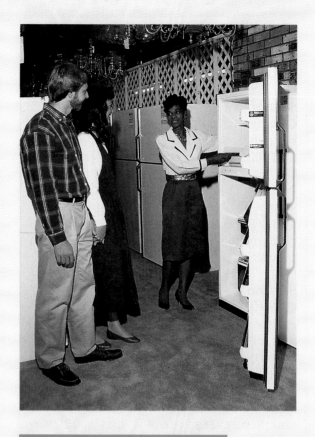

Current position:

"I sell appliances for a department store chain."

Responsibilities:

"I talk with customers to get a sense of what their needs and wants are. Then I show them the features of different appliances and answer any questions they may have."

Skills:

"To be good at this job, you must be able to put people at ease and communicate clearly. It helps to have a good memory for details so you can keep track of the features of many different appliances. Basic math skills are essential for writing out sales slips, figuring tax and discounts, and discussing payment plans."

Education:

"I have a high school diploma and previous retail experience."

Work environment:

"I work a lot of nights and weekends, and I have to be on my feet for long periods."

Favorite part of the job:

"I've always liked working with people. It's fun to be able to help them find exactly what they're looking for."

Biggest challenge:

"When a customer is rude or difficult, it can be frustrating. I just tell myself there must be some reason why this person is having a bad day. I can't take it personally or let it affect my attitude."

- Does Denise seem well suited to her job? Why or why not?
- Do you think you might enjoy working with the public as Denise does? Why or why not?

Summary

Section 14.1
Consumer Skills: Before you buy any kitchen equipment, make sure you need and will use it. If you decide to buy on credit, investigate the costs of borrowing. When you shop for equipment, consider your needs and wants. Gather information about several different products. Look for consumer safeguards and consider your purchase carefully.

Section 14.2
Choosing Kitchen Equipment: It's easier to shop for appliances, cookware, tools, and tableware when you are familiar with some of the basic options you will find. A wide range of choices is available. Some features are essential for safety and quality, while others depend on personal needs and preferences.

Section 14.3
Designing a Kitchen: An efficient kitchen is planned according to how it will be used and by whom. The floor plan should allow an uninterrupted work flow. Storage units and counter space should be adequate, accessible, and durable. Other elements, such as electricity, lighting, and plumbing, should provide safety and convenience. Life-span design helps make the kitchen easier to use for people of various ages and degrees of physical ability.

REVIEWING FACTS

1. Name one advantage and one disadvantage of buying on credit. (14.1)

2. What is an EnergyGuide label? How is it helpful when buying appliances? (14.1)

3. List four ways of being an active shopper. (14.1)

4. Identify three special features that may be found in refrigerator-freezers. (14.2)

5. List three things to consider when buying small appliances. (14.2)

6. Describe two signs of quality construction in knives. (14.2)

7. List four basic kitchen floor plans. (14.3)

8. In kitchen design, how does a peninsula differ from an island? What is the purpose of both? (14.3)

9. Why is good lighting important in a kitchen? (14.3)

10. Identify three features of good flooring. (14.3)

LEARNING BY DOING

1. **Simulation:** With one or two classmates, simulate an appliance-shopping trip. Pretend you are interested in buying one of the appliances in the foods lab. Through dialogue, identify the important points to consider when buying. Use the suggestions and checklists found in this chapter. (14.1, 14.2)

2. **Computer lab:** Using software that includes drawing tools, design an efficient kitchen floor plan. Include the location of large appliances and the dimensions of the work triangle. (14.3)

CHAPTER 14 REVIEW

THINKING CRITICALLY

1. **Determining credibility:** Sources of information about a product could include advertisements, reports in consumer magazines, and salespersons. Which do you think is most accurate and reliable? Explain your answer. (14.1)

2. **Analyzing decisions:** Which do you think is a greater problem when buying appliances: paying more for features that are seldom used, or not having needed features? Explain your answer. (14.2)

3. **Predicting consequences:** What might be the disadvantages of having work centers too close together? Too far apart? (14.3)

MAKING DECISIONS AND SOLVING PROBLEMS

What Would You Do?

1. One evening, you and your family go shopping for a microwave oven. At the first store you visit, you find a model that has most of the features you want and is on sale. You would like to compare it to other stores' selections, but the sale ends that day. (14.1)

2. You and your family are planning to buy a new refrigerator. The list of special features that family members would like is long and beyond your budget. You are having trouble reaching an agreement about which features are most important. (14.1, 14.2)

3. A new student in your foods lab group uses a wheelchair. The appliances, storage areas, and work space are sometimes difficult for him to use. Your teacher has asked you to suggest long-range and short-range solutions to the problem. (14.3)

LINKING YOUR STUDIES

1. **Math:** Compare the EnergyGuide labels on three different models of an appliance. Calculate the cost of using each one for one week, one month, and one year. Determine the difference in energy costs and rank the appliances from least to most expensive to use. (14.1)

2. **Social studies:** Choose one major appliance and research its development over time. How have the available options changed? What technological advances and social trends have made these changes in features possible and desirable? (14.2)

3. **Fine arts:** Plan and sketch an attractive, efficient kitchen design for a small apartment. Point out the features that make the kitchen efficient (either on the drawing or in a separate written description). Use colored pencils, paint chips, or wallpaper samples to show the color scheme. (14.3)

4. **Math:** Measure the distances between work centers in three different kitchens. Compare the results. Which kitchen would be most efficient for preparing food by one person? Two or more people at once? (14.3)

Unit Four

Foods for Meals and Snacks

CHAPTER 15

Convenience Foods

Objectives

After studying this section, you should be able to:

❖ Identify different types of convenience foods and their uses.

❖ Discuss the pros and cons of convenience foods.

Look for These Terms

analogues
formed product

What does the word "convenience" mean to you when it comes to food? Joanne thinks of convenience foods as those that are "easy to cook—no mess—no clean up." Ricco thinks of packaged mixes that save time. Chantel uses the term to describe any ready-to-eat foods, whether she buys them in a supermarket or from a vending machine.

Convenience Food Choices

In general, a convenience food is one that has been commercially processed to make it more convenient to store or use. Some convenience foods have been around for such a long time that they have become staples in the American food supply. Today you might not think of baked, sliced breads or bottled salad dressings as convenience foods. Yet when they first appeared, these products were time-saving innovations.

Many varieties of convenience foods are available. Besides those shown here, what other types can you think of?

Convenience foods include items that have been processed for a longer shelf life. For example, nonfat dry milk can be stored without refrigeration and kept for a longer time than fluid milk.

Another purpose of convenience foods is to reduce meal preparation time. Food that is partially prepared when purchased can save time in the kitchen. For example, you can buy cheese that is already shredded and vegetables that are already cleaned and cut up. Some foods are combined and packaged for specific uses, such as a mixture of frozen stew vegetables. Dry mixes are available for everything from macaroni and cheese to salad dressing to baked goods. Often you need only add one or two ingredients and complete a few simple steps to prepare the food.

Of course, convenience can go even further. You can buy snacks, main dishes, side dishes, desserts, and even complete meals that are already prepared. Some need only be thawed or heated, while others are ready to eat.

You can use granules of textured vegetable protein as a meat extender. Just mix the granules with ground meat or poultry for good nutrition at a lower cost. Egg substitutes can be scrambled or used in many recipes.

Manufactured Foods

As you have seen, processing can result in products that are more convenient. In addition, processing can result in manufactured foods—products developed to serve as substitutes for other foods. Many manufactured foods have been developed to meet special nutritional needs or to provide low-cost alternatives. There are several types of manufactured foods.

Analogues (AN-uh-logs) are foods made from a vegetable protein and processed to resemble animal foods. Textured vegetable protein, also known as TVP, is one of the most widely used analogues. When flavored and processed, it can be substituted for meat and poultry in foods such as meatless burgers, pot pies, and hot dogs. These products are generally low in fat and cholesterol, although they may be high in sodium. TVP can also be purchased as granules so you can make your own meatless main dishes.

Egg substitutes are another example of a manufactured food. They are usually made from egg whites with other ingredients added. Because they have no yolks, they have little or no saturated fat and cholesterol. They are usually sold in the freezer or refrigerator sections of the supermarkets. You can also buy ready-to-cook and ready-to-eat foods made with egg substitutes, such as baked goods.

A **formed product** is made from a less expensive food and substituted for a more expensive one. For example, surimi (soo-REE-mee) is made from white fish that is processed, flavored, and shaped to resemble expensive shellfish such as crab or lobster. The prices of imitation foods are lower than the prices of foods they replace. Such foods must be labeled "imitation" and can't be called by the name of the food they replace.

Sometimes manufactured foods are substituted for more expensive ones in convenience products. For example, "blueberry waffles" may not contain real blueberries. Instead, blueberry "buds" may be used which are made of sugar, oil, artificial flavor, salt, plus dyes and other additives.

Formed foods, such as products made with surimi, can be a good value. They are less expensive than the foods they replace.

The Pros and Cons of Convenience Foods

Every day, about 30 new convenience foods appear in the marketplace. The demand for new and more convenience foods emphasizes the important role they play in consumer food choices.

Most consumers are aware of the advantages of convenience foods. They cut down on the amount of preparation needed, saving time and energy. Because they need less preparation, less work space and equipment may be required. Many substitutes help people who are on special diets.

Although there are many advantages, there are also some disadvantages of convenience foods. They include cost, nutrition, and meal appeal.

Cost

Convenience is costly. Every additional step in processing adds to the price of the food. For example, at one supermarket, ready-to-cook meat loaf costs over twice as much as regular ground beef. Check the cost per serving of whole chicken versus cut-up chicken pieces. Will you save money if you cut up the chicken yourself?

Not all convenience forms have great price contrasts. To be certain, compare prices of different forms before buying.

Nutrition

Every step in processing usually destroys some nutrients. Heat, for example, destroys vitamin C. When grains are processed, much of the fiber and some of the nutrients are lost.

Frozen plain vegetables tend to lose the fewest nutrients during processing. In addition, no sodium, sugar, or fat is added to them.

Many convenience foods tend to be high in sodium, sugar, and fat. Even simple canned foods like vegetables usually have some salt added. Many fruits are canned in sugar syrups. Ready-to-cook and ready-to-eat foods often contain high amounts of sodium and fat.

Because the emphasis is now on good nutrition, low-sodium and low-fat convenience foods are becoming more common. Even so, the amounts of sodium and fat may still be above those recommended for good health. With careful shopping, you can buy nutritious convenience foods.

Food processing companies are making more nutritious convenience foods available, such as premixed salad ingredients.

Often, nutrients are added to convenience foods to increase the nutritional quality. Keep in mind that, even though many nutrients have been identified by scientists, there are probably others that are still unknown. When nutrients are added to food, only those that are known can be added. If you rely on convenience foods with nutrients added for good nutrition, you may be missing out on important nutrients that are present only in fresh foods.

Meal Appeal

Processing affects the flavor, color, and texture of food. Often, additives are used to make the final product resemble fresh ones. When it comes to convenience foods, the flavor and appearance may not compare with similar foods that are homemade.

Whether you choose convenience foods or the homemade versions, you may have to make some tradeoffs.

TIPS for Success

Buying Convenience Foods
* Read labels carefully. Choose products that are low in sodium, sugar, fat, and additives.
* Compare the cost of the convenience product with making it from scratch at home.
* Find out if any ingredients have to be added to the convenience food. How much will this add to the cost and preparation time?
* Ask yourself whether the product will help you have and enjoy a pleasant meal.

Section 15.1 Review

RECALL THE FACTS

1. What are the two main purposes of convenience foods? Give an example of a convenience food for each.

2. What is an analogue?

3. Name two ways in which convenience foods are often less nutritious or healthful than fresh foods.

DISCUSS YOUR IDEAS

4. With today's busy schedules, many people consider convenience foods essential and use them regularly in meals. What might be some effects of this trend?

APPLY YOUR LEARNING

5. Compare the cost and nutrition of at least three different convenience forms of a food. For example, you might want to compare different forms of macaroni and cheese (canned prepared, boxed mix, frozen). Which form might be the best choice? Why?

Objectives

After studying this section, you should be able to:

- Give suggestions for planning healthful meals around convenience foods.
- Describe general methods for preparing basic convenience foods.
- Discuss the benefits of making your own convenience foods.

Look for This Term

reconstitute

As you read this section, think of convenience foods in terms of your own food choices. Which convenience foods are you more likely to use? Why? How do you and your family use convenience foods in meals?

Planning Meals with Convenience Foods

Meals that use convenience foods can be nutritious and help you meet your daily food needs. Here are some guidelines for making daily food choices when you use convenience foods:

- If you use convenience products for one part of the meal, plan the rest of your choices carefully. Make other parts of the meal from fresh foods that can be prepared quickly. These include fresh fruits and vegetables, whole grain breads and cereals, and low-fat dairy products.
- When using dry mixes to make main dishes, side dishes, and sauces, reduce the amount of fat called for in the directions. Use skim milk or water instead of whole milk.
- Use quick-cooking grains as a side dish to add variety to meals. These include rice, bulgur, millet, kasha, and couscous. (For more information, see Chapter 17.)
- Keep shelf-stable or frozen main dishes and meals on hand for emergencies, but try to avoid using them regularly for meals.

When planning a meal around convenience main dishes, be sure to include nutritious fresh foods as well. Many require little preparation time.

Many convenience food packages include specific directions for preparing the food. Follow them exactly for best results. What cautions are given on the package directions shown here?

Preparing and Using Convenience Foods

Most convenience foods have directions for use on the package. Always read the directions carefully, even if you have used the product before. Manufacturers often change the ingredients or the preparation methods. Follow the directions exactly for best results.

If you want microwavable convenience foods, check the package directions before buying. Not all convenience foods can be successfully microwaved.

Here are some general guidelines for using common convenience foods. You'll also find information about specific convenience foods in later chapters.

❖ **Canned foods.** Many canned foods are ready to eat or need little preparation other than heating. Some canned soups must be mixed with water or milk. Once canned food is opened, any leftovers must usually be refrigerated.

❖ **Frozen foods.** Some frozen foods may need to be thawed. Others must be cooked without thawing. Check the package for special instructions, such as "Do not heat in toaster oven."

Before opening canned goods, wipe the top of the can with a clean, wet dishcloth. That will keep dirt and germs from getting into the food.

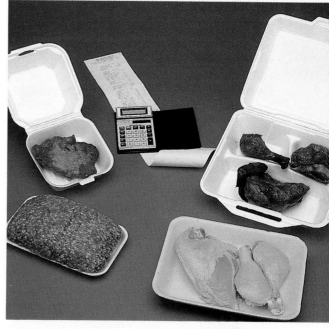

The cost of buying already-prepared foods is usually more than preparing similar recipes at home. Making your own convenience foods is an alternative that can save both time and money.

- ❖ **Chilled foods.** Use the same care in handling chilled convenience foods, such as fresh pasta and sauces, that you do when preparing foods from scratch. Keep them refrigerated until you are ready to use them. Use a chilled food product by the date shown on the package or check to see if it can be frozen. As an alternative, consider using it in a recipe which can be frozen.
- ❖ **Dried foods.** Many dried foods, such as nonfat dry milk, need to be reconstituted. To **reconstitute** means to add back the liquid that was removed in processing.
- ❖ **Dry mixes.** Most mixes contain the dry ingredients needed to prepare the food. You add other ingredients, such as liquids. Along with the basic directions, the package may have suggestions for variations.

Making Your Own Convenience Foods

Even though people are busy, they may be concerned about the cost or nutritional qualities of convenience foods. Some solve the problem by making their own convenience foods. Homemade convenience foods have several advantages:
- ❖ You decide on the kind and quality of ingredients to put into the product.
- ❖ You can control the amount of sodium, sugar, and fat used.
- ❖ Homemade convenience foods often cost less to prepare than the commercial ones.

- ❖ They have few or no additives.
- ❖ You enjoy meals with a homemade appearance and flavor.

Here are some ideas for making your own convenience foods.

Pre-prepared Ingredients

Perhaps there are some basic ingredients that you often use in recipes. You can save time by preparing a quantity of these foods ahead of time and refrigerating or freezing them.
- ❖ **Sautéed chopped vegetables.** Recipes often call for sautéed chopped garlic, onions, celery, or green pepper. Chop and sauté the combinations you use often. Freeze them in recipe-size quantities, such as 1/2 cup (125 mL). You can also freeze chopped vegetables without sautéing them, as long as you plan to cook them. Freezing softens crisp vegetables.

- ❖ **Dry beans and grain products.** Cook dry beans and grain products, such as rice and pasta, in quantity. Freeze them in 1-cup (125 mL) portions. Use them for salads, casseroles, soups, and side dishes.
- ❖ **Cubed or shredded cheese.** Cube or grate the kind of cheese you use frequently, such as cheddar or mozzarella. Store in a container with a tight-fitting cover and keep refrigerated or frozen until used.
- ❖ **Bread crumbs or cubes.** Cut bread into cubes and dry them. For crumbs, grind dried bread slices in a blender or food processor. You can also crush them with a rolling pin between two pieces of waxed paper or in a large, sealed plastic bag. Store the crumbs or cubes in an airtight container in the refrigerator or freezer. For added flavor and fiber, use whole wheat bread.

Frozen Main Dishes

At first, it may sound time-consuming to cook your own meals and freeze them. By preparing and freezing your own main dishes, however, you can save time and money in the long run. Considering the advantages, it may be worth the little extra time it takes.

Some busy people set aside one or two weekend days to "cook for the freezer." They prepare as many of their favorite recipes as they can and freeze them. Karen's mother gets the family involved in their "cooking weekend." They have a large freezer and can prepare enough main dishes to last about two months. Because everyone is involved, it has become a fun activity the family enjoys.

Others cook for the freezer regularly by preparing more than they need whenever they cook. The leftover food is frozen for future meals.

When packing the food, consider how it will be used. If family members eat at different times, freeze the food in single-serving packages.

When labeling the packages, include any instructions needed to serve the food. For example, if the recipe is to be served over rice, write that on the package so the rice can be thawed at the same time. (See pages 210-211 for information on packing and labeling foods to be frozen.)

Consider stocking your freezer with recipe ingredients that you have prepared ahead of time. They can cut down on the time needed to prepare recipes in the future.

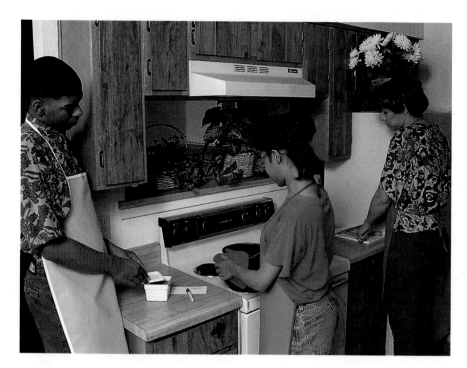

"Cooking for the freezer" is a way to use time efficiently. Several recipes can be prepared and frozen in one cooking session, especially when family members work together.

Homemade Mixes

You can make your own mixes for foods that you prepare regularly, such as quick breads or beverages. Seasoning mixes are great time-savers because you handle just one container instead of many different jars of herbs and spices.

The secret to making a successful mix is to be sure the ingredients are thoroughly combined and evenly distributed. Then, when you measure out the quantity you need, you will be sure to get the right amount of all the ingredients. Some ingredients may be heavier than others and may settle down in the container. Before measuring the amount you need, mix well to be sure the ingredients are evenly distributed.

Commercial mixes usually have preservatives added to extend the shelf life. You may not be able to store homemade mixes as long as commercial ones. Make only the quantity you think you will use before the mix spoils.

On page 404, you'll find an example of a basic baking mix and a recipe that can be prepared with it.

Section 15.2 Review

RECALL THE FACTS

1. List three tips for using convenience foods in meals.

2. Why is it important to read the directions on convenience foods even if you have used the product before?

3. Name two guidelines for using chilled convenience foods.

4. What are three benefits of making your own convenience foods?

DISCUSS YOUR IDEAS

5. How might you and your family use homemade convenience foods? What types of foods would be most helpful?

APPLY YOUR LEARNING

6. Plan a menu that combines a main-dish convenience food with easy-to-prepare fresh foods as side dishes. Evaluate the menu for nutrition, cost, and appeal.

Thinking About the Recipe

Read the recipes for "Favorite Wheat Pancakes" and "Whole Wheat Quick Bread Mix" and answer the following questions.

1. In what way does using a homemade mix like this one save time?
2. Why is it important to stir the quick bread mix before using it in the pancakes?

Favorite Wheat Pancakes

Customary	Ingredients	Metric
1	Egg, slightly beaten	1
1 ½ cups	Water	375 mL
2 Tbsp.	Oil	30 mL
2 ¼ cups	Whole Wheat Quick Bread Mix	550 mL

Yield: About 15 4-inch (10-cm) pancakes

Directions

Pan: Skillet

Temperature: Medium-high

1. Spray skillet with vegetable oil cooking spray. Preheat skillet.
2. Combine egg, water, and oil in a medium bowl.
3. Stir in Quick Bread Mix until just moistened.
4. Cook pancakes in hot skillet until browned on both sides, about 3 or 4 minutes.

Nutrition Information

Per 3-pancake serving : 257 calories, 8 g protein, 41 g carbohydrate, 7 g fat, 43 mg cholesterol, 425 mg sodium

Whole Wheat Quick Bread Mix

Customary	Ingredients	Metric
6 cups	Whole wheat flour	1500 mL
3 cups	All-purpose flour	750 mL
1 ½ cups	Instant nonfat dry milk	375 mL
1 Tbsp.	Salt	15 mL
1 cup	Sugar	250 mL
1/2 cup	Wheat germ	125 mL
1/4 cup	Baking powder	50 mL

Yield: About 12 cups baking mix

Directions

1. Combine all ingredients in a large bowl.
2. Put baking mix in a large container with a tight-fitting cover. Label with the name of the mix and the date.
3. Store baking mix in the refrigerator. Use within 12 to 14 weeks.

Note: Mix well again before measuring to use in recipes.

CAREER PROFILE

Marilyn Lakota
Processing Plant
Worker

Current position:

"I work in a large food processing plant. My current job involves inspecting and sorting ears of corn prior to freezing and packaging."

Skills:

"To be successful in this job, you must be able to handle repetitive tasks quickly and accurately. You also must be able to pay attention to details and work well as part of a team."

Education:

"In addition to my high school diploma, I have completed on-the-job training at the plant."

Work environment:

"My hours are steady—40 hours a week—and I work third shift. I work in a clean environment, though it can be noisy. Safety is always a factor with the various machines in the plant, so I have to be careful to follow all safety rules and pay attention to what I'm doing."

Future plans:

"I'm in line for a promotion to machine operator. My long-term goal is to become a supervisor or manager. As a first step, I volunteered for the quality-control team in my work unit."

- What are the advantages and disadvantages of Marilyn's work environment?
- What aspects of Marilyn's job do you find interesting? Why?

Summary

Section 15.1

Choosing Convenience Foods: Convenience foods include a wide variety of food items. They have been processed for longer shelf life, ease of preparation, or both. Manufactured foods are developed to serve as substitutes for other foods. Using convenience foods can save time and energy. However, convenience foods may be more costly, less nutritious, and less appealing than home-prepared or fresh foods.

Section 15.2

Cooking with Convenience: With careful planning, convenience foods can be part of a nutritious meal. Prepare convenience foods according to package directions. You can make your own convenience foods by pre-preparing ingredients, freezing main dishes, and making homemade dry mixes. Homemade convenience foods usually have advantages over store-bought versions, such as lower cost, better nutrition, and more meal appeal.

REVIEWING FACTS

1. In what way is nonfat dry milk more convenient than fluid milk? (15.1)

2. Name two reasons for the development of manufactured foods. (15.1)

3. What is TVP? How is it used? (15.1)

4. Identify two nutritional disadvantages of some convenience foods. (15.1)

5. What does "reconstitute" mean? (15.2)

6. Identify three types of recipe ingredients that you can pre-prepare. (15.2)

7. Describe two practices many people use to make and freeze main dishes. (15.2)

8. Do homemade dry mixes last as long as commercial varieties? Explain. (15.2)

LEARNING BY DOING

1. **Taste test:** Prepare a ready-to-cook entree or side dish and a similar recipe from scratch in the foods lab. Compare them for meal appeal and nutritional value. (15.1)

2. **Foods lab:** Pre-prepare different types of recipe ingredients. Divide them into convenient quantities, label them, and store them properly. Use these in a later foods lab. (15.2)

3. **Food science lab:** Using a recipe from this book or another source, prepare a dry mix. Store it and a similar commercial variety under identical conditions. Check both mixes regularly for texture and appearance. Prepare recipes using the mixes at regular intervals. How does time affect the quality of each mix? (15.2)

CHAPTER 15 REVIEW

4. **Foods lab:** Prepare a commercial dry mix according to the basic package directions. Prepare another batch using a variation suggested on the package or one of your own creation. Compare the two recipes for taste, texture, appearance, and nutritional value. (15.2)

THINKING CRITICALLY

1. **Identifying cause and effect:** Identify one positive effect and one negative effect of convenience foods on family life. (15.1)

2. **Identifying solutions:** How might convenience foods be used to help improve the global food supply? (15.1)

3. **Drawing conclusions:** You notice that your homemade convenience foods cost much less per serving than similar store-bought varieties. What do you think accounts for this price difference? (15.2)

MAKING DECISIONS AND SOLVING PROBLEMS

What Would You Do?

1. Your family uses convenience foods every day. You are worried about the effect on your family's health and budget. However, with everyone's busy, conflicting schedules, there doesn't seem to be much choice. (15.1)

2. You have promised to prepare a homemade pizza for your family's dinner tonight. However, you are late getting home from school and don't have time to prepare yeast dough crust or to simmer the tomato sauce. (15.2)

3. You are preparing your family's dinner when some old friends drop by. You would like to invite them to stay for the meal, but aren't sure you have enough food. You wonder how you can stretch the recipes using convenience foods. (15.2)

LINKING YOUR STUDIES

1. **Social studies:** Trace the history of convenience foods. What were some of the first commercially sold convenience foods? What technologies made them possible? How has their use affected family life? (15.1)

2. **Science:** Find information on the use of convenience foods by the armed forces and the space program. How has the technology used in preparing foods for these groups been applied to supermarket convenience foods, and vice versa? (15.1)

3. **Math:** Prepare a homemade convenience food. Calculate the cost per serving. Compare this to the per-serving cost of a similar commercial variety. Express the price difference in dollars and cents and as a percentage. (15.2)

4. **Writing:** Imagine that you can invent any kind of convenience food. Write a description of the product you would invent. Describe its appearance, texture, flavor, nutritional value, and how to store and prepare it. Then write an advertisement for your product. (15.1, 15.2)

Chapter 15: Convenience Foods   **407**

CHAPTER 16

Fruits and Vegetables

Section 16.1

Choosing Fruits and Vegetables

Objectives

After studying this section, you should be able to:

- ❖ Describe types of fruits and vegetables.
- ❖ Identify nutrients found in fruits and vegetables.
- ❖ Discuss guidelines for buying and storing fresh produce.
- ❖ Give suggestions for using convenience forms of fruits and vegetables.

Look for These Terms

drupes
tuber
cruciferous vegetables
unitized
mature fruits
ripe fruits

When she stopped at the supermarket one day, Marla was surprised to find that the produce section was being remodeled. "With all the emphasis on eating more fresh fruits and vegetables," said the manager, "we just didn't have enough space to handle the different kinds people want. So we're expanding."

Until that day, Marla was in the habit of eating only apples, bananas, potatoes, and carrots. She didn't even realize how many other kinds of fruits and vegetables are available. Now Marla likes to try a new one at least once or twice a month.

Types of Fruits and Vegetables

Think of the many varieties of fruits that are available. For example, there are:

- ❖ Melons, such as cantaloupe, honeydew, and casaba.
- ❖ Berries, including raspberries, strawberries, blackberries, and blueberries, as well as grapes.
- ❖ Citrus fruits, such as grapefruit, oranges, and tangerines.
- ❖ Many varieties of apples and pears.
- ❖ Cherries, plums, peaches, nectarines, and apricots. These fruits, called **drupes,** all have a central pit enclosing a single seed.
- ❖ Tropical fruits, including bananas, pineapple, and papayas.

In most supermarkets, you can find many other fruits from around the world. How many of the fruits and vegetables shown on page 410-411 have you tried?

Choose many different fruits for variety and good nutrition.

Carambola is also called star fruit because of its shape when cut. In taste and texture, it is similar to a blend of apples, grapes, and citrus fruit. Carambola is a good source of vitamin C and also supplies some vitamin A.

Atemoya has a sweet flavor and creamy, custard-like texture. It is a good source of vitamin C and potassium.

Lychees (LEE-chees) are small, round, sweet fruits about the size of cherries. The skin is bumpy and red to red-brown in color. Lychees are a good source of vitamin C and also supply potassium.

Pummelo (PAHM-uh-low) originated in the Far East. It resembles a large grapefruit, but is sweeter. It's a good source of vitamin C and potassium.

Calabaza is also called West Indian pumpkin. It may be green, tan, or orange and has bright orange flesh. Calabaza is a good source of vitamin A, vitamin C, and potassium.

Chayote (chy-OH-tay) is a tropical summer squash with a flavor similar to zucchini. It's a good source of vitamin C and also supplies potassium.

Malanga is a starchy vegetable popular in Cuba and in Puerto Rico, where it is called *yautia*. When boiled, the texture and flavor resemble a blend of dry beans and potatoes. Malanga is a good source of vitamin C.

Boniato is a tropical sweet potato. It's a good source of vitamin C and potassium.

Did you know that some "vegetables" are really fruits? Various parts of plants are eaten as vegetables.

- **Roots.** Carrots, beets, and turnips are examples of root vegetables. Roots store a plant's food supplies and send nutrients and moisture to the rest of the plant.
- **Stems.** Celery is a common stem vegetable.
- **Tubers.** A **tuber** (TOO-burr) is a large underground stem that stores nutrients. Potatoes are tubers.
- **Leaves.** Spinach, lettuce, and cooking greens such as kale and collards are leafy vegetables. Leaves are the plant's manufacturing areas. Through a process called photosynthesis (foe-toe-SIN-thuh-siss), they turn sunlight, carbon dioxide, and water into high-energy carbohydrates.
- **Bulbs.** Onions and garlic are examples of bulbs. A bulb is made up of layers of fleshy leaves surrounding a portion of a stem.
- **Flowers.** Broccoli is an example of a vegetable that includes the flowers of a plant, along with the attached stems.
- **Seeds.** Corn, beans, and peas are vegetables which come from the edible seeds of plants. Seeds are high in carbohydrates and other nutrients because they are the part of the plant from which new plants grow.
- **Fruits.** Some foods commonly called vegetables, including cucumbers, eggplants, and tomatoes, are really the fruit of the plant. The fruit is the part of the plant that holds the seeds.

Nutrients in Fruits and Vegetables

In general, fresh fruits and vegetables are excellent sources of vitamins, minerals, and fiber. Some have higher amounts than others. They are also low in fat and sodium and have no cholesterol.

As you may recall, only plant foods contain beta carotene, which the body uses to make vitamin A. Carotene gives food an orange color, so yellow or orange fruits and vegetables are excellent sources.

Dark green leafy vegetables, such as cooking greens and broccoli, are also excellent sources of beta carotene. Eat dark-green leafy vegetables several times a week—they are a good source of vitamins and minerals.

Research shows that a group of vegetables, called **cruciferous** (crew-SIH-fur-russ) **vegetables,** may also lower the risk of certain kinds of cancer. Cruciferous vegetables include broccoli, brussels sprouts, cabbage, collards, kale, mustard greens, cauliflower, rutabagas, and turnips.

Most people think of citrus fruits as the main source of vitamin C. However, many other fruits and vegetables are rich in this vitamin, including kiwi, strawberries, cantaloupe, cabbage, and potatoes.

Cruciferous vegetables are members of the cabbage family. They not only provide vitamins, minerals, and fiber, but may help protect against cancer. Make them a regular part of your food choices.

The Food Guide Pyramid recommends two to four servings of fruits each day and three to five servings of vegetables. Typical servings of fruit include 1 medium apple, banana, or orange; 1/2 cup (125 mL) of chopped, cooked, or canned fruit; or 3/4 cup (175 mL) of pure fruit juice. Vegetable servings might include 1 cup (250 mL) of raw, leafy vegetables; 1/2 cup (125 mL) of other vegetables (cooked or chopped raw); or 3/4 cup (175 mL) of vegetable juice.

Buying Fresh Produce

Some fruits and vegetables, such as bananas, apples, pears, grapes, spinach, and broccoli, are available all year. Others, such as asparagus, peaches, plums, and mangoes, have a specific growing season. During this season, the fruit or vegetable is plentiful,

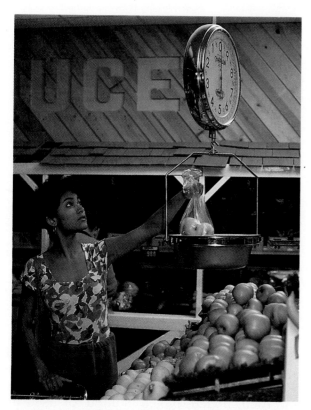

Produce is often priced by the pound. In many stores, you can check the weight of loose produce using the scale provided in the department.

prices usually are lower, and the quality is better. Seasonal items are often imported during the off-season months, but prices are higher. When shopping, look for items that are in season as well as year-round favorites.

Produce can be purchased loose, in a bag or plastic-covered tray, or unitized. **Unitized** means that large produce, such as broccoli, is held together with a rubber band or a plastic tie. If you want a smaller amount of produce than is in a package, ask a clerk to open it and repackage the amount you want.

Here are some additional general guidelines for buying produce.

❖ Buy top-quality fruits and vegetables. They will give you the most nutrients for the money and will last longer. Poor-quality produce is a waste of money.

❖ Buy only what you can store and use. Most high-quality fresh fruits and vegetables last about a week in the refrigerator.

❖ Inspect packaged produce carefully. If the package has stains or an unpleasant odor, it may be a sign of damaged or spoiled produce.

❖ Avoid any produce that looks wilted, shriveled, bruised, or decayed. Some produce may have natural blemishes, which do not affect quality. Grapefruit and oranges, for instance, may have a brownish scale.

❖ Buy by weight, when possible. Except for leafy vegetables, fruits and vegetables should feel heavy for their size.

Buying Fresh Fruits

Fruits are usually picked when they are mature. **Mature fruits** have reached their full size and color but may not have ripened. That means they are hard and have not yet reached full flavor.

Ripe fruits are tender with a pleasant aroma and fully developed flavors. To test for ripeness on most fruit, press very gently. The fruit should give a little under the pressure. Don't press so hard that you damage the fruit.

Bananas grow in the tropics. The large bunches are harvested while the fruit is still green. They will ripen naturally on the way to the marketplace or after purchase.

Fruits are easy to ripen. Place them in a brown paper bag at room temperature until they reach the stage of ripeness you want. If you use a plastic bag, punch holes in it to allow excess moisture to evaporate. Otherwise, the fruit may mold and decay before it ripens.

To avoid having fresh fruits ripen too quickly or all at once, buy fruits at different stages of ripeness. You can also refrigerate unripe fruits, which slows down the ripening process. As you need ripe fruit, take it out and let it ripen at room temperature.

When buying fresh fruits, look for fruit that is mature and at the stage of ripeness you want. Choose fruits that are typical in shape and size. Fruits that are much smaller than usual, or misshapen, are usually of lower quality.

Choose fruits that have reached their natural color, with no green showing anywhere. Green fruits, in most cases, will not ripen well. There are some exceptions:

❖ Some fruits are naturally green in color, such as certain varieties of pears, apples, and grapes.

❖ A few fruits, such as bananas, are picked green and will turn their natural color when they ripen.

❖ The skins of oranges sometimes turn green when exposed to light, but flavor and quality are not affected. Oranges, like all citrus fruits, must be ripe when picked.

In Puerto Rican cuisine, *plaintains* are a staple. A plaintain resembles a green banana, but because it is starchy, like a potato, it is cooked before eating. Plaintain can be roasted, fried, boiled, baked, stuffed, or used in casseroles.

Buying Fresh Vegetables

Fresh vegetables are already ripe when you buy them. Select those typical in shape and medium in size. Misshapen vegetables may not be of the best quality. Large vegetables might be overripe. Avoid vegetables that look like they have discoloring which indicates decay.

Storing Fresh Produce

Unless the produce is dirty, it should not be washed until you are ready to use it. The added moisture will speed up spoiling caused by bacteria. Moisture remaining on produce can also cause mold to grow. If it's necessary to wash produce before storing, be sure it is thoroughly dry before you refrigerate it.

Most fresh fruits and vegetables, except potatoes, sweet potatoes, and onions, should be stored in the refrigerator. Refrigerate produce in the crisper section or in brown paper bags. If you use plastic bags, punch holes in them so some of the moisture can escape. Don't line the bottom of the crisper with paper towels. They get soggy and might cause produce to decay or get moldy.

When potatoes are refrigerated, the starch turns to sugar, changing their flavor. Onions and sweet potatoes will mold and decay when refrigerated. Therefore, store potatoes, sweet potatoes, and onions in a cool, dark, dry place. Sometimes it's difficult to find such a spot in today's homes. If stored at room temperature, these foods will keep for a relatively short time. Therefore, buy only what you can use during that time.

Safety Check

Potatoes that are exposed to light may develop a greenish color. The green color itself is harmless. However, it indicates that the potato may contain a harmful, bitter-tasting compound called solanine. Potato sprouts also contain solanine. Cut away sprouts and green portions before using potatoes. Discard potatoes that have a bitter taste.

Storing potatoes and onions separately will lengthen their shelf life. What type of storage area is best?

Convenience Fruits and Vegetables

Here are some tips for buying and using convenience forms of fruits and vegetables:

* Canned fruits usually have less fiber than fresh fruits, but are still a good source of vitamins and minerals. Choose whole fruit, slices, or pieces, depending on how you will use them. To cut down on sugar, avoid fruits canned or frozen in heavy syrups.
* For a quick, low-fat dessert, try pureeing canned fruit in a blender and serving it over angel food cake.
* To serve frozen fruits, thaw them only partially. A few ice crystals should remain so the fruit is firm and cold, not mushy.
* Dried fruits are sweet and chewy—a concentrated form of energy. They can be eaten as snacks, cooked, or used in recipes.
* Most canned vegetables contain added sodium. To reduce the amount of sodium, drain the liquid from vegetables and rinse them before cooking. However, you will lose some nutrients that are found in the liquid, too.
* If you have freezer space, buy frozen vegetables in large bags so you can use just the amount you need. Cook frozen vegetables as directed before serving.
* Dried vegetables may be found in boxed casserole mixes and soup mixes. They must be rehydrated during the cooking process before you can eat them.
* Many fruit and vegetable juices are available. They do not contain fiber, but are good sources of many nutrients. If the label says "juice," the product must be 100 percent juice. Products that are not pure juice must be called by another name, such as fruit drink.

Convenience forms of fruits and vegetables give consumers more options.

Section 16.1 Review

RECALL THE FACTS

1. What is a tuber? Give an example of a tuber vegetable.
2. What is the difference between mature and ripe fruit?
3. Name three qualities to look for when choosing fresh vegetables.
4. Why should most produce be stored unwashed?
5. Give two suggestions for using convenience forms of fruits and vegetables.

DISCUSS YOUR IDEAS

6. Twenty years ago, supermarkets did not display as great a variety of fruits and vegetables as most do today. Discuss the reasons for this change. How does this benefit consumers?

APPLY YOUR LEARNING

7. Use the "Nutritive Value in Foods" chart in the Appendix to identify five fruits and five vegetables that are high in vitamins A and C.

Section 16.2
Preparing Raw Fruits and Vegetables

Objectives

After studying this section, you should be able to:

❖ Describe how to wash produce.

❖ Give suggestions for preparing and serving raw fruits and vegetables.

Look for This Term

enzymatic browning

Fresh fruits and vegetables, eaten raw, are nature's nutritious convenience foods. They need little preparation. In minutes, you can have a raw carrot for a snack, strawberry slices to top your cereal, or a pear for a quick dessert.

Unlike fruits, not all vegetables can be eaten raw. Those which can be include broccoli, carrots, cauliflower, celery, cucumbers, jicama, mushrooms, radishes, sweet peppers, and tomatoes.

Vegetables such as these, which are easy to chew and digest, can be eaten raw for snacks. How might raw vegetables be used in meals?

Washing Fresh Produce

Fresh fruits and vegetables should be washed before they are eaten or cooked. Washing helps remove pesticide residues, dirt, and germs. Even if you're going to peel or pare produce, washing helps keep chemicals and dirt from being transferred to the edible parts.

For tender fruits and vegetables, wash carefully in cool, clear water. Be sure all visible dirt is removed and that cracks and crevices are clean. Use a stiff brush to scrub thick-skinned produce, such as squash. Also scrub vegetables that might have a lot of dirt, such as potatoes. To minimize nutrient loss, do not let produce soak in water.

Cutting Fresh Produce

After it is washed, produce may need to be peeled, pared, or cut into pieces.

Cut or peel away the thick, inedible skins of some fruits, such as oranges and pineapples. A few vegetables may have to be pared, such as jicama. Also remove other inedible parts, such as the seeds of sweet peppers, the stems of fruits, and any soft spots or damaged areas.

Safety Check

Never use detergent to wash produce. The produce may absorb the detergent, which can make people ill if swallowed. In addition, it's possible that the detergent could react with any pesticides and waxes found on the produce. The reaction might produce other chemicals, possibly harmful ones.

TIPS for Success

Peeling Citrus Fruit

Here's an easy way to peel an orange or grapefruit. First, divide the peel into quarters by scoring it with a sharp knife. Begin the cuts at the stem end and continue around to the opposite end. Then pull each section of the peel away with your fingers.

To retain the most nutrients, don't pare produce with edible skins, such as apples. However, if you're concerned about removing wax and residues, pare the produce. Even though some nutrients will be lost in the skin, most will remain in the produce.

Fruits and vegetables can be cut into pieces to make them easier to eat or more attractive. To keep nutrient losses to a minimum, cut fruits and vegetables into the largest possible pieces. Also, serve them as soon after cutting as possible.

Fruits can be cut into many different shapes. For example, fruits such as bananas, oranges, and kiwis can be sliced crosswise. You might cut apples, pears, or peaches into wedges and remove the core or pit. Some fruits can be cut into cubes and served with wooden picks.

Vegetables may be cut in the same shapes as fruits or shredded on a grater. Most can also be cut into strips.

Preventing Cut Fruits from Darkening

Some fruits retain an attractive appearance after they are cut. These include citrus fruits, melons, pineapples, and kiwis. However, many other fruits will turn dark when the flesh inside is exposed to the air. The discoloration is due to a process called **enzymatic browning.**

The easiest way to keep fresh fruits from discoloring is to coat them with some form of ascorbic acid (vitamin C) as soon as they are cut. One solution is to dip the pieces of cut fruit in lemon juice. You can also buy an ascorbic acid powder to mix with water and sprinkle on cut fruit.

Unlike fruits, vegetables do not turn brown when they are cut. If they are allowed to stand for several days, however, they may begin to darken.

Lemon juice can keep banana slices from turning dark. Would you need to use lemon juice on any other fruits in this salad? Why or why not?

Science Connection

Chemistry:
Enzymatic Browning

Oxygen in the air will eventually cause any cut fruit to turn brown. However, the reaction occurs more quickly in fruits that contain a specific enzyme (called *polyphenoloxidase.*) The fruit, the enzyme, and oxygen in the air react to cause the discoloration. Enzymatic browning can be prevented with an acid, which slows down the action of the enzyme.

Serving and Storing Cut Produce

An assortment of cut-up raw fruits and vegetables is a welcome addition to any gathering. When arranging the fruits and vegetables on a platter, use your imagination. Don't just heap the food in any way. Instead, try to arrange it in an artistic pattern. That way, you have more fun preparing the food and your guests will enjoy the beauty of the arrangement. For instance, you could arrange the different kinds of produce into wedge-shaped sections, like pieces of pie. Keep in mind that color contrasts make a pleasing display.

If you've arranged the platter ahead of time, cover it tightly with plastic wrap, squeezing out as much air as possible. Refrigerate until serving time. You might want to serve the produce with a tasty low-fat dip, such as one made with yogurt.

A display of raw produce can be a work of art, as this example from Thailand shows. Simple arrangements using basic shapes can also be attractive and take little time to create.

Try keeping cut-up vegetables in the refrigerator as handy snacks. Store them in a tightly sealed plastic bag or on a plate covered with plastic. Squeeze out as much air as possible to keep nutrients from being destroyed by oxygen.

Section 16.2 Review

RECALL THE FACTS

1. How should thick-skinned produce be washed?

2. Name two ways to keep cut fruit from turning brown.

3. Why might you want to arrange raw fruits and vegetables in a pleasing pattern before serving?

DISCUSS YOUR IDEAS

4. How might people be encouraged to think of raw fruits and vegetables as convenience foods?

APPLY YOUR LEARNING

5. Plan an attractive platter of raw fruits or vegetables that you might serve at a party. What fruits or vegetables would you include? What shape would you use for each? Describe or sketch how the foods would be arranged on the platter. Evaluate your plan for nutrition as well as variety of shape and color.

Thinking About the Recipe

Read the recipe for "Strawberry Fruit Dip" and answer the following questions.

1. How would you prepare this recipe if you didn't have a blender or electric mixer?
2. What are some creative ways you could arrange and serve the fresh fruit and dip?

Strawberry Fruit Dip

Customary	Ingredients	Metric
8-oz. package	Nonfat or low-fat cream cheese	224-gram package
16-oz. package	Frozen sweetened strawberries, thawed	384-gram package
2 Tbsp.	Plain, nonfat yogurt	30 mL
	Assorted fresh fruit (strawberries, pineapple, banana, kiwi), cut into bite-size pieces	

Yield: 2 ¾ cups (675 mL)

Directions

Equipment: Blender or electric mixer
1. Place the cheese, strawberries, and yogurt in the blender or mixer bowl.
2. Whip until smooth.
3. Refrigerate for at least 2 hours before serving.
4. Serve dip with fresh fruit.

Nutrition Information

Per 1/4 cup (50 mL) serving (approximate): 78 calories, 2 g protein, 11 g carbohydrate, 3 g fat, 7 mg cholesterol, 109 mg sodium

Objectives

After studying this section, you should be able to:

❖ Identify the effects of cooking on fruits and vegetables.
❖ Describe methods for cooking fruits.
❖ Describe methods for cooking vegetables.

Look for This Term

chlorophyll

"I've never tasted vegetables this flavorful," thought Jolene as she enjoyed a meal with her friend's family. "The colors are so bright, too. I wonder what makes the difference?"

The difference Jolene noticed may have been due to the way the vegetables were prepared. Paying close attention to cooking methods can make a big difference in how cooked vegetables and fruits look and taste.

Effects of Cooking on Fruits and Vegetables

Cooking results in noticeable changes in fruits and vegetables, especially in texture, color, and flavor.

This image shows part of the leaf cell of a garden pea, greatly magnified by an electron microscope. Colors have been added to highlight the different areas. The green strands contain the chlorophyll pigments that give green plants their color. With proper cooking, vegetables such as peas stay bright green.

- **Texture.** Heat softens the cell walls, making fruits and vegetables more tender. Many vegetables, such as green beans and winter squash, must be cooked to be edible. Starchy vegetables are easier to digest when cooked. If overcooked, fruits and vegetables become mushy.
- **Color.** When properly cooked, fruits and vegetables retain pleasing colors. Green vegetables get their color from **chlorophyll** (KLORE-uh-fill), the chemical compound that plants use to turn the sun's energy into food. If overcooked, green vegetables can turn an unpleasant olive green.
- **Flavor.** The heat of cooking releases flavors, making them more noticeable. Fruit flavors mellow somewhat and taste less acid. Herbs, spices, or other foods can be added during cooking, allowing their flavors to mingle with the natural flavor of the fruit or vegetable. When overcooked, fruits and vegetables lose their flavor and may even develop an unpleasant flavor.

Cooking can also result in nutrient losses. To minimize loss of vitamin C when cooking fruits and vegetables, keep them whole or in large pieces. Cook them quickly using methods that require only a small amount of water, such as simmering in a tightly covered pan or microwaving. Serve cooked vegetables and fruits with the cooking liquid whenever possible.

Cooking Fresh Fruits

Cooking fruits is a way of adding variety to your food choices. Cooked fruits can be served hot or chilled. They may be part of the main course, a snack, or a dessert.

Before cooking, remember to wash fresh fruits as described in Section 16.2. Fruits can be cooked by several different methods.

Poaching Fruits

Poaching, or stewing, is a method of cooking fruit in simmering liquid. The goal is to retain the shape of the fruit as it cooks.

Fruits that can be poached include plums, berries, apples, and pears. Small fruits, such as berries, are left whole. Apples and pears may be cut in large pieces.

When poaching, use enough water to cover the fruit. Add sugar at the beginning of cooking. The sugar is not just for sweetness, but to help retain the shape of the fruit. Sugar added at the beginning of cooking strengthens the cell walls so that the heat won't break down the texture.

For flavoring, you may also want to add lemon or orange rind, a cinnamon stick, or vanilla. Simmer, uncovered, until the fruit is tender but still holds its shape.

Poaching is a way to add flavor to fruit while retaining the shape for an attractive presentation.

Fruit Sauces

Fruit sauces, such as applesauce, are also made by cooking the fruit in liquid. In this case, however, the goal is to break down the texture. Therefore, sugar is not added until after cooking.

Besides apples, many fruits—such as peaches, plums, apricots, and pears—can be made into a sauce. Try combining two kinds of fruit for a different flavor.

To make a fruit sauce, pare the fruit and cut it into small pieces for faster cooking. Add water to a saucepan to a depth of about 1/4 inch (0.6 cm). Put the fruit in the saucepan. Bring to a boil, lower the heat to simmer, and cover the pan. Cook, stirring occasionally, until the fruit has broken down. The time will vary, depending on the kind of fruit and the size of the pieces. Sweeten as desired with sugar, honey, or syrup. Spices or other flavorings may also be added.

Baking Fruits

Care must be taken when you bake fruits to avoid overcooking. Best results are obtained with firm fruits, such as apples, pears, and bananas, that are whole or in large pieces.

Apples are probably the most popular baked fruit. They are easy to prepare and make a delicious ending to any meal. Use a variety of apple suited to cooking, such as Rome Beauty. Before cooking, core the apples and cut a thin strip of skin from around the middle. This will enable the apples to expand as they cook so they will not burst. You can fill the core cavity with raisins and seasonings such as cinnamon or nutmeg. Place the apples in a baking dish and pour hot water around them to a depth of 1/4 inch (6 mm). Bake at 350°F (180°C) until tender, about 45 to 60 minutes.

Microwaving Fruits

Fruits are easy to prepare in the microwave oven. They cook quickly and keep their fresh flavor and their shape.

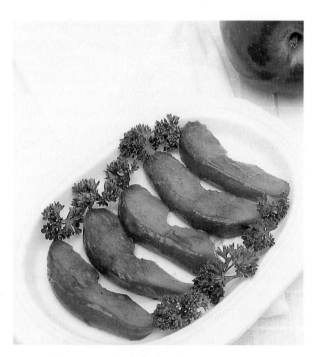

For variety, try baking sliced apples instead of the whole fruit. Seasonings such as cinnamon and nutmeg can give the flavor of apple pie with less fat and fewer calories.

Because they are so tender, however, they can easily overcook. Watch the timing carefully.

Cover fruits when microwaving them, but leave a small opening for excess steam to escape. If you're cooking whole fruits, such as plums, puncture them with a fork in several places to keep them from bursting.

The basic steps in poaching, making a fruit sauce, and baking fruit are similar for microwave and conventional cooking. Power level and cooking time will vary, so check the owner's manual or a microwave cookbook.

Cooking Fresh Vegetables

Before cooking vegetables, wash them carefully and trim away inedible parts. If necessary, pare and cut the vegetables into pieces. Small pieces will cook faster than larger ones, but will also lose more nutrients.

Fresh vegetables can be cooked by several different methods. The timing and method depends on the tenderness of the vegetable and the size of the pieces.

Simmering Vegetables

Vegetables can be simmered in a covered pan in a small amount of water. Allow about 1/2 cup (125 mL) water for four servings of vegetables. Pour the water into a medium-size saucepan, cover, and bring to a boil. Add the vegetables, cover, and bring to a boil again. Then lower the heat until the water just simmers. Cook, covered, until vegetables are tender.

Steaming Vegetables

Steaming is a nutritious way to cook vegetables. Fewer nutrients are lost because the vegetables are not cooked in water. However, steaming sometimes takes a little longer than simmering.

Place the steamer basket in a saucepan with a tight-fitting cover. Add water to a depth just below the bottom of the steamer. Cover the pan and bring the water to a boil. Add the vegetables to the steamer basket and cover. Reduce the heat slightly, but not so much that the water stops boiling and producing steam. Steam the vegetables until tender.

Microwaving Vegetables

Microwaving cooks vegetables quickly using only a small amount of water. Therefore, the vegetables lose few nutrients and keep their color, texture, and flavor.

Remember, larger pieces will take longer to cook than smaller ones. Pieces that are the same size and shape will cook more evenly.

When cooking whole vegetables that have a skin, such as potatoes or squash, pierce the skin with a fork to keep them from bursting.

If parts of a vegetable are more tender than others, arrange the tender parts toward the center and the less tender ones toward the edge of the baking dish. For instance, the stems of broccoli and asparagus are less tender and would be placed toward the edge.

Always cover the container to retain moisture. Follow directions in the owner's manual or cooking guide for cooking times and special instructions.

TIPS for Success

Retaining Color in Vegetables

❖ Some red vegetables, such as red cabbage and beets, can turn blue if simmered in water that contains certain minerals. To avoid discoloration, add a small amount of an acid food, such as lemon juice or vinegar, to the water during cooking.

❖ Don't add baking soda when simmering vegetables. Although it helps retain color in green vegetables, baking soda destroys vitamins and creates a mushy texture. For a bright green color, avoid overcooking the vegetable.

Recipes for cooking red cabbage or beets often include lemon juice or vinegar. Why?

Vegetables are naturally low in fat. To keep them that way, go easy on the high-fat foods sometimes added to vegetables at the table or during cooking. These include butter, margarine, salad dressings, mayonnaise, cheese, and the rich sauces that come with some frozen vegetables. Instead, use low-fat seasonings to add "zip" to fresh vegetables or plain frozen ones. Try lemon juice, flavored vinegar, herbs, spices, or low-fat salad dressings.

Baking Vegetables

Vegetables with a high moisture content, such as winter squash, potatoes, and sweet potatoes, can bake in the dry heat of an oven.

Winter squash is usually cut in half, the seeds removed, and the halves placed on a baking sheet. Squash usually bakes at 350°F (180°C) for 30 minutes or longer, until it is tender. The time depends on the variety and size of the squash.

Potatoes are baked in the skins are usually placed right on the oven rack. They can bake at any temperature between 300°F (150°C) and 450°F (230°C). The baking time will depend on the temperature. Such flexibility in temperatures makes it possible to bake potatoes with other foods that need more exact temperatures. For example, you can bake muffins at 375°F (190°C) and still bake potatoes at the same time.

Sweet potatoes can also be baked with the skins on. Put them in a shallow pan in case juices begin to run out. They bake best at 400°F (200°C).

Pared whole vegetables such as carrots, onions, and potatoes can be baked in the same pan with a roast. This method adds fat to the vegetables, but it also browns them and gives them a flavorful crust.

There are many varieties of potatoes. All-purpose types, such as round white potatoes, can be either baked or simmered with good results. The round red type is better when simmered.

Frying Vegetables

Vegetables such as chopped onions, garlic, celery, and sweet peppers are sometimes sautéed before they are used in recipes. Sautéing brings out the flavor of the vegetables. Stir-frying is also a popular method of cooking.

Many people enjoy the flavor of deep-fried vegetables, such as potatoes, zucchini slices, cauliflower, mushrooms, and onions. Except for potatoes, deep-fried vegetables are usually covered with a batter first.

Keep in mind that frying in even a small amount of oil adds fat and calories to any vegetables. If a large amount of fat is used, as in deep-fat frying, much more fat is absorbed by the vegetables.

Cooking Convenience Fruits and Vegetables

❖ Canned vegetables may be simmered in liquid on the range top or heated in the microwave oven.

❖ Frozen vegetables may be steamed, simmered in liquid, or cooked in the microwave oven. Follow package directions for best results.

❖ Dried fruits may be poached in water or fruit juice and served as a tasty side dish or dessert.

Vegetables are often stir-fried with other foods. Use just a small amount of oil.

Section 16.3 Review

RECALL THE FACTS

1. Name three undesirable changes that can occur if fruits or vegetables are overcooked.

2. Identify two ways poaching fruit differs from making a fruit sauce. What is the reason for the differences?

3. Describe two differences between simmering and steaming a vegetable.

DISCUSS YOUR IDEAS

4. Which do you think might be the best way to cook vegetables? Why?

APPLY YOUR LEARNING

5. Write an article for the local newspaper's food page, giving ideas for cooking vegetables to retain nutrients, appearance, texture, and flavor.

Thinking About the Recipe

Read the recipe for "Herbed Vegetable Combo" and answer the following questions.

1. If you planned to make this recipe, how much time would you allow for pre-preparation tasks?
2. Do you consider this to be a healthful method for cooking vegetables? Why or why not?

Herbed Vegetable Combo

Customary	Ingredients	Metric
2 Tbsp.	Water	30 mL
1 cup	Zucchini squash, thinly sliced	250 mL
1 1/4 cups	Yellow summer squash thinly sliced	300 mL
1/2 cup	Green pepper, cut into 2-inch (50 mm) strips	125 mL
1/4 cup	Celery, cut into 2-inch (50 mm) strips	50 mL
1/4 cup	Onion, chopped	50 mL
1/2 tsp.	Caraway seed	3 mL
1/8 tsp.	Garlic powder	0.5 mL
1 medium	Tomato, cut into wedges	1 medium

Yield: 4 servings

Directions

Pan: Large skillet
Temperature: Medium

1. Heat water in skillet.
2. Add zucchini, yellow squash, green pepper, celery, and onion.
3. Cook, covered, over medium heat for about 4 minutes, or until vegetables are tender-crisp.
4. Sprinkle seasonings over vegetables. Top with tomato wedges.
5. Cook, covered, over low heat for about 2 minutes, or just until tomato wedges are heated.
6. Serve hot.

Nutrition Information

Per serving (approximate): 32 calories, 2 g protein, 7 g carbohydrate, trace of fat, 0 mg cholesterol, 12 mg sodium

CAREER PROFILE

Ed Quintero
Wholesale Buyer

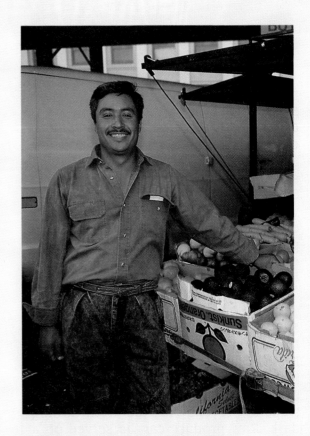

Current position:

"I'm a produce buyer for a grocery wholesaler."

Responsibilities:

"I purchase produce from farmers and other wholesale firms for resale to clients such as grocery stores, school cafeterias, and restaurants."

Skills:

"My job requires some knowledge of accounting and marketing to stay informed about prices and availability. And, of course, you must be familiar with produce!"

Education:

"I have a four-year college degree in purchasing, and a background in produce sales."

Work environment:

"This can be a highly competitive job with long hours and a certain amount of travel. During a typical day, I might get together with some of our vendors, meet with store executives, and discuss sales promotions with the advertising department."

Favorite part of the job:

"I enjoy the variety of working with many different people."

- Does Ed seem well qualified for his job? Why or why not?
- What aspects of Ed's job do you think you might find challenging? Why?

Summary

Section 16.1
Choosing Fruits and Vegetables: You can choose from a wide variety of produce. Fruits and vegetables are excellent sources of vitamins, minerals, and fiber. Shop carefully for the best quality and value on in-season and year-round produce. Some fruits can be ripened after purchase. Store fresh produce properly to preserve its quality. Convenience forms of fruits and vegetables give you still more options.

Section 16.2
Preparing Raw Fruits and Vegetables: Fresh produce should be washed before it is used. To retain the most nutrients, keep paring and cutting to a minimum. Take steps to prevent cut fruits from turning dark. Raw produce can be served on a platter for a party or kept on hand in the refrigerator for snacks.

Section 16.3
Cooking Fruits and Vegetables: Cooking affects the texture, color, and flavor of fruits and vegetables. Overcooking can result in discoloration and loss of texture, flavor, and nutrients. Fresh fruits may be poached, baked, made into sauces, or prepared in a microwave oven. Fresh vegetables may be simmered, steamed, baked, or prepared in a microwave oven. They may also be fried in oil, which adds flavor but also fat.

REVIEWING FACTS

1. Why are roots high in nutrients? (16.1)

2. Give three examples of cruciferous vegetables. What is a possible benefit of eating them? (16.1)

3. Give three tips for buying fresh produce. (16.1)

4. Why should you wash produce, even if you're going to peel it before eating? (16.2)

5. What is the process that causes cut fruit to darken? How can it be prevented? (16.2)

6. How should cut produce be stored? (16.2)

7. Give three tips for minimizing vitamin C loss when cooking fruits and vegetables. (16.3)

8. What characteristics make some fruits better for baking than others? (16.3)

9. Explain how to simmer vegetables. (16.3)

10. Give three tips for microwaving vegetables. (16.3)

LEARNING BY DOING

1. ***Food science lab:*** Select two potatoes. Store one in a cool, dry, dark place. Store the other in the refrigerator. After at least one week, bake the potatoes. Compare their taste and texture. What caused the difference? (16.1)

2. ***Demonstration:*** Using your knowledge of handling fresh produce and of meal appeal, demonstrate how to create an attractive fresh fruit or vegetable platter. (16.2)

3. **Food science lab:** Cut an apple into wedges. Sprinkle half of the wedges with lemon juice. Let all the wedges stand at room temperature. Record any changes in appearance after 5, 10, and 15 minutes. Explain what happened and why. (16.2)

4. **Foods lab:** Select one fruit or vegetable and prepare it using three of the methods described in this chapter. Compare the results on appearance, taste, texture, and convenience. Identify when you might want to use each method. (16.3)

THINKING CRITICALLY

1. **Predicting consequences:** What are some possible consequences of not getting enough fruits and vegetables in your diet? (16.1)

2. **Forming hypotheses:** A hypothesis is sometimes called an "educated guess." Based on what you know about the effect of lemon juice on cut fruit, do you predict that any other juices would have the same effect? Which ones? How could you test your hypothesis? (16.2)

3. **Comparing and contrasting:** Compare and contrast the advantages and disadvantages of the cooking methods described in this chapter. (16.3)

MAKING DECISIONS AND SOLVING PROBLEMS

What Would You Do?

1. The supermarket is having a sale on fruits and vegetables. However, they are packaged in quantities that are too large for your family's use. You want to take advantage of the low price, but are afraid some of the produce will spoil before you can eat it. (16.1)

2. You are watching your neighbor's children, ages seven and nine, and are responsible for making sure they eat their dinner. Your neighbor has warned you that they do not like to eat vegetables. You wonder how you can make vegetables more appealing to the children. (16.2, 16.3)

LINKING YOUR STUDIES

1. **Science:** Research and report on the ways fruits and vegetables are classified by scientists. (16.1)

2. **Math:** Use newspaper ads or visit a supermarket to conduct a price survey. Compare the per-serving price of several similar fruits or vegetables (for example, different types of berries or cruciferous vegetables). Compare the prices of different forms such as fresh, frozen, and canned. Make a bar graph showing your findings. What are some possible reasons for the price differences? (16.1)

3. **Fine arts:** Many artists have included arrangements of fruits or vegetables in their works. Using art books, find such artworks by at least five different artists. Be prepared to discuss the works and your reactions to them in class. Suggested works: Henri Rousseau, *Still Life with Tropical Fruit;* Paul Cezanne, *Fruit Bowl, Glass, and Apples;* Gabriel Metsu, *Vegetable Market at Amsterdam.* (16.1, 16.2)

4. **Social studies:** In cookbooks, magazines, and other sources, find recipes for cooked fruits and vegetables that are popular in other cultures. Identify the cooking methods used. (16.3)

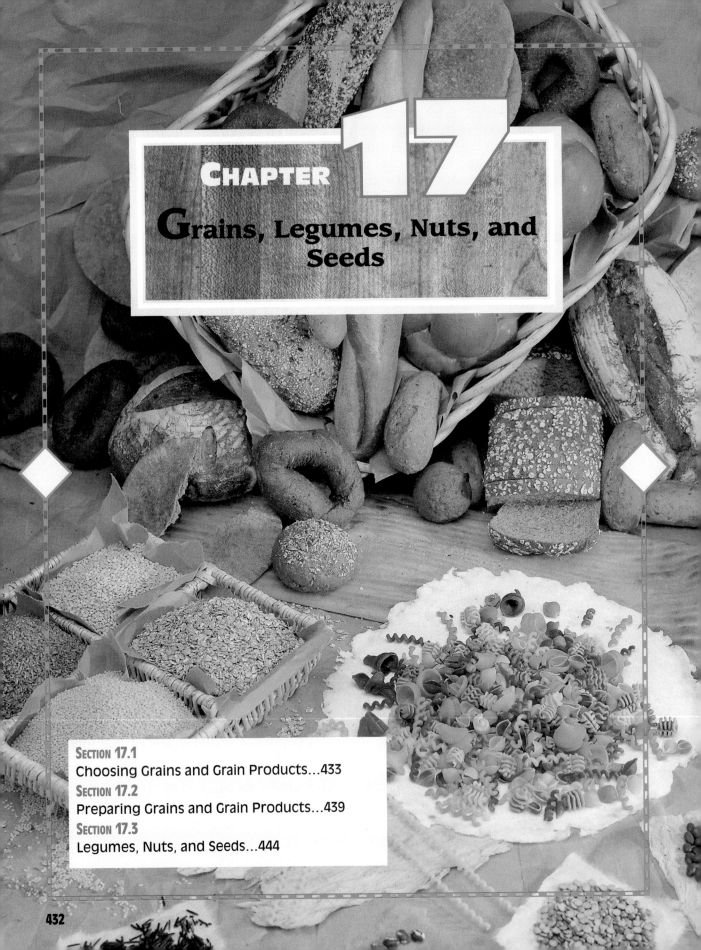

CHAPTER 17
Grains, Legumes, Nuts, and Seeds

Objectives

After studying this section, you should be able to:

❖ Describe the nutrients in grains and grain products.
❖ Identify different grain products and their uses.
❖ Give guidelines for buying and storing grain products.

Look for These Terms

germ
endosperm
bran
enrichment
fortified

Grains have been the most important staple in the world's food supply for thousands of years. How many grains and grain products can you name? After reading this section, you may be familiar with a few more than before.

What Are Grains?

Grains are the seeds of plants in the grass family. Common grains in North America include wheat, rice, corn, buckwheat, oats, rye, triticale (trih-tih-KAY-lee), barley, and millet.

Besides grains, a number of other foods also come from the seeds of plants: dry beans and peas, nuts, and sunflower seeds, for example. All of these edible seeds are alike in some ways. The seed is usually encased in a container of some kind—a soft pod (beans and peas), a hard shell (nuts and seeds), or a husk of dried plant material (grains). The seed itself has several parts:

❖ A tiny embryo that will grow into a new plant. In grains, this is called the **germ.**

❖ A food supply for the embryo, made up of proteins, starches, and other nutrients. In grains, this part of the seed is called the **endosperm.**
❖ An outer protective coat or skin. In grains, it is called the **bran.**

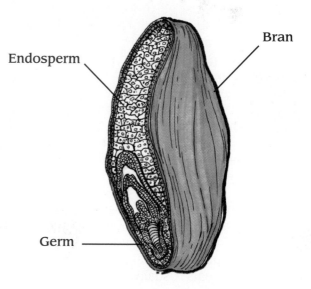

The three parts of the grain kernel are each nutritious.

After they are harvested, all grains are processed. However, some undergo more processing than others. Products made with the whole grain retain most of the nutrients found in the kernel.

Nutrients in Grains

Like all plant seeds, grains are packed with nutrients. The endosperm is high in complex carbohydrates and proteins. The bran is rich in fiber, B vitamins, and some minerals. The germ provides B vitamins, vitamin E, iron, zinc, and other trace minerals, along with unsaturated fat.

All grains must be processed before consumers can use them. The outer husk is removed, leaving the actual grain seed, called a kernel. The nutrients in the grains and grain products you eat depend on the way they are processed from that point on.

Sometimes the entire kernel is used to make whole grain products. Examples include whole wheat flour, brown rice, and whole grain breakfast cereals. These products contain most of the kernel's original nutrients.

In another method, the bran and germ are removed, along with the fiber and nutrients they contain. The remaining endosperm is made into products such as white flour or breakfast cereals. Usually, some of the nutrients lost in the processing are added to the product so the total is close to the original levels. This is known as **enrichment.** Some products are **fortified,** which means that the manufacturer has added 10 percent or more of the daily value for that nutrient.

The Food Guide Pyramid recommends eating 6 to 11 daily servings of enriched or whole grains and grain products. Typical servings include one slice of bread, 1/2 cup (125 mL) cooked cereal, rice, or pasta, or one ounce (28 g) ready-to-eat cereal.

Buying Grains and Grain Products

When you buy grains and grain products, keep nutrition in mind. Choose whole grain products as much as possible. Otherwise, be sure the product is enriched. Look for products low in fat, sugar, and sodium. Try different grains for variety.

When buying, read the labels to make certain you get the product you want. If the grain is visible in the package, inspect it carefully to be sure you are getting good quality. For example, be sure pasta is not cracked or broken.

The following information will help you select specific types of grains and grain products.

Rice

Several different varieties of rice are grown. You can choose from rice with short, medium, or long grains.

❖ **Short grain.** The grains are almost round. When cooked, the rice is moist and the grains stick together. Short-grain rice is a good choice for creamy dishes, molded rice rings, or eating with chopsticks.

❖ **Medium grain.** The grains are plump, tender, and moist. They stick together, but not as much as short-grain rice.

❖ **Long grain.** When cooked, the grains are fluffy and dry and stay separated.

Rice can also vary in the way it is processed. *Brown rice* is the whole grain form of rice. Only the outer hull has been removed; the bran and germ remain. *White rice* has had the bran and germ removed. *Converted rice* has been parboiled (briefly boiled) to save nutrients before the hull is removed. It takes longer to cook than regular white rice. *Instant rice* has been precooked and dehydrated. It takes only a few minutes to prepare.

Other Cooked Grains

Besides rice, many other types of grain can be cooked and served as a side dish. Cooked grains are also popular as a hot breakfast cereal. Some can be used in baking or other recipes. Here are some types of grains you might want to try:

❖ **Oats.** Usually eaten as a breakfast cereal or used in cooking. Quick-cooking types are available.

❖ **Cornmeal.** Coarsely ground dried corn. Available in yellow or white types. Used as a breakfast cereal and in baked goods.

The type of rice you choose may depend on how you plan to use it. What else would you consider when buying rice?

Many of the grain products you may find in the supermarket originally came from different places around the world. For example:

❖ Basmati (bahz-MAH-tee) rice is a variety from India, now also grown in America. It is fragrant with a rich, nutty flavor.

❖ Ramen (RAH-men) are Japanese noodles made of wheat and deep-fried. (Low-fat ramen are available.)

❖ Couscous (described on page 436) is very popular in the Middle East.

❖ Chapati (chah-PAH-tee) is a flat bread from India.

❖ Tortillas originated in Mexico.

Oats, shown here in kernel form, are just one of many grains that can be used as a breakfast cereal, as a side dish, or in recipes. How many different kinds have you tried?

* **Grits.** Coarsely ground endosperm of corn. Used as a breakfast cereal or side dish.
* **Bulgur.** Wheat kernels that have been steamed, dried, and crushed. Tender with a chewy texture. Used in main dishes, salads, and as a side dish.
* **Wheat berries.** Whole, unprocessed wheat kernels. Can be cooked as a cereal or added to other foods.
* **Couscous** (KOOS-koos). Steamed, cracked endosperm of wheat kernel. Has a nutty flavor. Used as a cereal, in salads and main dishes, or sweetened for dessert.
* **Cracked wheat.** Very hard with tough and chewy texture. Often added to bread.
* **Barley.** Mild-flavored grain. Usually used in soups and stews.
* **Kasha** (KAH-shah). Roasted buckwheat that is hulled and crushed. Has a pleasant, nutty flavor. Used as a breakfast cereal or side dish.
* **Millet.** Small, yellow grains with a mild flavor. Used as a breakfast cereal or side dish.

* **Triticale** (trih-tih-KAY-lee). A cross between wheat and rye, with more protein than wheat. Can be used in cereals and main dishes and combined with other cooked grains.
* **Brans.** The ground bran of oat, rice, or wheat can be purchased to use as a hot cereal or in cooking. All are high in fiber.

Instant and Ready-to-Eat Cereals

Some of the hot cereals already described, such as oats and grits, are also available in instant forms. Cooking time is shorter. Often sugar and other flavorings have been added.

Dry, ready-to-eat cereals come in many different varieties. Use the nutrition information on the label to help you make wise choices. Look for cereals that are high in complex carbohydrates and fiber, low in sugar and sodium. It's not necessary for a cereal to provide 100 percent of the nutrients you need in a day. You can get a nutritious product at a lower cost by buying cereals that are not so highly fortified.

Another ready-to-eat grain product is wheat germ. It has a pleasant, nutty flavor and is an excellent source of proteins, vitamins, and minerals. Wheat germ can be added to other foods for more nutrition. For example, you might sprinkle it on cereal or use it in recipes.Use wheat germ in small amounts—it contains fat, which could add up to more than you need.

Pasta

Pasta (PAH-stah) is an Italian word that means "paste." To make pasta, dough made from flour and water is rolled thin, then formed into hundreds of different shapes. Examples include spaghetti and macaroni.

Both enriched and whole-wheat pasta is available. Sometimes pasta is flavored and colored with other foods, such as spinach. Noodles are pasta made with eggs.

Pasta comes in many different shapes and colors for use in a variety of recipes.

Packages of dried pasta are found in the grocery section with other shelf-stable foods. You may find fresh pasta in the refrigerated section.

Breads

Breads range from enriched white bread to whole wheat and mixed whole grains. They come in assorted flavors, shapes, and sizes, including individual rolls.

Leavened (LEV-uhnd) breads are made with leavenings, ingredients such as yeast or baking powder that cause them to rise. Unleavened, or flat, breads—such as tortillas—are made without leavenings. Pita (PEE-tuh), also called pocket bread, is a flat bread that can be split horizontally to make a pocket which can be filled with food.

When buying bread, read the label carefully. "Whole wheat" means the product is made from the whole grain. If only the word

Leavened breads have a very different texture from unleavened breads. What makes the difference?

"wheat" is used, it usually means some part of the grain has been removed or white flour is used. Some dark breads are made with white flour colored with caramel or molasses.

Storing Grains and Grain Products

To maintain the quality of grains and grain products, follow these storage guidelines:

❖ Store whole grains and whole grain products in the refrigerator. Because they contain oil, they can spoil at room temperature if not used quickly.

❖ Refrigerate fresh pasta.

❖ Store other uncooked grains and grain products, such as white rice and dried pasta, in a cool, dry place in tightly covered containers.

❖ Store breads at room temperature for short-term storage. Otherwise, freeze. If bread is refrigerated, it gets stale faster. However, in humid weather, refrigerate bread to prevent mold from growing.

❖ Store cooked grains in the refrigerator if they will be used within a few days. For longer storage, freeze.

A label that says "wheat bread" doesn't necessarily mean the bread is made from the whole grain. Remember, wheat is used to make both whole wheat flour and enriched white flour.

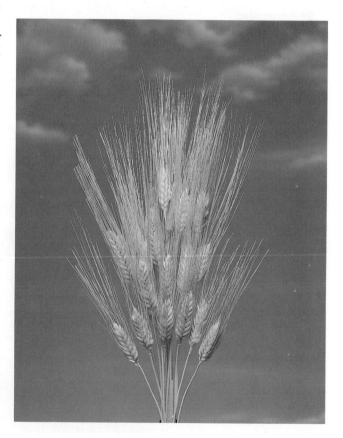

Section 17.1 Review

RECALL THE FACTS

1. Identify the three parts of the grain kernel and the nutrients found in each.

2. Name four grains that can be cooked and eaten as a side dish.

3. What should you look for when choosing a nutritious ready-to-eat cereal?

4. How should bread be stored?

DISCUSS YOUR IDEAS

5. What qualities have made grain products so popular around the world?

APPLY YOUR LEARNING

6. Find three recipes that each use a different grain or grain product. Identify the type of grain or grain product and describe its nutritional value.

Objectives

After studying this section, you should be able to:

❖ Explain the general principles of cooking grains.
❖ Describe how to successfully prepare rice and other grains, pasta, and breakfast cereals.

Look for This Term

al dente

Properly prepared, grains can be a nutritious, flavorful part of any meal, from breakfast to a meal for company. You can serve them plain or use recipes that might add vegetables, seasonings, and sauces. Some can even be served as desserts if sweeteners and fruit are added.

Principles of Cooking Grains

Because they are dry, grains must be cooked in water. They need enough time to absorb the amount of water needed to make them edible.

Even though most grains are cooked in a similar way, cooking methods and times do vary. Always follow package or recipe directions.

Unless package directions state otherwise, do not rinse enriched grains before cooking. Rinsing causes loss of the added B vitamins.

Microwaving grains is not always practical. Because grains need time to absorb the liquid and soften, microwaving does not usually save time. Pasta, for instance, takes just

as long to microwave as it does to cook conventionally. However, check the package for microwave directions.

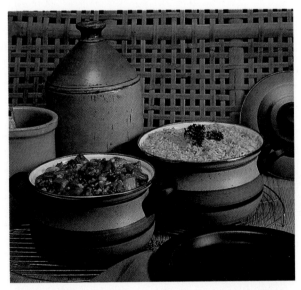

Grains are a delicious part of many dishes, such as this mulligan stew served with rice.

Preparing Rice and Other Grains

Rice is usually simmered, using just the amount of water that the grain can absorb. Bring the water to a boil, add the rice, cover, and bring to a boil again. Then reduce the heat so the rice simmers gently.

Package directions may tell you to stir the rice at intervals as it cooks. Do not stir long-grain rice unless necessary. Stirring scrapes off starch, making the grains stick together.

Near the end of cooking time, check the rice for doneness. It should be tender but firm. There should be no water left. If any water remains, continue cooking without the cover until the excess water evaporates.

Many other grains, such as barley, grits, and kasha, are cooked in much the same way. The chart below gives information about cooking different grains.

Instant rice requires a slightly different method. Follow package directions.

Preparing Pasta

Unlike rice and other grains, pasta is cooked, uncovered, in a large amount of boiling water. Pasta is one of very few foods that must be boiled. The boiling helps circulate the pasta so it cooks evenly.

TIPS for Success

Cooking Pasta

Pasta sometimes tends to stick together during or after cooking. Here are some suggestions to prevent sticking:

❖ Use plenty of water.
❖ Bring the water to a rapid boil. Then add the spaghetti slowly so the boiling does not stop.
❖ Stir frequently during cooking.

Cooking Grains

To cook 1 cup (250 mL) dry grain, use the amount of water shown and cook for the time indicated.

Grain	Amount of Water	Cooking Time	Cooked Yield (approx.)
Barley (pearl)	2 ½ cups (625 mL)	40-45 min.	3 cups (750 mL)
Bulgur	2 cups (500 mL)	30 min.*	2 ½ cups (625 mL)
Cornmeal	4 cups (1 L)	25 min.	3 cups (750 mL)
Grits (regular)	4 cups (1 L)	25 min.	3 cups (750 mL)
Kasha	2 cups (500 mL)	15 min.	2 ½ cups (625 mL)
Millet	2 ½ to 3 cups (625 to 750 mL)	35 to 40 min.	3 ½ cups (875 mL)
Rice (long or medium grain)	2 cups (500 mL)	45 min. (brown) 15 min. (white)	3 cups (750 mL)

*Do not cook bulgur; pour boiling water over it and let stand 30 minutes.

After the water has come to a rapid boil, add the pasta slowly. That way it will be less likely to stick together.

Check the package for the amount of water to use. With spaghetti, for example, use about 1 quart (1 L) of water for every 4 ounces (112 g) of spaghetti. Be sure the pot is large enough for the amount of water used and the boiling action of the water.

Pasta is generally cooked to a doneness stage known as **al dente** (ahl DEHN-tay), which means it is firm to the bite. Cooking time varies from 5 to 20 minutes, depending on the thickness of the pasta. If the pasta is to be further cooked in a recipe (such as lasagne), cook it for a shorter time so it is slightly more firm.

Unless directions state otherwise, fresh pasta will cook in a fraction of the time needed by dried pasta. Otherwise, the methods are the same.

After cooking, drain the pasta in a colander or strainer. Never rinse pasta after cooking—it loses valuable nutrients. To keep cooked pasta hot, set the colander or strainer over a pan of hot water and cover.

The chart at the bottom of the page gives the yield of cooked pasta from a given amount of dry.

If you have leftover cooked pasta, freeze it. First, stir 1 tsp. (5 mL) cooking oil into the hot drained pasta to keep it from sticking. Freeze in serving-size portions.

Healthy Attitudes

Pasta, in itself, is a low-fat, low-calorie, high-protein and high-carbohydrate food. However, sauces and other foods added to pasta can greatly increase fat and calories. Look for low-fat sauces for pasta, or adapt recipes to lower the fat.

Dry Pasta Quantities

Type of Pasta	Dry Weight	Dry Volume	Cooked Yield (approx.)
Small pasta, such as macaroni, shells, spirals, twists	4 oz. (112 g)	1 cup (250 mL)	2 ½ cups (675 mL)
Long, slender pasta, such as spaghetti, linguini	4 oz. (112 g)	1-inch diameter bunch	2 cups (500 mL)

Preparing Breakfast Cereals

Follow the package directions for cooking hot breakfast cereals. Some can be cooked in either water or milk. Instant hot cereals usually require only that you add boiling water. Some ready-to-eat cereals can be microwaved to serve hot.

Cereals, cold or hot, are usually eaten with milk. For natural sweetness and added nutrients, try adding fresh or dried fruit, such as strawberries, raisins, dried apricots, or sliced bananas. If more sweetness is desired, you can add a small amount of sugar, honey, molasses, or syrup.

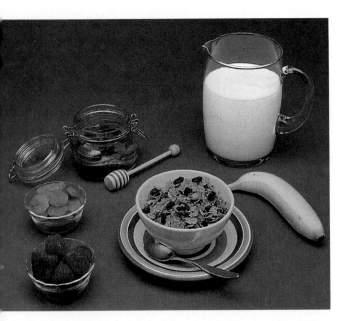

Try adding your own toppings to breakfast cereals for added flavor and nutrients. It's usually more economical than buying cereal with fruit already in it.

There are many ways to use grains in meals. How many can you think of?

■ Section 17.2 Review ■

RECALL THE FACTS

1. Why shouldn't you rinse grains before cooking them?

2. Does microwaving grains save time? Explain.

3. How can you tell when rice is properly cooked?

4. How does the preparation of pasta differ from that of most other foods? What is the reason for using this preparation method?

DISCUSS YOUR IDEAS

5. What are some creative ways to use grains in meals?

APPLY YOUR LEARNING

6. Find recipes for a variety of pasta sauces. Which appear to be low in fat? How might you reduce the fat in the other recipes?

Thinking About the Recipe

Read the recipe for "Western Beans with Rice" and answer the following questions.

1. What foods provide most of the protein in this recipe?
2. If you wanted to reduce the sodium in this recipe, what changes would you make?

Western Beans and Rice

Customary	Ingredients	Metric
(See package directions)	Instant brown rice	(See package directions)
(See rice package directions)	Water	(See rice package directions)
1 Tbsp.	Vegetable oil	15 mL
1 cup	Chopped onion	250 mL
1 cup	Diced celery	250 mL
3 cups	Canned pinto beans, drained	750 mL
8-oz. can	Tomato sauce	224-g can
1/2 cup	Water	125 mL
1/4 tsp.	Hot pepper sauce	1 mL

Yield: 6 servings

Conventional Directions

Pan: Saucepan; large skillet
Temperature: High, then low

1. Prepare instant brown rice in saucepan, according to package directions, using amount of rice and water to make 3 cups cooked rice.
2. While rice is cooking, heat oil in skillet. Cook onions and celery in oil until tender.
3. Stir in beans, tomato sauce, 1/2 cup water, and hot pepper sauce.
4. Heat mixture thoroughly..
5. Serve over hot rice.

Microwave Directions

Pan: Saucepan; 1-qt. (1-L) microwave-safe dish with cover
Power level: 100 percent power

1. Prepare rice as in Step 1 of conventional directions.
2. Combine onions and celery in microwave-safe dish. Cover.
3. Cook onions and celery at 100 percent power for 2 minutes, stirring after 1 minute.
4. Stir in beans, tomato sauce, 1/2 cup water, and hot pepper sauce. Cover.
5. Cook mixture at 100 percent power for 5 to 8 minutes, stirring after 4 minutes.
6. Serve over hot rice.

Nutrition Information

Per serving—coventional directions (approximate): 246 calories, 9 g protein, 46 g carbohydrate, 4 g fat, 0 mg cholesterol, 752 mg sodium

Objectives

After studying this section, you should be able to:

❖ Identify the nutrients in legumes, nuts, and seeds.

❖ Give guidelines for buying, storing, and preparing legumes, nuts, and seeds.

Look for This Term

legumes

Legumes are plants whose seeds grow in pods. They include beans, peas, and lentils.

Legumes come in different shapes, sizes, and colors. In one form or another, they are available in most parts of the world. They are considered to be the second most important food in the world, after grains.

Legumes are excellent sources of complex carbohydrates, proteins, fiber, B vitamins, iron, calcium, potassium, and some trace minerals. Except for soybeans, they are low in fat.

Nutrients in Legumes

As explained in Section 17.1, all edible seeds have several parts. The inside of a legume contains the embryo, the tiny seedling that will grow into a plant under the right conditions. Surrounding the seedling is its food supply, rich in proteins, carbohydrates, vitamins, and minerals.

When beans and peas are green, they are eaten as vegetables. At that stage in their growth, however, they have not yet developed the proteins and some of the other nutrients found in legumes. As legumes mature, they store up nutrients for the embryo's food supply.

Legumes store up nutrients as they mature. Here, lima beans are being harvested.

The combination of grains and legumes, as in this lasagne made with dry beans, provides complete protein. What are the advantages of using legumes and grains as protein sources?

Legumes are included in the Meat, Poultry, Fish, Dry Beans, Eggs, and Nuts Group in the Food Guide Pyramid. Health experts urge people to eat dry beans, peas, or lentils at least twice a week instead of meat. When counting your servings, 1/2 cup (125 mL) of cooked dry beans counts as 1 ounce (28 g) of lean meat.

Legumes and grains work perfectly as a team. Each has the amino acids the other one lacks. By eating both sometime during the day, you can get the essential amino acids needed for good health. Grains and legumes make up about two-thirds of the protein eaten by people around the world.

ting good quality. Look for bright color, no visible damage, and uniform size. Mixed sizes result in uneven cooking, since smaller ones cook faster than larger ones.

Store dry legumes in a cool, dry place. Once the package has been opened, transfer the remainder to a tightly covered container.

Cooked legumes should be stored in the refrigerator if they will be used within a few days. For longer storage, freeze. When putting the beans in freezer containers, add enough cooking liquid to cover them so they will not dry out. Frozen cooked beans can be thawed in a microwave oven or in the refrigerator.

Buying and Storing Legumes

Many types of legumes are available. The box on page 446 describes some examples.

When buying legumes, purchase only as much as you will use within six months. Legumes continue to dry out when stored. The drier they are, the longer they will take to cook.

If legumes are visible in the package, inspect them carefully to be sure you are get-

Preparing Legumes

Like grains, legumes are prepared by cooking in water. They need time to absorb water until they become soft enough to eat. Always follow package or recipe directions.

Cooked beans can be served as a side dish or used in recipes such as casseroles, soups, and salads. Preparing dry beans takes time, but is relatively easy. Lentils and dry peas cook in less than an hour. Dry peas are usually used in soup. Lentils are used in soup or as a side dish.

Type of Legume	Typical Uses
Black beans (turtle beans) Black skin, cream-colored inside, sweet flavor.	Soups, other dishes. Popular in Latin American and Asian cooking.
Black-eyed peas Actually beans, not peas. Small, oval, with black "eye" on one side.	Main dishes; "Hoppin' John" (popular Southern recipe).
Dry peas Available whole or split, green or yellow.	Soups.
Garbanzo beans (chickpeas) Round, roughly shaped, nut-like flavor, firm texture. Hold their shape when cooked.	Appetizers, salads, main dishes.
Lentils Thin, tiny, disc-shaped. Come in colors ranging from grayish brown to green to reddish orange.	Soups, stews, salads, side dish. Main ingredient in East Indian dish *dal*.
Lima beans White, flat beans in assorted sizes. Baby limas are smallest with mild flavor. Butter beans are largest with a rich, buttery flavor.	Soups, casseroles, side dish.
Pink and red beans Vary in size, flavor, and intensity of color. Kidney beans are largest with a hearty flavor.	Chili and other Latin American main dishes.
Pinto beans Pink and white, speckled. Similar in flavor and texture to pink and red beans.	Mexican foods, such as chili and refried beans.
Soybeans Distinct flavor. High in fat and protein. Difficult to digest.	Usually eaten in form of soy products, such as tofu and soy milk.
White beans Vary in size and flavor, but all have a firm texture. Great Northern are largest.	Navy beans are medium size. Soups, baked beans.

Sorting, rinsing, and soaking are the first steps in preparing beans.

Sorting and Rinsing

Before cooking, sort legumes carefully. Pick out foreign material such as pebbles and stems. Also discard any legumes that are damaged, are smaller than the others, or have a greenish tint.

Rinse the legumes carefully by placing them in cool water. Drain them and rinse again. Repeat, if necessary, until the water is clear.

Soaking Beans

Beans normally take from one and a half to three hours to cook. Soaking before cooking can cut down on the cooking time by 15 to 30 minutes. Dry peas and lentils do not have to be soaked.

To soak beans, use a large pot. For every pound (500 g) of any kind of beans, sorted and washed, add 10 cups (2500 mL) hot water. Simmer for two to three minutes, then turn off the heat and cover the beans. Let them soak for at least an hour. The longer beans soak, the less cooking time they need.

Healthy Attitudes

People sometimes avoid beans because they may produce gas in the digestive system. The effect is caused by certain complex sugars in the beans that cannot be digested. Here are some suggestions that may help minimize the problem.

- Add beans to your food choices gradually. Start with a small amount once a week and gradually work up to larger amounts. This helps your body adapt.
- Soak beans before cooking. Change the soaking water several times. Use fresh water for cooking.
- Try different varieties of beans. Some cause more gas than others.

Most people find that if they add beans to their food choices gradually, they are better able to digest them.

Simmering Beans

The next step is to cook the legumes. If beans have been soaked, drain and rinse them first.

Place the beans in a large pot—they double in volume as they cook. Add water, using the amount specified in the package directions as a guide. More water may be needed if the legumes are older and drier. If desired, you can add chopped onions, garlic, and dried herbs for a flavorful broth.

Cover the pot and bring the water to a boil. Then lower the heat to a simmer.

Use the package directions as a guide for cooking time. For best results, start checking at the minimum cooking time given. If the beans are not tender enough, continue cooking. If the beans will be used in a salad or further cooked in a recipe, cook them a shorter time so they are a little more firm. If you plan to mash them, cook longer so they are a little more soft.

TIPS for Success

Cooking Beans

❖ Simmer beans gently. If boiled, they get mushy and the skins break.

❖ Leave the cover slightly ajar during cooking. If the pot is tightly covered, the cooking liquid foams up and can boil over.

❖ Check several times during cooking to make sure the beans are always covered with water. If more water is needed, add hot water, not cold.

❖ Salt and acid foods, such as vinegar and tomatoes, toughen beans. Add them near the end of the cooking time, if desired.

If you were cooking beans to use in a salad such as this one, would you shorten or lengthen the cooking time? Why?

When done, the beans should have only a little cooking liquid left. Serve the liquid with the beans—it contains B vitamins. If you plan to use only the beans, save the liquid for soups, sauces, or broth.

Other Methods

An easy way to cook beans is with a slow cooker. Do not presoak them. Check the owner's manual of the slow cooker for exact directions. In general, the beans are combined with boiling water in the cooker. Mix well, cover, and cook on the high setting. This method generally takes three to eight hours, depending on the kind of beans.

Beans can also be cooked in a pressure cooker. Follow directions in the owner's manual.

Convenience Forms of Beans

If you don't have time to cook dry beans, don't let that stop you from using them in meals. Canned beans are a time-saver because they are already cooked. Use plain canned beans in recipes as you would cooked dry beans. Rinse them first to cut down on sodium. They can be mashed by hand or in a blender to make dips, sandwich spreads, and fillings for tacos. You can also buy canned beans with sauces and seasonings added.

Sunflower seeds are a popular type of edible seed. What nutrients do they provide?

Legumes can be cooked in the microwave, too. It takes about the same amount of time as conventional cooking. If you want to prepare a bean recipe in the microwave oven, use canned beans to save time.

Nuts and Seeds

Like legumes, nuts and seeds are included in the Meat Group in the Food Guide Pyramid. Nuts and seeds are high in protein and B vitamins. Because they are also very high in fat, however, they should be used sparingly.

A wide assortment of nuts are available, including almonds, filberts, cashews, Brazil nuts, and walnuts. Even though peanuts are legumes, most people use them as they do other nuts. The most popular edible seeds include pumpkin, squash, sunflower, and sesame.

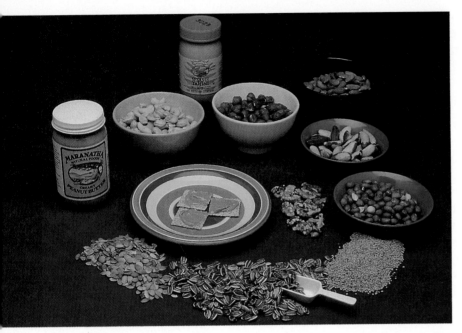

Nuts and seeds, and spreads made from them, can add flavor, texture, and nutrients to many recipes.

Buying and Storing Nuts and Seeds

Nuts and seeds are sold with or without the shell. Some are roasted with oil, which adds more fat. Dry roasting is a special process that roasts nuts and seeds without adding oil.

Nuts and seeds can be ground into a thick, spreadable paste. Peanut butter is a common example. Tahini (tuh-HEE-nee) is a spread made from ground sesame seeds. It is popular in Middle Eastern cooking as a spread and flavoring.

When buying nuts and seeds, avoid those in shells that are cracked or broken. Harmful germs may be present in the edible parts.

Store nuts and seeds in the refrigerator. Because they contain oil, they can spoil at room temperature if not used quickly.

Using Nuts and Seeds

You can enjoy nuts and seeds in a variety of ways. Chopped or ground nuts and seeds add flavor and texture to baked goods, salads, cereal, and yogurt. They can also be used in meatless main dishes for added protein. Nut butters and spreads can be used in sandwiches or recipes.

Section 17.3 Review

RECALL THE FACTS

1. Name five nutrients supplied by legumes.

2. Within how many months should dry legumes be used? Why?

3. What are the three basic steps in preparing dry beans?

4. Why should nuts and seeds be used sparingly?

DISCUSS YOUR IDEAS

5. What characteristics of legumes might account for their importance in the world food supply?

APPLY YOUR LEARNING

6. Look through cookbooks to find recipes that use legumes in each of the following: a vegetarian main dish, a main dish with meat or poultry, a soup, a salad, and a side dish. Be prepared to discuss how the recipe directions relate to the preparation principles you have learned in this section.

CAREER PROFILE

Steve Helman
Farmer

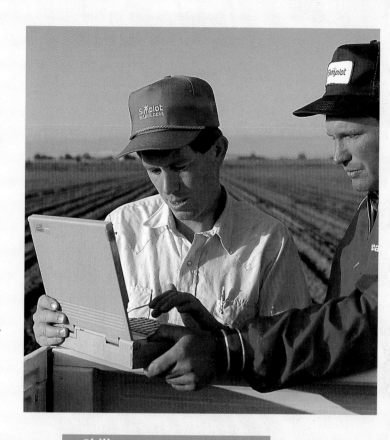

Job description:

"I own a Midwestern crop farm that's been in my family for five generations."

Responsibilities:

"When most people think of farming, they picture you out in the field on a tractor, planting and harvesting. That's part of the job, of course, but there's a lot more to it. Our farm is a family business. We have to plan how to use our land, what type of seed to buy, what yield to expect, when to buy new equipment—everything involved in getting a crop to market."

Why I chose this job:

"I grew up on this farm, and I couldn't imagine ever leaving it. To me, farming is not just a job, but a way of life."

Education:

"I took time off from farming to earn a four-year college degree in agriculture. When I was in high school I participated in the Future Farmers of America and 4-H."

Skills:

"Besides the physical stamina you need to be a farmer, you must be organized and able to plan ahead. You also have to be aware of outside influences, such as the weather and fluctuations in prices, and you must be able to keep financial and inventory books."

Favorite part of the job:

"It's very rewarding to be my own boss. My goal is to produce the highest yield of top-quality corn and soybeans possible."

- In what ways could a personal computer be useful in managing the business aspects of a farm?
- What aspects of Steve's job do you think you might enjoy? Why?

Summary

Section 17.1
Choosing Grains and Grain Products:
Grain kernels are made up of the germ, endosperm, and bran. Grains are generally high in complex carbohydrates, proteins, fiber, vitamins, and minerals. However, the nutrition of grains depends on how they are processed. Cooked grains are popular as side dishes and breakfast cereals. Grain products include instant and ready-to-eat cereals, pasta, and breads. Look for nutrition and quality when buying. Store grains and grain products properly to maintain their quality.

Section 17.2
Preparing Grains and Grain Products:
Grains must be cooked before eating. Although cooking methods for many grains are similar, always check the package directions. Rice and many other grains are simmered in only as much water as they can absorb. Pasta is boiled in a large amount of water, then drained. Breakfast cereals are served hot or cold, often with milk and fruit.

Section 17.3
Legumes, Nuts, and Seeds: Legumes are high in protein, fiber, and other nutrients. Most are low in fat. The many types of legumes can be used in main dishes, side dishes, and salads. Dry beans require long cooking in water. Soaking dry beans first decreases the cooking time. Nuts and seeds are high in protein, but also fat. They may be eaten plain or added to baked goods and other dishes.

REVIEWING FACTS

1. What is the difference between whole grain and enriched products? (17.1)

2. Describe the following grain products and tell how they are used: couscous, kasha, triticale. (17.1)

3. Name three specific instances of grains or grain products that should be refrigerated. (17.1)

4. Why must grains be cooked before they are eaten? (17.2)

5. What type of rice should not be stirred during cooking? Why? (17.2)

6. What term is used to describe properly cooked pasta? What does it mean? (17.2)

7. Describe the following legumes and tell how they are used: garbanzo beans; lentils; soybeans. (17.3)

8. Give three guidelines for buying legumes. (17.3)

9. Briefly describe how to cook beans. (17.3)

10. What is dry roasting? (17.3)

LEARNING BY DOING

1. **Taste test:** Prepare a variety of different grains, such as couscous, bulgur, and millet. Compare them for taste, texture, and appearance. Decide what types of dishes or recipes each grain might be used in. Give reasons for your answers. (17.1, 17.2)

2. **Foods lab:** Prepare a dessert dish using rice or pasta. What nutritional value does rice or pasta add to the dessert? (17.2)

3. **Foods lab:** Make your own spread from nuts or seeds. (Look in a cookbook for a basic peanut butter recipe and adapt it to use different nuts or seeds if desired.) Evaluate the results on taste, texture, and appearance. Explain how you might use the product. (17.3)

THINKING CRITICALLY

1. **Drawing conclusions:** Why do you think the bran and germ are sometimes removed when processing grains, even though it results in a less nutritious product? (17.1)

2. **Recognizing fallacies:** A friend of yours who wants to lose weight avoids pasta because he thinks it is fattening. Do you agree? Explain your answer. (17.1, 17.2)

3. **Identifying cause and effect:** Your friend tells you that the last time she cooked beans, they were tough and chewy. What are some possible explanations for this? (17.3)

MAKING DECISIONS AND SOLVING PROBLEMS

What Would You Do?

1. Your family relies mostly on processed grain products and eats very few whole grains. You would like to start introducing more whole grains to make your family's meals more nutritious. (17.1)

2. You have cooked too much rice for your family's dinner. You wonder what to do with the leftovers. (17.2)

3. You would like to cook beans for your family's dinner tonight, but you will be out of the house all day. (17.3)

LINKING YOUR STUDIES

1. **Social studies:** Using library sources, write a report on a grain that is popular in a specific foreign country. How was the grain introduced in that country? Why is it popular? How is it used? What percentage of the population is employed in growing and processing the grain? (17.1)

2. **Math:** Draw a graph comparing the cooking times of various grains and legumes. (17.2, 17.3)

3. **Science:** Write a short report on scientist George Washington Carver. What contributions did he make to the use of peanuts? What were some of his creations or discoveries? How do you benefit today from his work? (17.3)

CHAPTER 18

Dairy Foods and Eggs

Objectives

After studying this section, you should be able to:

❖ Identify nutrients in dairy foods.
❖ Describe the types of dairy foods available.
❖ Give guidelines for buying and storing dairy foods.

Look for These Terms

nonfat milk solids
pasteurized
ultra-pasteurization
homogenized
cultured
ripened cheese
unripened cheese

Dairy foods include milk and the many products made from milk, such as yogurt and different kinds of cheeses.

Nutrients in Dairy Foods

Milk has been called an "almost-perfect" food. It is especially high in proteins, vitamin A, riboflavin, vitamin B_{12}, calcium, phosphorus, magnesium, and zinc. When fortified, it is an excellent source of vitamin D.

Milk also contains saturated fat and cholesterol. Some or most of the fat can be removed to produce skim and low-fat milk. These products also have less cholesterol.

The fat in other dairy products depends on the kind of milk from which they are made. Those made with skim or low-fat milk have less fat.

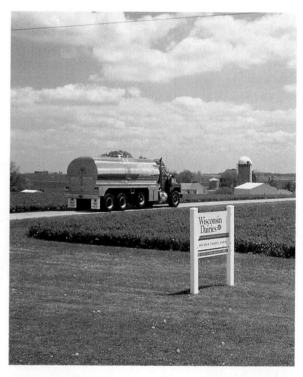

Wisconsin produces more dairy products than any other state. Other leading dairy states include California, Minnesota, New York, and Pennsylvania.

The Food Guide Pyramid recommends two to three servings a day from the Milk Group. A typical serving includes 1 cup (250 mL) of milk or yogurt, 1½ ounces (42 g) of natural cheese, or 2 ounces (56 g) of processed cheese.

Types of Dairy Foods

An array of dairy foods are available in the marketplace. They include fresh and convenience forms of milk, cheeses, cream, butter, and frozen dairy desserts.

Milk

As stated earlier, milk is available with varying fat content. The dairy industry measures fat in milk by weight. From a nutrition standpoint, however, it is more useful to know the percentage of calories that come from fat.

* *Whole milk* is 3.3 percent fat by weight with 48 percent of the calories from fat.
* *Low-fat milk* is 1 to 2 percent fat by weight with 16 to 38 percent of calories from fat.
* *Skim milk* contains only a trace of fat.

Fresh whole milk contains about 87 percent water and 13 percent solids. Some of the solids are milkfat. The **nonfat milk solids** contain most of the protein, vitamins, minerals, and lactose (milk sugar) found in milk.

Processing of Fluid Milk

Before milk reaches the marketplace as a beverage, it must be processed. Government regulations state that milk must be **pasteurized,** or heat-treated to kill enzymes and harmful bacteria. Enzymes in milk can make it spoil quickly. **Ultra-pasteurization** heats milk to a higher temperature, which means it can be kept refrigerated longer than pasteurized milk.

UHT (ultra-high temperature) milk is processed the same as ultra-pasteurized milk. It is packaged in aseptic containers (sometimes called "juice boxes"), which makes it a shelf-stable product.

Milkfat is lighter than other milk fluids and easily separates, rising to the top of the milk. When milk is **homogenized,** the fat is broken down and evenly distributed in the milk so it does not separate.

Inspectors test milk during and after processing to ensure quality and safety.

When milk is skimmed, most of the vitamin A is removed. By law, any vitamin A removed when making low-fat and skim milk must be replaced. In addition, some manufacturers voluntarily fortify milk with vitamin D.

Other Types of Milk

Besides plain fluid milk, various flavored milks and convenience products are available.

Some milk products are **cultured**. This means a harmless bacteria culture is added to them after pasteurization. The bacteria cause fermentation to take place. This gives cultured dairy products, such as yogurt and buttermilk, a characteristic tangy, acidic flavor.

❖ **Buttermilk** has a tart, buttery flavor and smooth, thick texture. It was originally a fluid left after cream was churned into butter. Now it is made from cultured low-fat or skim milk. Often nonfat dry milk solids are added.

❖ **Chocolate milk** has chocolate or cocoa and sweetener added.

❖ **Kefir** (keh-FUR) is a beverage similar in flavor to yogurt. The authentic Middle Eastern beverage is made of fermented camel's milk. In the United States, kefir is made from cultured cow's milk.

A variety of milk products are available for use as beverages or in cooking.

❖ **Nonfat dry milk** is a powdered form of skim milk. When reconstituted, use and refrigerate as you do liquid skim milk. The instant variety mixes with water more easily. Add the powder directly to recipes to increase nutrients, especially protein and calcium, without adding fat.

❖ **Evaporated milk** is canned whole or skim milk that contains only half the amount of water as regular milk. Use evaporated skim milk as a nonfat cream substitute in beverages.

❖ **Sweetened condensed milk** is concentrated, sweetened canned milk. It is used to make candy and desserts.

Yogurt

Yogurt is made by adding a harmless bacteria culture to milk, resulting in a thick, creamy, custard-like product with a tangy flavor. Yogurt may be purchased plain or with added flavorings such as vanilla and fruits.

Science Connection

Chemistry:

Coagulating Milk Protein

Milk contains many different proteins, but two major ones are involved in making milk products such as yogurt and cheese. The two proteins are casein (kay-SEEN) and whey (way). When an acid food or milk-clotting enzymes such as rennin (REH-nihn) are added to milk, the two proteins separate. Casein clumps together into solid groups called curds, as in cottage cheese. The whey is a thin, bluish liquid that remains after the curds clump. By turning proteins into curds, many different dairy products are made.

Yogurt is a concentrated form of milk and is therefore higher in nutrients. For example, 1 cup (250 mL) of nonfat yogurt has 452 milligrams of calcium, while a cup (250 mL) of skim milk has 302 milligrams.

Cheeses

Cheese is made from curds with the whey drained off. There are two basic categories of cheeses—ripened (also called aged) and unripened.

Ripened cheese is made from curds to which ripening agents, such as bacteria, mold, yeast, or a combination of these, have been added. The cheese is then aged under carefully controlled conditions. Aging time depends on the kind of cheese. The result is a cheese that can be stored for a relatively long time.

The texture of ripened cheeses can be categorized as soft, semi-soft, semi-hard, hard, and very hard cheeses.

Specialty cheeses are created by combining several ripened cheeses by either cold or hot processing methods. *Cold pack* cheese is a blend of ripened cheeses processed without heat. Flavorings and seasoning are often added. *Pasteurized process cheese* is a blend of ripened cheeses processed with heat. Examples include process American cheese, cheese spread, and cheese food.

Unripened cheese is made of curds that have not been aged. Most unripened cheeses will keep only a few days in the refrigerator.

The chart on page 459 describes some different varieties of cheeses.

Cream

Cream is a liquid separated from milk. Several types are available that vary in fat content. Heavy cream, the highest in fat, whips easily. Light cream, which is not as high in fat, is used in coffee. Half and half is a mixture of milk and cream. Sour cream, made by adding lactic acid bacteria to cream, is thick and rich with a tangy flavor.

Cheese is made by adding enzymes or other ingredients to milk, causing it to thicken and form curds. The curds are then separated from the whey and further processed into cheese.

Types of Cheese

RIPENED CHEESES	Appearance	Texture and Flavor
Blue Cheese	White cheese with a blue vein.	*Semi-soft.* Tangy flavor.
Brick	Light yellow in color.	*Semi-soft.* Sweet, mild but pungent flavor.
Brie (bree)	White, edible crust with a creamy yellow interior.	*Soft.* Mild to pungent flavor.
Camembert (KAM-ehm-behr)	White, edible crust with a creamy yellow interior. Similar to Brie.	*Soft.* Mild to pungent flavor.
Cheddar	White to orange in color.	*Hard.* Mild to sharp in flavor.
Colby	Similar to Cheddar, but more moist.	*Hard.* Mild to sharp in flavor.
Edam (EE-duhm)	Creamy yellow Dutch cheese with red wax coating.	*Semi-hard.* Mild, nut-like flavor.
Feta (FAY-tuh)	White, crumbly cheese.	*Semi-hard.* Salty "pickled" flavor.
Gouda	Creamy yellow cheese with red wax coating. Similar to Edam, but higher in fat.	*Semi-hard.* Mild, nut-like flavor.
Monterey Jack	Creamy white cheese with tiny cracks.	*Semi-soft.* Mild flavor.
Muenster (MUHN-stir)	Orange exterior and white interior.	*Semi-soft.* Mild flavor.
Parmesan (PAHR-muh-zahn)	Creamy white, granular cheese.	*Very hard.* Tangy, robust flavor.
Provolone (proh-vo-LOW-nee)	Creamy golden yellow, plastic-like cheese.	Hard. Bland to sharp, smoked. flavor.
Romano (roh-MAH-noh)	Creamy white, similar to Parmesan.	Very hard. Rich, tangy flavor.
Swiss	Creamy white cheese with holes in it.	Hard. Firm with a nut-like flavor.
UNRIPENED CHEESES	Appearance	Texture and Flavor
Cottage Cheese	Moist, soft cheese with large or small curd.	Bland flavor, but flavorings such as chives may be added May be creamed.
Cream Cheese	Smooth, spreadable white cheese.	Mild, slightly acid flavor. Flavorings such as strawberry may be added.
Farmer's Cheese	Firm and dry. Similar to cottage cheese.	Bland flavor.
Mozzarella	Creamy white, plastic-like cheese.	Semi-soft. Mild flavor.
Ricotta	Moist, white cheese.	Mild, sweet flavor.

Butter

Butter is made from milk, cream, or a combination of both. Because it is high in saturated fat and also contains cholesterol, it should be used in moderation.

Butter is graded for quality by the USDA. *Grade AA* is superior in quality. It has a delicate sweet flavor, a smooth creamy texture, and spreads well. It may be purchased salted or unsalted. *Grade A* butter is very good in quality and has a pleasing flavor with a smooth texture. *Grade B* butter is made from sour cream and has a pleasing flavor.

Frozen Dairy Desserts

Several different types of frozen desserts are available. They differ in fat content and ingredients. All come in a variety of flavors. Here are some examples:

* ❖ **Ice cream** is a whipped frozen mixture of milk, cream, sweeteners, flavorings, and other additives.
* ❖ **Ice milk** is similar to ice cream, but has less fat and usually more sugar.
* ❖ **Sherbet** also has less fat and more sugar than ice cream. Besides milkfat and sugar, it contains water, flavorings, and other additives.

* ❖ **Frozen yogurt** is similar to ice milk but with yogurt cultures added. Some frozen yogurt has about the same amount of fat as ice milk. Nonfat frozen yogurt is also available.

Buying and Storing Dairy Foods

When buying dairy products, look for the date on the package. Most milk products can be safely used up to five days beyond the "sell by" date if they have been stored properly. Yogurt and some ripened cheeses may be stored for longer periods of time. Make sure containers are sealed tightly and have not been opened before you buy them.

Dairy foods are highly perishable. Store them immediately when you get home from shopping. Refrigerate all dairy foods in their original containers, if possible.

The different types of frozen dairy desserts differ in ingredients, fat, and calories. Check the label to be sure you know which kind you are buying.

Cheese can be frozen for later use in cooked dishes, such as this turkey and rice casserole.

Here are some additional tips for storing dairy foods:

* Tightly close milk and cream containers. These products can pick up aromas from other foods and develop off-flavors.
* Store milk away from light. Light destroys the riboflavin (a B vitamin) in milk.
* Keep cheeses tightly wrapped.
* Hard cheeses can be frozen, but the texture will change. Freeze in 1/2 pound (250 g) portions. Use crumbled, shredded, or in cooked dishes.
* Refrigerate butter up to several weeks. For longer storage, freeze up to nine months.
* Store ice cream tightly covered in the freezer.

Safety Check

After pouring milk, return the container to the refrigerator immediately. Do not pour milk that has been sitting in a serving pitcher back into the original container. Instead, if the milk has been at room temperature less than two hours, refrigerate it in a separate container and use soon. Discard milk that has been left at room temperature more than two hours.

Section 18.1 Review

RECALL THE FACTS

1. Identify four nutrients in milk products.
2. Why is milk pasteurized?
3. What is the difference between ripened and unripened cheese?
4. Give three tips for storing milk.

DISCUSS YOUR IDEAS

5. Discuss the benefits of using nonfat yogurt instead of other dairy foods in cooking.

APPLY YOUR LEARNING

6. Use the chart "Nutritive Value in Foods," in the Appendix, to compare the nutrients in various dairy products. Which are highest in calcium? Which are lowest in fat?

Objectives

After studying this section, you should be able to:

❖ Identify ways to prevent problems when cooking with milk.

❖ Discuss ways to use yogurt in recipes.

❖ Identify guidelines for preparing cheese.

Look for This Term

scalded milk

Dairy foods are delicate proteins. They must be cooked carefully at moderate temperatures and for a limited amount of time.

Cooking with Milk

Milk can be the base for preparing delicious cooked foods, including cocoa and soups. However, when cooking milk, several problems can arise.

❖ **Skin.** When milk cooks, liquid evaporates. The protein solids clump together, forming a skin on the surface. To keep a skin from forming, cover the pan or stir the mixture regularly. If a skin forms, use a wire whisk to beat it back into the mixture. If you remove it, you also remove nutrients.

❖ **Scorching.** Milk can scorch, or burn, easily. The milk solids fall to the bottom of the pan, stick, and burn. To prevent scorching, use low heat. Also, stir the mixture to keep the solids circulating.

❖ **Curdling.** When milk curdles, it has separated into curds and whey. Curdling may occur when milk is heated with acid foods, such as vegetables and fruits. It can also be caused by salt or high heat. To prevent curdling, use low temperatures, stir the mixture, and combine milk with acid foods gradually.

When milk-based recipes are cooked carefully, the result is smooth and flavorful.

TIPS for Success

Making Hot Cocoa

❖ Cocoa powder by itself is difficult to mix with liquids. To prevent lumping, mix the cocoa powder and sugar thoroughly. Gradually add a little liquid, stirring well to make a smooth paste. Then continue adding the rest of the liquid, stirring constantly.

❖ To cut down on fat, use skim milk. For greater richness and more nutrients, add nonfat dry milk when combining the cocoa and sugar.

❖ Use low heat to prevent scorching.

❖ For a flavor variation, add vanilla or peppermint extract, cinnamon, or nutmeg.

Cocoa is one of the favorite hot beverages prepared with milk. It can be prepared on the range or in the microwave.

Some recipes call for **scalded milk.** This means the milk is heated to just below the boiling point. Use low heat and cook only until bubbles appear around the sides of the pan.

Milk and milk-based recipes can be prepared easily in the microwave oven. Be sure to use a large enough container in case the milk foams up.

Using Yogurt in Recipes

Yogurt can be a nutritious substitute for ingredients such as sour cream, cream cheese, milk, and mayonnaise. It can be used in many recipes, from soups to main dishes to salads.

Here are some basic guidelines to remember when cooking with yogurt.

❖ Yogurt can be cooked, baked, or frozen. The active bacterial cultures may not survive, but the nutrients will still be the same.

❖ Whey may separate from the curd in yogurt when it is stored. Stir it back into the yogurt before you use it.

❖ Cook yogurt at moderate temperatures for only the time needed. Yogurt is just as delicate as other dairy foods. If overcooked, it will curdle.

❖ To keep yogurt from separating during cooking, blend 1 Tbsp. (15 mL) cornstarch with a small amount of yogurt. Combine with the remaining yogurt and use according to recipe directions.

A yogurt maker is an appliance that can be used to make yogurt at home. Packaged yogurt starter can supply the bacterial culture.

- You can thicken yogurt by letting the whey drain off. Line a strainer with a double thickness of cheesecloth. Empty the yogurt into the strainer and set the strainer over a bowl. (The bowl should be a size and shape that prevents the strainer from touching the bottom.) Refrigerate up to 12 hours or until enough whey has drained off to give the desired thickness. If thick enough, you can use the yogurt as a cheese. Use the nutrient-rich whey in soups and casseroles, or substitute it for water, buttermilk, or milk in baking.

Yogurt can also be used as a salad dressing, dip, sauce, or dessert topping. For example, top cooked vegetables such as asparagus with plain yogurt and sprinkle with chopped nuts and minced chives.

Preparing Cheese

Unripened cheeses, such as cottage cheese and cream cheese, should be served chilled. They can be used to make dips by adding seasonings and chopped vegetables.

Ripened cheese tastes best when served at room temperature. Remove it from the refrigerator at least 30 minutes before serving to allow it to reach room temperature. You can also bring it to room temperature by microwaving it at 30 percent power for about 20 seconds, then letting it stand five minutes. Times will vary, depending on size and texture of the cheese. Repeat if necessary.

Follow these guidelines when cooking cheese:
- Heat cheese just long enough to melt it. If overcooked, cheese gets stringy and tough.
- To speed up cooking time, shred, grate, or cut cheese into small pieces.
- Be careful when microwaving cheese— the fat in it attracts microwaves. The cheese may be hotter than the rest of the microwaved food.
- To lower the fat in recipes with cheese, choose sharp-flavored varieties. Since they have more flavor, you can use less cheese.

When cheese is used as a topping, it is often shredded or grated and added near the end of cooking time. Then only brief heating is needed to melt it, reducing the chance of overcooking.

Section 18.2 Review

RECALL THE FACTS

1. List two ways to prevent milk from curdling.

2. How can yogurt be used as a substitute for cheese?

3. What happens to cheese if it is overcooked?

DISCUSS YOUR IDEAS

4. What are some ways to use milk and dairy products in cooking to meet the nutritional needs of someone who doesn't like plain milk?

APPLY YOUR LEARNING

5. Locate a recipe for homemade cream of tomato soup. Read through the directions carefully. What does the recipe recommend to prevent curdling? How might you improve upon the directions?

Thinking About the Recipe

Read the recipe for "Easy Macaroni and Cheese" and answer the following questions.

1. Why is the cheese cut into cubes before it is cooked?
2. What are some low-fat foods you could serve with this dish to make a nutritionally balanced menu?

Easy Macaroni and Cheese

Customary	Ingredients	Metric
8 oz.	Elbow macaroni	224 g
4 oz.	Process cheese spread (sold in loaves)	112 g
1/2 cup	Green pepper, chopped	125 mL
1/4 cup	Onion, finely chopped	50 mL
1 tsp.	Margarine	5 mL
1 cup	Evaporated skim milk	250 mL
1/4 tsp.	White pepper, ground	1 mL
1/2 cup	Bread crumbs	125 mL
1 tsp.	Margarine, melted	5 mL

Yield: 4 servings

Directions

Pans: Saucepan; 1 ½ quart (1.5 L) casserole dish
Oven Temperature: 350°F (180°C)

1. Cook and drain macaroni according to package directions. Set aside.
2. Cut cheese into cubes and set aside.
3. Sauté green pepper and onion over medium-low heat in 1 teaspoon (5 mL) margarine, about 1 to 2 minutes, stirring constantly.
4. Stir in evaporated skim milk and cheese cubes.
5. Cook over medium-low heat, stirring constantly, until cheese is melted and mixture is well blended. Stir in pepper.
6. Combine milk and cheese mixture with macaroni in casserole dish. Mix gently.
7. Combine bread crumbs and 1 teaspoon (5 mL) melted margarine.
8. Sprinkle bread crumb mixture over macaroni and cheese mixture.
9. Bake at 350°F (180°C) 20 to 30 minutes until hot and bubbly.
10. Serve hot.

Nutrition Information

Per serving (approximate): 274 calories, 15 g protein, 28 g carbohydrate, 11 g fat, 30 mg cholesterol, 531 mg sodium

Objectives

After studying this section, you should be able to:

❖ Describe the structure of an egg.
❖ Identify the nutrients provided by eggs.
❖ Give guidelines for buying and storing eggs.
❖ Explain how to cook eggs by conventional and microwave methods.

Look for These Terms

albumen
chalazae
coagulate
shirred eggs

Eggs are an economical food source and can be prepared in a variety of ways. Many people enjoy them for breakfast. However, they can be featured in other meals as well.

The Structure of an Egg

The egg is shaped like an oval, with one end more narrow than the other. It has a hard outer shell lined with several membranes. The shell color may be brown or white, depending on the breed of hen. The color does not affect the nutrients in the egg. A pocket of air occupies the space between the shell and membrane at the wide end. As the egg ages, the air pocket grows.

Inside the egg is a thick, clear fluid called the **albumen** (al-BYOU-men). It is commonly called the egg white. The yolk is the round, yellow portion of the egg, floating in the albumen. **Chalazae** (kuh-LAH-zuh) are twisted, cordlike strands of albumen that anchor the yolk in the center of the egg.

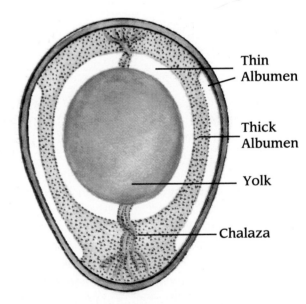

Thin Albumen

Thick Albumen

Yolk

Chalaza

Whether the shells are brown or white, eggs have the same nutrients and the same structure.

Nutrients in Eggs

Eggs are an excellent source of protein, riboflavin, and iodine. In addition, they are good sources of vitamin A, some other B vitamins, vitamin D, iron, and trace minerals. However, egg yolks also contain saturated fats and cholesterol.

Eggs are part of the Meat, Poultry, Fish, Dry Beans, Eggs, and Nuts Group. When counting servings from that group, one egg counts as 1 ounce (28 g) of meat. However, because whole eggs are so high in cholesterol, health experts recommend that people eat no more than four a week. There is no limit on eating egg whites because they are cholesterol-free.

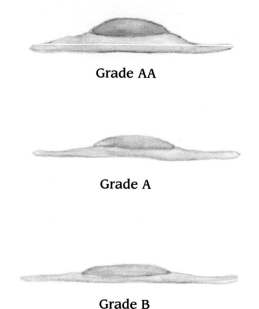

Grade AA

Grade A

Grade B

Egg grades indicate thickness and appearance.

Buying and Storing Eggs

Eggs are sold according to size and grade standards set by the USDA. Both size and grade are clearly marked on the package.

The USDA grade shield on the package means that the eggs have been federally inspected for wholesomeness. The grade is determined by the inner and outer quality of the egg at the time it was packaged. It has nothing to do with the freshness of the egg or the size.

The three egg grades are AA, A, and B. There is no difference in nutritive value among them. However, there is a difference in appearance when cooked. Grade AA and

A eggs have a thicker white and are used when appearance is important, such as with fried or poached eggs. Grade B eggs are used when appearance is not important, such as in baked products or scrambled eggs. As a rule, grades AA and A are most common in supermarkets. The illustration above shows the differences in the grades.

The size is determined by the minimum weight for a dozen eggs, as shown in the chart below. The sizes most commonly sold are "large" and "extra large." As a general rule, recipes assume that large eggs will be used.

Jumbo	X-Large	Large	Medium	Small	Peewee
30 OZ.	27 OZ.	24 OZ.	21 OZ.	18 OZ.	15 OZ.

Egg sizes indicate the minimum weight of a dozen eggs. About how much would a single large egg weigh?

Harmful bacteria in raw or under-cooked eggs have caused food-borne illness. To make sure that eggs are safe to eat, follow these guidelines:

❖ Do not use eggs that are cracked or broken. They may contain harmful bacteria.

❖ Always cook eggs thoroughly until the whites and yolks are firm.

❖ Use the proper sanitation procedures when preparing eggs. (See Section 7.3, pages 195-197 and 201-202).

❖ Serve cooked eggs and egg-rich foods right after cooking.

❖ Never eat raw eggs or any foods containing raw eggs, such as homemade eggnog, homemade ice cream, and raw cookie dough. (Raw eggs in commercial products are usually pasteurized, which destroys harmful bacteria.)

To reduce the risk of illness, egg-rich dishes should be cooked thoroughly and served right away.

Eggs are usually priced according to size and supply. Check the unit price to determine which size is the best buy. Be sure to open the carton and inspect the eggs. They should be clean and whole, without any cracks.

Eggs are highly perishable. Store them immediately when you get home from shopping. Refrigerate eggs in the original carton. Do not put them in the egg tray commonly found on the refrigerator door—the drop in temperature each time the door is opened may cause eggs to lose quality more quickly. In addition, egg shells are porous and pick up aromas from other foods if stored uncovered. Do not wash eggs before storing—washing destroys the egg's natural protective covering.

Leftover raw yolks or whites should be refrigerated in a covered container if they will be used within two to four days. For longer storage, freeze them. Refrigerate cooked egg dishes immediately and use them within three days.

TIPS for Success

Freezing Eggs

❖ To freeze whole raw eggs, beat the eggs until well-blended and pour them into freezer containers. Three tablespoons (45 mL) of beaten whole egg equals one large egg.

❖ To freeze raw whites, place the white of one egg in each compartment of an ice cube tray. After freezing, put frozen cubes in a tightly sealed freezer container and use as needed. Two tablespoons (30 mL) of egg white equals one large white.

❖ Use frozen eggs only in dishes that will be thoroughly cooked.

Preparing Eggs

Like dairy foods, eggs are delicate proteins. They must be cooked at moderate temperatures for a limited amount of time. When overcooked, egg whites shrink and become tough and rubbery. When egg yolks are overcooked, they toughen and turn gray-green on the surface.

Eggs can be prepared easily, either on top of the range or in a microwave oven. There are a few differences in basic cooking principles, depending on which method you use.

In conventional cooking, use medium to low heat. Time the eggs carefully to make sure they are thoroughly cooked. The whites will **coagulate,** or become firm, before the yolks.

When eggs are cooked in a microwave oven, the yolks cook faster than the whites. That is because the fat in the yolks attracts more microwaves than the whites. Eggs are usually removed from the microwave oven while still moist and soft. Standing time completes the cooking.

Eggs can be prepared in several basic ways: cooked in the shell, fried, baked, poached, or scrambled.

Before microwaving, pierce egg yolks. If you don't, trapped steam could cause the yolk to burst.

Eggs Cooked in the Shell

When cooking eggs in the shell, place a single layer of eggs in a saucepan. Add water to a level at least 1 inch (2.5 cm) above the eggs. Cover the saucepan and bring the water just to boiling. Turn off the heat (and remove the pan from the heating unit, if using an electric range). Let the eggs stand in the hot water, covered. If you want soft-cooked eggs, let them stand about four to five minutes for a safe doneness. For hard-cooked eggs, let stand about 15 minutes if using large eggs (about 18 minutes if using extra large eggs).

After cooking, immediately run cold water over the eggs to stop the cooking process. To serve soft-cooked eggs, break the shell with a knife and scoop the egg out of the shell into a serving dish. To remove the shell from a hard-cooked egg, gently tap the egg all over to crackle the shell. Roll the egg between your hands to loosen the shell. Peel the shell away starting at the large end.

Fried Eggs

Eggs can be fried in a small amount of fat or using a vegetable oil cooking spray. Heat a skillet over medium-high heat until it is hot enough to sizzle a drop of water. Gently break one egg at a time into a small bowl or custard cup. If the yolk breaks, save the egg for another use. Otherwise, gently slip the egg from the bowl into the heated pan. Reduce the heat to low immediately. Cover the pan and cook the eggs slowly until done. Turn the eggs over to cook both sides.

Baked Eggs

Baked eggs are sometimes called **shirred eggs.** Break the eggs into a small bowl, then slip them into a greased, shallow baking dish or custard cup. You can use individual dishes or place several eggs in one dish. Top the eggs with a small amount of milk, if desired.

To bake conventionally, place in an oven preheated to 325°F (160°C). Bake until done—about 12 minutes for two eggs.

To microwave, first pierce the yolks with the tip of a knife or a wooden pick so that steam can escape. Otherwise, the eggs may burst. Cover the baking dish with plastic wrap and vent it to allow steam to escape. Follow the power level and timing instructions in the owner's manual or recipe book.

Baked eggs are easy to prepare. If you like, you can sprinkle on toppings such as chopped parsley, ham, or mushrooms.

When poaching, start with fresh, cold eggs—they will hold their shape better. Drain poached eggs well before serving.

Poached Eggs

Poaching is a method of cooking eggs, out of the shell, in simmering water. To poach eggs conventionally, bring the water to a boil in a saucepan or deep skillet, then reduce the heat to a gentle simmer. Break one egg at a time into a small dish. Hold the dish close to surface of the water and slip the egg in. Simmer about five minutes or until done.

Eggs can also be poached in the microwave oven. Follow the directions in the owner's manual or recipe book. Be sure to pierce the yolks first to let steam escape.

After cooking, use a slotted spoon to lift the eggs out of the water and drain them. Serve the eggs in a dish or over toast.

Scrambled Eggs

When making scrambled eggs, beat the eggs together with water or milk. Use one tablespoon (15 mL) liquid for each egg.

To cook conventionally, melt a small amount of butter or margarine in a skillet, or use a vegetable oil cooking spray. Pour the egg mixture into the hot skillet. As the mixture starts to thicken, gently draw a spatula across the bottom and sides of the pan. This forms large curds and allows the uncooked egg to flow to the bottom of the skillet. Continue this procedure until the eggs are thickened and no visible liquid remains. Do not stir the eggs constantly. They will get mushy.

To make scrambled eggs in the microwave oven, cook the egg mixture in a custard cup or other microwave-safe container. Follow the power level and timing instructions in the owner's manual or recipe book. Stir once or twice during cooking and again at the end of the cooking time. Let stand to complete cooking.

Basic Omelet

A basic omelet, also called a French omelet, is made with beaten eggs, just as scrambled eggs are. However, an omelet is cooked in a skillet without stirring. The result is shaped somewhat like a large pancake. During cooking, occasionally lift the edge of the omelet to allow uncooked egg to flow to the bottom. When the omelet is almost done, you may add a filling, such as sautéed vegetables. Fold the omelet in half to serve.

There are many variations of omelets. The recipe on page 473 is for an Italian-style omelet, called a *frittata* (frih-TAH-tuh). In the next section, you will learn how to make a puffy omelet using beaten egg whites.

WORLD **of** variety

"Thousand-year eggs" are a Chinese delicacy. However, they are not really that old. The eggs are cooked, preserved in a mixture of fine ash, clay, and salt, and then wrapped in straw. After about 45 days, they are considered ready to eat.

"Thousand-year eggs" are usually made from duck eggs. The unique preservation method gives the eggs a distinctive flavor and appearance.

Section 18.3 Review

RECALL THE FACTS

1. What is another name for the white of an egg?

2. Name four nutrients found in eggs.

3. What does the grade shield on an egg carton tell you?

4. Why shouldn't whole eggs in the shell be cooked in the microwave oven?

DISCUSS YOUR IDEAS

5. What are the advantages and disadvantages of the various cooking methods for eggs?

APPLY YOUR LEARNING

6. Design an advertisement to promote the use of eggs. You may want to focus on their versatility or nutritional value.

Thinking About the Recipe

Read the recipe for "Italian Frittata" and answer the following questions.

1. How does the preparation method for this recipe differ from that for scrambled eggs?
2. Name two ways you might reduce the amount of fat in the frittata.

Italian Frittata

Customary	Ingredients	Metric
1/4 lb.	Fresh mushrooms, thinly sliced	112 g
2	Green onions, minced	2
1 ½ Tbsp.	Margarine	20 mL
6	Eggs	6
3 Tbsp.	Fresh parsley, chopped	45 mL
1/2 tsp.	Basil, dried and crumbled	2 mL
1/4 cup	Grated Parmesan cheese	50 mL
	Salt and pepper to taste	

Yield: 4 servings

Conventional Directions

Pan: Large skillet with oven-safe handle
Oven Temperature: Broil

1. Sauté mushrooms and onions in margarine over medium heat until tender-crisp.
2. Preheat broiler.
3. Beat eggs in medium bowl.
4. Add parsley, basil, salt and pepper, and half the cheese to the eggs. Mix well.
5. Pour egg mixture over vegetables in skillet. Cook over medium heat, without stirring, until edges are lightly browned.
6. Sprinkle with remaining cheese.
7. Broil until top is golden brown.
8. Cut into wedges and serve hot.

Microwave Directions

Pan: 9-inch glass pie pan, microwave-safe
Power level: 100% power

1. Combine mushrooms, onions, and margarine in glass pie pan. Cover with plastic wrap and vent.
2. Cook 2 to 3 minutes at 100% power, rotating the pan after 1 minute.
3. Beat eggs, parsley, basil, salt, pepper, and half the cheese in a small bowl.
4. Pour egg mixture over vegetables.
5. Cook at 70% power 4 to 5 minutes.
6. .Move cooked portions to center of dish and uncooked parts to outside. Lightly level the top. Rotate pan.
7. Cook 4 to 5 minutes more at 70% power until eggs are set but glossy.
8. Sprinkle remaining cheese on eggs
9. Cook 2 to 3 minutes. at 70% power.
10. Let stand 2 to 3 minutes. Cut into wedges and serve hot.

Nutrition Information

Per serving (approximate): 188 calories, 13 g protein, 3 g carbohydrate, 14 g fat, 324 mg cholesterol, 263 mg sodium

Objectives

After studying this section, you should be able to:

❖ Describe the difference between stirred custard and baked custard.
❖ Explain how to separate and beat egg whites.
❖ Identify uses for beaten egg whites.

Look for These Terms

quiche
soufflé
meringue

Eggs perform different functions in recipes. They add richness and nutrients. They bind ingredients together, as in a meat loaf. They are also used for thickening foods such as sauces. When beaten, they incorporate air and can be used to help baked products rise.

Custards

One example of a recipe made with eggs is custard. Custard is a tender blend of milk thickened with eggs. It serves as the base for main dishes, such as **quiche** (keesh). Quiche

is a pie with a custard filling that contains foods such as chopped vegetables, cheese, and chopped cooked meat. Sweetened, flavored custard is a popular dessert.

There are two types of custard, stirred and baked.

❖ *Stirred custard* is also known as soft custard. It is cooked on top of the range, stirred constantly, until it thickens enough to coat a spoon. It is pourable, creamy, and can be served as a pudding or as a sauce over cake or fruit.
❖ *Baked custard* is baked in the oven. It has a firm, delicate consistency, similar to yogurt. If prepared in individual custard cups, the cups are set in a pan of hot water to keep the mixture from overcooking. The custard is baked until a knife inserted in or near the center comes out clean. Baking time varies, depending on the size of the pans. If overbaked, the custard will curdle. If not baked long enough, it will not set.

Custards are versatile combinations of milk and eggs. What is the difference between stirred and baked custard?

Separating Eggs

Sometimes recipe directions call for only the yolk or white of the egg. In that case, you need to separate the egg. Eggs separate more easily when they are cold.

An easy, sanitary way to separate whites from yolks is to use an inexpensive egg separator. Simply break the egg into the separator. The white will flow through, leaving the yolk in the separator.

Beating Egg Whites

When egg whites are beaten, air is incorporated into them. Beaten egg whites can be used to add volume and lightness to baked products. For example, they can be used to prepare soufflés. A **soufflé** (soo-FLAY) is

Safety Check

The traditional method for separating whites calls for passing the yolk back and forth from shell half to shell half. This method is no longer recommended. Bacteria may be present in the pores of the shell and could be picked up by the yolks and whites.

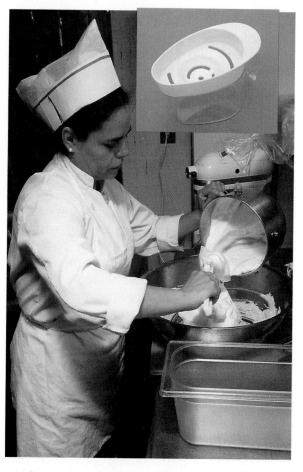

Professional chefs and bakers use beaten egg whites in many creative dishes. You can, too, if you know the "secrets" to successfully beating egg whites.

made by folding stiffly beaten whites into a sauce or batter, then baking the mixture in a deep casserole until it puffs up.

Here are some guidelines for beating egg whites:

- ❖ When separating the yolks from the whites, be careful that no yolk mixes with the whites. Yolks contain fat, and even a drop of fat can keep whites from reaching full volume.
- ❖ Before beating, let egg whites stand at room temperature for 30 minutes. This will allow them to reach the fullest volume when beaten.
- ❖ Use beaters and bowls that are clean and completely free of fat. Plastic bowls tend to absorb fat, so use only glass or metal bowls.

As egg whites are beaten, they turn white and foamy and begin to form peaks. The peaks reach two different stages.

❖ **Soft peak stage.** The peaks bend over slightly when the beaters are lifted out of the whites.

❖ **Stiff peak stage.** The peaks are glossy and hold their shape when the beaters are lifted out of the mixture.

Stop beating egg whites as soon as they reach the stage called for in the recipe. Do not try to beat past the stiff peak stage. If the whites are overbeaten, they will turn dry and dull and begin to fall apart. They cannot be used since they have lost air and moisture.

When used in mixtures, beaten egg whites must be folded in. If they are stirred or beaten, the whites lose air and volume. To fold beaten whites into a mixture, add them to the bowl containing the mixture. Use a flat tool, such as a rubber scraper, for folding. (See Section 8.4 for directions on folding.)

Puffy Omelet

Beaten egg whites can be used to make a puffy omelet. A puffy omelet is made by separating the eggs and beating the whites and yolks separately. The stiffly beaten whites are folded into the yolks. The mixture is poured into a skillet with an ovenproof handle. It is first cooked on top of the range until puffed and lightly browned on the bottom, about five minutes. Then it is baked at 350°F (180°C) for 10 to 12 minutes or until a knife inserted in the center comes out clean.

The omelet can be served open-faced or folded. To serve the omelet folded, cut partially through the center of the omelet for ease in folding. The omelet can be filled with foods such as cheese, vegetables, and meats.

Meringues

A **meringue** (mehr-ANG), a foam made of beaten egg white and sugar, is used for desserts. There are two types of meringue, soft and hard. Soft meringue is used to top precooked pies and puddings. Hard meringue is used to make baked meringue shells that can be filled like a pie.

To make a meringue, beat the whites until they are foamy. Sometimes cream of tartar is added to the whites before beating to make the meringue more stable. When the whites are foamy, gradually beat in the sugar, one tablespoon at a time. Most soft meringue recipes call for 1 to 2 Tbsp. (15 to 30 ml) sugar per egg white. A hard meringue may use 4 Tbsp. (50 mL) sugar per egg white. Continue beating until the sugar is dissolved.

A puffy omelet is light in texture and lends itself to a variety of nutritious fillings.

To find out if the sugar is dissolved, rub a little meringue between the thumb and forefinger. If it feels gritty, all the sugar is not dissolved.

Spread soft meringue over hot, pre-cooked pie filling or pudding. On a pie, the meringue should touch the crust all around the edge or it may shrink during baking. Bake it in a pre-heated oven according to recipe directions until the peaks are lightly browned.

Sometimes a liquid accumulates between the meringue and pie filling, a condition known as "weeping." This happens when the sugar is not completely dissolved or the meringue is not beaten to the soft-peak stage. Meringue weeps less when put on a hot filling.

Hard meringue can be baked on a baking sheet. Line the sheet with parchment paper (a special paper used for baking in the oven), waxed paper, or foil. Shape the meringue into individual or large shells using a spoon, spatula, or pastry tube.

A baked hard meringue is crispy. It must bake at a low enough temperature to dry out thoroughly, but not overcook. Unless it dries well, the meringue may be sticky and chewy. Bake according to the time and temperature in the recipe directions. Turn off the oven and leave the meringue in it for at least another hour to dry out.

Section 18.4 Review

RECALL THE FACTS

1. What is the difference between a baked custard and a stirred custard?

2. What is the safest way to separate egg whites from the yolks?

3. Give three guidelines for beating egg whites.

4. Name two dishes that use beaten egg whites.

DISCUSS YOUR IDEAS

5. What might baked meringue shells be filled with?

APPLY YOUR LEARNING

6. Beat one egg white using 1/8 teaspoon (0.5 mL) cream of tartar. Beat another egg white without cream of tartar. Compare the results.

Lemon meringue pie is a popular dessert. Which type of meringue is used to make the fluffy, delicate topping?

Thinking About the Recipe

Read the recipe for "Meringue-Swirled Fruit" and answer the following questions.

1. What combination of fruits would you use in this recipe?
2. What should you check for when beating the egg whites?

Meringue-Swirled Fruit

Customary	Ingredients	Metric
4 cups	Fresh or frozen fruit (any combination, such as blueberries, strawberries, orange sections, banana slices)	1 L
2 Tbsp.	Cherry or almond extract	30 mL
5	Egg whites	5
2/3 cup	Sugar	150 mL

Yield: 6 servings

Directions

Pans: Six large custard cups; cookie sheet
Temperature: 500°F (260°C)

1. Preheat oven.
2. Mix fruit and extract together. Chill.
3. Beat egg whites in large bowl until foamy.
4. Add sugar gradually, about 2 Tbsp. (30 mL) at a time, beating after each addition. Stop beating when stiff peaks form.
5. Divide fruit mixture evenly among custard cups.
6. Top and seal each dish of fruit with meringue. Use spoon to swirl meringue to a decorative peak.
7. Place custard cups on cookie sheet. Bake at 500°F (260°C) for 3 minutes or until meringue is golden. Serve immediately.

Nutrition Information

Per serving (approximate): 147 calories, 4 g protein, 35 g carbohydrate, trace of fat, 0 mg cholesterol, 48 mg sodium

CAREER PROFILE

Kristen Todd
Dairy Writer

Current position:

"I'm a public relations writer for a dairy industry organization."

Responsibilities:

"I research and write articles for company newsletters as well as for public distribution. My articles are intended to keep the public and other interest groups aware of our organization's activities and accomplishments."

Skills:

"Organization is a key skill, since I usually have several projects going at once. Creativity and strong communication skills are also necessary."

Education:

"I have a four-year college degree with a double major in communications and home economics."

Work environment:

"The majority of my time is spent at my desk doing research or writing on a computer. I also meet weekly with other staff members in my department. I usually work 40 hours a week, but must sometimes work extra hours to meet deadlines."

Favorite part of the job:

"Writing has always been my first love. I enjoy being able to gather facts and put them all together in an article that people will find informative and interesting to read."

- Does Kristen seem well suited to her job? Why or why not?
- What aspects of Kristen's job do you think you might enjoy? Why?

Summary

Section 18.1
Choosing Dairy Foods: Milk is high in protein, vitamin A, and B vitamins. You can choose from whole, low-fat, or skim milk as well as a variety of flavored and convenience milk products. Yogurt is made by adding live bacterial culture to milk. The many kinds of cheese fall into two basic categories, ripened and unripened. Other dairy products include cream, butter, and frozen dairy desserts. Dairy foods are highly perishable and must be refrigerated or frozen.

Section 18.2
Preparing Dairy Foods: When heating milk, use care to avoid scorching, curdling, and skin formation. Yogurt can be a nutritious substitute for higher-fat dairy products. Unripened cheese should be served chilled, while ripened cheese tastes best at room temperature. Avoid overcooking cheese.

Section 18.3
Egg Basics: Eggs are good sources of protein, several vitamins, and iron. The yolks are high in fat and cholesterol. Eggs are sold by size and grade. They should be refrigerated in their original cartons. When cooking with eggs, take steps to prevent food-borne illness. Eggs may be cooked in the shell, fried, baked, poached, scrambled, or made into a basic omelet.

Section 18.4
Using Eggs in Recipes: Eggs perform different functions in recipes. They thicken and add richness to custards and quiches. Egg whites can be beaten to add volume and lightness to soufflés, puffy omelets, and meringues.

REVIEWING FACTS

1. Identify the percent of calories from fat in whole, low-fat, and skim milk. (18.1)

2. Give two examples of cultured milk products. (18.1)

3. How is pasteurized process cheese made? (18.1)

4. What causes skin formation in milk? How can you prevent it? (18.2)

5. Why should you save the whey from thickened yogurt? How can it be used? (18.2)

6. Give two reasons why you should not store eggs in the egg tray on the refrigerator door. (18.3)

7. Describe how to freeze leftover raw egg whites. (18.3)

8. Briefly describe the procedure for making hard-cooked eggs. (18.3)

9. Describe the characteristics of egg whites beaten to the soft-peak stage and the stiff-peak stage. (18.4)

10. Identify two ways of keeping meringue from "weeping." (18.4)

LEARNING BY DOING

1. **Food science lab:** Add 1 Tbsp. (15 mL) lemon juice to 1 cup (250 mL) room-temperature milk. Let the milk stand for ten minutes. Describe the results. What do you think is happening to the milk? What is this process called? (18.1)

2. **Foods lab:** Select a recipe calling for sour cream. Prepare it first as directed. Prepare again using yogurt instead of sour cream. Compare the results on taste, texture, appearance, and nutritional value. (18.2)

3. **Foods lab:** Develop your own recipes for scrambled eggs. Experiment by adding seasonings and other ingredients. Evaluate the results for taste, appearance, nutritional value, and cost per serving. (18.3)

4. **Demonstration:** Demonstrate the proper method for making baked meringue shells, including beating the egg whites, forming the shells, and baking the meringue. (18.4)

THINKING CRITICALLY

1. **Forming hypotheses:** Why do you think food manufacturers developed UHT milk and canned milk? In what situations would these products be valuable? (18.1)

2. **Making generalizations:** Would you try to dovetail other food preparation tasks with cooking dairy products? Why or why not? (18.2)

3. **Recognizing alternatives:** How can you reduce the amount of cholesterol in recipes that use eggs? (18.3)

4. **Comparing and contrasting:** Compare the texture and composition of quiches and soufflés. Explain when you might want to serve each dish. (18.4)

MAKING DECISIONS AND SOLVING PROBLEMS

What Would You Do?

1. You have found a recipe for a cheese sauce that you would like to try. However, it calls for Edam and Gouda cheese, which you have not been able to find in your local food stores. You wonder if you can substitute other types of cheese. (18.1)

2. You offer to make a dip for a friend's party. You want to make it attractive and tasty, but low in fat and cholesterol as well. (18.2)

3. You want to reduce a recipe that calls for three eggs by one-half. (18.3)

4. You want to make meringue shells for your family's dessert tonight. However, it will take half an hour for the egg whites to come to room temperature, and you don't have that much time. (18.4)

LINKING YOUR STUDIES

1. **Social studies:** Using library resources, find information on milk products that are popular in other cultures. Present your findings to the class. (18.1)

2. **Math:** Compare the per-serving price and nutritional value of sour cream and its lower-fat substitutes, including yogurt and reduced-fat sour cream products. Record your findings on a chart or bar graph. Also tell how each product's nutritional value affects your decision about which is the best buy. (18.2)

3. **Writing:** Select your favorite cheese and trace its history. Write an article for a popular food magazine, including historical information, how the cheese is produced, and some ways to use it. (18.2)

4. **Science:** Using library resources, find more information on the reproductive purposes of the egg. How does the yolk develop? What is the purpose of the albumen? What is the shell's composition? Share your findings with the class in a short report. (18.3)

5. **Social studies:** Write a report on the international origins of dishes mentioned in this section. Where and when did soufflés and meringues originate? What other international dishes use beaten egg whites? (18.4)

CHAPTER 19

Meat, Poultry, Fish, and Shellfish

Looking at Meat, Poultry, Fish, and Shellfish

Objectives

After studying this section, you should be able to:

❖ Identify nutrients in meat, poultry, fish, and shellfish.
❖ Discuss factors affecting tenderness.
❖ Give guidelines for comparing costs of meat, poultry, fish, and shellfish.

Look for These Terms

cut
marbling

Cerise looked at the long meat display case in the supermarket. It seemed like hundreds of different packages of meat were on display to her left and poultry to her right. Beyond the poultry, she could see dozens of different kinds of fresh fish and shellfish.

Cerise wondered how all these different foods compared to one another. Were some more nutritious than others? How else did they differ? How could she find the best buys?

Your Choices

Like Cerise, you face many choices when shopping for meat, poultry, fish, and shellfish. Each of these categories includes foods from several different sources.

❖ Meat includes beef (from mature cattle), lamb (from young sheep), pork (from hogs), and veal (from young cattle).
❖ Poultry refers to birds raised for food, such as chicken, turkey, duck, and goose.
❖ Dozens of different fish and shellfish are available, from cod and salmon to lobsters and clams.

When you shop for meat, poultry, fish, and shellfish, consider nutrition, tenderness, and cost.

Within each category, you can choose from many different fresh or frozen cuts. A **cut** refers to a particular edible part of meat, poultry, or fish as it is sold in the marketplace. For instance, cuts of beef include steaks, chops, roasts, and organ meats (such as liver).

You can also buy cured meat and poultry products, such as ham, bacon, cold cuts, and sausages. Many other convenience forms are available as well. (For more information on choosing convenience foods, see Chapter 15.)

How can you make wise decisions when shopping for meat, poultry, fish, and shellfish? Start by taking a look at how the different choices vary in nutrition, tenderness, and cost.

Nutrition of Meat, Poultry, Fish, and Shellfish

Meat, poultry, fish, and shellfish are all nutritious foods. They are excellent sources of complete protein. All three provide B vitamins, phosphorus, and certain trace minerals.

The Food Guide Pyramid recommends two to three servings daily from the Meat, Poultry, Fish, Dry Beans, Eggs, and Nuts Group. A typical serving can be 2 to 3 ounces (56 to 84 g) of cooked lean meat, poultry, or fish.

Many Americans eat larger servings of meat, poultry, and fish than the recommended portions. That means they eat more protein than needed. The larger servings may also add more fat and cholesterol to daily food choices.

Fat and Cholesterol Content

Because they are animal foods, meat, poultry, fish, and shellfish all contain cholesterol. All animal muscle contains about the same amount of cholesterol per ounce. Organ meats have more cholesterol.

Fat content varies. Most fish is very low in fat. So is turkey breast meat. Other poultry and meat cuts generally have more fat, but the amount varies depending on the cut and the preparation method. Meat, poultry, fish, or shellfish that has less than 10 grams of fat in a 3 ½ ounce (100 gram) serving is considered lean.

Besides the amount of fat, another consideration is the type of fat that is present. In general, beef has the largest amount of saturated fat. Pork has more polyunsaturated fats than beef or lamb. Chicken and turkey generally have less saturated fat than red meat. Fish has the least amount of saturated fat and the most polyunsaturated.

Meat and poultry include both invisible fat—which is part of the chemical composition of the food—and visible fat. In poultry, most of the visible fat is located in the skin

Healthy Attitudes

Here are some suggestions for enjoying meat, poultry, and fish while limiting fat and cholesterol.

- Follow the Food Guide Pyramid recommendations for serving sizes.
- Combine moderate amounts of meat, poultry, or fish with grains and vegetables.
- Substitute legumes for meats at least several times a week.
- Choose cuts with less fat. (You'll learn more about choosing cuts in later sections.)
- Trim fat layers from meat. Remove poultry skin before eating.
- Use low-fat cooking methods, such as broiling or roasting. Avoid cooking methods that add fat, such as frying.

Comparing Fat and Cholesterol Content

The following chart lists just a few examples of meat, poultry, fish, and shellfish. It shows the approximate amount of fat, saturated fat, and cholesterol in each. Notice that within each category, some choices are higher and some are lower in fat. How does the cholesterol content compare?

Type of food (3 oz. [84 g] serving)	Total Fat (g)	Saturated Fat (g)	Cholesterol (mg)
Fish and shellfish:			
Cod, cooked	1	0	47
Tuna, canned in water	1	0	48
Mackerel, cooked	15	4	64
Shrimp, cooked	1	0	166
Poultry:			
Chicken, light meat, without skin, roasted	3	0	73
Chicken, dark meat, without skin, roasted	4	1	80
Turkey, breast meat, without skin, roasted	1	0	71
Meat:			
Beef, top round, trimmed, broiled	5	2	71
Beef, ground, regular, broiled	18	7	76
Beef liver, pan-fried	7	2	410
Pork loin, trimmed, roasted	11	4	77

Marbling

Layer of Fat

Visible fat in meat occurs in two ways—as fat layers surrounding muscle sections and as marbling within muscle sections.

and in layers under the skin. In meat, there may be a layer of visible fat surrounding the lean muscle portion of the cut. In addition, small white flecks, called **marbling,** may appear within the muscle tissue of meat.

Factors Affecting Tenderness

Tenderness is another consideration when shopping for meat, poultry, and fish. As you will see later on, tenderness can affect your choice of cooking method.

Different cuts of meat, poultry, and fish may vary in tenderness. Why? To answer that question, it helps to know a little about the composition of meat, poultry, and fish.

A cut may contain four basic types of tissue: muscle tissue, connective tissue, fat, and bone. When it comes to tenderness, the most important factors are muscle tissue and connective tissue.

Composition of Meat and Poultry

Meat and poultry have very long, thin muscle cells (sometimes called "muscle fibers").

Some are as long as 12 inches (30 cm). They are thinnest in young animals and in parts of the animal that get little exercise (such as the back). As animals get older, the fibers thicken. They are thickest in those parts that get the most exercise (such as the legs). Thicker muscle fibers give the meat or poultry a tougher, coarser texture.

Tenderness also depends on the amount and type of connective tissue that is present. Connective tissue is a protein material that surrounds cells. The more connective tissue, the tougher the cut of meat or poultry.

There are several kinds of connective tissue in meat and poultry, but two are important when it comes to tenderness and cooking.

❖ *Collagen* (KAHL-eh-jen) is a thin, white or transparent connective tissue. When meat or poultry is cooked using moist-heat methods, such as simmering in liquid, the collagen softens and turns into a gelatin.

❖ *Elastin* (ee-LASS-tin) is a yellowish, very tough connective tissue. It cannot be softened by heat. Other tenderizing methods, such as pounding, cutting, or grinding, must be used to break down elastin.

Beef and Poultry Muscle

Single Muscle Cell

Connective Tissue

Bundle of Cells

Single Cell

Many bundles of cells form muscle tissue

Fat content can also have an effect on tenderness. Meat that has more marbling seems more tender. In addition, fat gives meat and poultry flavor and helps keep it juicy as it cooks.

In meat and poultry, the muscle tissue is made up of long fibers held together in bundles by connective tissue. The thicker the fibers, the less tender the meat.

TIPS for Success

Cutting Across the Grain

The lengthwise direction of the muscle cells is known as the "grain." One solution for less tender cuts of meat is to cut across the grain. The long fibers are cut into pieces and the meat can be easier to chew. Most meats are generally cut this way for retail sale. It's also a good way to cut cooked meat and poultry for serving.

Safety Check

When shopping for meat, poultry, or fish, be sure the department smells fresh. Foul odors could indicate leaking packages or temperatures that may be too high for safety. The fish department may have a characteristic fish aroma, but should have no foul odors. (See Section 12.3 for more shopping tips.)

Fish Muscles Are Different

The muscles in fish are arranged differently. Instead of the long fibers found in meat and poultry, fish have very short fibers that are arranged in layers. The layers are separated by sheets of very thin, fragile connective tissue. When heated, this connective tissue turns into gelatin. As a result, all fish and shellfish is very tender. When cooked, the flesh "flakes" or breaks up into small pieces because the muscle fibers are short.

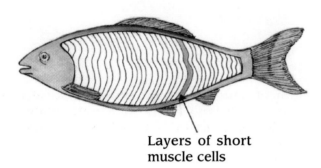

Layers of short muscle cells

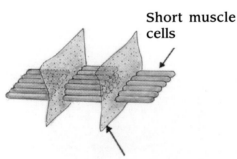

Short muscle cells

Very thin sheets of connective tissue divide muscle cells

Fish is naturally tender because it has short muscle fibers and fragile connective tissue.

Comparing Costs

When shopping, cost is an important point of comparison. Meats, poultry, fish, and shellfish are generally the most expensive part of the food budget. However, cuts can vary widely in cost.

Remember to compare the cost per serving of different cuts of meat, poultry, and fish. (Refer to Section 12.3, page 341.) If you find a bargain that's not on your shopping list, consider changing your plans. You may save a considerable amount.

Here are some general guidelines:

❖ Tender cuts are often more expensive than less tender cuts. Knowing how to cook less tender cuts can help you save money.

❖ Boneless meat and poultry is generally more expensive than cuts sold with the bone. You may be able to save money by removing the bones yourself. Remember, however, that boneless cuts yield more servings per pound. Be sure to check the cost per serving.

Section 19.1 Review

RECALL THE FACTS

1. List three nutrients found in meat, poultry, and fish.

2. Identify two factors that affect the tenderness of meat and poultry.

3. What is the most accurate way to compare the cost of different cuts of meat, poultry, or fish?

DISCUSS YOUR IDEAS

4. What factors might affect the price of meat, poultry, and fish?

APPLY YOUR LEARNING

5. In magazines and cookbooks, find at least six recipes for meat, poultry, or fish. Identify the cut and preparation method for each recipe. Why do you think some preparation methods are preferred for certain cuts?

Objectives

After studying this section, you should be able to:

* Describe the four basic types of meat.
* Identify tender and less tender cuts of meat.
* Identify processed meat products.
* Give guidelines for storing meat.

Look for These Terms

wholesale cuts
retail cuts
variety meats
curing

The more you know about meat, the easier it will be to find the best buys. Even though there are many different cuts of meat, with an understanding of just a few basic guidelines you can become a smart meat shopper.

Types of Meat

Each of the four basic types of meat has a distinct flavor and appearance. When shopping, look for color typical of the meat.

* **Beef** is meat from cattle over one year old. It has a hearty flavor. The cuts have bright red flesh. The fat is firm with a white, creamy white, or yellowish color.
* **Veal** is meat from very young calves, one to three months old. It has a mild flavor and light pink color with very little fat. "Special fed veal" has been fed a special milk-base diet; the flesh is more tender with a grayish-pink color and white fat.

* **Lamb** has a mild but unique flavor. Cuts are a bright pink-red color with white, brittle fat. The fat is sometimes covered with a "fell," a colorless connective tissue.
* **Pork** has a mild flavor. Fresh meat is a grayish-pink color with white, soft fat.

Because of changes in breeding and feeding practices, the pork produced today is leaner than in the past.

Cuts of Meat

For marketing, meat is first divided into large **wholesale cuts** (also called primal cuts). Wholesale cuts for beef, veal, pork, and lamb are identified in the illustrations on this page.

These wholesale cuts are divided into the smaller **retail cuts** which you find in the supermarket. For example, one of the wholesale cuts of beef is the chuck, from the shoulder area. Retail cuts from the chuck include blade roast and chuck short ribs.

The price label on the meat package identifies the cut. The type of meat is listed first (beef, veal, pork, or lamb). The wholesale cut is listed second. This tells you the part of the animal the meat comes from, such as chuck, rib, or round. The retail cut, such as spareribs, chops, or steak, is listed third.

Compare the wholesale cuts for the four types of meat animals. In what ways are they similar? How are they different?

Beef

Pork

Veal

Lamb

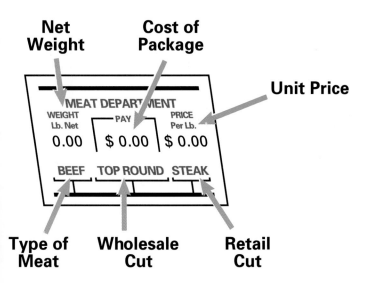

Net Weight

Cost of Package

Unit Price

MEAT DEPARTMENT
WEIGHT
Lb. Net
0.00

PAY
$ 0.00

PRICE
Per Lb.
$ 0.00

BEEF TOP ROUND STEAK

Type of Meat

Wholesale Cut

Retail Cut

Meat labels can help you identify the cut. They also provide information about the size of the package and the price.

Which Cuts Are Lean?

When shopping for meat, lean choices (less than 10 grams of fat in a 3½ ounce [100 gram] serving) include:

❖ *Beef* roasts and steaks: round, loin, sirloin, chuck arm.
❖ *Pork* roasts and chops: tenderloin, center loin, ham.
❖ *Veal* cuts: all except ground veal.
❖ *Lamb* roasts and chops: leg, loin, fore shanks.

When shopping, you can also use appearance as a clue to leanness. Inspect the package carefully. How much fat can you see? The fat that surrounds the cut should be trimmed to less than 1/4 inch (0.6 cm). If there is more, you pay for the excess and waste money.

Using Bone Shape to Identify Cuts

Each wholesale cut has a distinctive bone shape. Therefore, you can use bone shape as a method to identify meat cuts. The bone shape for a particular area of the animal is almost identical in beef, pork, lamb, and veal, although the bones differ in size.

The bones are also your clue to the tenderness of the cut. For example, the rib or T-shaped bones, which are part of the backbone, indicate the meat is tender. Knowing whether a cut is tender will help you decide what cooking method to use.

The diagram on page 492 shows typical bone shapes for the wholesale cuts of meat. It also identifies which wholesale cuts are tender.

Lean cuts of meat can be a part of an overall low-fat eating plan.

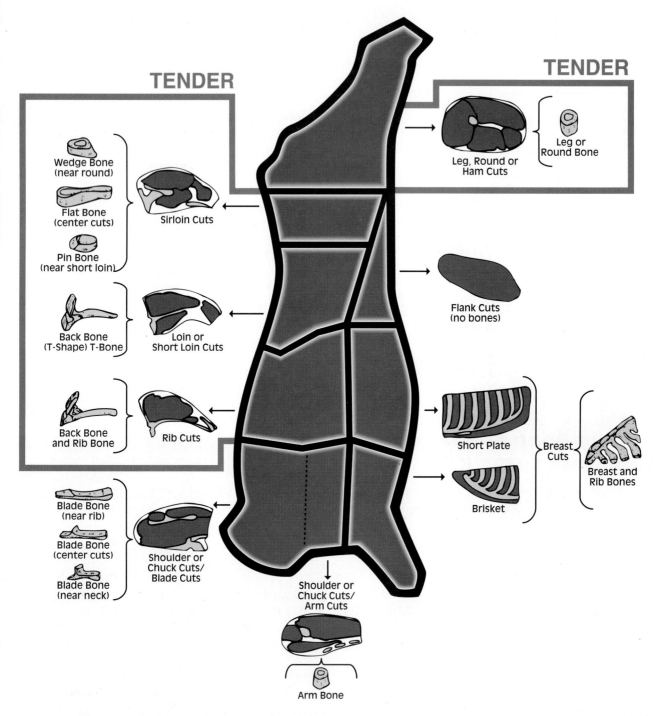

TENDER

TENDER

Wedge Bone (near round)

Flat Bone (center cuts)

Pin Bone (near short loin)

Sirloin Cuts

Back Bone (T-Shape) T-Bone

Loin or Short Loin Cuts

Back Bone and Rib Bone

Rib Cuts

Blade Bone (near rib)

Blade Bone (center cuts)

Blade Bone (near neck)

Shoulder or Chuck Cuts/ Blade Cuts

Leg, Round or Ham Cuts

Leg or Round Bone

Flank Cuts (no bones)

Short Plate

Breast Cuts

Brisket

Breast and Rib Bones

Shoulder or Chuck Cuts/ Arm Cuts

Arm Bone

Bone shapes can help you decide how tender meat is and what cooking method to use. Notice the typical bone shapes for each part of the animal. An example of a retail cut is also shown for each wholesale cut. Tender cuts include those from the rib, loin or short loin, sirloin, and leg or round.

These stuffed peppers are just one example of the many uses for ground meat. When buying, look for an indication of fat content on the label. For example, "85 percent lean" would mean that the ground meat is 15 percent fat by weight.

Ground Meat

Ground beef is made from beef trimmings, the meat attached to the bone. By law, ground beef cannot have more than 30 percent fat by weight. Lean ground beef is available, although it may cost more.

You may also find packages of ground lamb, pork, and veal. If not, you can ask to have meat ground for you.

Organ Meats

Edible animal organs are usually called **variety meats.** Here are some examples.
* Liver is highly nutritious and tender, with a pronounced flavor.
* Lamb and veal kidneys are tender with a mild flavor. Beef and pork kidneys are strong flavored and less tender.
* Chitterlings usually refers to the intestines of pigs, but they may also come from calves. They are thoroughly cleaned and sold whole in containers.

Other organ meats include brains, heart, tongue, tripe (stomach lining of cattle), and sweetbreads (thymus gland).

Inspection and Grading

Meat is inspected before it can be sold. The USDA inspects meat for wholesomeness. A round inspection mark is stamped on the meat with a harmless vegetable dye. The inspection mark is stamped in only a few places on the animal, so you will probably not see it on retail cuts.

Meat may also be graded. Grading is a voluntary program available to the meat industry, which pays for the service. Meat is graded according to standards which include amount of marbling, age of the animal, and texture and appearance of the meat. Following are the most common grades for beef.
* *Prime* is the highest and most expensive grade. The meat is well marbled with fat. It is very tender and flavorful.
* *Choice* is the most common grade sold in supermarkets. It has less marbling than prime but is still tender and flavorful.
* *Select* contains the least amount of marbling and is least expensive. It is sometimes sold as a store brand.

Meat that has been graded is identified by a grade shield. Which of these grades is least expensive?

Lamb and veal are also graded. The same grades are used, except that "Good" replaces "Select." Pork is not graded because the meat is more uniform in quality.

Processed Meats

Meats can be processed into products such as ham, bacon, sausage, and cold cuts. Processed meats give consumers a wider variety of products from which to choose. About 35 percent of the meat produced in the United States is processed.

Processing involves treating the meat to extend its shelf life and to create a distinctive flavor. One common processing method is **curing.** This method uses a mixture of salt, sugar, nitrite, ascorbic acid, and water. The meat may be soaked in the solution or the solution may be pumped into the meat.

Other processing methods include drying, salting, and smoking. Drying and salting help preserve the meat. Smoking originally meant exposing meat to wood smoke to preserve and flavor it. Today, liquid smoke is used for flavoring only.

Often, more than one of these processing methods is used. For example, bacon is cured and smoked. Chipped beef has been dried, salted, and smoked.

Ham is pork that has been cured and either smoked or canned. Check the label carefully for instructions. Some hams are precooked, but others must be cooked before eating. If the label does not specify, cook the ham.

Healthy Attitudes

Processed meats should be eaten in moderation. Many of them are high in sodium, fat, or both. In addition, nitrites and nitrates found in cured meats may be linked to certain types of cancer. The National Cancer Institute and the American Cancer Society recommend that people eat fewer smoked, salt-cured, and nitrate-cured foods.

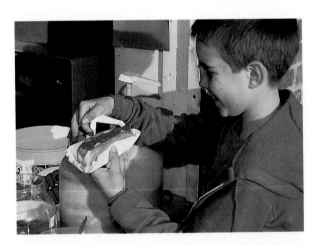

Many people enjoy the flavor of hot dogs and other cured meats. Health experts recommend such meats be eaten only occasionally, since most are high in fat and sodium.

Sausages are made from ground meat, often mixed with fat, salt, sugar, preservatives, seasonings, and other additives. Many different types of sausages are available. Some, such as fresh pork sausage, must be cooked before eating. Others are ready to eat, although they may be heated. Again, check the label carefully.

Cold cuts are processed meats that have been sliced and packaged. They are ready to eat.

Storing Meat

Meat requires cold storage. Ground meat and variety meats, if stored in the refrigerator, should be used within one to two days. Other fresh meat will keep in the refrigerator for three to five days. For longer storage, freeze the meat. See the chart in Section 7.4, pages 208-209, for more specific storage times, including leftovers.

Kielbasa, or Polish sausage, is an example of a sausage associated with a particular country or region. Others include chorizo from Spain, pepperoni from Italy, and braunschweiger from Germany.

Section 19.2 Review

RECALL THE FACTS

1. How does pork differ from beef in flavor and color?

2. Name three wholesale cuts of beef that are considered tender.

3. Give four examples of processed meat products.

4. How long can fresh meat be stored safely in the refrigerator?

DISCUSS YOUR IDEAS

5. How do you think the cut and grade of meat affect its price?

APPLY YOUR LEARNING

6. Bring to class several price labels from packages of meat. (Clean them thoroughly first.) Using the information found on the labels, identify the type of animal, the wholesale cut, the retail cut, the unit price, and the total price for the package.

Poultry is an increasingly popular food. Some poultry is relatively low in fat, which makes it a good choice for health-conscious consumers. Its mild flavor lends itself to many different recipes.

Types and Market Forms of Poultry

The different types of poultry—chicken, turkey, duck, and goose—are sold in a wide variety of market forms.

Chicken

Chicken has light and dark meat. The light meat is leaner and has a milder flavor.

Tenderness and cooking method are determined by the age of the bird. The terms used on the label give an indication.

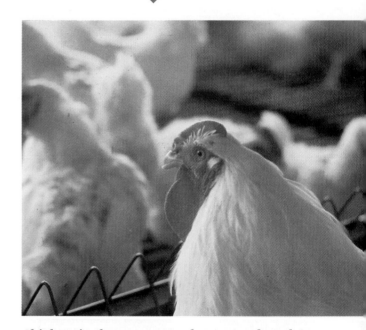

Chicken is the most popular type of poultry in the United States. Why do you think this is so?

- **Broiler-fryer** chickens are the most tender and most common. They can be cooked using almost any method.
- **Roaster** chickens are raised to be roasted whole. They are slightly larger and older than broiler-fryers and yield more meat per pound.
- **Stewing chickens** are older, mature birds. Since they are less tender than others, they must be cooked in moist heat.
- **Rock Cornish game hens** are young, small chickens of a special breed. They have less meat in relation to size than other chickens. One hen usually makes one serving. They can be broiled or roasted.
- **Capons** are desexed roosters under 10 months old. Tender and flavorful, they are best roasted.

Chicken can be purchased in various market forms. Broiler-fryers are sold whole or cut up. You can also buy specific parts, such as chicken breasts (including boneless) or legs. Other types of chicken are usually sold whole, either fresh or frozen.

Turkey

Turkeys are larger than chickens and have a stronger flavor. The light meat is leaner and more tender with a more mild flavor than the dark meat.

When buying a whole turkey, you can choose from several types. They differ mainly in size. All are suitable for roasting, the most common cooking method for turkey.

To cut up a whole chicken, follow these steps...

1. Slice the skin between one leg and the body.

2. Bend the leg to crack the joint. Then cut through the joint and remove the leg. Repeat for the other leg and the wings.

3. If desired, separate the drumstick from the thigh by cracking the joint and cutting through it.

4. Use kitchen shears to cut along the backbone on both sides, separating the breast from the back.

5. Hold the breast skin side down and snap it in two.

6. Cut the breast in half, leaving the breastbone on one of the halves.

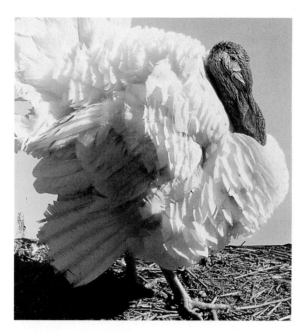

Turkeys are categorized by size.

the word "meat" is part of the description, such as "ground turkey breast meat" or "ground chicken meat," the poultry was ground without the skin. Poultry ground without skin is leaner.

Ground poultry can be used instead of ground beef, but it gives a drier, more bland product. Usually, a little more liquid and seasonings must be used in the recipe.

Giblets

Edible poultry organs are called **giblets** (JIB-lets). Giblets are usually included in a package stuffed inside of whole cleaned poultry. They include the liver, gizzard (stomach), and heart. Chicken livers and gizzards are also sold separately.

Processed Poultry

Turkey is processed the same as meat into products such as ham and bacon. Turkey and chicken are also processed into sausages, such as frankfurters.

- ❖ **Beltsville or fryer-roaster** turkeys are smallest, with an average weight of 5 to 9 lbs. (2.5 to 4.5 kg). They are not always available.
- ❖ **Hen** turkeys (female) weigh about 8 to 16 lbs. (4 to 8 kg).
- ❖ **Tom** turkeys (male) can weigh up to 24 lbs. (12 kg).

Whole turkeys are sold fresh or frozen. You can also buy turkey parts, such as drumsticks, thighs, and wings. Turkey breast is sold bone-in, boneless, or cut into tenderloins and cutlets.

Ducks and Geese

Ducks and geese have all dark meat, which is very flavorful but relatively high in fat. Usually, only whole, frozen ducks and geese are sold.

Ground Poultry

Ground chicken or turkey can be purchased. Read the label carefully. If it states "ground turkey breast" or "ground chicken," both the flesh and skin were used. As you may recall, most of the fat is in the skin. If

Strings of ducks hang in Hong Kong, in preparation for use in popular dishes of the region.

Biochemistry:

Light and Dark Meat

Why does poultry have light and dark meat? The difference in color is due partly to the amount of exercise that different parts of the bird get. Muscles that get frequent, strenuous exercise need more oxygen than others. The oxygen is stored in a red-colored protein pigment called *myoglobin* (MY-uh-GLOW-bin). The amount of myoglobin in the muscle tissue determines the color. Dark meat is found in those parts of chickens and turkeys that get the most exercise, such as the legs. Because chickens and turkeys do not fly, their breast and wing muscles do not need as much oxygen to function. The tissue does not contain as much myglobin, which makes breast meat a lighter color.

■ ■ ■

Inspection and Grading

Poultry is inspected and graded by the USDA. Grading is a voluntary program, just as it is with meat. The inspection and grade

Processed chicken or turkey products may be lower in fat and sodium than processed meats. Check the nutrition facts on the label.

marks can appear on the label or on a wing-tag attached to the bird.

Grade A is the grade of poultry most commonly found in supermarkets. It indicates the poultry is practically free of defects, has a good shape and appearance, and is meaty.

Buying and Storing Poultry

When buying poultry, look for plump, meaty birds. The skin should be smooth and soft. Color of the skin may vary from a creamy white to yellow, depending on the food eaten by the bird. Avoid poultry with tiny feathers or bruised or torn skin.

When stored in the refrigerator, poultry should be used within one to two days. For longer storage, freeze. See the chart in Section 7.4, pages 208-209, for more specific storage times, including leftovers.

Section 19.3 Review

RECALL THE FACTS

1. Tell which cooking method is best for each of the following types of chicken: broiler-fryer, stewing chicken, capon.

2. What is the main difference among types of turkeys?

3. How are ducks and geese usually sold?

4. List three characteristics of good quality poultry.

DISCUSS YOUR IDEAS

5. Review the different market forms of poultry. When might you prefer to buy each one?

APPLY YOUR LEARNING

6. Make a list of as many different ways of using poultry in recipes as you can. Identify the type or form of poultry that might be used in each.

Objectives

After studying this section, you should be able to:

❖ Describe different types and market forms of fish.
❖ Identify different types and market forms of shellfish.
❖ Give guidelines for buying and storing fish and shellfish.

Look for These Terms

crustaceans
mollusks

Fish and shellfish have long been favorite foods of people living in coastal regions. Today, people almost everywhere can enjoy the nutrition and flavor of the many varieties of fish and shellfish that are available.

Types and Market Forms of Fish and Shellfish

What is the difference between fish and shellfish? Fish have fins and a bony skeleton with a backbone. Shellfish have no fins or bones but have a shell instead.

Some fish and shellfish come from inland waters such as lakes, rivers, and ponds. They are known as freshwater varieties. Saltwater varieties, also known as seafood, come from oceans and seas. Today, both freshwater and saltwater fish and some shellfish are being raised on fish farms.

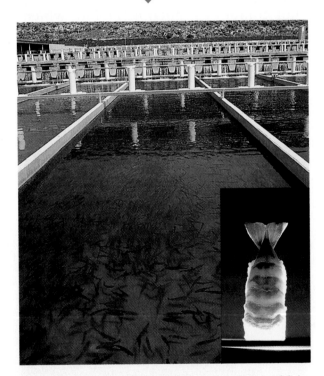

Fish farms provide much of the fish sold in the U.S. today, as well as some shellfish.

Types of Fish

There are dozens of varieties of fish. However, when it comes to cooking, many of them are similar to one another. If a specific fish recommended in a recipe isn't available, a fish similar in color and texture can be substituted. The box at the bottom of the page gives some examples.

As you have learned, most fish are very low in fat. A few of the darker fish have a higher fat content.

Drawn

Market Forms of Fish

Fish can be purchased in several market forms. The most common are:

❖ **Drawn:** Whole fish with scales, gills, and internal organs removed.
❖ **Dressed or pandressed:** Drawn fish with head, tail, and fins removed.
❖ **Fillets:** Sides of fish cut lengthwise away from bones and backbone. Usually boneless. Large fillets may be cut into smaller ones.
❖ **Steaks:** Cross sections cut from large, dressed fish. May contain bones from ribs and backbone.

Dressed

Fillet

Fish Choices

Fish with a light color, mild flavor, and tender texture:

Catfish	Perch	Sole
Cod	Pike	Trout
Flounder	Pollock	Turbot
Haddock	Pompano	Whitefish
Halibut	Red Snapper	

Fish with a dark color, more pronounced flavor, and firm texture:

Bluefish	Salmon	Tuna
Mackerel	Swordfish	

Steaks

You can purchase drawn or dressed fish, fillets, or steaks. Which would you choose if you wanted boneless fish?

Shellfish

Shellfish generally have a mild, sweet flavor. Almost all shellfish come from oceans and seas, but a few come from fresh water. There are two types of shellfish: crustaceans and mollusks.

Crustaceans

Crustaceans (kruss-TAY-shuhns) have long bodies with jointed limbs, covered with shells. They include crabs, crayfish, lobsters, and shrimp.

❖ **Crabs** have a round shell with eight legs and two claws. Different varieties and sizes are available. Whole crabs are sold live, cooked, or frozen. Crab legs and claws are sold cooked and frozen. Cooked crabmeat is available refrigerated, frozen, and canned.

❖ **Crayfish** are freshwater crustaceans. They are also called "crawfish" or "crawdads." They look like small lobsters. Crayfish are sold whole, live, or cooked.

❖ **Lobsters** have a long, jointed body with four pair of legs and two large claws, all covered with a hard shell. Average weight is from 1 ¼ lb. (625 g) to 2 ¼ lb. (1125 g). Maine lobster is the most popular. Fresh lobster is sold live.

❖ **Shrimp** vary in size and color. They are usually sold frozen or previously frozen and thawed. You can buy raw shrimp, with or without the shell, as well as shelled, cooked shrimp.

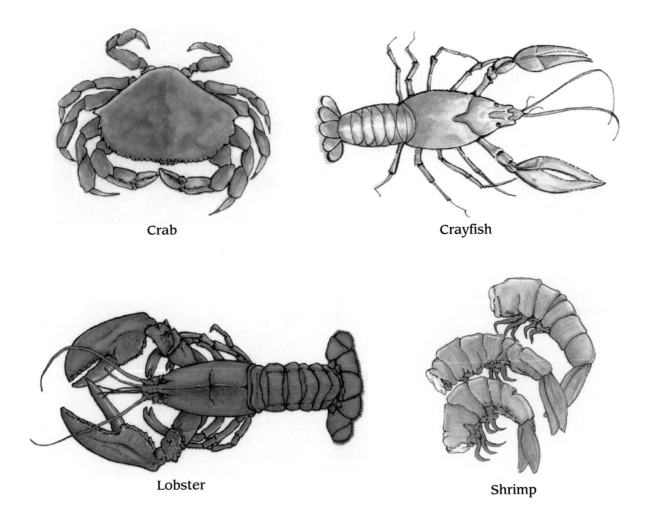

Crab

Crayfish

Lobster

Shrimp

Mollusks

Mollusks have soft bodies that are covered by at least one shell. They include clams, mussels, oysters, scallops, and squid.

❖ *Clams* have two shells hinged at the back with edible flesh inside. Many varieties are available, from small to large. They are sold live (still in the shell) or shucked (removed from the shell).

❖ *Mussels* have a thin, oblong shell. Depending on type, the length varies from 1½ inches (3.8 cm) to 6 inches (15 cm). Shell colors also vary. The flesh is creamy tan and not as tender as oysters or clams. Mussels are sold live in the shell.

❖ *Oysters* have a rough, hard, gray shell. They come in different sizes. The flesh varies in color, flavor, and texture. Oysters are sold live or shucked.

❖ *Scallops* grow in beautiful fan-shaped shells. Only the muscle that hinges the two shells is sold. Bay scallops are very tiny, about 1/2 inch (1.3 cm) in diameter, sweet and tender. Sea scallops are larger (about 1½ inches (3.8 cm) in diameter) and not as tender as bay scallops.

❖ *Squid* is also known as calamari (cah-lah-MAH-ree). It is sold fresh. Squid is popular in Asia and the Mediterranean area and is becoming popular in the United States.

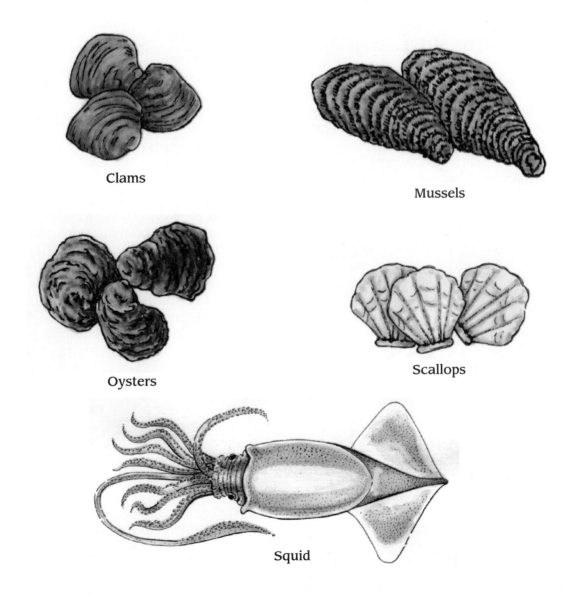

Clams

Mussels

Oysters

Scallops

Squid

Processed Fish

Fish may be dried, pickled, smoked, or cured. Sometimes more than one method is used. For example, lox is a type of cured, smoked salmon. Cod is often salted and dried. Herring may be cut into chunks, pickled in vinegar and spices, and then packed in jars.

Canned fish is ready to eat as is, heat, or use in recipes. To cut down on fat, look for fish packed in water instead of oil. If fish is packed in oil, drain well and rinse off the oil before using. Many other convenience forms of fish are available, such as frozen, breaded fish sticks.

Inspection and Grading

A voluntary inspection and grading program is carried on jointly by the Food and Drug Administration (FDA) and the National Marine Fisheries Service of the U.S. Department of Commerce. The program attempts to focus on those parts of fish processing that may be risks to consumer safety. Some state and local fish inspection services are also available.

Fish that has been inspected carries this seal. Look for it on the package.

Buying and Storing Fish and Shellfish

Buy fish from a reliable source. When buying fresh fish, notice the way it is displayed. If layers are piled on ice, the top layer may be too warm for safe keeping. Don't buy ready-to-eat fish that is piled next to fresh fish. Harmful bacteria from the fresh fish may have transferred to the ready-to-eat products.

Judge the quality of fresh fish by its appearance and aroma. Fresh fish should have shiny skin and a glistening color. It should have a mild, fresh aroma, similar to cucumbers or seaweed. The skin should spring back when pressed. Whole fish should have clear, full eyes and bright red or pink gills.

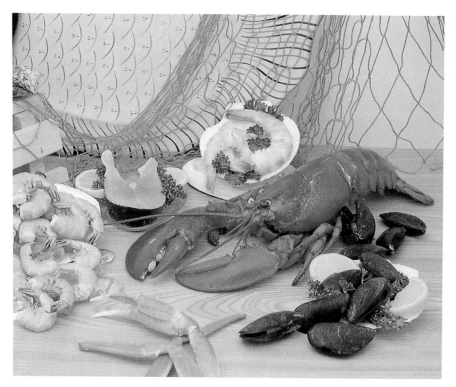

Remember to look for signs of quality when buying fish and shellfish. How would you store the varieties shown here?

Some shellfish must be live if bought fresh. Look for signs that they are live, such as movement in lobsters. Mollusk shells should be closed when they are tapped.

Fresh fish and shellfish that have gone bad will smell "fishy" or have an unpleasant ammonia odor.

After you bring fish home, store it in the refrigerator or freezer immediately. Refrigerate live shellfish in containers covered with a clean, damp cloth. They need breathing space to stay alive. Do not put live saltwater shellfish in fresh water—they will not live.

Fish stored in the refrigerator should be used within one to two days. For longer storage, freeze. See the chart in Section 7.4, pages 208-209, for more specific storage times, including leftovers.

Section 19.4 Review

RECALL THE FACTS

1. How are drawn fish and dressed fish alike? How are they different?

2. Define "crustacean" and "mollusk." Give three examples of each.

3. List four signs to look for when buying fresh fish and shellfish.

4. How should live shellfish be stored?

DISCUSS YOUR IDEAS

5. Do you think it would be safe to eat fish that you and your friends had caught on a fishing trip? Why or why not?

APPLY YOUR LEARNING

6. Find recipes for fish and shellfish in magazines or cookbooks. Identify whether each recipe calls for a light-colored fish, dark-colored fish, crustacean, or mollusk.

Preparing Meat, Poultry, Fish, and Shellfish

Meat, poultry, fish, and shellfish are different in some ways. However, when it comes to cooking, there are also many similarities. Many of the same basic cooking methods can be used for each.

Principles of Cooking Meat, Poultry, and Fish

When cuts from animal foods cook, several changes occur in color, flavor, and texture.
❖ **Color.** The red color changes to brown. For instance, beef, which is dark red, turns a dark brown. Pork and the white meat of poultry, which are a light pink, turn beige.
❖ **Flavors.** Heat develops the flavors by creating chemical reactions within the cut.
❖ **Texture.** When heated, a cut loses fat and moisture. As a result, it shrinks. In addition, muscle fibers get firmer and connecting tissue becomes more tender.

When cooked in dry heat, animal foods lose some juices, carrying off some B vitamins. Some thiamin is destroyed by high temperatures. In general, however, few nutrients are lost unless the food is overcooked.

When properly cooked, meat is tender and flavorful and retains most of its nutrients.

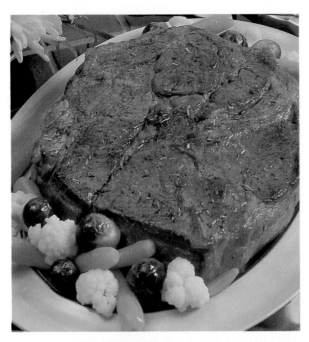

Moist heat methods are a good choice for less tender cuts. Why?

When a cut is overcooked in dry heat, it dries out and gets tough, stringy, and chewy. In moist heat, an overcooked cut gets mushy and loses its flavor. When overcooked in a microwave oven, the cut can get so hard that it cannot be chewed.

Choosing a Cooking Method

The cooking method depends on the tenderness of the cut. Tender cuts can be cooked using dry heat methods, such as broiling and roasting. Broiling, the fastest of the two methods, cooks tender cuts in a matter of minutes. Examples of tender cuts include steaks, rib and loin roasts, certain kinds of chops, ground meat and poultry, broiler-fryers, fish, and some shellfish.

Less tender cuts include blade roasts, arm steaks, stewing hens, and some shellfish.

These cuts can be tenderized using cooking methods that involve moist heat, such as simmering, stewing, and braising. These methods involve long, slow cooking which breaks down the collagen in the meat and makes it tender.

Moist heat methods also give you an opportunity to add seasonings, sauces, and other foods to the dish. You can create many different flavor combinations in this way. You may sometimes choose to cook tender cuts in moist heat for this reason. When tender cuts are cooked in moist heat, the cooking time is generally shortened. Otherwise, the cut can easily be overcooked and fall apart.

Preparing to Cook

For best results, thaw frozen raw meat, poultry, and fish before cooking. Follow the guidelines for safe thawing in Section 7.3, page 203. If the cut is not thawed, the cooking time will have to be increased. In general, increase the cooking time by about 50 percent. For example, if the normal cooking time is 40 minutes, the cooking time for frozen cuts would be about 60 minutes. However, the extra time needed depends on size of the food and whether or not it was partially thawed.

Before cooking meat, poultry, or fish, be sure the cut is clean. Rinse it under cold water and pat dry with a paper towel. If you are cooking whole poultry, first remove the giblets and neck from the body and neck cavities. Rinse the cavities of whole poultry and whole fish several times. Remove any foreign matter that may be present in the cavities.

Trimming Fat

Before cooking meat and poultry, remove as much fat as possible. Trim visible fat from meat as shown in the illustration on page 508.

A boning knife is useful for trimming fat from meat. First cut away visible fat from around the outside of the meat (left). Then cut the muscle sections apart (right) and trim away the fat found between them.

As you have learned, much of the fat in poultry is in or just under the skin. When cooking poultry in moist heat, remove the skin. However, when using dry heat methods, leave the skin on to keep the poultry from drying out. Most of the fat will melt and drip away during cooking. Remove the skin before eating.

Judging Doneness

Doneness means that the cut has cooked long enough for the necessary changes to take place so it is a pleasure to eat. All cuts must be cooked long enough so they are safe to eat. If any part is not cooked, there is a risk of food-borne illness.

Safety Check

Once you start to cook a cut, regardless of the method, finish cooking it. Don't cook food partially and then complete the cooking later. Partial or interrupted cooking often produces conditions that encourage the growth of harmful bacteria.

Testing Meat and Poultry for Doneness

To be safe to eat, all meat and poultry should reach an internal temperature of at least 160°F (71°C). This insures that harmful bacteria have been destroyed.

When roasting or microwaving cuts more than two inches (5 cm) thick, use a meat thermometer to check for doneness. The thermometer, when inserted into the thickest part of the cut, will tell you the internal temperature. The chart on page 509 gives internal temperatures for meat and poultry cooked in dry heat.

With other cooking methods, with thinner cuts, or if you do not have a meat thermometer, test for doneness by checking the inside color. With a sharp knife, pierce the cut about halfway through. The juices running out should be clear, with no pink color. The center of the meat should not show any pink color.

When testing chicken, you may find the meat has turned dark around the bones. This is common in young broiler-fryers. Their bones have not hardened completely. During cooking, color pigment from the inside of the bone seeps out. The meat is safe to eat.

Safety Check

Trichinosis is an illness caused by a parasitic worm sometimes found in pork or wild game. It can cause diarrhea, nausea, vomiting, and other symptoms. Thorough cooking to an internal temperature of 160°F (71°C) destroys the parasite.

The parasite that causes trichinosis is shown here greatly magnified. Trichinosis is much less common now than in the past. Still, cook pork to the recommended temperature to reduce the risk of any food-borne illness.

Internal Temperatures for Meat and Poultry

Cooking food to an internal temperature of 160°F (71°C) usually protects against food-borne illness. However, some foods are considered more tasty when they are cooked to a higher internal temperature. The higher temperatures in this chart reflect a greater degree of doneness.

Food	Internal Temperature	
	°F	°C
Beef		
Rare (some bacterial risk)	140	60
Medium	160	71
Well Done	170	77
Pork, Lamb, Veal		
Medium	160	71
Well Done	170	77
Poultry		
Whole poultry	180	82
Turkey breasts or roasts	170	77
Stuffing (cooked alone or in bird)	165	74
Ham		
Fresh (raw) or shoulder	160	71
Precooked (to reheat)	140	60
Ground meat and poultry		
Turkey, chicken	170	77
Beef, veal, lamb, pork	160	71

When testing small pieces or cubes of meat or poultry, pierce with a fork. If it slides easily to the bottom, the cut is done.

Meat and poultry cooking times vary, depending on the method and cut used. The cooking time given in the recipe is just a guide. Begin testing meat and poultry for doneness about ten minutes before the end of the cooking time.

Testing Fish for Doneness

Fish is very tender and cooks in a short time. When using conventional cooking methods, remember the "ten-minute rule." Cook fish ten minutes for every inch (2.5 cm) of thickness, as measured at the thickest part. However, there are a few exceptions. If fish is being baked in a sauce, add about five minutes to total cooking time. Some moist heat recipes may call for longer cooking times to allow flavors to blend. Remember to increase the cooking time if the fish is frozen.

Begin to check fish for doneness about two or three minutes before the cooking time is up. Fish is done when its flesh turns opaque. When gently lifted with a fork, the flesh flakes easily.

Basic Cooking Methods

A number of different cooking methods can be used for meat, poultry, fish, and shellfish. They include roasting, broiling, poaching, and microwaving. You may want to review basic information on these cooking methods in Sections 9.3 and 9.4.

Roasting or Baking

When roasting or baking meat, poultry, or fish, it is usually not necessary to preheat the oven. However, follow recipe directions. The roasting temperatures in a conventional oven should be at least 325°F (160°C) to keep harmful bacteria from growing. Fish can bake at high temperatures, such as 450°F (230°C).

When roasting whole poultry, make the bird as compact as possible. Some turkeys, like this one, have a small plastic cylinder that pops up to indicate doneness. However, check the internal temperature with a thermometer to be sure.

The way you prepare meat, poultry, and fish for roasting or baking varies:

❖ **Large meat roasts.** Put the roast, fat side up, on a rack in the pan to hold the cut out of the drippings. Some rib cuts of meat form a natural rack. Insert the meat thermometer so the tip is in the center of the roast. The thermometer should not touch bone, fat, or thick connective tissue.

❖ **Whole poultry.** Make the bird as compact as possible so it cooks evenly. Tie the legs together. Tuck tips of wings under the back. Insert the thermometer deep into the thickest part of the thigh next to the body. Be sure it is not touching bone or fat.

❖ **Poultry pieces.** Place in a shallow pan, skin side up.

Safety Check

Roasting whole poultry with stuffing requires a few special precautions.

❖ Do not stuff the poultry ahead of time. The inside of a refrigerated stuffed bird does not chill fast enough for safe storage. Harmful bacteria will multiply. Instead, stuff the poultry just before roasting.

❖ Allow extra cooking time for poultry with stuffing. If you want to shorten the cooking time, bake the stuffing separately.

❖ After cooking, use a meat thermometer to make sure the stuffing has reached an internal temperature of 165°F (74°C).

❖ Remove stuffing from poultry immediately after cooking.

❖ Store leftover poultry and stuffing separately, divided into small portions.

❖ **Fish.** Place the fish in a lightly oiled, shallow baking dish. If baking fillets, place skin side down so you can test for doneness. To keep the fish moist, brush with seasoned melted fat or a sauce. It can also be breaded. If so, dot the fish with a teaspoon (5 mL) of butter or margarine after breading.

Follow recipe directions for turning the food. Generally, large roasts and fish do not have to be turned. Poultry pieces may need to be turned after half the cooking time.

For low-fat cooking, use broth or juice for basting instead of drippings.

Roast or bake for the time specified in the recipe. Remove from the oven when done.

Broiling

Many tender cuts are suitable for broiling. These include many steaks and chops; hamburgers; chicken halves, quarters, or pieces; fish steaks, fillets, or whole fish; and some shellfish, such as shrimp. Do not broil whole turkey pieces—they are too thick. However, thinner cuts may be broiled, such as cutlets or ground turkey patties.

By broiling tender cuts, you can prepare delicious main dishes, such as this broiled mullet, in a short time.

Follow the guidelines for broiling in Section 9.4. Here are some additional tips:

❖ Slash the fat around the edges of meat before broiling. This will keep the cut from curling.
❖ When broiling chicken, begin with the skin side down. Halfway through the broiling time, turn skin side up.
❖ Because fish is lean, brush it lightly with melted butter or margarine to keep it from charring.
❖ To add flavor to broiled foods, brush them with a sauce, such as barbecue or salsa.

For variety, make kabobs (kuh-BOBS). Cut meat, poultry, or firm fish into cubes. Put them on a skewer, alternating with pieces of vegetables such as tomato quarters, mushrooms, and green pepper chunks. Brush with melted butter or margarine, or a sauce, to keep vegetables from drying out. Broil, turning so that all sides are done.

Fish fillets can be poached in seasoned liquid. Add the fillets to the simmering liquid, cover, and cook gently until done.

Poaching

As you may recall, poaching involves simmering whole foods in a small amount of liquid. Fish is one of the foods most commonly poached. Many people consider poached fish a delicacy, and it is often served in fine restaurants.

Whole drawn fish, fillets, or steaks may be poached. The cooking liquid may be plain water, water with lemon or grapefruit juice, fish or vegetable stock, or milk. Usually, it is seasoned to add more flavor to the fish. Try using herbs or spices, such as dill or grated fresh ginger, and sautéed vegetables, such as onions and green peppers.

To poach fish fillets:
1. Pour the cooking liquid (seasoned as desired) into a large, deep skillet. Bring to a boil, then immediately reduce the heat to a simmer.
2. Place the fillets in a single layer in the pan. Add enough liquid, if necessary, to cover the fish by at least 1 inch (2.5 cm).
3. Cover the pan and simmer gently until the fish is just opaque throughout. Do not turn the fish while poaching.

To poach whole fish or fish steaks, first wrap the fish in cheesecloth. Allow enough length at the ends so the cheesecloth can be twisted, knotted, and used as handles to lower and raise the fish. Otherwise, follow the same procedure as for fillets.

If you like, you can serve hot poached fish with a sauce made from the cooking liquid. After removing the fish from the pan, boil the cooking liquid to reduce the amount of liquid and reach the desired flavor.

Poached fish may also be eaten chilled. You might serve cold poached fish with dill or cucumber sauce or use it in a salad.

Microwave Cooking

All types of meat, poultry, fish, and shellfish can be microwaved. When buying for microwaving, choose cuts that are uniform in shape and size. Frozen raw meat, poultry, fish, and shellfish should be completely thawed before cooking in the microwave.

For best results, follow the directions in microwave recipes exactly. Here are some general guidelines.

A cooking bag can be used when microwaving roasts and whole poultry. What are the advantages of this method?

Safety Check

Do not use a conventional meat thermometer inside the microwave oven. Use a thermometer made for the microwave, or wait until after cooking to use a conventional thermometer.

Microwaving Meat and Poultry

Remember that microwave ovens do not always cook evenly. This is especially important when microwaving large cuts, such as meat roasts or a whole turkey. Follow recipe directions exactly to be sure the meat or poultry cooks completely throughout.

When microwaving pork roasts, special care must be taken to cook the meat thoroughly. Place the meat in a covered dish or in a loosely sealed microwave-safe cooking bag. This will hold in moist heat to help ensure even cooking and tender, juicy meat. If you like, add a small amount of liquid such as water, broth, fruit juice, or a sauce. A cooking bag can also be used for whole poultry, if desired.

When microwaved, roasts and whole poultry are cooked to a lower internal temperature than with conventional cooking. That is because the internal temperature continues to rise during standing time. If the microwave oven has a temperature probe, you can program the oven to shut off when the food reaches the desired temperature.

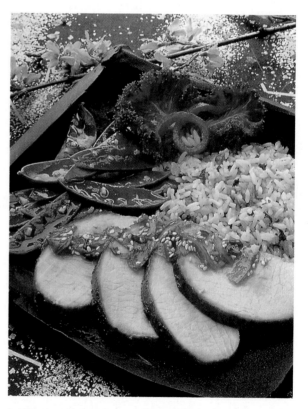

Follow microwave directions carefully for meat that is evenly cooked, tender, and juicy. Use a sauce, a browning grill, or a broiler to add color to the surface of the meat.

During standing time, cover roasts loosely with foil to hold heat in. After standing time, check the meat or poultry in several spots with a meat thermometer to be sure it has reached the proper internal temperature throughout.

Light-colored cuts cooked in a microwave oven may look unappetizing because they have not browned. You may want to use one of the following methods to create a "browned" effect:

❖ Before cooking, brush or rub with a dark-colored sauce such as barbecue, tamari, or Worcestershire.
❖ Use a browning dish or grill. It is specially made so it becomes extremely hot. Small cuts can be pressed down against the bottom to brown them.
❖ After microwaving, put the cut in the broiler for a few minutes to brown it.

Microwaving Fish

When microwaving fish, allow about three to six minutes per pound (500 g) at 100 percent power. Thick fillets and whole fish take a little more time than thin ones.

Take care to avoid overcooking—fish is tender and the microwave cooks quickly. Remove the fish from the microwave when it is still slightly underdone in the center. Let it stand five minutes to complete the cooking, then test for doneness.

Shellfish cooks quickly, so be careful not to overcook. If you do, it will get tough and rubbery.

Other Cooking Methods

Meat, poultry, fish, and shellfish may be pan-fried. Often the food is breaded or dipped in batter first. Remember, however, that food absorbs fat as it fries. Other cooking methods are lower in fat.

Healthy Attitudes

The microwave oven gives you an easy, healthy way to cook ground meat for use in recipes. Crumble the meat in a microwave-safe colander. Set the colander in a large microwave-safe bowl or casserole dish. Cook on high power for the time specified in the oven's instruction book. As the meat cooks, the fat drains into the bowl or dish. Discard the fat and use the meat as desired.

Since most meat has fat of its own, you do not need to fry it in added fat. Pan-broil it instead.

Batter-dipped fried chicken is a traditional favorite, but adds more fat than you may want or need. What are some alternative cooking methods that give a similar texture and flavor?

If you do fry, use as little fat as possible. For example, when sautéing small pieces of meat, poultry, fish, or shellfish, use no more than 1 tsp. (5 mL) of oil or a vegetable oil spray.

Most meat (except veal) is marbled with fat. Therefore, it can be pan-broiled—cooked in a skillet without added fat—instead of fried. For instance, you can pan-broil hamburgers, bacon, or tender steaks and chops. Be sure to remove the fat that accumulates during cooking.

Some cooking methods—such as stewing, braising, and stir-frying—usually involve cooking several different foods together, such as meat and vegetables. These methods are discussed in Chapter 20, "Food Combinations."

Section 19.5 Review

RECALL THE FACTS

1. Name two specific cooking methods you might use for tender cuts and two you might use for less tender cuts.

2. Name three steps that might be involved in preparing raw meat or poultry for cooking.

3. Name two signs that fish is done cooking.

4. Briefly explain how to prepare whole poultry for roasting.

DISCUSS YOUR IDEAS

5. What is the advantage of knowing basic guidelines for a number of different methods of cooking meat, poultry, and fish?

APPLY YOUR LEARNING

6. Choose one of the cooking methods discussed in this chapter. Write the name of the method vertically down the left-hand side of a piece of paper. Next to each letter, write a sentence that begins with that letter and gives a fact about the cooking method.

Thinking About the Recipe

Read the recipe for "Breaded Perch with Parmesan" and answer the following questions.

1. If the fish fillets are 1½ inches thick at the thickest part, about how long will they take to cook?
2. What other types of fish could you substitute for perch? (See Section 19.4.)

Breaded Perch with Parmesan

Customary	Ingredients	Metric
1/2 cup	Dry bread crumbs	125 mL
2 Tbsp.	Grated Parmesan cheese	30 mL
1/2 tsp.	Oregano, thyme, or basil	3 mL
1 lb.	Perch fillets	0.45 kg
1/4 cup	Skim milk	50 mL
1 Tbsp.	Margarine, melted	15 mL

Yield: 4 servings

Directions

Pan: Shallow baking pan
Temperature: 425°F (220°C)

1. Preheat oven. Grease baking pan.
2. Combine bread crumbs, Parmesan cheese, and choice of herbs.
3. Dip fillets in milk, then coat with bread crumb mixture. Lay in single layer on baking pan.
4. Drizzle fillets with melted margarine.
5. Bake at 425°F (220°C) until fish flakes easily with a fork (approximately 10 minutes per inch of thickness).

Nutrition Information

Per serving (approximate): 197 calories, 26 g protein, 10 g carbohydrate, 5 g fat, 104 mg cholesterol, 260 mg sodium

Thinking About the Recipe

Read the recipe for "Simply Deluxe Microwave Chicken" and answer the following questions.

1. Why is it important to arrange and turn the chicken pieces as specified in the recipe?
2. What is the purpose of the soy sauce?

Simply Deluxe Microwave Chicken

Customary	Ingredients	Metric
4	Boneless, skinless chicken breast halves	4
2 Tbsp.	Soy sauce	30 mL
1/2 cup	Plain nonfat yogurt	125 mL
1/2 tsp.	Grated onion	3 mL
1/2 tsp.	Prepared mustard	3 mL
1/4 tsp.	Seasoned salt	1 mL
Dash	Pepper	Dash

Yield: 4 servings

Directions

Pan: Round microwave-safe dish with removable rack

Power level: 100% power

1. Brush chicken pieces with soy sauce.
2. Arrange chicken on rack close to edges of dish. Cover loosely with waxed paper.
3. Microwave at 100% power for 6 minutes.
4. Mix together yogurt, onion, and mustard in small bowl. Set aside.
5. Remove chicken pieces from rack. Turn pieces over and place in bottom of dish, arranging them in a circle around the edge.
6. Sprinkle chicken with seasoned salt and pepper. Spoon yogurt mixture over each piece.
7. Cover loosely with waxed paper. Microwave at 100% power for about 6 minutes, or until fork can be inserted in chicken with ease.
8. Sprinkle with additional salt and pepper, if desired. Let stand, covered, 2 minutes before serving.

Nutrition Information

Per serving (approximate): 148 calories, 29 g protein, 3 g carbohydrate, 3 g fat, 73 mg cholesterol, 739 mg sodium

Thinking About the Recipe

Read the recipe for "Beef Patties with Herbs" and answer the following questions.

1. What other cooking methods could you use for ground beef patties?
2. If you substituted ground turkey meat for ground beef, what other changes might you need to make in the recipe? Why?

Beef Patties with Herbs

Customary	Ingredients	Metric
1 lb.	Extra-lean ground beef	0.45 kg
1/2 tsp.	Black pepper, ground	3 mL
1/2 tsp.	Rosemary, dried	3 mL
1/2 tsp.	Thyme, dried	3 mL
4 slices	Tomato	4 slices
4 thin slices	Onion	4 thin slices
4	Crusty rolls, split	4

Yield: 4 servings

Conventional Directions

Pan: Nonstick skillet
Temperature: Medium

1. Combine ground beef, pepper, and herbs until well blended.
2. Shape the ground beef mixture into four patties about 1/2 inch (1 cm) thick.
3. Panbroil ground beef patties about 8 minutes, turning once.
4. Serve patties with tomato and onion slices on crusty rolls.

Microwave Directions

Pan: Microwave-safe dish
Power level: 100% power

1. Follow Steps 1 and 2 of conventional directions.
2. Place ground beef patties in microwave-safe dish. Cover with waxed paper.
3. Cook patties for about 6 minutes at 100% power, turning once after 2 minutes.
4. Let stand 1 minute.
5. Serve patties with tomato and onion slices on crusty rolls.

Nutrition Information

Per serving (approximate): 382 calories, 27 g protein, 33 g carbohydrate, 16 g fat, 70 mg cholesterol, 374 mg sodium

CAREER PROFILE

Bill Mayokok
Fisherman

Current position:

"I'm a boatswain (a highly experienced deckhand) on a large fishing vessel."

Responsibilities:

"Basically, I help carry out the ship's sailing and fishing operations. After removing the catch from the nets, we have to see that it's washed, salted, iced, and properly stored. Once we're back on land, we help unload the catch."

Skills:

"This work can be physically demanding, so you must be in good health. You also must have a certain amount of mechanical aptitude to work the equipment. And you must be patient and able to work as a team with others."

Education:

"This line of work is learned on the job. I sometimes attend workshops on the newest improvements in fishing gear."

Work environment:

"I prefer to work outdoors, so this job suits me. The days can be long and hot, but at the same time satisfying and relaxing. Sometimes the job can be hazardous, though, when an unexpected storm or fog blows up."

Career goals:

"I'm hoping to obtain my license from the U.S. Coast Guard to captain my own fishing vessel someday."

- Why do you think teamwork is so important in Bill's job?
- What aspects of Bill's job do you think you might enjoy? Why?

Summary

Section 19.1
Looking at Meat, Poultry, Fish, and Shellfish: Meat, poultry, fish, and shellfish are sources of complete protein, B vitamins, and several minerals. They also contain cholesterol and varying amounts of fat. Cuts of meat and poultry that include thicker muscle fibers or more connective tissue are less tender. Meat, poultry, fish, and shellfish are usually the most expensive part of the food budget.

Section 19.2
Meat Selection and Storage: Beef, veal, lamb, and pork each have a characteristic flavor and color. You can identify cuts of meat by the package label or by bone shape. The USDA inspects meat for wholesomeness. Grading for quality is a voluntary program. Some meats are processed by curing and other methods. Store meat properly to retain its quality.

Section 19.3
Poultry Selection and Storage: Chicken and turkey may be purchased fresh or frozen, whole or in parts. Ducks and geese are usually available whole and frozen. Poultry is inspected, and may be graded, by the USDA. Poultry requires cold storage.

Section 19.4
Fish and Shellfish Selection and Storage: Fish that are similar in color and texture can be substituted for one another. Fish may be bought fresh or frozen in several market forms. Shellfish include crustaceans and mollusks. Many are sold live. Fish may also be dried, pickled, smoked, or cured. Judge the quality of fish and shellfish by appearance and aroma. Fish should be refrigerated or frozen.

Section 19.5
Preparing Meat, Poultry, Fish, and Shellfish: Tender cuts can be cooked with dry heat methods. Less tender cuts need moist heat methods. Cuts should be thawed, cleaned, and trimmed of fat before cooking. You can test for doneness by using a meat thermometer or checking the color and texture of the cut. Basic cooking methods include roasting or baking, broiling, poaching, and microwaving.

REVIEWING FACTS

1. Of beef, pork, chicken, and fish, which generally has the most saturated fat? The least? (19.1)

2. What is elastin? Why is it a factor in meat and poultry preparation? (19.1)

3. Give two examples of lean cuts of each of the following: beef; pork; lamb. (19.2)

4. List and describe three grades of meat. (19.2)

5. Name three types of chicken suitable for roasting. (19.3)

6. What is the difference between "ground turkey" and "ground turkey meat"? (19.3)

7. What does "seafood" refer to? (19.4)

8. What is the difference between fish fillets and fish steaks? (19.4)

9. Describe how cuts from animal foods change in color, flavor, and texture when they are cooked. (19.5)

10. Give three tips for broiling meat, poultry, or fish. (19.5)

LEARNING BY DOING

1. **Demonstration:** Choose a less tender cut of meat. Demonstrate ways of tenderizing it before cooking. (19.1, 19.2)

2. **Taste test:** Compare the taste of different types of processed meat, poultry, or fish. Identify the processing method used and tell what characteristics it gives the food. (19.2, 19.3, 19.4)

3. **Foods lab:** Choose a recipe calling for ground meat. Prepare it once using meat, then using ground poultry instead. Compare the results. (19.3)

4. **Demonstration:** Demonstrate how to judge the quality of fresh fish. (19.4)

5. **Foods lab:** Cook a thicker cut of meat or poultry. Test for doneness by using a meat thermometer and by piercing with a knife. Which method do you think is more reliable? (19.5)

THINKING CRITICALLY

1. **Analyzing decisions:** Besides cost and tenderness, what other factors might affect your choice when buying meat, poultry, and fish? (19.1)

2. **Recognizing bias:** A friend refuses to try organ meats, giblets, or shellfish. She is sure she won't like them. Why might she feel this way? What might be some benefits of trying these foods? (19.2, 19.3, 19.4)

3. **Predicting consequences:** How do you think overcooking affects the appearance, flavor, and texture of fish? (19.5)

MAKING DECISIONS AND SOLVING PROBLEMS

What Would You Do?

1. You would like to reduce the amount of money you spend on meat, poultry, and fish, while still providing your family with good-tasting, quality protein foods. (19.1)

2. You have just moved to a new town and would like to prepare dinner for some new friends. You choose a favorite recipe that calls for loin of lamb, but discover that none of the stores in your area carry it. (19.2)

3. A supermarket is having a sale on fresh, whole catfish. You enjoy catfish, but you don't know how to dress them. (19.4)

4. You are cooking a blade roast in the oven and figure it will be done in about 15 minutes. You get a phone call from the school that your ten-year-old sister attends. The school explains that your sister is not feeling well. You know that it will take at least half an hour to pick her up and bring her home. (19.5)

LINKING YOUR STUDIES

1. **Social studies:** Find information about which foods from animal sources are most popular in another culture. (19.1)

2. **Science:** Find information about meat processing methods. How were meats treated for preservation and flavoring in the past? How is this done today? What chemicals and chemical processes are involved? If possible, conduct an experiment or demonstration showing these principles at work. (19.2)

3. **Math:** Compare the prices of similar forms of chicken and turkey in your area. Figure the cost per serving for each. Show your findings on a bar graph. Also list the possible reasons for any price differences. (19.3)

4. **Science:** Write a report about the latest studies on the relationship between the amount of fish eaten and the occurrence of heart disease. (19.4)

CHAPTER 20
Food Combinations

Objectives

After studying this section, you should be able to:

- Describe how to make sandwiches using a variety of breads and fillings.
- Give suggestions for nutritious snacks.
- Explain how to pack an interesting, nutritious lunch and keep it safe to eat.

Look for These Terms

club sandwich
vacuum bottle

In the last three chapters, you have learned about specific types of foods, ranging from fruits to fish. Different kinds of foods can be put together to make pleasing combination dishes. For example, a variety of nutritious foods can be used in making sandwiches, snacks, and packed lunches. All three are an important part of daily food choices.

Making Sandwiches

When making a sandwich, focus on healthful ingredients. Start with whole grain breads. As a change from sliced bread, make sandwiches with rolls, pita bread, taco shells, bagels, or tortillas. Try toasting the bread.

The variety of fillings is limited only by your imagination. Try leftover cooked lean meat, poultry, or fish; mashed, cooked dry beans; egg or fish salad; or low-fat cottage cheese mixed with chopped fruit. Choose luncheon meats that are low in fat.

Top the fillings with other foods. Use fruits and vegetables such as tomatoes, lettuce, pickles, onions, shredded carrot, sliced apples, and cucumbers. Mustard and salsa are often added for extra flavor.

Sandwiches can be heated easily in a microwave oven. Prepare the sandwich, omitting fresh vegetables and fruit which would wilt during heating. Add those later. Wrap the sandwich in a paper towel and microwave it on 100 percent power for 30 to 60 seconds.

Here are several basic ways to make sandwiches:

❖ *Traditional sandwich.* Use two slices of bread and your choice of fillings. To keep moist fillings from soaking the bread, spread one side of each slice with a very thin coat of butter or margarine. Place the filling between the two buttered slices of bread. For easier eating, cut the sandwich into halves or quarters.

❖ *Fancy sandwiches.* Cut the bread into fancy shapes with cookie cutters before or after you add the filling. Serve these sandwiches at formal events or on special occasions.

❖ *Club sandwich.* A **club sandwich** uses three slices of bread and two different kinds of fillings, such as turkey and ham. Prepare a traditional sandwich. Then butter the top slice, add a second filling, and top it with third slice of bread, buttered side down. Cut the sandwich into quarters. Secure quarters with decorative toothpicks, if necessary.

❖ *Filled pocket sandwiches.* Make pocket sandwiches with pita bread or hard rolls. Taco shells can also be used to hold a filling. To make a pocket from a pita, first warm the pita briefly in the microwave oven to make it easier to handle. Then cut the pita in half with a sharp knife. Gently slit or pull the two sides apart. To make a pocket from a hard roll, slice off the top and scoop out the bread to form a hollow for the filling. (Dry the leftover bread and crust for bread crumbs.) To keep pockets from absorbing the filling, line them first with shredded lettuce or alfalfa sprouts.

By using different breads, fillings, and flavorings, you can create an endless variety of sandwiches. Can you identify the basic types of sandwiches shown here?

Healthful Snacks

As you have learned, snacks are as much a part of your daily eating plan as meals are. (If you need to review information about snacks and eating patterns, see Section 4.1.)

There are many simple, nutritious ways to satisfy between-meal hunger. For instance, fresh fruits and vegetables are easy to prepare. You could also have a glass of skim milk, a small sandwich, or a cup of soup with whole grain crackers as a snack.

Here are more ideas for healthful, tasty snacks to make in a jiffy:

- *Fruit shake:* Put 1 cup (250 mL) of frozen fruit, such as strawberries or peaches, in a blender. Add 1 cup (250 mL) of skim milk, 2 teaspoons (10 mL) of honey, and 1/2 teaspoon (2.5 mL) of vanilla extract. Cover and blend until smooth. Serve immediately.
- *Yogurt pops:* Pour flavored yogurt into a paper cup. Put a wooden popsicle stick or a plastic spoon in the center. Freeze the yogurt pop for at least an hour. The stick or spoon serves as a handle.
- *Frozen fruit bites:* Freeze whole grapes or strawberries. They make candy-like snacks.
- *Low-fat tortilla or pita chips:* Cut tortillas or pita bread into six or eight wedge-shaped pieces. Spread a single layer in a baking pan. Bake them in a preheated oven at 450°F (230°C) for about five minutes or until the wedges are crispy.

Packing a Lunch

It's estimated that about 30 percent of American workers carry a packed lunch. Their reasons vary from saving money to having a better choice of foods. Packed lunches can be taken to school, too.

With a little organization, packed lunches can be easy to assemble. Here are a few simple guidelines:

Fruit shakes make nutritious beverages or snacks. Try blending orange juice, nonfat yogurt, and honey for a refreshing treat.

- Keep hot foods hot and cold foods cold. Since the lunch may have to stand at room temperature four to five hours before eating, use an insulated lunch bag or containers such as vacuum bottles. You can also buy a freezer gel pack, freeze it, and pack it with the lunch.
- To pack foods such as hot soup, chili, or stew, use a wide-mouth vacuum bottle. A **vacuum bottle** has a vacuum space between the outer container and the inner liner, which is made of glass or metal. Vacuum bottles do a better job of keeping foods hot than less expensive foam-insulated bottles. Before packing the vacuum bottle, preheat it—fill it with hot tap water and let it stand a minute or two. Empty the water, fill the bottle with piping hot food, and close tightly.
- Pack foods that are easy to handle. Avoid foods that are drippy or oily. If foods must be cut up, cut them before packing the lunch.

When packing a lunch, keeping the food safe and fresh is an important consideration. So is avoiding waste. How can these items help?

❖ To speed up lunch packing, set aside an area in the freezer, refrigerator, and a nearby cabinet for lunch foods and equipment.
❖ Make packing lunches a family affair. Take turns as the "designated lunch packer" for everyone.

Assembling the Lunch

To prepare an interesting and nutritious lunch, use a variety of foods, following the guidelines in the Food Guide Pyramid. Use your imagination. Think of leftover foods you enjoy eating cold—barbecued chicken, meat loaf, roast turkey, or pizza. You can also heat up leftover chili, stew, or soup to pack in a vacuum bottle.

If you take salads with greens, mix the fruits and vegetables but pack the dressing and any crunchy additions separately. Add them just before you eat.

Bean dips and spreads make tasty sandwich fillings. Try using them as dips for fresh fruits and vegetables, too.

Earth Watch

When you pack a lunch, remember to reduce, reuse, and recycle. For example, plastic containers from yogurt, sour cream, and cottage cheese can be washed out and used to pack foods. Reuse plastic bags from the grocery store as lunch sacks. Save used aluminum foil if it can be recycled in your area. Avoid one-use containers and wraps. Use a cloth napkin instead of paper ones. These tips will help you save money and cut down on waste.

Be sure your food choices include whole grain breads or rolls as well as fresh fruits and vegetables.

What will you choose for a beverage? Remember that a regular soft drink has about 10 teaspoons (50 mL) of sugar and very few nutrients. Milk and fruit juice, on the other hand, are both flavorful and nutritious.

Don't forget to include such nonfood items as forks, spoons, and napkins. Tuck in a wet wipe or a wet washcloth in a plastic bag when you pack foods that are especially messy.

Nutritious packed lunches are based on the Food Guide Pyramid. How would you rate this lunch?

Thinking About the Recipe

Read the recipe for "Apple-Tuna Sandwiches" and answer the following questions.

1. Which food groups are represented in this sandwich?
2. What ingredients might you add or substitute for a flavor variation?

Apple-Tuna Sandwiches

Customary	Ingredients	Metric
7-oz can	Water-pack tuna, drained and flaked	198-g can
1/2 cup	Celery, finely chopped	125 mL
2 Tbsp.	Onion, finely chopped	30 mL
1/2 cup	Mayonnaise, nonfat variety	125 mL
4	Lettuce leaves	4
4 slices	American cheese (optional)	4 slices
1	Apple, cored and thinly sliced— about 12 slices	1
4	Whole wheat buns, split	4

Yield: 4 servings

Directions

1. Combine tuna, celery, onion, and mayonnaise.
2. Cover the bottom of each bun with a lettuce leaf. (Be sure leaves are dry.)
3. Place a cheese slice on top of the lettuce leaf, if desired. (For a decorative effect, try cutting each cheese slice in half diagonally to form two triangles.)
4. Spread tuna mixture on top of lettuce or cheese slices on each bun. Place apple slices on top of tuna. Cover with top half of bun.

Nutrition Information

Per serving (approximate): 119 calories, 6 g protein, 11 g carbohydrate, 7 g fat, 16 mg cholesterol, 302 mg sodium

Objectives

After studying this section, you should be able to:

❖ Describe how to select, wash, store, and serve several kinds of salad greens.

❖ Plan and assemble a salad using a variety of methods and ingredients.

❖ Identify ways to serve salads.

Look for These Terms

emulsion
base
body

A salad is a versatile combination of foods. It can be simply an assortment of greens served as a side dish, or it can be a hearty main dish. Fresh fruit salads can serve as desserts or refreshing snacks any time of day. Depending on the ingredients, a salad can provide servings from each of the five food groups.

Ingredients for Salads

Almost any solid, ready-to-eat food from the five food groups can be used in a salad. Some of the basic foods include:

❖ **Salad greens.** Lettuce is the most common salad green. It comes in many varieties, such as iceberg, romaine, bibb (also known as Boston or butterhead), and red or green leaf lettuce. Other greens include spinach, escarole, chicory, and radicchio (rah-DEE-kee-oh). Remember, the darker the color, the more nutrients the greens contain. Flavors vary from mild to slightly bitter.

❖ **Other vegetables and fruits.** Any fresh fruits and fresh or cooked vegetables may be used in salads. They can be sliced, diced, shredded, quartered, or cubed.

Salad greens include (clockwise from lower left): iceberg lettuce, spinach, leaf lettuce, curly endive, escarole, romaine lettuce, and (center) bibb lettuce.

- ❖ **Cooked grains, legumes, meat, poultry, fish, or eggs; cheese.** Make hearty main dish salads by mixing these foods with fruits and vegetables. For example, combine leftover rice with cooked dry beans, chopped onions, chopped tomatoes, seasonings, and greens. Any cooked, chilled pasta can be used in salads, too.

Salad Dressings

Salad dressings are sauces poured on salads to give them richness and flavor. They also act as binding agents to hold salads together. There are several basic types of dressings.

- ❖ **Oil-based dressings** are also called "French," "Italian," or "vinaigrette" (vihn-uh-GREHT) dressings. They are a mixture of oil, vinegar, and seasonings. Oil-based dressings separate easily and must be mixed again each time you use them.
- ❖ **Mayonnaise** is made with oil, vinegar or lemon juice, seasonings, and eggs. Eggs create an emulsion, which keeps the oil and vinegar from separating. An **emulsion** is an evenly blended mixture of two liquids that do not normally stay mixed.
- ❖ **Cooked dressings** are similar to mayonnaise, but use white sauce to replace some of the eggs and oil.
- ❖ **Dairy dressings** include "ranch-type" dressings. They have buttermilk, yogurt, sour cream, or cottage cheese as a main ingredient. Seasonings are added.

Salad dressings have traditionally been high in fat and calories because of the oil used in making them. Today, however, there are many low-fat and fat-free dressings available. Check the fat content on the label when you are selecting salad dressings. Remember, the nutrients listed on the label are for one serving of 2 tablespoons (30 mL). Many people use far more than that.

Try using nonfat yogurt to make a flavorful, low-calorie salad dressing. Add your favorite seasonings or a dry prepared mix to vary the flavor. For example, stir a little prepared mustard into the yogurt for a main dish salad dressing.

Many different types of salad dressings can be purchased. You can also flavor salads with vinegar or lemon juice, or use nonfat yogurt to make your own dressings.

Science Connection

Chemistry:
Emulsifying Agents in Mayonnaise

Oil and water do not ordinarily stay mixed. If they are shaken together, the oil is broken down into tiny droplets. As soon as you stop shaking the mixture, however, the oil droplets begin to combine with one another. Soon the oil and water are separate again.

The egg yolks in mayonnaise contain a natural substance that acts as an *emulsifying agent*. This agent coats the oil droplets and causes them to repel one another. It also reduces the ability of the vinegar (which is mainly water) to repel the oil. Therefore, the oil stays in small droplets that remain evenly mixed throughout the dressing.

■ ■ ■

Before washing iceberg lettuce, remove the core. Striking the head against a flat surface loosens the core so that it can be removed easily with the fingers.

Making a Salad

What kind of a salad should you make? First, decide how you plan to serve it. *Appetizer salads* are small, tasty salads served at the beginning of a meal to stimulate your appetite. For example, a shrimp cocktail or small tossed salad might be served. An *accompaniment salad* is a small salad served with a meal. Coleslaw, fruit salads, and tossed salads are examples. *Main dish salads* make up the main course of a meal. They generally contain a protein food along with grains, fruits, and vegetables. For instance, a chef's salad is made with cooked meat, poultry, and eggs, as well as cheese, on a thick bed of lettuce. A main dish salad is a great way to use leftovers. *Dessert salads* are usually made with fruit.

Preparing Salad Greens

Refrigerate salad greens as soon as you get home from the supermarket. You can wait to clean them until you use them, or you may clean them first so they will be ready to use.

❖ *Iceberg lettuce.* Hold the head in your hands, core side down. Hit the core on the counter once or twice to loosen it. Remove the core from the head. Let cold water run into the cavity for a minute or two until it pours out between the leaves.

Place the head, core-side down, in a colander and let it drain. Store the drained lettuce in a covered plastic container or bag in the refrigerator.

❖ **Leafy greens.** Pull the leaves away from the core and wash them under cold running water. Place each leaf, stem side down, in a colander so the water can drain off easily. You may also need to pat the greens dry before storage. Put the washed greens in a plastic container with a cover or in a large plastic bag and store them in the refrigerator.

Assembling the Salad

Salads are fun and easy to assemble. Be creative! Choose colorful combinations of greens, fruits, vegetables, and other foods for an attractive, healthful dish.

A salad can be served in a small or large bowl or on a plate, depending on the foods used. For an attractive touch, line the bowl or plate with greens first—creating a **base** for the salad. Other salad ingredients make up the **body**, or main part of the salad.

Salad ingredients can be combined in many different ways. Here some common methods:

❖ **Tossed or mixed salads.** Greens and vegetables can be gently tossed together. Ingredients may be stirred together with a dressing, as in potato salad. They may also be put together in layers instead. For example, you might layer shredded greens, cooked mashed beans, chopped tomatoes, and yogurt in a dish.

❖ **Arranged salads.** Salad ingredients may be arranged in an attractive pattern, usually on a base of greens. For example, you might arrange fresh fruit slices around a mound of cottage cheese.

❖ **Molded salads.** Any salad mixture that holds its shape can be molded in a decorative container. Many molded salads are made with gelatin.

Making an arranged salad is an opportunity to develop your artistic skills.

Tossed or mixed salads lend themselves to a wide variety of ingredients. What are some of your favorite combinations?

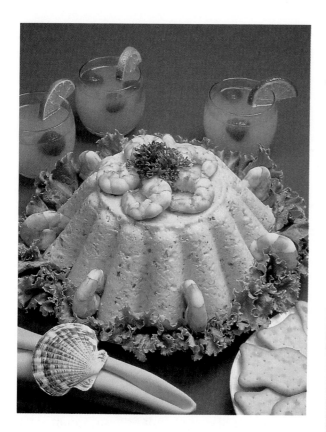

A fruit-and-gelatin mixture is not the only possibility for a molded salad. This shrimp mousse could be served as an appetizer or snack.

Serving Salads

Salads may be dressed up with decorative vegetables, such as green or red pepper rings or carrot sticks, and sprinkled with seeds, chopped nuts, or raisins.

Add the dressing to a tossed salad just before serving it. If dressing is added too soon, the greens will wilt. Better still, serve the salad without dressing. Pass the dressings separately at the table, so people can add their own.

Thinking About the Recipe

Read the recipes for "Garbanzo Salad" and "Honey-Mustard Dressing" and answer the following questions.

1. Name one substitution you might make for each ingredient in the recipe.
2. What could you do to keep the chopped apple from turning brown while you make the dressing?

Garbanzo Salad

Customary	Ingredients	Metric
8 leaves	Romaine lettuce	8 leaves
16-oz. can	Garbanzo beans	454-g can
1 large	Apple	1 large
1 medium	Red or green pepper	1 medium
1/2 cup	Raisins	125 mL

Yield: 4 servings

Conventional Directions

1. Tear lettuce into bite-size pieces.
2. Rinse and drain garbanzo beans.
3. Core apple. Chop apple and pepper into bite-size pieces.
4. Toss all ingredients in salad bowl.
5. Serve with Honey-Mustard Dressing.

Honey-Mustard Dressing

Customary	Ingredients	Metric
2 tsp.	Prepared mustard	10 mL
2 Tbsp.	Vinegar	30 mL
2 tsp.	Oil	10 mL
2 tsp.	Honey	10 mL
1/4 tsp.	Celery seed	1 mL

Yield: 4 servings

Directions

1. Mix together mustard and vinegar in small bowl.
2. Add oil, honey, and celery seed. Mix well.

Nutrition Information

Per serving (approximate—salad plus dressing): 227 calories, 7 g protein, 42 g carbohydrate, 4 g fat, 0 mg cholesterol, 487 mg sodium

Objectives

After studying this section, you should be able to:

❖ Describe how to prepare clear, vegetable, and cream soups.
❖ Explain how to make and use white sauce and gravy.

Look for These Terms

bouillon
white sauce
aromatic vegetables
au jus

People often think of homemade soups as delicious foods that take a long time to prepare. While that may have been true in the past, today's quick and easy methods can result in soups as flavorful as the ones great-grandma used to make. As you will see, there are also ways to make soups and sauces with less fat than traditional versions.

Kinds of Soups

There are basically three kinds of soups:

❖ *Clear broth* is also called stock, consommé (kahn-soh-MAY), or **bouillon** (BOOL-yon). It is the seasoned liquid made from cooking meat, poultry, fish, or vegetables. The liquid is strained to remove any solids. Serve broth as part of a meal or as a snack. It is also used as a base for sauces and other soups.

A hearty soup is almost a meal in itself. Broth or cream soup might be served as an appetizer or a meal accompaniment.

- **Hearty vegetable soups** are thick soups, made with assorted vegetables, legumes, and grain products. Chunks of cooked meat, poultry, or fish can be added.
- **Cream soups** are traditionally made with a **white sauce**—a milk-based sauce thickened with starch—plus cooked vegetables, poultry, or shellfish. Cream soups made this way can be high in fat.

Soups are usually highly nutritious. Some B vitamins and vitamin C may be destroyed by heat, especially if the soup is cooked for a long time. Other water-soluble vitamins and minerals, however, remain in the liquid.

Making Soups

Many people today use canned convenience broths or bouillon cubes as a base for making soup. You can also combine broth with a seasoned vegetable juice for additional flavor. Here are some easy, basic ways to make vegetable and cream soups.

The first step in making most soups is to sauté **aromatic vegetables,** such as chopped onions, garlic, celery, and green peppers, in a small amount of fat. These vegetables are used in small amounts to flavor most soups. Sautéing them first helps develop the flavors. Use a stockpot and about 1 teaspoon (5 mL) of oil.

Vegetable Soup

To make vegetable soup, combine the sautéed aromatic vegetables with broth. Add other vegetables according to the recipe or make up your own combinations. Use at least three or four different vegetables for a rich flavor.

When adding the vegetables, begin with those that take the longest to cook. Then add the remaining vegetables according to the time needed for cooking. Season the soup with herbs and spices. Cover and simmer the soup only until the vegetables are tender.

For variety, flavor, and nutrients, add other foods such as cooked legumes or grain products (pasta, rice, or barley). These foods contain starch and will thicken the soup. You can also add cooked leftover meat and poultry sliced in thin strips or cut into small cubes.

Homemade soup doesn't have to take all day. Try starting with ready-made broth or vegetable juice. Add vegetables, grains, and leftover meat or poultry. A stockpot is useful for making large amounts of soup.

Cream Soup

A traditional cream soup is thickened with a white sauce (see page 538).

You can also make a cream soup using pureed cooked vegetables and nonfat dry milk. This method is quick, easy, and low in fat. The recipe on page 540 is an example of this type of soup. You can vary the recipe by substituting other vegetables, such as chopped broccoli or cauliflower. Just be sure to include either potatoes or 1/4 cup (60 mL) cooked rice to thicken the soup. If you prefer a smooth soup rather than a chunky one, puree all the cooked vegetables (and the rice, if used).

Cooking Soup in the Microwave Oven

Try making your own broth in the microwave oven. It takes much less time than by conventional cooking. Check a microwave cookbook for directions.

Vegetable soups can be easily prepared in the microwave oven. Chop the vegetables into uniform pieces and add hot water or broth. The hot liquid will help speed up the cooking process. Cook larger quantities of soup in a covered container to speed up cooking time. Still, you may find that larger quantities of soup take longer than on a conventional range.

Milk-based soups may foam up during microwave cooking. Follow the directions in the owner's manual for the best results. Be sure to use a large enough container. You may prefer to cook milk-based soups on the conventional range.

Convenience soups can be heated quickly in the microwave oven. When using a temperature probe, heat cream soups to about 140°F (60°C) and other soups to about 160°F (71°C).

Sauces and Gravies

Sauces and gravies are thickened liquids used to add flavor to cooked food. There are many different kinds of sauces and gravies. Most, however, are variations on a few basic types. Added ingredients and seasonings give each variation a distinct flavor.

Basic White Sauce

The most common sauce is white sauce. It is made by thickening milk with flour.

Flour contains starch granules which lump together as they cook. If flour alone were added to the milk, the mixture would be lumpy. For a smooth sauce, the flour is cooked in fat. The fat coats the starch granules and helps keep them from lumping.

For a medium-thick sauce, use 2 tablespoons (30 mL) each of butter and flour for every 1 cup (250 mL) of milk. For a thinner sauce, use 1 tablespoon (15 mL) each of butter and flour.

Melt the fat and add the flour. Cook the mixture over low heat, stirring constantly, for about two minutes or until the mixture is smooth and bubbly. Gradually add the milk while continuing to stir. Cook the mixture, stirring constantly, until it thickens. The sauce should be thick enough to coat the back of a wooden spoon.

Pan Gravy

Pan gravy is made like white sauce, but with meat juices instead of milk. Remove the meat from the pan and pour the juices into a measuring cup. Skim off and reserve the fat.

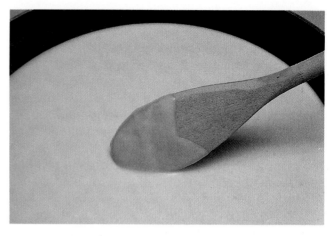

When making white sauce, stir constantly until the mixture is thick enough to coat a spoon.

Gravy made with pan juices adds flavor to meat. How can you reduce the fat in the gravy?

TIPS for Success

Rescuing Lumpy Sauce or Gravy

If a few lumps occur, put the sauce or gravy through a strainer or blender. Reheat the mixture, stirring constantly, and serve.

Measure the remaining liquid. For each 1 cup (250 mL) of liquid, use 2 tablespoons (30mL) each of fat and flour. Heat the fat, then blend in the flour and cook the mixture until it is smooth and bubbly. Gradually add the remaining liquid and stir constantly until smooth and thickened. Scrape the bottom of the pan to loosen browned meat particles that add flavor to the gravy.

Lower-Fat Alternatives

White sauce and gravy are high in fat. Consider using seasoned nonfat yogurt in place of white sauce. Instead of serving roasts with gravy, try serving them **au jus,** or "in the juice." Use the pan drippings after the fat has been skimmed off.

To make lower-fat gravy, remove the meat from the pan and skim the fat from the meat broth. Measure the broth. You may need to add some water or boullion to obtain enough broth for gravy. Measure out 2 tablespoons (30 mL) of flour or cornstarch and 1/4 cup (50 mL) of cold water for every 1 cup (250 mL) of broth. (Note: Mixing starch with cold water before adding it to a hot mixture prevents lumping.) Shake the starch and water mixture together in a covered container. Add the starch mixture to the broth and heat the mixture to boiling, stirring constantly. Cook the mixture until it thickens, about one minute.

Traditional French cooking—famous throughout the world—relies on rich sauces for its delicious flavors. *Nouvelle cuisine* ("new cooking") is a more recent style of French cooking. The emphasis has shifted to smaller portions, attractive presentations, more vegetables, and sauces that are lower in fat.

Section 20.3 Review

RECALL THE FACTS

1. Describe how to make a clear broth.

2. Name three aromatic vegetables. Why are they sautéed?

3. Why must flour be coated with fat when making a white sauce?

4. What is a lower-fat alternative to gravy served with roasted meat?

DISCUSS YOUR IDEAS

5. How might a family's food budget be stretched by serving soup as the main dish?

APPLY YOUR LEARNING

6. Create a recipe for a hearty vegetable soup that you can prepare in one hour. What pre-preparation tasks could you do beforehand to cut down even further on the cooking time?

Thinking About the Recipe

Read the recipe for "Creamy Vegetable Soup" and answer the following questions.

1. What is used to thicken this soup?
2. How could you prepare a low-sodium version of this recipe?

Creamy Vegetable Soup

Customary	Ingredients	Metric
1	Green pepper, chopped	1
1	Onion, small, chopped	1
3	Celery stalks, chopped	3
1	Garlic clove, chopped or pressed	1
1 tsp.	Oil	5 mL
32-oz. can	Stewed tomatoes	896-g can
3	Potatoes, pared and cubed	3
1 cup	Carrots, sliced	250 mL
1 cup	Corn, frozen or canned	250 mL
1 cup	Green beans, frozen or canned	250 mL
1 cup	Water	250 mL
2	Beef boullion cubes	2
1/2 cup	Instant nonfat dry milk	125 mL

Yield: About 4 servings

Directions

Pan: Dutch oven
1. Sauté green pepper, onion, celery, and garlic in oil.
2. Add stewed tomatoes (with liquid), potatoes, carrots, corn, green beans, water, and beef boullion cubes to sautéed vegetables.
3. Simmer mixture over medium heat until vegetables are tender.
4. Drain the cooking liquid from the vegetables, reserving the liquid.
5. Puree half of the cooked vegetables in a blender or food processor.
6. Return pureed vegetables to the Dutch oven. Thin the mixture with reserved cooking liquid.
7. Add the instant nonfat milk and remaining vegetables. Mix well.
8. Simmer until thoroughly heated.
9. Season to taste and serve hot.

Nutrition Information

Per serving (approximate): 268 calories, 10 g protein, 58 g carbohydrate, 2 g fat, 1.5 mg cholesterol, 1315 mg sodium

Objectives

After studying this section, you should be able to:

❖ Plan and prepare hearty one-dish meals using a variety of ingredients, including those low in fat.
❖ Explain several methods used to prepare one-dish meals.

Look for These Terms

extender
binder

Depending on the foods used, combination dishes can often provide servings from the five food groups. To complete the meal, add a salad and whole grain bread. Some main dishes can be served over a grain. A stir-fry or stew, for example, tastes great over cooked rice or noodles.

Some common main dish combinations are stews, braised meats with vegetables, stir-fries, pizza, and casseroles.

Stews

Stewing is an efficient way to cook less tender cuts of meat or poultry. Cut meat into cubes, but leave poultry in pieces. Remove poultry skin to reduce fat. Browning meat before stewing it adds flavor and color to the gravy.

Fish and shellfish stews are delicious, too. Oyster stew, for instance, is traditional for some people during holiday seasons.

Many different kinds of vegetables can be used in stews. Starchy ones, such as potatoes, add thickness. If you're not following a recipe, make up your own combination. Also consider using fruits, such as dried apricots.

An oyster stew is one example of a hearty main dish combination. What would you serve with it to make an appealing, nutritionally balanced meal?

Although water is the basic liquid in stew, try substituting other liquids, such as broth or vegetable juice, for part of it. Tomato juice, for example, contains acid which helps tenderize meat and adds flavor.

Cooking time depends on the tenderness of the meat. Beef may need two or three hours to cook, while poultry may cook in an hour. Because fish is already tender, fish stews take little time to cook. As a rule, cook them just until the fish flakes and the flavors are blended.

Cooking times also vary with the appliance used. A beef stew can cook in thirty minutes in a pressure cooker, an hour in a microwave oven, two and one-half hours on the range top or in a conventional oven, or about nine hours in a slow cooker.

Vegetables and fruits may need different amounts of cooking time, depending on tenderness and the size of the pieces. Add them to the stew according to the amount of cooking time needed. Those that will take longest to cook, such as fresh carrot pieces, should be added early in the process. Those that

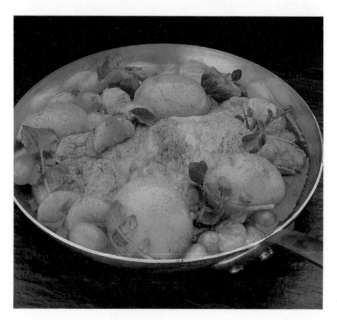

Fresh or dried fruits can be included in stews. They add nutrients and complement the flavor of the other ingredients.

take less time to cook, such as frozen corn, can be added later. Add canned vegetables or leftover cooked vegetables near the end of cooking time.

To stew meat on the range top, brown cubes of meat without added fat in a large pan. Remove the meat to a clean plate. Sauté aromatic vegetables in a small amount of fat, then return the browned meat to the pan. Add seasonings and enough liquid to cover the meat. Cover the pan and simmer until tender, adding the other ingredients during the cooking time as explained above.

Braised Foods

Braising is used to cook large, less tender cuts of meat and poultry. It can also be used to give flavor to tender cuts. For example, fish is sometimes braised in a flavorful sauce.

Meat is often browned before braising; usually poultry is not. Place the meat or poultry in a Dutch oven or heavy pot. Add enough liquid to cover the bottom and create steam. Add seasonings such as onions, garlic, herbs, and spices. Cover the pan and bake at 350°F (180°C) or simmer on top of the range.

Add other vegetables as the meat braises. The timing depends on how long they will take to cook. Use large pieces of vegetables, such as halved or quartered potatoes and carrot halves. Add quick-cooking vegetables, such as peas and corn, near the end of the cooking time.

Check the food regularly to make sure there is enough liquid covering the bottom of the pan. Add hot water when needed. Cold water will increase the cooking time. To thicken the gravy, add a diced potato an hour before serving.

The cooking time depends on the size and cut of the meat. Cook until the ingredients are tender and the flavors are well blended.

The French term *fricassee* (FRIK-uh-SEE) means to cut up meat, stew it or fry it, and serve it in a sauce or its own gravy. In America the term has come to refer to stewed dishes of chicken or veal.

Consider using fresh or canned fruit to flavor the sauce. Some tasty combinations are pork with apples (applesauce or peeled and quartered fresh apples), poultry with pineapple or orange juice, fish with lemon or grapefruit juice, beef with prunes or dried apricots, and lamb with canned plums.

Stir-Frying

Stir-frying is a quick and easy way to make a flavorful, nutritious dish. It can be a low-fat dish if you choose the ingredients carefully.

The secret of a successful stir-fry is to cut up all the ingredients and assemble them in the order in which they are to be cooked. Because stir-frying is fast, there's no time to stop and cut up foods while you're cooking.

Cut raw meat or poultry across the grain into thin, narrow strips. Meat that has been chilled in the freezer will be easier to slice. Cubes or strips of tofu or cooked meat, poultry, or fish can also be used.

Select a variety of vegetables. Cut each into pieces of the same size for even cooking.

The wok is ideal for stir-frying. It has a rounded bottom and sits on a metal ring which is placed on the range. Electric woks are also available. If you don't have a wok, you can use a large skillet.

Heat just a small amount of oil in the skillet or wok. High heat is necessary to cook food quickly and give vegetables a crispy texture. The wok or skillet is hot enough for cooking when a few drops of water sizzle and evaporate immediately. Add seasonings and cook for a few seconds to flavor the oil. Stir foods constantly as they cook, or they will burn.

Begin stir-frying raw meat, poultry, or fish first. When cooked, remove it to a clean platter. Next, cook dense, fibrous vegetables

You can use almost any combination of protein foods, fruits, vegetables, seasonings, and sauces in a stir-fry. Be sure to slice each type of food uniformly for even cooking.

Stir-Fry Suggestions

❖ **Seasonings:** 1/4 to 1/2 teaspoon (1 to 3 mL) grated raw ginger, pressed garlic, crushed dried thyme or marjoram.

❖ **Protein:** 1 cup (250 mL) tofu, meat, poultry, or fish.

❖ **Vegetables or fruits:** 3 cups (750 mL) of at least three vegetables and fruits.

❖ **Sauce:** Mix 1 tablespoon (15 mL) cornstarch with 1 tablespoon (15 mL) tamari sauce, soy sauce, or prepared mustard to make a paste. Add 1 cup (250 mL) canned broth, fruit juice, or vegetable juice and mix well.

such as broccoli, carrots, and cauliflower. (You can also precook them in the microwave oven.) Then cook the other vegetables. Add the cooked meat, poultry, or fish when the vegetables are done.

As you cook, avoid overloading the pan. Putting too much food in the pan at one time will result in vegetables that are steamed, not stir-fried.

After all the foods in the stir-fry have been cooked, add a sauce for flavor. The sauce is usually mixed ahead of time and allowed to stand until needed. Stir it just before adding it to the wok or skillet.

The box on this page will give you ideas for making stir-fries. The recipe on page 545 shows one possible combination of ingredients.

Pizza

Pizza is a hearty main dish served on a crust. Traditional pizza calls for a yeast bread crust topped with a tomato-based sauce, cheese (generally mozzarella), and other toppings. However, many variations are possible. Pizza can be baked in any large shallow pan.

Here are some suggestions for making pizza. For a low-fat pizza, use smaller amounts of low-fat or fat-free cheese.

❖ **Base.** One ready-made or homemade crust.

❖ **Seasonings.** Small amounts of garlic, oregano, basil, marjoram, pepper, cayenne, cinnamon, nutmeg, or chili powder.

❖ **Sauce.** Canned pizza, pasta, taco, or chili sauce; salsa; pureed fresh or canned fruit.

❖ **Toppings.** Chopped broccoli, cauliflower, green or red peppers; grated carrots; sliced mushrooms, onions, or pineapple slices; cooked or canned meat, poultry, or fish; browned, drained ground beef or sausage.

❖ **Grated cheese.** Mozzarella, feta, Gouda, Cheddar, Swiss, or Parmesan.

Pizza is generally baked in an oven preheated to 425°F (220°C). The cooking time may vary depending on the size pizza you are making and the ingredients used. Check a cookbook for cooking times.

It's easy to make pizza at home. Try new combinations, such as a rice crust with vegetable toppings.

Thinking About the Recipe

Read the recipe for "Whitefish Stir-Fry" and answer the following questions.

1. What would you do if you did not have already-cooked fish on hand to use in the recipe?
2. How can you tell when the oil is hot enough for cooking?

Whitefish Stir Fry

Customary	Ingredients	Metric
1 Tbsp.	Cornstarch	15 mL
1 Tbsp.	Tamari sauce	15 mL
1 cup	Pineapple juice	250 mL
1 Tbsp.	Oil	15 mL
1/2 tsp.	Fresh ginger, grated	2 mL
1	Garlic clove, pressed	1
1 cup	Snow peas	250 mL
1/2 cup	Green bell pepper, chopped	125 mL
1/2 cup	Red bell pepper, chopped	125 mL
1/2 cup	Water chestnuts, sliced	125 mL
1 cup	Pineapple chunks	250 mL
1 cup	Whitefish fillets, cooked and cubed	250 mL
	Hot cooked rice	

Yield: 4 servings

Directions

Pan: Wok or large skillet

Temperature: Medium-high

1. Combine cornstarch with tamari sauce. Add pineapple juice and set aside.
2. Heat oil in wok. Add ginger and garlic and cook for a few seconds to flavor the oil.
3. Add snow peas, green and red pepper, water chestnuts, and pineapple chunks to wok. Cook, stirring constantly, until snow peas and pepper are tender but still slightly crisp.
4. Add cooked whitefish to vegetables in wok.
5. Mix the sauce from Step 1 and pour it over the food. Cook, stirring constantly, until mixture is thickened and fish is hot.
6. Serve over hot cooked rice.

Nutrition Information

Per serving (approximate—without rice): 226 calories, 13 g protein, 28 g carbohydrate, 7 g fat, 34 mg cholesterol, 286 mg sodium

Casseroles

A casserole is a tasty blend of cooked ingredients which are heated together to develop flavor. The base of a casserole provides its main texture and flavor. A casserole also needs an **extender,** such as pasta or rice, to help thicken it, and a liquid **binder** to hold it together. Seasonings and aromatic vegetables give more flavor and texture.

Here are some suggestions for casserole combinations:

❖ *Base.* Cubed, cooked meat, poultry, or fish; browned, drained ground beef or turkey; grated or cubed cheese.

❖ *Vegetables.* Any cooked or canned vegetables.

❖ *Extenders.* Dry bread crumbs; cooked diced potatoes, pasta, rice, grits, or barley; cooked, mashed dry beans.

❖ *Aromatic vegetables.* Chopped celery or parsley; sautéed mushrooms, onions, or chives.

❖ *Seasonings.* Dried, crushed oregano, basil, thyme, or marjoram; ground ginger, mace, cinnamon, chili powder, cayenne or black pepper. Start out using 1/4 teaspoon (1 mL). You can always add more to taste.

❖ *Binder.* Skim milk, broth, fruit juice, soup, or a thickened sauce.

To make a casserole for four people, try combining 1 cup (250 mL) of each ingredient choice (except seasonings) in a greased 1½ quart (1.5 L) baking dish with a cover. Bake the casserole about 30 minutes in an oven preheated to 350° F (180° C). Remove the cover after 20 minutes if the liquid needs to thicken.

To microwave a casserole, combine the ingredients in a ungreased baking dish with a cover. Cook the casserole at 100 percent power for six to 18 minutes, depending on the ingredients. Stir once or twice during cooking and rotate the casserole after half the cooking time.

In what ways do casseroles save time and energy when planning and preparing meals?

Section 20.4 Review

RECALL THE FACTS

1. What kind of meat works well for stewing and braising? Give two examples.

2. Why must stir-fry ingredients be cut up and assembled before you start cooking?

3. Name the main parts of any casserole. Give an example of each.

DISCUSS YOUR IDEAS

4. Discuss reasons why food combinations are good, economical choices for many families.

APPLY YOUR LEARNING

5. Develop a list of at least six ingredients that you could use in making three of the one-dish meals discussed in this section. What foods might you need to have on hand for "emergency" one-dish meals?

Rick Joseph
Pizza Maker

Current position:

"I'm a college student working part-time at a pizza restaurant."

Responsibilities:

"I make the dough, prepare the other ingredients, and then put them all together to make the pizzas. When I'm not cooking, I make sure my area of the kitchen is clean. I also help train new workers."

Skills:

"Employers are looking for people who can handle responsibility and get along well with other workers. The food preparation skills can be learned through on-the-job training. My previous experience as a short-order cook helped me get this job. Oh, and you have to be willing to follow rules about personal hygiene and kitchen sanitation. They're very important for any food service worker."

Work environment:

"I work mostly nights and weekends, and spend a lot of time on my feet in a hot kitchen!"

Favorite part of the job:

"I've always enjoyed cooking, and pizza is especially fun to make. I like using my creativity to come up with new flavor combinations for our weekly specials. And I love to hand-toss the dough the traditional way—it gives my work a special flair, and it entertains the customers."

- Does Rick seem to enjoy his work? Explain.
- What aspects of Rick's job do you think you would enjoy? Why?

Summary

Section 20.1
Sandwiches, Snacks, and Packed Lunches: Sandwiches can be as varied, nutritious, and hearty as the ingredients from which they are made. Choose breads, fillings, and toppings creatively. Nutritious, easy-to-prepare snacks are part of a healthful eating plan. When packing lunches, keep hot foods hot and cold foods cold.

Section 20.2
Salads and Dressings: Salads tend to be nutritious and low in calories. They may include greens, fresh fruits or vegetables, cheese, and cooked grains, legumes, meat, poultry, fish, or eggs. Basic dressings include oil-based, mayonnaise, cooked, and dairy varieties. Salads are assembled and served in a number of ways.

Section 20.3
Soups and Sauces: There are three basic kinds of soup: clear broth, hearty vegetable, and cream soup. Soups, which are usually very nutritious, often rely on aromatic vegetables for flavoring. You can use quick and easy methods to make low-fat soup. Sauces and gravies can add flavor to cooked foods. You can make a basic white sauce from a mixture of fat, flour, and seasonings added to milk. Pan gravy is made with meat juice as the liquid.

Section 20.4
Casseroles and Other Combinations: One-dish meals can be healthful choices, depending on the ingredients. Types of one-dish meals include stews, braised dishes, stir-fries, pizza, and casseroles. Combination dishes lend themselves to variety and creativity in the kind and amounts of ingredients used.

REVIEWING FACTS

1. What are the differences between a traditional sandwich, a fancy sandwich, and a club sandwich? (20.1)

2. Name two kinds of bread, other than sliced bread, which can be used to make sandwiches. (20.1)

3. What are two ways to keep packed lunches cold? Why is the temperature of the food important? (20.1)

4. What is the basic difference between an oil-based dressing and a mayonnaise dressing? (20.2)

5. How should leafy greens be washed? (20.2)

6. Name one way cream soups and hearty vegetable soups are the same and one way they are different. (20.3)

7. When making a sauce, how can you keep the flour from becoming lumpy? (20.3)

8. Why is meat often browned before stewing? (20.4)

9. When braising, how much liquid should you add to the pan? (20.4)

10. Why is high heat essential for stir-frying? (20.4)

LEARNING BY DOING

1. **Taste test:** Plan and prepare one or two sandwich fillings and toppings. Use a variety of breads to make up enough sandwiches so that members of the class can sample a piece of each sandwich. (20.1)

2. **Foods lab:** Plan and prepare a salad luncheon and invite some teachers to share it. (20.2)

3. **Foods lab:** In groups, choose and pre-

pare several foods to stir-fry. Chop vegetables and slice meats uniformly and arrange them in cooking order. One group should prepare a mixture to make sauce. Another could cook rice to serve with the stir-fry. Choose a designated "stir-fryer" or take turns stirring the mixture. (20.4)

THINKING CRITICALLY

1. *Identifying cause and effect:* You decide to take packed lunches to school. Will your lunches the first week or so of school be different from those later on during the year? Why or why not? If your lunches tend to be the same, what effect will that have on you? (20.1)

2. *Determining accuracy:* Compare the labels of several popular salad dressings including some varieties lower in fat. Rate them in terms of fat content and primary ingredients. How do their ratings compare with the claims or descriptions on the label? (20.2)

3. *Comparing and contrasting:* Examine a can of ready-made gravy, a package of gravy mix, and a can of cream soup, such as mushroom, that may be used for gravy. Using the same serving size for each, calculate the calories and fat. Which rates the best? The worst? How do your findings compare with the commonly-held assumption that gravies are a calorie-laden addition to a meal? How do they compare to other sauces? (20.3)

4. *Recognizing alternatives:* You have all the ingredients to make stew for dinner—all except the stew meat. Could you alter the recipe using another meat or no meat at all? Why or why not? How? (20.4)

MAKING DECISIONS AND SOLVING PROBLEMS

What Would You Do?

1. Your sports team is leaving for an all-day tournament in the morning. The coach told each of you to pack one meal to eat at noon and another to eat in the evening because there will be no stops along the way. (20.1)

2. Your family needs to cut down on cholesterol. Tossed salad is on your menu often—as well as oil-based and mayonnaise vsalad dressings.. (20.2)

3. It's your turn to cook soup and you're short of fresh ingredients. You do, however, have loads of leftovers. (20.3)

LINKING YOUR STUDIES

1. *Social studies:* Use library references or cookbooks to find out what sandwiches and salads are popular in other cultures. Report to the class. (20.1, 20.2)

2. *Math:* Alter the yield of a soup recipe to make one or two servings. Using a microwave cookbook (or experimenting on your own), figure out how long it would take to cook the soup in a microwave oven as compared to a conventional range. What can you conclude about cooking a single serving of soup in the microwave? (20.3)

3. *Writing:* Write a short essay on one of the following topics:

A. The sandwiches I ate as a child were memorable. (20.1)

B. If I were a salad, I would be a (name a type of salad) because... (20.2)

C. Soup is more than a meal: it is a way of showing you care. (20.3)

D. Pizza is an almost perfect food. (20.4)

CHAPTER 21
Baking

Look for These Terms

gluten
leavening agent
knead

How can just a few basic ingredients make such taste-tempting treats as a cinnamon yeast roll, a rich buttery cake, or an apple pie with a crust that melts in your mouth? The secret lies in the amounts of the ingredients used and how they are combined and baked. With a little understanding of baking ingredients and techniques, you can prepare a wide array of delicious baked products.

Ingredient Basics

All baked products are made by using a combination of the following basic ingredients: flour, liquid, leavening agents, fat, sweeteners, eggs, and flavoring. Some of these ingredients affect the nutrient density. Baked goods are generally nutritious, but many are high in fat, sugar, and calories.

Ingredients such as these are common to many different baked goods. Each ingredient has a specific role to play in the mixture.

While all-purpose flour is the most commonly used type, there are others. Top row, left to right: pastry, durum, oat, soy, and triticale flours. Middle row, left to right: barley, millet, rice, and buckwheat flours. Bottom row, left to right: unbleached flour, whole wheat flour, cornmeal, and rye flour.

Flour

Flour is usually one of the main ingredients in baked products. The protein and starch in flour make up most of the structure. One of the proteins is called **gluten** (GLOO-ten). Gluten affects the texture of the product and helps determine how a product will rise. As you will see later on, other ingredients also affect the texture.

When liquid and flour are mixed, the starch absorbs some of the liquid. More is absorbed as the product bakes.

There are many types of flours, which vary in gluten content. *All-purpose flour*—a wheat flour—gives good results for most products. *Bread flour* has the highest gluten content and gives bread a strong structure. *Cake flour* contains less gluten and gives cakes a tender structure.

Whole wheat flour has weaker gluten than all-purpose flour. Products made with only whole wheat flour rise less and have a heavy texture. Other whole grain flours, such as rye or cornmeal, have either weak gluten or no gluten. They are generally combined with all-purpose flour in equal proportions. Stir whole grain flours rather than sift them—the particles are too large to go though a sifter.

Whole grain flours should be stored in the refrigerator to keep them fresh. Store other flours in an airtight container in a cool, dry place.

Liquid

Liquid is needed to help form the structure of the product. It takes part in the many physical and chemical changes that occur during baking. Water and milk are the most common liquids used in baking. Milk adds flavor and nutrients and helps baked goods brown better. To reduce fat in a recipe, use skim milk instead of whole milk.

Some recipes call for buttermilk, which gives a slightly tangy flavor. Buttermilk also makes the mixture more acid and affects the kind of leavening needed.

Leavening

Most baked products include a leavening agent. **Leavening agents** provide air, steam, or gas to help baked products rise. This makes the baked product less compact and gives it a softer texture.

Here is a description of how each leavening agent works:

❖ **Air** is trapped in mixtures as they are beaten. Creaming fat and sugar, sifting flour, and adding beaten egg whites are some of the ways to add air. When the mixture is heated, the air expands and the product rises. Angel food cake is leavened mainly by air in beaten egg whites.

❖ **Steam** leavens products that contain high amounts of water. As the product bakes, the water heats and produces steam. Steam expands, causing the product to rise. Popovers and cream puffs use steam for leavening.

❖ **Yeast** is a microorganism that produces carbon dioxide gas as it grows. It needs food (such as flour or sugar), liquid, and a warm temperature to grow. Several forms of yeast are available. *Active dry yeast* and *quick-rising dry yeast* come as dry granules in a packet. The quick-rising type leavens the dough about twice as quickly. Both can be stored at room temperature. *Compressed yeast* comes in individually wrapped cakes and must be refrigerated. Use yeast before the expiration date on the package.

Under the right conditions, yeast cells multiply (shown here greatly magnified). They also produce carbon dioxide, which causes the dough to rise.

❖ **Baking soda** is used whenever the recipe calls for an acid liquid such as buttermilk, yogurt, or sour milk. It produces carbon dioxide gas when combined with liquids.

❖ **Baking powder** is leavening made of baking soda and a powdered acid such as cream of tartar. The most common type, double-acting baking powder, releases some carbon dioxide gas when it is first mixed with a liquid. The remainder is released when it is heated.

Fat

Fat adds richness, flavor, and tenderness to baked products. Fats can be solid or liquid. Shortening, lard, butter, and margarine are solid fats. Oils are liquid fats.

Solid and liquid fats cannot be substituted for one another. In place of butter or shortening, you can use regular margarine, but do not use soft, whipped, or liquid margarine or spreads. They may contain water or oil which can affect the results. You can also substitute solid shortening for butter or margarine. Any cooking oil may be used in baking, as long as it has a mild flavor.

Refrigerate lard, butter, and margarine. Store shortening and oils at room temperature unless the label directs otherwise.

Eggs

Eggs add flavor, nutrients, richness, and color to baked products. They also help to form the structure. When beaten, eggs add air to the mixture. To reduce fat and cholesterol, two egg whites can usually be substituted for one whole egg.

Sweeteners

Sugar is the most commonly used sweetener. It helps make baked products tender, adds sweetness and flavor, and helps the crust to brown. Granulated white sugar and brown sugar are used in many recipes. Other sweeteners include honey, corn syrup, molasses, and powdered sugar. Some artificial sweeteners are suitable for baking, but others are not. Follow the manufacturers' recommendations.

Store most sweeteners in tightly covered containers in a cool place. Some sweeteners should be refrigerated after opening. Follow label directions.

Flavorings

Fruits and nuts add both flavor and texture to baked goods. Herbs, spices, and extracts are used in small amounts to add flavor. Extracts are flavorings in a liquid form. Vanilla and almond are two common varieties. Store herbs, spices, and extracts in tightly closed containers.

Combining the Ingredients

The characteristics of a baked product depend on not only what ingredients are used, but how they are combined. During the mixing process, changes take place that affect the texture of the finished product.

The Role of Gluten

When flour and liquid are mixed together, the gluten in flour "develops," or becomes strong and elastic. It forms a network of tiny air cells. Air, steam, or gas produced by the leavening agent is trapped by these cells. When heated, the trapped gasses expand and the product rises.

The longer the mixing time, the greater the extent to which gluten is developed. For example, ingredients for cakes and quick breads are mixed only long enough to combine them. As a result, the gluten is not strong. The cells remain small and the network stretches very little. This results in a fine, tender texture.

Yeast breads, on the other hand, are mixed much longer than cakes. The dough for yeast bread is worked with the hands to develop the gluten. As a result, the gluten is very elastic and expands easily. Larger air cells are produced, giving yeast breads a coarser texture.

Sugar cane is one of the sources of granulated sugar, a common sweetener in baked goods.

Hawaii

Batters and doughs have different consistencies—thick or thin, soft or firm. Waffle batter and cookie dough are two examples.

Batters and Doughs

The amount of liquid in relation to the flour determines whether a mixture is a batter or dough and affects how you handle the mixture. Batters have more liquid than doughs. There are four kinds of batters and doughs:

❖ *Pour batters* are thin enough to pour in a steady stream. They are used to make cakes, pancakes, and waffles.
❖ *Drop batters,* which are thick, are usually spooned into pans. They are used to make some quick breads and cookies.

❖ *Soft doughs* are soft and sticky but can be touched and handled. Rolled biscuits, yeast breads and rolls, and some cookies start with soft doughs.
❖ *Stiff doughs* are firm to the touch. Easy to work with and cut, they form the basis for pie crust and some cookies.

Methods of Mixing

There are several basic methods for combining ingredients. Other methods are usually variations. Use the method described in the recipe you have chosen. The chart on page 556 summarizes common mixing methods used in baking. You will read more about these later in the chapter.

Unless the recipe directs otherwise, have all ingredients at room temperature before mixing. Thirty minutes is long enough to warm refrigerated items.

Some doughs must be kneaded after they are mixed. To **knead** dough means to work it with the hands in order to further mix the ingredients and develop gluten. For directions, see "Tips for Success" on this page.

When making biscuits and yeast breads, knead the dough by pushing, folding, and turning it.

TIPS for Success

Kneading Dough
1. Turn the dough out on a very lightly floured surface.
2. With the heel of your hands, push down on the edge of the dough nearest to you.
3. Fold the dough in half toward you and give it a quarter turn.
4. Continue pushing, folding, and turning for the time directed in the recipe.

Summary of Common Mixing Methods

Method	Uses	Highlights	Where Described
Standard mixing method	• Cakes • Quick breads • Cookies	• Cream solid fat and sugar • Add dry ingredients alternately with liquids	• Section 21.4, page 572
Muffin method	• Muffins and other quick breads • Some cakes and cookies	• Use liquid fats • Pour liquids all at once into dry ingredients	• Section 21.2, page 560
One-bowl method	• Cakes • Cookies • Quick breads	• Use solid fat • Only one bowl needed	• Section 21.4, page 572
Pastry and biscuit method	• Pastry • Rolled biscuits	• Use pastry blender to mix solid fat and flour	• Section 21.2, page 562

Preparing to Bake

The baking pans you choose can affect the results of baking. Use the size and type of pan specified in the recipe. If the pan is too large or small, the product will not bake properly.

Pan materials are important, too. Most recipes are developed for light-colored metal pans. If you use glass pans, lower the temperature by 25°F (14°C). Glass retains more heat than metal, and at the higher temperature, a dark, thick crust may result.

Dark pans also retain more heat than light ones and can create a thick crust. If you use dark metal pans, you may have to lower the oven temperature by about 10°F (6°C).

Glass bakeware or special microwave bakeware must always be used when baking in the microwave oven.

Pan Preparation

Baking pans must be properly prepared so products can easily be removed from the pans. Follow recipe directions carefully. The pans should be prepared before the ingredients are mixed.

Here are several different methods for preparing pans:

❖ **Grease and flour** means to lightly grease a pan and dust it with flour. Use waxed paper to spread the fat. Sprinkle a little all-purpose flour into the pan. Tilt the pan to different angles until the flour is spread evenly. Turn the pan upside down over the sink and tap it gently to remove any excess flour. The flour allows the product to come out of the pan easily. Never grease and flour pans for microwave baking—they become sticky.

In order to make the finished product easy to remove, you may need to prepare the pans. If so, the recipe will tell you which method to use. Some recipes require ungreased pans—otherwise the product will not rise properly.

* **Vegetable oil cooking spray** is the easiest method, but may not work with all products. Follow the directions on the label.
* **Lining a pan with paper** requires parchment paper. Do not use brown paper or waxed paper. Brown paper contains chemicals that may be transferred to the food when it is heated. The wax in waxed paper may melt. Parchment paper is made for cooking and baking. Cut a piece of parchment the same shape and size as the pan bottom. Grease the pan and line the bottom with the parchment paper. When the product is removed, peel the paper off the bottom. This method is used for rich cakes, such as fruitcake.

Conventional and Microwave Baking

Most batters and doughs are baked. In a conventional oven, the dry heat creates desirable changes. The product browns and, depending on the ingredients, a crispy crust may develop. Because a microwave oven cooks with moist heat, baking results differ from a conventional oven. Microwave baked products do not brown or develop a crispy crust. They have more of a steamed texture than a baked one and are very tender and moist.

Unless the recipe states otherwise, preheat the conventional oven. Before you turn on the oven, make sure the oven racks are in the proper position. See page 282 to review proper pan placement.

Brownies are an example of a cookie that can be baked in the microwave oven with good results. Use a recipe written for the microwave.

After you put the pans in the oven, set a timer for the baking time. Begin to check the product for doneness about five minutes before the time is up.

Only certain kinds of cakes, quick breads, and cookies can be baked successfully in a microwave oven. Follow the directions in the owner's guide or in a microwave recipe.

Removing Baked Products from Pans

Some baked products must be removed from the pans immediately when they come out of the oven. Others must cool for a few minutes. Still others need to stay in the pan until they are completely cool. Follow the recipe directions.

Use cooling racks so baked goods will cool faster and stay crisp. When baked goods are allowed to cool on a solid surface, such as a cutting board, moisture collects and baked goods become soggy.

Storing Baked Products

Fruit pies and products with cream filling must be refrigerated to prevent spoilage. Studies show that other baked products get stale quickly when stored at refrigerator temperatures. Store them at room temperature if they will be used within three days. To store them longer, freeze them in airtight freezer containers.

RECALL THE FACTS

1. List the basic ingredients in baked products. Identify one function of each.

2. Identify three methods for combining ingredients.

3. What type of paper is used for lining baking pans? Why?

4. In general, how do microwaved baked products differ from conventionally baked products?

DISCUSS YOUR IDEAS

5. Discuss the pros and cons of microwave baking versus conventional baking. When might you choose each?

APPLY YOUR LEARNING

6. Locate a basic muffin recipe. Identify the function of each ingredient.

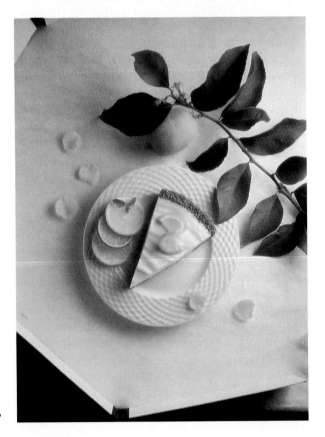

How should this chiffon pie be stored?

Objectives

After studying this section, you should be able to:

❖ Suggest several additions to quick breads which increase the nutritional value.
❖ Discuss the differences and similarities between the muffin method and the pastry method of mixing.
❖ Describe the quality characteristics of properly mixed and baked muffins and biscuits.

Look for These Terms

cut in
rolled biscuits
drop biscuits

As their name implies, quick breads are quick and easy to make. Most use baking powder as a leavening agent. Muffins, biscuits, pancakes, corn bread, and fruit breads are common examples.

Quick breads are good sources of carbohydrates, protein, B vitamins, and iron. Using whole grains adds fiber and trace minerals. If fruits and nuts are included, they provide more vitamins and minerals.

Some quick breads are high in fat. By choosing wisely, though, you can use quick breads to add variety, flavor, and nutrition to your meals and snacks.

Quick breads can add nutrients and variety to meals. What are some of your favorite types of quick breads?

Muffins

Muffins are prepared using the muffin method of mixing. The most important part of this procedure is properly mixing the dry and liquid ingredients.

Muffin method:

1. Sift together or mix all dry ingredients (flour, sugar, baking powder, spices) in a large bowl. Make a well in the center of the dry ingredients using the back of a spoon.
2. Beat all liquid ingredients (eggs, milk or water, oil or melted fat, liquid flavorings) together in a small bowl until they are well blended.
3. Pour the liquid into the center well of the dry ingredients. Mix just enough to moisten the dry ingredients. A few floury spots can remain and the batter should be lumpy.
4. Fold ingredients such as chopped nuts and raisins in gently.

It is important not to overmix the batter. Muffins that are properly mixed have a rounded, pebbly top with a coarse but tender texture inside. Overmixed muffins will have peaks on the tops and be tough and heavy. The inside will have long, narrow tunnels.

The flavor of muffins can easily be varied with different ingredients. Fresh and dried fruits are often included. Try cranberries, blueberries, chopped dates, or dried apricots. Muffin recipes may also include yogurt or sour cream, tofu, raw vegetables (zucchini and carrots, for example), or cooked vegetables (such as sweet potatoes and winter squash). These ingredients add flavor and important nutrients, too. Adding extra ingredients to just any recipe may not work. Instead, start with recipes that already include them.

To add fiber to muffins, substitute 1/2 cup (125 mL) bran for an equal amount of flour. More than that will affect the texture.

Instead of greasing muffin pans, you can line them with paper baking cups. Fill the cups only two-thirds full. If you add more than that, the batter will overflow and the muffins will have odd shapes.

When baking muffins, test them for doneness about five minutes before the end of the baking time. They are done when they are nicely browned. A wooden pick inserted in the center should come out clean. Serve warm.

Mix the dry ingredients and make a well in the center.

Beat the liquid ingredients together.

Add the liquids to the dry ingredients all at once. Stir briefly—do not overmix.

With what other foods might quick loaf breads such as these be served?

Loaf Breads

Many quick loaf breads are mixed in the same manner as muffins. They often have the same basic ingredients. Cranberry-orange-nut bread, for instance, is a holiday favorite. Other breads, such as corn bread, are less sweet. Some loaf breads are flavored with herbs.

Quick breads are generally baked in greased loaf pans. If the bread contains dried fruit and nuts, line the bottom of the pan with parchment paper so the loaf can be removed easily.

Check for doneness as you would with muffins. Don't be surprised if the top of the loaf cracks. That is typical for quick breads.

Biscuits

Biscuits are delicate, small breads. Properly made, they have a tender but crisp crust and are an even, light-brown color. The inside is slightly moist, creamy white, and peels apart in tender layers.

There are two kinds of biscuits—rolled and dropped. Both are made using the pastry and biscuit method of mixing.

Mixing Biscuit Dough

In the pastry and biscuit method, the fat is cut into the flour. To **cut in** means to mix solid fat and flour using a pastry blender or two knives and a cutting motion. This technique leaves the fat in fine particles in the dough. During baking, the fat melts between layers of flour, giving a flaky texture.

A pastry blender is a tool designed for cutting fat into flour.

Handle the dough as little as possible. If the shortening and flour are overmixed, the texture will be mealy, not flaky.

Pastry and biscuit method:

1. Sift together or mix the dry ingredients in a large bowl. Sifting ensures the ingredients are distributed evenly.
2. Cut the shortening into the flour until the particles are the size of peas or coarse bread crumbs.
3. Make a well in the center of the dry ingredients and add the liquids. Stir just until the ingredients are blended and form a soft dough.

Making Rolled Biscuits

Rolled biscuits are rolled out to an even thickness and cut out with a biscuit cutter. If you don't have a biscuit cutter, you can use the rim of a water glass.

To make rolled biscuits, mix the dough as explained above. If necessary, use your hands to form a ball of dough.

Turn the dough out on a lightly floured board and knead about ten strokes. (See page 555 for specific kneading instructions.) The goal is to blend the ingredients but not develop too much gluten. Overkneading results in tough, compact biscuits.

Next, roll the dough out until it is about ½-inch (1.3 cm) thick. Cut the biscuits out with a biscuit cutter that is slightly dusted with flour. Press the cutter straight down, so the biscuits have straight sides and even shapes. Don't twist the cutter.

Place the biscuits on an ungreased baking sheet, about 1 inch (2.5 cm) apart. Bake according to recipe directions.

Making Drop Biscuits

Drop biscuits contain more liquid than rolled biscuits. This creates a batter that is too sticky to handle but which can be dropped from a spoon. Although these biscuits have irregular shapes, they are just as flavorful and flaky as the rolled variety.

After kneading biscuit dough, roll it out to an even thickness so the biscuits will be uniform in size.

Cut the biscuits out, being careful not to pull or tear the dough. You can reroll the leftover dough to make more biscuits.

Mix drop biscuits using the same method as rolled biscuits. Drop the batter in mounds on a greased cookie sheet about 1 inch (2.5 cm) apart. Bake according to recipe directions. You can also spoon drop biscuits onto a casserole as a topping.

Drop biscuits save time because you do not have to knead or roll dough.

Serving Biscuits

Biscuits are best when they are eaten warm, right out of the oven. Serve them with meals or use them for sandwiches. Biscuits can be made ahead of time, frozen, and then reheated in the microwave oven.

Traditionally, biscuits provide the base for one of America's favorite desserts—strawberry shortcake. See the recipe on page 564.

See the recipe on page 564.

Biscuits and muffins are usually served fresh from the oven or reheated.

Section 21.2 Review

RECALL THE FACTS

1. List five ingredients you can add to quick breads to vary the nutritional value.

2. Name two ways that the muffin method and biscuit method are similar and two ways they are different.

3. Describe the characteristics of a well-made muffin after baking.

4. What are the differences between a drop biscuit and a rolled biscuit?

DISCUSS YOUR IDEAS

5. Brainstorm ways that you can use quick breads to add variety to meals.

APPLY YOUR LEARNING

6. Find three recipes for quick breads. Identify the mixing method used in each.

Thinking About the Recipe

Read the recipe for "Strawberry Shortcake" and answer the following questions.

1. What other fruits or combinations of fruits could you use to make shortcake?
2. What tools can be used to cut the margarine into the dry ingredients?

Strawberry Shortcake

Customary	Ingredients	Metric
2 cups	Fresh or frozen strawberries, sliced	500 mL
1/4 cup	Sugar (optional—omit if using frozen strawberries)	50 mL
1 cup	All-purpose flour	250 mL
1 Tbsp.	Sugar	15 mL
1 ½ tsp.	Baking powder	7 mL
1/2 tsp.	Salt	2 mL
2 Tbsp.	Margarine	30 mL
1/2 cup	Skim milk	125 mL
1/2 cup	Whipped topping or low-fat vanilla yogurt	125 mL

Yield: 4 servings

Directions

Pan: Baking sheet
Temperature: 450°F (232°C)

1. Thaw strawberries if frozen. If using fresh strawberries, clean and slice. Add 1/4 cup (50 mL) sugar to the fresh strawberries and refrigerate for about an hour to draw out the juices.
2. Preheat the oven. Lightly grease the baking sheet.
3. Sift flour, 1 Tbsp. (15 mL) sugar, baking powder, and salt together into a bowl.
4. Cut the margarine into the flour mixture until it resembles coarse bread crumbs. Make a well in the center of the mixture.
5. Add the milk and stir with a fork until ingredients are moistened and form a drop batter.
6. Drop biscuits onto baking sheet about 1 inch (2.5 cm) apart.
7. Bake at 450°F (232°C) about 15 minutes or until golden brown.
8. For each serving, tear a warm biscuit in half and place the bottom half in a small bowl.
9. Spoon 1/2 cup (125 mL) strawberries and juice over each biscuit half.
10. Cover the berries with the top half of the biscuit. Add 2 tablespoons (30 mL) whipped topping or yogurt to each shortcake. Serve.

Nutrition Information

Per serving (approximate): 102 calories, 1 g protein, 11 g carbohydrate, 6 g fat, trace of cholesterol, 168 mg sodium

Yeast Breads and Rolls

Objectives

After studying this section, you should be able to:

❖ Identify ways to simplify bread making.
❖ Describe the procedure for making yeast breads.
❖ Explain how to tell when yeast breads are done baking.

Look for This Term

quick-mix method

As their name indicates, yeast breads use yeast for leavening. The yeast also gives the bread a characteristic flavor and contributes to the wonderful aroma of baking.

Time Savers

Many people think that baking yeast bread is too time-consuming for today's fast-paced lifestyles. With a little organization, however, bread baking can be a part of regular food preparation. Making yeast dough is a flexible process. The tasks can be timed to fit into the cook's schedule.

Several appliances can help speed up the bread-making process. Use a microwave oven to heat the liquid before adding it to yeast, to bring refrigerated ingredients to room temperature, and to let the dough rise. Check the owner's manual for specific directions. These vary, depending on the power and controls.

A heavy-duty mixer with dough hook or a powerful food processor will mix yeast dough quickly. They will knead it in about six minutes compared to eight or ten minutes by hand.

As different as these breads appear, all use yeast for leavening.

Technology Tidbit

Do you think that you don't have time to make bread? Automatic bread makers allow you to make bread with almost no effort. All you do is accurately measure the ingredients into the machine. This handy appliance mixes, kneads, allows the dough to rise, and then bakes it. Depending on the type of bread you make, you have a loaf of bread in about four hours.

Steps in Making Yeast Bread and Rolls

There are just a few easy steps to follow in making yeast bread and rolls. These include mixing the dough, kneading it, letting it rise, shaping it, and finally baking it.

Mixing the Dough

Yeast bread is simply a mixture of flour, salt, sugar, liquid, fat, and yeast. Sugar provides food for the yeast so that it will grow. Salt controls the action of the yeast. Consult a recipe for the exact ingredients and amounts.

Bread flour is ideal for yeast breads. However, most recipes for homemade bread call for all-purpose flour. It is more readily available than bread flour and makes a loaf with good texture.

If a recipe uses only all-purpose flour, you can mix whole grain flour with it for added fiber and nutrients. For yeast doughs, a general rule is to use at least one-third all-purpose flour. The other two-thirds can be whole grain flours such as whole wheat or rye. Other amounts of ingredients remain the same.

Before you begin, be sure the ingredients are at room temperature and the liquid is

Use a thermometer to check the temperature of the liquids.

After mixing the liquid and dry ingredients, use a spoon to beat in the additional flour. The amount needed will vary. It depends on the moisture content of the flour and even the humidity in the air that day.

heated to the right temperature. Yeast will not grow if the liquid is too cold. If the liquid is too hot, it will kill the yeast.

The **quick-mix method** combines active dry yeast with the dry ingredients. A standard mixer will work for the first part of the mixing until the dough thickens and becomes too heavy for it. Beat the rest of the flour in with a wooden spoon.

Quick-mix method for yeast bread:

1. Combine part of the flour with the undissolved active dry yeast, sugar, and salt in a large bowl.
2. Heat the liquid and fat to 120°F to 130°F (49°C to 54°C).

Yeast goes to work during the rising time. Cover the dough to keep it from drying out.

Gently "punching" the dough after the first rising eliminates excess gas bubbles. It also helps ensure that yeast, warmth, and moisture are evenly distributed throughout the dough.

3. Add the liquid to the dry ingredients, beating them with a mixer until they are well blended. At this point, the gluten is beginning to develop.
4. Beat in enough of the remaining flour to make the kind of dough specified in the recipe. You may need more or less flour than the recipe calls for. Some kinds absorb more liquid than others.

Kneading the Dough

Turn the dough out on a lightly floured surface. Knead the dough until it becomes a smooth, shiny ball, about 8 to 10 minutes. Use just enough flour to keep the dough from sticking to the work surface or to your hands. Too much flour will give a tough texture.

Don't be concerned if bubbles develop in the dough. That's a clue that gluten is developing. The cell walls are becoming elastic and expanding with carbon dioxide given off by the yeast.

Letting Dough Rise

Shape the dough into a ball and place it in a well-oiled bowl to rise. Turn the dough over so all sides are coated with oil. Put a piece of plastic wrap over the top of the

dough to keep it from drying out. Cover the bowl with a clean dish towel. Set the bowl in a warm (not hot), draft-free place for about an hour to rise.

After the first rising, "punch" the dough down by gently pressing your fist down in the center. Gently pull the dough from the sides of the bowl to the center and press down to eliminate the large air bubbles. If you're not ready to shape the dough, let it rise again.

Thinking About the Recipe

Read the recipe for "Honey Whole Wheat Bread" and answer the following questions.

1. What is the name of the mixing method used in this recipe?
2. Why isn't an exact amount of all-purpose flour specified?

Honey Whole Wheat Bread

Customary	Ingredients	Metric
2 ½ to 3 cups	All-purpose flour	625 to 750 mL
3 cups	Whole wheat flour	750 mL
2 tsp.	Salt	10 mL
1 pkg.	Active dry yeast	1 pkg.
1 cup	Skim milk	250 mL
1 cup	Water	250 mL
1/4 cup	Honey	50 mL
3 Tbsp.	Shortening	45 mL

Yield: Two loaves

Two-day Directions

Pan: Small saucepan; two 9 x 5 x 3 inch (23 x 13 x 8 cm) loaf pans
Temperature: 400°F (200°C)

Day One

1. Mix 1 cup (250 mL) all-purpose flour, 1 cup (250 mL) whole wheat flour, salt, and undissolved active dry yeast in a large bowl. Set aside.
2. Combine milk, water, honey, and shortening in a small saucepan.
3. Heat liquids over low heat until warm, about 120°F(49°C). Shortening does not have to melt.
4. Add the heated liquid to the dry ingredients.
5. Blend at low speed with a mixer about 2 minutes. Occasionally scrape the bowl.
6. Add another 1/2 cup (125 mL) all-purpose flour and 1/2 cup (125 mL) whole wheat flour to the mixture.
7. Beat about 2 minutes at medium speed, scraping the bowl occasionally.
8. Stir in 3/4 cup (175 mL) all-purpose flour and 1 ½ cups (375 mL) whole wheat flour with a wooden spoon until the mixture forms a soft dough. If necessary, add more all-purpose flour.

Honey Whole Wheat Bread (cont.)

9. Put the dough on a lightly floured surface.
10. Knead the dough about 8 to 10 minutes until it is smooth and elastic.
11. Place the dough in a large, well-oiled bowl. Turn the dough in the bowl to be sure all sides are oiled.
12. Cover the dough with a piece of plastic wrap. Place a clean dish towel over the bowl.
13. Refrigerate the dough overnight.

Day Two
1. Remove dough from the refrigerator.
2. Gently push your fist into the center of the dough. Pull the sides of the dough toward the center.
3. Turn the dough out of the bowl onto a lightly floured surface. Allow the dough to rest 10 to 15 minutes.
4. Divide the dough into two equal portions.
5. Shape the dough into two loaves.
6. Put each loaf into a well-greased loaf pan.
7. Cover the loaves with a clean dish towel and let them rise in a warm place until doubled in size, about one hour, or until finger indentations remain.
8. Preheat the oven to 400°F (200°C).
9. Bake the loaves about 25 to 30 minutes or until done.
10. Remove loaves from pans and cool on a cooling rack away from drafts.

Nutrition Information
Per serving (1 slice or 1/20 of loaf—approximate): 80 calories, 2 g protein, 15 g carbohydrate, 1 g fat, trace of cholesterol, 110 mg sodium

You can also cover the dough and refrigerate it overnight. It will rise in the refrigerator and be ready to shape the next day.

Shaping the Dough

Shape the dough into loaves or rolls, according to recipe directions. Place the bread in greased pans or on baking sheets. Cover the pans and let the shaped dough rise until double or until finger indentations remain when you lightly press the dough.

Baking

Bake as directed in the recipe. Bread and rolls are nicely browned when done baking. Tap the loaf with your finger. If it sounds hollow, it is done baking. Remove the bread from the pans and let the loaves stand about 20 minutes for easier cutting.

After shaping, bread dough is allowed to rise a final time in the pan.

Yeast dough can be shaped in many creative ways, such as this braided ring. Notice the evenly browned crust.

Section 21.3 Review

RECALL THE FACTS

1. What appliances can help speed up the bread-making process? Why?

2. What happens if the liquids in yeast breads are too hot or too cool?

3. How can you tell if dough is ready to shape and bake?

4. How can you tell if a loaf of bread is done baking?

DISCUSS YOUR IDEAS

5. Discuss the pros and cons of making yeast breads yourself by hand versus using an automatic bread maker or commercially frozen bread dough.

APPLY YOUR LEARNING

6. Using cookbooks or other references, describe at least five different ways of shaping yeast breads or rolls other than a loaf.

Objectives

After studying this section, you should be able to:

* Describe types of cakes, cookies, and pies.
* Give guidelines for preparing cakes, cookies, and pies.

Look for These Terms

shortened cakes
foam cakes

Who doesn't enjoy a freshly-baked cookie or a warm slice of homemade pie? Cakes, cookies, and pies are among the most popular baked goods. While many are nutritious, most are high in fat, sugar, and calories, so eat them sparingly. When you do prepare sweet treats for your family and friends, there are some choices you can consider.

Cakes

Although cakes are easy to make, accurately measuring ingredients is essential for good results.

Cake recipes sometimes call for cake flour, which is low in gluten. If you do not have cake flour, substitute all-purpose flour. For each 1 cup (250 mL) of cake flour, use 1 cup (250 mL) minus 2 tablespoons (30 mL) of all-purpose flour.

There are two basic kinds of cakes, shortened and foam cakes.

Besides being beautifully decorated, these desserts have something else in common— they are all shortened cakes.

Shortened Cakes

Shortened cakes are rich and tender. They most often contain a solid fat such as shortening, butter, or margarine, but may contain oil. Shortened cakes appear in a variety of flavors including chocolate, lemon, and spice. Some contain chopped nuts and dried fruits.

As you learned in Section 21.1, several methods can be used for mixing cakes. The standard method is most common for shortened cakes. An electric mixer is helpful for creaming and beating the ingredients.

Standard method for mixing cakes:

1. Cream the solid fat and sugar until the mixture is light and fluffy, as in whipped cream.
2. Beat the eggs into the mixture thoroughly, usually one at a time.
3. Sift the dry ingredients together.
4. Mix the liquids together.
5. Add the dry ingredients to the creamed mixture alternately with the liquid. Begin and end with the dry ingredients. This helps keep the fat from separating, which could affect the texture. Add the dry ingredients in fourths and the liquids in thirds. After each addition, beat the batter just enough to mix the ingredients.

You can also use the *one-bowl method* to mix shortened cakes. The dry ingredients are combined by sifting or mixing. Solid fat, liquids, and flavorings are added and beaten with the dry ingredients until well blended. The eggs are beaten in last.

You can bake shortened cakes in pans of many shapes and sizes, from individual cupcakes in muffin pans to large sheet cakes. Fancy molds can turn an ordinary cake into a centerpiece for a special event.

To check a shortened cake for doneness, insert a wooden pick in the center. If it comes out free of wet batter, the cake is done.

A shortened cake should have a slightly rounded top with a tender, shiny crust. When the cake is cut, it should have a fine, even grain and be moist and tender.

The one-bowl method saves time because there are fewer steps in mixing. How else might this method save time and personal energy?

Foam Cakes

Foam cakes are leavened with beaten egg whites, which give them a light, airy texture. Angel food, sponge, and chiffon cakes are examples.

Angel food cakes use only beaten egg whites for leavening. They have neither egg yolks nor fat. This makes them good choices for low-fat, low-calorie desserts. In sponge cakes, beaten egg yolks are added to the batter before the batter is folded into the egg whites. Some foam cake recipes call for baking powder as well. Chiffon cakes include yolks, oil, and baking powder, which are blended and then folded into beaten egg whites.

Foam cakes must be baked in ungreased pans. As the batter rises during baking, it clings to the sides of the pan. If the pan were greased, the cake would not be able to rise. A tube pan is often used for foam cakes.

Foam cakes have a light texture because they include beaten egg whites.

To test a foam cake for doneness, touch the top lightly. It should spring back.

Foam cakes are generally cooled upside down in the pan to keep them from losing volume or falling. If the tube pan does not have legs to support it upside down, use an empty glass bottle with a slender neck or a large metal funnel turned upside down. Invert the tube pan over the neck of the bottle or funnel.

When the cake is cool, gently loosen the cake from the sides with a spatula. Turn the pan upside down to remove the cake. If the pan has a removable bottom, use a spatula to loosen the cake from the bottom.

TIPS for Success

Using a Tube Pan

Most tube pans are made in two parts. The bottom (which contains the center tube) detaches from the sides, making it easy to remove the cake. If the pan is in one piece, line the bottom with parchment paper so the cake can be removed more easily.

Decorating Cakes

Cakes are often frosted. Since frostings are usually high in fat, sugar, and calories, you may want to try one of these alternatives.

* Make a glaze with confectioners' sugar and lemon, orange, or pineapple juice. Drizzle it over the cake and let it flow down the sides.
* Sift a little confectioners' sugar over the top of the cake. Try putting a cutout paper design, such as a snowflake, on top before sifting the sugar.

You may also serve the cake with fresh or frozen fruit instead of icing.

These simple cake toppings are attractive, easy to make, and lower in calories than frosting.

Cookies

Cookies are easy to prepare. Many people consider homemade cookies well worth the little time and effort they require. The main difference between cakes and cookies is that cookies have little, if any, liquid. This gives cookies a heavier texture than cakes.

Cookies vary in texture from soft to crisp. They can be made in assorted shapes and decorated in many ways. The thousands of cookie varieties can be divided into six basic kinds.

* *Bar cookies* are baked in square or rectangular pans and then cut into bars, squares, or diamonds. They can be made from a batter or a soft dough that is pressed into a pan. Textures vary from cake-like to chewy. Brownies are one example of bar cookies. Usually, bars are cooled in the pan and then cut.
* *Drop cookies* are made from a soft dough that is dropped from a teaspoon onto cookie sheets. During baking, the dough spreads out to make a thick cookie. Remember to allow enough space between cookies so they can spread without touching. Most chocolate chip cookies are drop cookies.
* *Cut-out cookies* (also called rolled cookies) are made from stiff dough that is rolled out and cut with cookie cutters.
* *Molded cookies* are formed by shaping the dough by hand into balls. These balls can be rolled in chopped nuts or other toppings before baking, or they can be flattened with a fork or the bottom of a glass.
* *Pressed cookies* are made by pushing dough through a cookie press, which can create a variety of shapes. Spritz cookies are an example of pressed cookies.
* *Sliced cookies* (sometimes called refrigerator cookies) are made by forming a soft dough into a long roll and refrigerating it. When the roll is chilled and firm, the cookies are sliced and baked.

Cookies range from simple to decorative. Try baking and freezing batches of different kinds until you have an assortment. Then you can put together a sampler for a homemade gift.

Most cookies are baked on cookie sheets —flat pans with only one edge. Let cookie sheets cool before baking more cookies. Otherwise, the warm pan will soften the dough and the cookies will lose their shape.

Bar cookies are done baking when they pull away slightly from the sides of the pan. A slight impression remains when they are tapped gently. Other cookies are done when the bottoms are lightly browned and the edges are firm.

Store cookies in covered containers. Waxed paper between layers will keep them from sticking together.

Pies

A pie is a flaky crust filled with either a sweet or a savory mixture. A sweet pie may contain a fruit, custard, or cream filling and is generally served as dessert. A savory pie, filled with a meat or a custard and vegetable mixture, is served as a main dish. Two examples are quiche and potpie.

Pies can have one or two crusts made with flour, fat, salt, and water.

WORLD of variety

Dutch immigrants introduced cookies to America in the early 1600s. The Dutch word *koekjes,* which means "little cakes," soon was Americanized to "cookies."

A lattice crust is made with strips of dough.

To mix pastry, use the pastry and biscuit method. Follow the same steps as you would to mix biscuit dough (see page 562). For a flaky pastry, handle the dough as little as possible.

Use a lightly floured surface to roll out pastry dough. Roll the dough in a large, round circle about 1/8 inch (0.3 cm) thick and 2 inches (5 cm) larger than an inverted (upside-down) pie pan. If the dough cracks or tears, patch it with another piece of dough. Moisten the area to be patched with a little water and press a piece of dough over it. Sprinkle some flour over the patched area and continue to roll it with rolling pin.

For a two-crust pie, fold a rolled pastry circle in half and gently place it in a pie pan. Unfold the circle and fit it into the pan without stretching the pastry. Trim the pastry even with the edge of the pan. Fill it with a sweet or savory mixture. Place another circle of pastry over the filling to form the top crust. Trim it so that 1/2 inch (1.3 cm) extends over the edge of the pan. Moisten the bottom pastry around the edge with water. Tuck the top pastry under the bottom edge of the pastry and gently pinch the layers together. Make a decorative edge that also seals the top and bottom crusts. (See "Tips for Success," p. 577, for directions.)

Roll pastry dough from the center outward to form a circle of even thickness.

Make several small slits in the top crust to allow steam to escape.

When making a one-crust pie, roll out one pastry circle for the bottom crust. Put the pastry into the pie pan. Trim it, leaving a 1/2-inch (1.3 cm) overhang. Turn the overhang under to form a double thickness along the pan rim. Flute the edge or make a forked edge.

Fold the pastry so that you can transfer it to the pan without stretching or tearing it.

Trim the pastry with kitchen shears. Will this be a one-crust or two-crust pie? How can you tell?

Some recipes call for a baked pie shell. The filling is added later. If you bake the pie shell before filling it, pierce the bottom with a fork about every 1 inch (2.5 cm) to prevent the crust from bubbling up while baking.

One-crust pies can also be made with crumb crusts. Mix fine crumbs from graham crackers or gingersnaps with melted butter or margarine and press them into the pan. These crusts are usually used with unbaked fillings.

Pecan pie is an example of a pie that is traditionally made without a top crust. What others can you name?

TIPS for Success

Making a Decorative Edge

The edge of a pie crust can be finished in several ways. Here are two you can try:

❖ **Forked edge.** To make a forked edge, dip the tines of a fork in flour. Use the fork to press the pastry crust against the edge of the pan around the entire crust.

❖ **Fluted edge.** To make a fluted edge, place the index finger of one hand on the inside edge of the crust and the thumb and index finger of the other hand on the outside edge. Gently push the crust to form a curved shape. Repeat this process around the entire crust edge.

Section 21.4 Review

RECALL THE FACTS

1. What are the two basic kinds of cakes? Name two ways they are different and two ways they are alike.

2. What are six basic kinds of cookies?

3. Give two examples of dessert pies and one example of a savory pie.

4. What should you do if pastry dough tears as you are rolling it?

DISCUSS YOUR IDEAS

5. Why do you think homemade cakes and pies were more common (and perhaps more popular) 60 or 70 years ago?

APPLY YOUR LEARNING

6. In small groups, locate several pie recipes in magazines and food advertisements. Write down any shortcut ingredients or preparation methods suggested in the recipes. Make suggestions for modifying the recipes to make them lower in fat.

Thinking About the Recipe

Read the recipe for "Apple Bran Bars" and answer the following questions.

1. What are two other methods you could use to test the bars for doneness?
2. How might you adapt this recipe for microwave preparation?

Apple Bran Bars

Customary	Ingredients	Metric
1 cup	100 percent bran cereal	250 mL
1/2 cup	Skim milk	125 mL
1 cup	All-purpose flour	250 mL
1 tsp.	Baking powder	5 mL
1/2 tsp.	Cinnamon, ground	2 mL
1/4 tsp.	Nutmeg, ground	1 mL
1/3 cup	Margarine	75 mL
1/2 cup	Brown sugar, packed	125 mL
2	Egg whites	2
1 cup	Pared, chopped apple	250 mL

Yield: 16 servings

Directions

Pan: 9 x 9 inch (23 x 23 cm) baking pan
Temperature: 350°F (180°C)

1. Preheat oven. Grease baking pan.
2. Soak bran in milk until milk is absorbed.
3. Mix flour, baking powder, cinnamon, and nutmeg thoroughly in a bowl. Set aside.
4. Beat margarine and sugar until creamy in a separate bowl. Add the egg whites and beat again.
5. Add the dry ingredients to the creamed mixture.
6. Stir in apples and the bran mixture; mix well.
7. Put mixture into greased baking pan.
8. Bake at 350°F (180°C) about 30 minutes or until a toothpick inserted in the center comes out clean.
9. Cool. Cut into bars and serve.

Nutrition Information

Per serving (approximate): 107 calories, 2 g protein, 17 g carbohydrate, 4 g fat, trace of cholesterol, 106 mg sodium

CAREER PROFILE

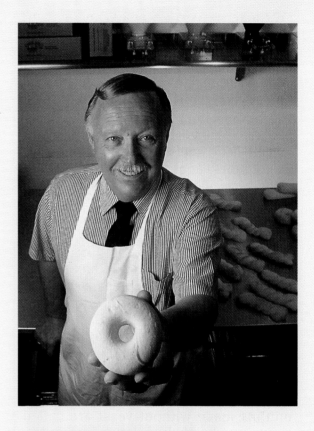

Cal Chandler
Retail Bakery
Manager

Current position:

"I manage the bakery department of a large supermarket."

Responsibilities:

"It's my job to see that the bakery runs efficiently and profitably. Among my specific duties are ordering supplies, hiring and supervising employees, and managing the payroll."

Skills:

"Leadership abilities are important. In managing my staff, I've had to learn how to build a strong team out of individuals with very different personalities. Good communication skills and the ability to handle many details at one time also are necessary to succeed in this job."

Education:

"I have a bachelor's degree in food service management. While I was in college, I worked part-time as a baker for a doughnut chain."

Typical day on the job:

"During a typical day, I might interview potential employees, prepare the next week's schedule, arrange for the repair of faulty equipment, and meet with a dissatisfied customer to try to make things right."

Favorite part of the job:

"I enjoy working with people, and this job certainly gives me ample opportunity to do that. I also like to see that operations run smoothly and that customers are happy with our services."

- What are some examples of leadership skills that a manager might need?
- What parts of Cal's job appeal to you? Why?

Summary

Section 21.1
Ingredients and Techniques for Baking: Basic ingredients for baked products include flour, liquid, leavening agents, fat, sweeteners, eggs, and flavoring. Each plays a specific role in the mixture. When flour and liquid are mixed, gluten develops. The mixture forms a batter or dough. Recipes use different mixing methods depending on the desired results. Follow recipe directions for the size and type of pans to use and how to prepare them for baking. Conventional and microwave baking produce different results. After baking, remove products from pans and store them properly.

Section 21.2
Quick Breads: Breads, biscuits, and muffins made without yeast are called quick breads. They are mixed using the muffin method or the pastry and biscuit method. Quick breads can be nutritious, but some are high in fat and calories .

Section 21.3
Yeast Breads and Rolls: You can use time-saving techniques to speed up yeast bread preparation. Yeast bread dough consists of flour, salt, sugar, liquid, fat, and yeast. After kneading and rising, the dough can be shaped and baked a number of ways.

Section 21.4
Cakes, Cookies, and Pies: There are two basic kinds of cakes, shortened cakes and foam cakes. Foam cakes generally rely on beaten eggs instead of a chemical leavening agent. Cookies can be shaped in a variety of ways. Pies can have sweet or savory fillings, and can be made with one or two crusts. These baked goods are often high in fat and calories.

Reviewing Facts

1. Name two kinds of batters and two kinds of doughs. (21.1)

2. What can air, steam, and carbon dioxide do for baked goods? How do they work? (21.1)

3. What is the difference between using a dark pan or a light pan for baking? (21.1)

4. Which baked goods should be refrigerated? Which should not? Why? (21.1)

5. What are three kinds of quick breads? (21.2)

6. Why are quick breads mixed only briefly? (21.2)

7. When making whole grain yeast dough, how much all-purpose flour should be used in the dough? (21.3)

8. When and how is dough "punched" down? (21.3)

9. What are two examples of low-fat ways to decorate a cake? (21.4)

10. What are the six basic kinds of cookies? (21.4)

Learning by Doing

1. **Food science lab:** Demonstrate the action of leavening agents. Dissolve one package of yeast in water. Add both sugar and water to another package of yeast. Combine baking powder with water and baking soda with water. Compare the results of all the samples. (21.1)

2. **Foods lab:** Prepare yeast dough and freeze it. At a later time, allow it to thaw and rise in the refrigerator overnight. Bake it the next day. Evaluate the results. (21.3)

3. **Foods lab:** Prepare enough pastry for a two-crust pie. Roll out all the dough in a large square. Sprinkle one-fourth of it with cinnamon and sugar, cut it into strips, and put the strips on a baking sheet. Re-roll the rest of the dough, sprinkle cinnamon and sugar on one-third of it, cut it into strips, and place the strips on another sheet. Repeat this process two more times. You should have four baking sheets of dough strips. Keep track of which sheet which. Bake them and compare the results. Which pastry is more flaky and tender? Why? (21.4)

THINKING CRITICALLY

1. **Recognizing alternatives:** To cut down on fat and calories, Mick has decided to streamline his bread recipe to include only flour, water, and yeast. Will his "no-frills" bread be a satisfactory product? Why or why not? What are some alternative plans? (21.1)

2. **Predicting consequences:** Jan is baking bread for 45 minutes in a disposable aluminum pan. Because she plans to throw the pan out after using it, she doesn't grease it. What are two problems using this pan might cause? (21.1)

3. **Determining accuracy:** Paula's friend heard that you could substitute applesauce for oil in a muffin recipe to cut down on fat. How can Paula find out whether this is true? (21.2)

4. **Forming hypotheses:** Bread has been called the staff of life. Those selling homes are sometimes encouraged to bake bread before showing their house so it smells appealing. Why do you think bread has such importance? (21.3)

MAKING DECISIONS AND SOLVING PROBLEMS

What Would You Do?

1. A friend invites you over to make cookies for a party. She says that she likes to bake by just throwing a bunch of ingredients together. Directions are not for her. (21.1, 21.4)

2. Your life is hectic, with school sports, music lessons, and other activities. Your grandmother, who lives with you, is turning eighty later this week. You know she would love to have fresh yeast rolls for her birthday breakfast. (21.3)

3. Some family friends drop by just before dinner time. Your dad asks you to prepare a special dessert within an hour. (21.4)

LINKING YOUR STUDIES

1. **Science:** Research and report on one of the following topics: What is yeast and how does it grow? What is in baking powder and baking soda that brings about a chemical reaction to form carbon dioxide? Why does baking soda need to be mixed with an acid? (21.1)

2. **Social studies:** Use your school or public library to find out how the American colonists (or other groups) baked bread before the invention of the kitchen range. (21.3)

3. **Social studies:** Read about ancient Egypt and find out how bread baking developed. Report to the class. (21.3)

4. **Math:** Make a chart comparing one kind of pie made in several ways: totally from scratch; using a purchased crust and canned filling; or purchased from a bakery. Rate each kind in terms of preparation time, cost, and fat and calorie content. (21.4)

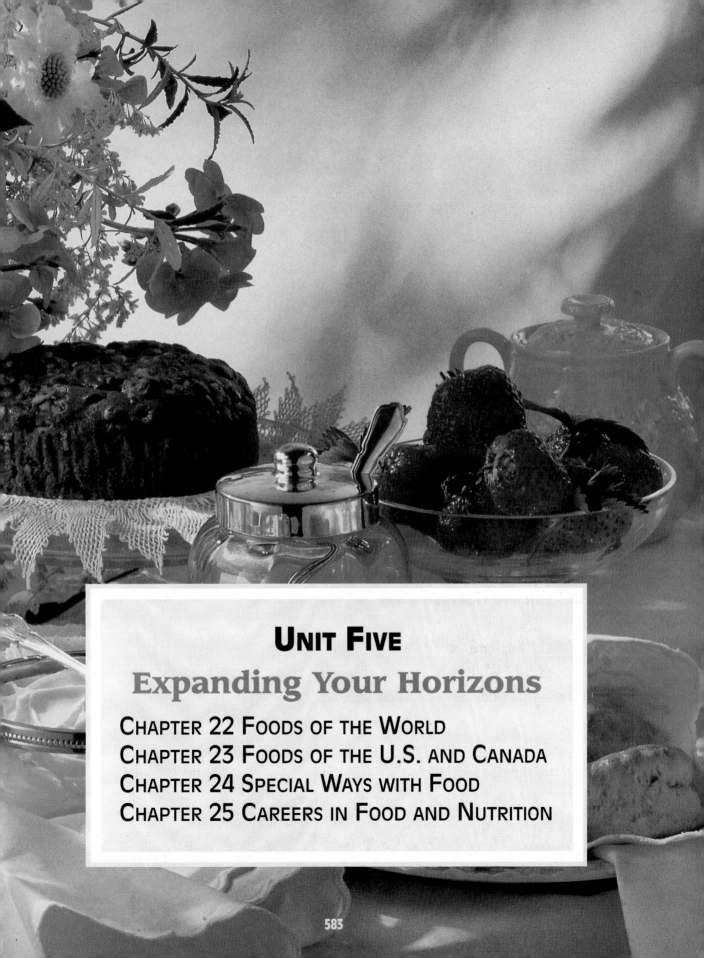

UNIT FIVE

Expanding Your Horizons

CHAPTER 22

Foods of the World

Objectives

After studying this section, you should be able to:

❖ Describe food choices available in the various regions of Latin America.
❖ Identify the cultural influences on foods in Latin America.

Look for This Term

maize

Over twenty countries in Central and South America make up what is called Latin America—the land where people speak languages based on Latin (Spanish, French, Portuguese). This region of over 300 million people stretches from Mexico and the Caribbean Islands to the tip of South America. It contains the fastest growing city in the world, Mexico City.

The early history of this area is dominated by three native cultures: Aztec, Inca, and Maya. The Aztecs flourished in Mexico, the Incas in South America, and the Mayans in Central America.

Because the area is so vast, it includes climates and geographical features of all kinds—tropical rain forests, snow-capped mountains, arid deserts, and temperate zones. Foods vary according to the growing conditions, but there are many similarities from country to country.

Corn, or **maize,** is the staple grain in much of Latin America. Wheat and rice are grown in some areas.

Beans are a common protein source in Latin America. They can be combined with other foods, such as the wild rice and chopped onions shown here, to make a great variety of dishes.

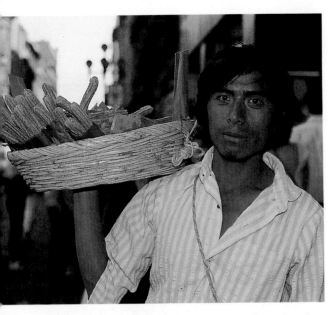

This street vendor in Mexico holds a basket of churros, fried pastries sprinkled with sugar and cinnamon.

❖ **Tostadas** begin with a crispy fried tortilla spread with the same kinds of foods used to make tacos.
❖ **Enchiladas** are made from a soft tortilla rolled around a meat, bean, or cheese filling and topped with salsa and grated cheese.
❖ **Frijoles** are cooked dry beans. *Frijoles refritos* are cooked dry beans that are mashed and fried in lard.
❖ **Tamales** are made of finely chopped fillings encased in masa dough, wrapped in corn husks or banana leaves, and steamed.
❖ **Moles** are Mexican sauces. Mole poblano is made from tomatoes, chili, fruit, seasonings, and chocolate, which gives it richness.

Mexicans like to finish off a meal with a popular dessert called *flan*, a sweet custard topped with a sauce of caramelized sugar.

Mexico

Mexico's wide variety of foods have developed both from the native foods which abound and the influence of the Spanish conquerors.

Cornmeal, rice, cooked dry beans, and chili peppers are basic to Mexican food. The bland taste of corn and beans provides a mild contrast to the variety of spicy peppers.

Here are some foods that are common in Mexican meals:

❖ **Tortillas** are thin discs of bread. They are generally made from *masa,* dried corn that is soaked in limewater and ground while wet.
❖ **Tacos** are folded tortillas filled with foods such as meat, chicken, refried beans, avocadoes, onion, lettuce, cheese, tomatoes, and salsa, a spicy sauce.

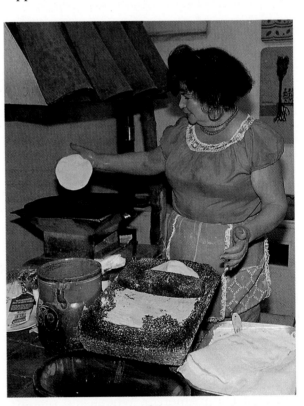

With years of experience and centuries of tradition behind her, this Mexican woman makes a batch of tortillas. She uses the traditional tools: a metate to hold the dough and a metlalpil to roll it.

Central America

A bridge of seven countries connects Mexico to South America: Belize, Costa Rica, El Salvador, Guatemala, Honduras, Nicaragua, and Panama. This is where the Mayan empire flourished. People who live in these countries today are of Mayan, European, African, and mixed descent. The cooking has Mayan and Aztec roots with Spanish and Caribbean influences.

Corn and beans are the staple crops. Bananas, coffee, coconuts, and cacao are exported to other countries.

Chicken is widely eaten in Central America. It might be prepared with pineapple, or in a mixture of ingredients such as pumpkin seeds, tomatoes, and raisins.

A favorite food is the chayote, a crisp vegetable with a delicate flavor. (See the illustration in Section 16.1, page 411). Chayote is often sliced and simmered. Costa Ricans mix it with cheese and eggs, while cooks in the Dominican Republic may fry it with eggs, tomatoes, and hot peppers.

The Caribbean

The tropical islands of the Caribbean Sea are to the south and east of Mexico, between Florida and South America. Caribbean nations include Cuba, Jamaica, Haiti, the Dominican Republic, and Puerto Rico.

Columbus landed on the islands on his trek to find spices and a shorter route to India. The Spanish came later as did the Dutch, Portuguese, British, and French. All of these cultures left their mark on the people who live there today, in the languages they speak, their customs, and their food.

Fish and shellfish are staple foods on the islands. Flying fish, conchs, shrimp, codfish, clams, grouper, and red snapper are just a few of the choices available.

Tropical fruits and vegetables grow in abundance. Mangoes, bananas, coconuts, papayas, pineapples, sweet potatoes, yams, pumpkins, and chili peppers are basic in island cooking. Islanders use coconut milk and fruit juice to prepare many kinds of foods.

The staple food is the *plantain*, a starchy food that looks like a green banana and is cooked as a vegetable. It can be roasted, fried, boiled, or baked, as well as combined in dishes with meat and cheese.

Cooking techniques and sauces vary, giving each island unique dishes even though many of the ingredients are the same.

This buffet from the island of Barbados includes beans, rice, plaintain, fish, pineapple, and other locally available foods.

Fruit is plentiful in the Caribbean, as you can see from the colorful assortment in this outdoor market in Grenada.

Here are some examples of foods found among the Caribbean Islands:

❖ *Moros y cristianos* is a Cuban national dish made with black beans and rice.

❖ *Djon-djon* are black mushrooms found only on Haiti. Haitian food generally reflects French and African influences.

❖ *Jamaican Saturday Soup* includes hot peppers (originally from Africa), carrots, turnips, and pumpkin added to beef stock.

❖ *Conchs* are shellfish that come from beautiful shells. The meat must be beaten before it is tender enough to eat.

❖ *Crapaud*, a huge bullfrog which lives in the mountaintops of the island of Dominica, is considered a delicacy.

For dessert, a pudding or ice cream made with an exotic fruit would be a popular choice.

South America

Twelve nations make up South America, the southern half of the Western Hemisphere: Argentina, Bolivia, Brazil, Chili, Colombia, Ecuador, Guyana, Paraguay, Peru, Suriname, Uruguay, and Venezuela. It also includes French Guiana, a European possession.

As in the rest of Latin America, the population is of native Indian, European, and African ancestry. The climate, culture, people, and growing conditions vary greatly from country to country and from rural area to city.

Brazil

Brazil, the largest country in South America, is located on the eastern part of the continent. It produces great amounts of beef, coffee, and cocoa. The people of Brazil are mainly a mixture of native Indians, Portuguese, and Africans.

Brazilian food reflects this mixture. From West Africa comes *dende* or palm oil (which gives a bright yellow-orange color to foods), *malagueta* peppers, and coconut milk. All are

Healthy Attitudes

In many Latin American countries, staple foods include grains, beans, and fresh fruits and vegetables. These food choices are relatively low in fat, sugar, and sodium. How might the food customs that originated in the past benefit people now and in the future?

widely used to prepare food in Brazil. From the Portuguese comes the love for sausages and kale in soups.

Here are some examples of foods you might find in Brazil:

❖ *Feijoada* is the national dish of Brazil. It's made of stewed black beans, smoked sausages, dried beef, pork, onions in hot sauce, rice, collard greens, and sliced oranges.

❖ *Churrasco* is beef that is marinated and barbecued.

❖ *Mariscada* is a fish stew made with an assortment of fish: clams, mussels, codfish, shrimp, and crabmeat. They are all cooked together with tomatoes and spices.

Black beans are a staple in Brazil. What popular Brazillian dish is made with black beans?

Peru

Peru is located on the Pacific coast of South America. When Pizarro, the Spanish conqueror, came to Peru in the 16th century, the local people were eating corn, potatoes, squash, beans, cassava, sweet potatoes, peanuts, tomatoes, avocados, and chili peppers. While these foods are still popular, today Peru is also noted for its fishing industry. The potato remains its staple food. Popular meats include seafood, beef, and guinea pig.

Peru was a Spanish colony for almost 300 years. The Spanish influence can be seen in foods such as *gazpacho*, a cold tomato-based soup of Spanish origin. (See the recipe on page 590).

Ceviche is a native Peruvian dish in which raw fish is marinated in lime. Other foods often eaten in more affluent (wealthy) areas include meat, poultry, vegetables, and grains that are highly seasoned with onions, garlic, and hot peppers. Rice, potatoes, and bread accompany the main meals.

In poorer areas, meals include potatoes, corn, squash, and soups made of wheat and barley. The foods of those living in jungle areas consist of a variety of fish, small game, fruits, and nuts.

Argentina

South of Brazil, along the eastern coast of South America, lies Argentina. Today most of its inhabitants are of European descent.

Raising beef is one of Argentina's major industries, and as a result most people eat beef. It is often grilled outdoors and served with spicy sauces. *Puchero* is a meat and vegetable stew.

Another widely-eaten dish is the *empanada*, a turnover of dough filled with vegetables, meat, fruit, or a combination of the three. Meats are also combined with fruits in local stews such as *Carbonada Criolla*—beef mixed with peaches.

This gaucho, or South American cowboy, is engaged in producing one of Argentina's largest exports—beef.

Section 22.1 Review

RECALL THE FACTS

1. What is the staple grain in most of Latin America?

2. What is the most popular type of bread in Mexican cooking?

3. What cultures have influenced Caribbean food?

DISCUSS YOUR IDEAS

4. What factors influence the food customs of a particular area?

APPLY YOUR LEARNING

5. In groups, make a list of the foods described in this section with which you are familiar. Can you think of other Latin American foods that you have tasted that were not listed in the text? What ingredients appear regularly in the dishes you listed?

Thinking About the Recipe

Read the recipe for "Gazpacho" and answer the following questions.

1. How does this recipe illustrate European influence on Latin American food customs?
2. How might you puree the ingredients if you didn't have a blender?

Gazpacho (Cold Vegetable Soup)

Customary	Ingredients	Metric
16-oz. can	Whole tomatoes, with liquid	454-g can
1/2 cup	Finely chopped green peppers, divided	125 mL
1/2 cup	Finely chopped cucumber, divided	125 mL
1/4 cup	Chopped onion, divided	50 mL
1 Tbsp.	Vegetable oil	15 mL
1½ tsp.	Ground cumin	7 mL
1½ tsp.	Cider vinegar	7 mL
1/4 tsp.	Salt	1 mL
1/4 tsp.	Pepper	1 mL
1/2 cup	Croutons, unseasoned	125 mL

Yield: 4 servings

Directions

1. Put in a blender: tomatoes (with liquid), 1/4 cup (50 mL) of green pepper, 1/4 cup (50 mL) of cucumber, 1/4 cup (50 mL) of onion, the vegetable oil, cumin, cider vinegar, salt, and pepper. (Save remaining ingredients to serve as accompaniments to the soup.)
2. Cover and blend ingredients on medium speed until smooth.
3. Place blended mixture in a covered container. Refrigerate for 1 hour or longer.
4. Serve soup cold with the croutons and remaining chopped ingredients as accompaniments.

Nutrition Information

Per serving (approximate): 71 calories, 2 g protein, 9 g carbohydrate, 4 g fat, 0 mg cholesterol, 330 mg sodium

Africa and the Middle East

Objectives

After studying this section, you should be able to:

❖ Describe food choices available in Africa and the Middle East.
❖ Identify the cultural and geographical influences on the foods of Africa and the Middle East.

Look for These Terms

berebere
kibbutz

Although Africa is an ocean away from Latin America, the two continents share some of the same foods. This is the result of journeys by explorers and settlers, the transportation of Africans to the New World as slaves, and the similarities in climate.

The mixing of cultures and food traditions often makes it difficult to determine the origins of particular foods. Unleavened breads, for example, are common in many cultures. Variations of pita bread can be found throughout the Middle East and much of Africa. For example, a staple bread of Ethiopia, a country in eastern Africa, is *injera*, a giant pancake baked on a griddle. It is used to wrap and scoop other foods.

The Sahara Desert forms a natural east-west dividing line through Africa. It separates the five nations in the north, along the Mediterranean Sea, from the rest of the continent.

The people living south of the Sahara are mainly Africans. Those living north of the Sahara are mostly Arabs, with a culture similar to the Middle East. For purposes of discussion, the five countries north of the Sahara will be included later in this section, in "North Africa and the Middle East."

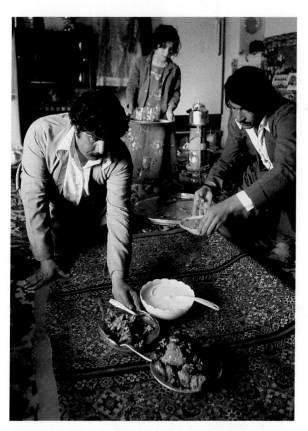

Members of a Middle Eastern family gather for the evening meal. By tradition, the diners sit on the floor.

Africa Below the Sahara

The area south of the Sahara Desert is sometimes known as the sub-Sahara region. Most of this area has a tropical or subtropical climate. However, there is a wide range in geographical features, including mountains, coastlines, river valleys, tropical rain forests, and the Sahara Desert. Consequently, different foods are raised in various regions.

Historically, African society has been based on kinship groups of related people. These kinship groups linked together into clans, and clans formed into tribes that might have thousands of members. Clans often lived together in villages and jointly owned the surrounding farmland. Food traditions are often linked to these associations rather than the political borders of specific countries.

Large cities are scattered throughout Africa, centers of business, trade, and government. International settlers in these cities brought their customs with them. Thus the lifestyles and foods in cities differ from those in rural areas. People in less developed areas eat foods traditional to that particular region.

At this market in the West African nation of Mali, peanuts and yams are among the foods sold.

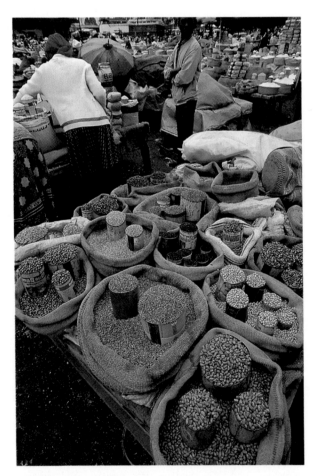

Shoppers in this Nairobi, Kenya, market have a wide variety of beans from which to choose.

This peanut snack shows an African influence. According to some historians, peanuts were brought to Africa from South America over two hundred years ago.

Climate varies, which influences the kinds of crops that can be grown. Western and central Africa are wet, tropical areas. Their chief crops include plantains, rice, bananas, yams, and cassava. In the grasslands in the east and south, corn, millet, and sorghum are among the crops grown. Wheat is grown in many areas, along with foods such as onions, garlic, plantains, pumpkins, watermelons, cucumbers, chili, dates, and figs.

Chickens, cattle, sheep, and goats may be raised wherever possible. Small herds of animals have traditionally provided income, as well as food, for small farmers and herders. Meat, however, is usually eaten just for special occasions. People living along waterways, such as rivers, lakes, and seacoasts, have an abundant supply of fish.

Over the centuries, food crops introduced from other continents were incorporated into African food traditions. Coconuts were introduced from Asia in the 1500s. Sweet pota-

toes and corn came from America at roughly the same time. In the 1600s, cassava became an important food source. It thrived in much of Africa, even in difficult growing conditions. In the 1700s, peanuts were introduced, possibly from South America.

Yams continue to be important in Africa. The traditional way to prepare them is to boil, peel, and slice or pound them until they form a paste called *fufu*. In West Africa, cooks mash and deep fry them, make them into croquettes, or slice and bake them. In some areas, cooks make fufu by mashing cassava and plantains.

Most Africans eat one large meal a day, and this is generally in the evening. A typical meal may include a grain such as millet cooked into a porridge or a vegetable such as yams. This is served with a seasoned stew made with vegetables and flavored with meat, poultry, or fish, if available. During the rest of the day, Africans eat light snacks.

The meal is always a social occasion. The food may be served in one large bowl, set on the ground. People sit around the bowl, using either pieces of bread or their fingers to scoop up the food.

In many areas of Africa, spicy hot foods are preferred. Cooks make up their own seasoning mixes, based on the many kinds of hot chili and spices available. One blend, called **berbere,** is commonly used in Ethiopia in soups and stews. It is a spicy hot combination of garlic, red and black peppers, salt, coriander, fenugreek, and cardamom. Other spices are added, depending on the cook's preference.

South Africa was visited and also settled by many waves of Europeans looking for trade routes or escaping persecution. These French, Dutch, British, and German Europeans brought their own food preferences and preparation methods. African cooks modified them with local produce and techniques. *Bredie*, for example, is a stew made with meat or fish, vegetables, onions, and chili peppers.

North Africa and the Middle East

The five main countries in North Africa include Libya, Egypt, Algeria, Morocco, and Tunisia. The population is clustered along the Mediterranean, in desert oases, or in irrigated parts of Egypt along the Nile.

The Middle East is located just east of North Africa, between Southeast Europe and Southwest Asia. The countries of the Middle East include Lebanon, Syria, Iran, Iraq, Israel, Jordan, Kuwait, Turkey, and Saudi Arabia, along with many others.

Because of its location between Asia, Europe, and southern Africa, this area has been well-traveled. Its cuisine reflects the influence of those early travelers. The use of rice as a staple and the variety of produce are some of the results of foreign visitors.

Most of the inhabitants of this area share many food traditions. Because all of these nations were occupied by European countries some time in the past, there is also French and British influence in the food customs.

The fruit-filled triangles on the left are made with phyllo, very thin sheets of pastry. Phyllo dough is common in Middle Eastern cuisine and can hold either sweet or savory fillings. Stuffed vegetables are also popular, such as these onions stuffed with ground meat and spicy stuffed artichokes.

Tabbouleh is a popular, refreshing salad from the Middle East. It is made with bulgur (steamed, dried, crushed wheat kernels).

Staples in this area are wheat and barley. Other commonly used foods include olive oil, rice, yogurt, chickpeas (or garbanzo beans), fava beans, lentils, lamb, and goat. Fruits include apricots, pomegranates, dates, figs, grapes, and oranges. Vegetables include eggplant, peppers, olives, cucumbers, and tomatoes. Seasonings include parsley, dill, mint, cinnamon, lemon juice, pine nuts, onion, and garlic. *Tahini*, a sesame seed paste, is popular.

Most people in this area are Arabs. Israel, which is a Jewish nation, is the exception.

Arab Countries

There are many similarities in the foods of these countries. The names and some seasonings may vary, but the ingredients and cooking methods are similar.

While lamb is commonly eaten, chicken and fish are also used when they are available. Chicken is sometimes an ingredient in stews made with lentils, beans, rice, and vegetables.

Tabbouleh is a popular salad made with bulgur, olive oil, tomatoes, mint, parsley, and onions.

Healthy Attitudes

Throughout much of Africa, meat is used as a flavoring ingredient rather than as the main focus of the meal. The people get more of their protein from combinations of plant foods, such as rice and beans. Plant proteins are a staple in Latin America and the Middle East, also. As you have learned, health experts encourage Americans to use plant foods as a source of protein more often. What might Americans learn about healthful eating from their global neighbors?

A major food in this area is yogurt. Depending on where you are, you might find yogurt made from the milk of cows, goats, camels, or buffalo. In several countries, yogurt is called *leban*. Leban is often mixed with vegetables, especially cucumbers and dates, for a side dish or part of a main dish.

Here are some other dishes commonly found in this area.

❖ **Felafel** are patties made from ground chickpeas, well-seasoned and fried. They are served in pita bread with tahini and vegetables.

❖ **Kubaybah or kibbi** is a mixture of ground lamb, bulgur, cinnamon, and allspice.

❖ **Stuffed vine leaves** are filled with a rice and meat mixture and served with a sauce made of yogurt, garlic, and mint.

❖ **Herrira,** a mutton and vegetable soup, is eaten often during Ramadan, the month when Muslims fast during daylight hours.

❖ **Pastilla,** a dish from Morocco and Algeria, is a pigeon pie made with phyllo dough, eggs, vegetables, spices, and nuts.

❖ **Couscous** has a double meaning. It refers to a type of pasta popular in this region, which looks like tiny beads of dough. It also refers to the main dish that is made with a variety of stews served over steamed couscous.

❖ **Kebabs** are made of marinated cubes of lamb on a metal skewer and grilled with herbs. Ground meat is also formed into long patties and cooked on skewers.

In Iran, Iraq, and Lebanon, some of the following dishes might be served:

❖ **Chelo** is steamed rice accompanied by a meat or vegetable dish.

❖ **Koresh** is a stew of meat or poultry with vegetables, fruit, nuts, seasoning, and perhaps cereal. Most Iranians will eat a *chelo koresh* for one meal a day.

Desserts in this area are often fresh, seasonal fruits. In the winter, a compote of dried fruits may be served. Sweeter treats include *baklava* (phyllo dough layered with nuts and syrup), *halva* (a sweetened candy), and rice pudding.

For a feast, such as a wedding, it is common to roast a whole sheep and serve it with couscous. A salad of tomatoes, peppers, cucumbers, mint, oranges, melon, grapes, dates, and figs might be included.

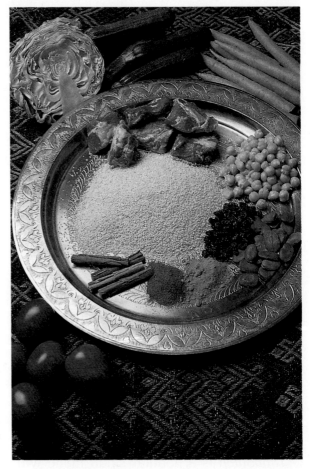

Soon these ingredients will become a tasty North African stew, or tagine, of lamb, chickpeas, vegetables, raisins, and spices, served over couscous. The mild flavor of the couscous is a fitting background for stronger-flavored foods.

Israel

Israel includes people native to the Middle East along with others from around the world. Consequently, its food customs combine Middle Eastern traditions with those of many other countries. Customs also reflect Jewish food traditions and laws.

Traditional condiments which find their way into most recipes include *zhoug, shatta,* and tahini. *Shatta* is a red chili pepper mixture. *Zhoug* is a combination of green chili peppers, parsley, coriander, cumin, garlic, olive oil, and salt and pepper.

Some Israelis live in a **kibbutz,** a communal organization which raises its own food. Breakfasts at a kibbutz are known to be substantial. They may consist of fresh produce, cold meats, cheese, fish, eggs, condiments, vegetable salads, and hot coffee.

Chicken and lamb are widely used. Many main dishes are prepared using slow cooking procedures. Traditional Jewish religious laws forbid cooking on the Sabbath, a day of rest and worship. Slow cooking allowed foods to be started the day before.

Traditional Jewish dishes are familiar in America and elsewhere, as well as in Israel. They include (above) challah bread, gefilte fish, blintzes, and knishes, among others. Another Jewish tradition is the seder plate (left), part of the Passover holiday. Each of the foods on the plate has a symbolic meaning.

Section 22.2 Review

RECALL THE FACTS

1. What are two important food plants which found their way from the Americas to Africa?

2. What is couscous?

3. How has location influenced the food customs of the Middle East?

4. Give an example of how religion influences eating habits in Middle Eastern countries.

DISCUSS YOUR IDEAS

5. How does global travel influence the exchange of food customs today? How does this compare with the influence of travel in the past?

APPLY YOUR LEARNING

6. Find a recipe for making yogurt (using milk and a small amount of cultured yogurt). Come up with a work plan for making some at home or in a foods lab.

Thinking About the Recipe

Read the recipe for "Senegalese Couscous" and answer the following questions.

1. What other grains might you substitute for couscous if it is unavailable?
2. What suggestions do you have for lowering the fat in this recipe?

Senegalese Couscous

Customary	Ingredients	Metric
8-oz. package	Couscous mix	226-g package
1/4 cup	Pistachio nuts, shelled	50 mL
1/4 cup	Almonds, blanched	50 mL
1/2 cup	Golden raisins	125 mL
1 Tbsp.	Orange peel, grated	15 mL
1 oz.	Semisweet chocolate, grated (optional)	28 g
1/2 tsp.	Cinnamon, ground	3 mL
1 tsp.	Margarine, lowfat	5 mL
Dash	Salt	Dash
2 Tbsp.	Powdered sugar	30 mL
1/4 cup	Dates, pitted and chopped	50 mL

Yield: 4 servings

Directions

Pan: Medium saucepan

1. Prepare couscous according to package directions, but *omit* any seasoning packet enclosed.
2. Grind remaining ingredients, except dates, in a food processor until well mixed.
3. Stir the dates, nut mixture, and couscous together in a large bowl.
4. Mound the couscous mixture on a platter and form it into a pyramid shape.
5. Serve.

Nutrition Information

Per serving (approximate): 373 calories, 11 g protein, 63 g carbohydrate, 11 g fat, 0 mg cholesterol, 60 mg sodium

Objectives
After studying this section, you should be able to:
- Identify foods commonly found in Western and Eastern Europe.
- Identify ways that culture, history, geography, and climate influence European foods.

Look for These Terms
scones
high tea
haute cuisine
nouvelle cuisine
antipasto

The European countries tend to be small and there is considerable travel among them. They share many food customs and seasoning choices, especially neighboring countries with similar climates. On the other hand, most European countries have had distinctive histories and traditions which give their foods national identities.

Western Europe

Western Europe includes the British Isles, France, Spain, Portugal, Germany, Austria, Italy, Greece, and Scandinavia.

The European nations have much in common, yet each has its own identity. This scene shows a French fishing village on the Mediterranean coast.

Plum pudding is a Christmas tradition in England. It is a heavy food made with raisins, currants, nuts, and flavorings, steamed for many hours.

- ❖ **Shepherd's pie** is a meat pie that is covered with mashed potatoes and baked. It is often made with leftover ground lamb or beef cooked with onions, garlic, tomatoes, and seasonings.
- ❖ **Cornish pasties**, popular in the south of England, are a combination of steak, onions, chopped potatoes and carrots, baked in a pastry crust. In former times, these baked turnovers were carried to work by miners and eaten cold.
- ❖ **Bubble and squeak** uses chopped leftover meat and vegetables. They are mixed with mashed potatoes and fried until brown and crisp.
- ❖ **Finnan haddie** is smoked haddock prepared with milk, onion, lemon juice, pepper, and parsley.

The British also enjoy a variety of game—pigeon, quail, pheasant, and deer. Fish such as sole, salmon, turbot, monkfish, and shellfish are also common to British menus.

The British Isles

The British Isles are an island group just off the European continent. The two largest islands are Great Britain—which includes England, Scotland, and Wales—and Ireland.

British food tends to be hearty and cooked by plain, simple methods. Beef, mutton (meat from older sheep), pork, and fish are favorite foods. Many Britons eat four meals a day: breakfast, lunch, tea, and dinner (or supper).

Breakfast has historically been a meal of great variety and quantity. Today it tends to be smaller. Even so, it usually includes cereal, toast and marmalade, tea, and either eggs, bacon, sausage, tomatoes, or fried bread. In Scotland, oatmeal porridge is standard breakfast fare.

Here are some dishes often served at lunch or dinner:

- ❖ **Roast beef and Yorkshire pudding** consists of beef baked in the oven, with a popover-like mixture cooked in the pan drippings. Roast beef is usually served with a horseradish sauce or mustard.

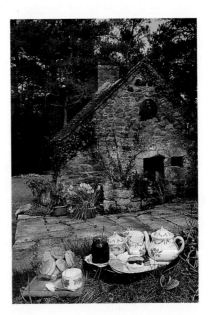

This English tea, served in the garden of an old stone cottage, features scones topped with thick clotted cream and blueberry preserves.

A meal which is uniquely British is "four o'clock tea." Tea itself, the national beverage, was brought from China to England by Dutch traders at the beginning of the 1600s. Most Britons add milk to their tea. Tea, the meal, is generally served with a bread of some kind or dessert. The bread may be sandwiches made with cucumbers, watercress, or meat or fish fillings. Crumpets, which are similar to what Americans call English muffins, may also be served. **Scones,** a tasty variation of baking-powder biscuits, are served with butter and jam in parts of Britain. In Scotland, tea may be served with oatcakes or oatmeal biscuits.

Another British favorite is the *savory*, a dish somewhere between an appetizer and a main dish. *Welsh rarebit*, for example, is seasoned melted Cheddar cheese on toast. Adding a savory to tea and serving it a bit later turns a regular tea into **high tea,** which then may replace the supper meal.

Often, dessert is fresh fruit and cheese or a pastry. Cookies are called *biscuits*. *Shortbread*, a rich mixture of butter, flour and sugar, is usually associated with Scotland.

Popular British condiments include marmalade, lemon curd, and mincemeat. Another is chutney, one of the dishes brought back from India when it was a British territory.

France

France has long been known for the quality and complicated preparation of its food. The goal of French cooking is to blend foods and seasonings to either enhance one another or to create a new flavor altogether. One flavor does not dominate the dish.

The classic dishes of France have been called **haute cuisine,** or "high cooking"—food that is elaborately and skillfully prepared. Originally, great chefs prepared huge numbers of these time-consuming dishes for the aristocrats of France. Preparing food was considered a fine art, just as painting was. Rich sauces, elegantly decorated dishes, exotic ingredients, and puff pastries characterized haute cuisine. Today this type of food is found mainly in expensive restaurants.

Modern French cooking is called **nouvelle cuisine,** or "new cooking." The trend is to lower flour, sugar, and fat content.

French people rarely eat between meals. A typical breakfast might be tea or coffee and some kind of bread—toast, a croissant, or *brioche*, a round roll made from a rich yeast dough. Lunch or dinner might include an *hors d'oeuvre* (appetizer), a light fish course, a main dish of meat and vegetables, a salad, bread and cheese, and fresh fruit or a sweet dessert. This menu sounds hearty, but remember that there are no between-meal snacks. Portion sizes are moderate. Food is eaten slowly and enjoyed.

Many French dishes vary from region to region and from city to rural area. Local food customs make up a style called provincial cooking, a much simpler type of cooking than haute cuisine. Hearty one-dish meals are characteristic of provincial cooking.

Here are some examples of popular French foods:

❖ **Ragout** is a flavorful stew made with vegetables and meat, poultry, or fish. It is often named after the region where it originated.

In France, one often sees shoppers carrying fresh, unwrapped bread home from the bakery. The long loaves are called baguettes.

This pot of bouillabaisse includes many different kinds of seafood, shells and all.

* **Pot-au-feu** is a popular soup of beef and veal cooked with vegetables such as carrots, celery, onions, and turnips.
* **Beef Bourguignon** is a famous French stew of cubed beef, onions, mushrooms, carrots, and seasonings served over boiled potatoes.
* **Bouillabaisse** is a hearty soup that combines several types of fish and shellfish, tomatoes, and herbs.

French people enjoy salads after the main course. They are made with salad greens topped with seasoned oil and vinegar. Vegetables are usually enhanced with a sauce.

Spain and Portugal

Spain and Portugal have access to the sea, so many of their dishes contain at least one kind of fish. The cooking of Spain varies greatly from region to region.

Breakfast in Spain is similar to breakfast in France. It generally consists of coffee or hot chocolate and a bread. The bread might be *churros*, fried strips of dough.

Lunch often consists of a salad, fish, a meat course, and fruit or a light dessert. Supper at home may be a light meal, but at a restaurant, it may be another large meal.

There are a few dishes which are enjoyed throughout the country. These include chicken and garlic, garlic shrimp, potato omelets, *gazpacho* (cold vegetable soup), and *paella*. Paella has a base of rice, olive oil, and saffron. From there cooks add a mixture of ingredients such as meats, vegetables, legumes, and especially fish and seafood.

Portuguese cooking is similar to Spanish cooking, except the Portuguese prefer spicier food. The cuisine was greatly influenced by travelers to India, South Africa, and South America. Portuguese foods tend to be rich because they contain more cream and butter.

Appetizers, or tapas, are favorites in Spain. This assortment features peppers, ground meat, eggs, and olives.

A paella of shrimp, clams, chicken, vegetables, and rice makes a colorful meal.

Germany and Austria

Generally speaking, German food tends to be rich and heavy. Sausages abound, with different combinations and seasonings in each region. Familiar favorites include liverwurst, bratwurst, knockwurst, and frankfurters.

Pork is probably the most popular meat, although beef and veal are common, too. Poultry is important, but fish is not popular.

Two characteristics of German cooking are the use of one-dish meals and the blending of fruit, meat, and vegetables to get sweet-sour flavors. Pork, for example, may be served with applesauce or cooked prunes.

People in Austria, a nation south of Germany, share a common language with the Germans and have many similar food customs. Austrian cooking has also been influenced by that of its Eastern European neighbors.

Here are some examples of German and Austrian foods:

❖ **Sauerbraten** is a beef roast marinated for several days in a sweet/sour sauce, then simmered in the same sauce. It is served with noodles, dumplings, or boiled potatoes.

❖ **Schnitzel** means "cutlet" in German. The meat cutlet is usually dipped in egg, breaded, and fried.

❖ **Kartoffelsalat** is a potato salad made with red potatoes, oil, vinegar, herbs, mustard, and other seasonings. It is served lukewarm. Bacon is sometimes added to potato salads.

Germans are famous for their rye and pumpernickel breads as well as *stollen*, a yeast bread with raisins and candied fruit. Another favorite is *streusel-kuchen*, a coffee cake topped with a mixture of flour, sugar, butter, nuts, and cinnamon.

Cabbage is important in German cooking. This meal includes both red cabbage slaw and sauerkraut, or fermented cabbage, along with potato pancakes, apples, sausages, and pumpernickel bread.

German desserts include rich cakes and cookies. *Bavarian cream* is a delicious mold of custard and cream. *Marzipan*, a rich mixture of ground almonds and sugar formed into exotic shapes, has its origins in Germany. So does *nürnberger lebkuchen*, better known as gingerbread.

Austrians are famous for rich desserts, most notably their cakes or tortes. For example, *linzertorte* is cake made with ground walnuts which is spread with jam.

Italy

Where did pasta come from? The most popular explanation is that Marco Polo brought it to Italy from China. Today pasta is still the national dish of Italy. It is made from durum wheat, the staple grain of Italy, which is not suitable for baking but perfect for pasta. Pasta is prepared in many ways, depending on the region.

In Northern Italy, the cooking is similar to that of France. It is characterized by herbs and rich sauces as well as the use of butter and lard.

In the south of Italy, foods are heartier. Tomato sauces and garlic are commonly used.

Here are some popular Italian dishes:

❖ *Cannelloni* are large pasta tubes that are cooked, stuffed with a meat or cheese filling, then baked in a sauce.

❖ *Ravioli* are pasta "pillows" filled with a savory mixture which varies by region.

❖ *Polenta* is cornmeal cooked in milk or water, cooled, and sliced. It's a staple food in Northern Italy.

❖ *Risotto* is a grain dish made from rice which is sautéed and then cooked in stock and flavorings.

Pasta sauces often, but not always, depend on tomatoes for a base. Some have a cream sauce base. *Pesto* is a sauce of fresh basil leaves, garlic, olive oil, grated cheese, and pine nuts.

Italians eat a variety of meat, poultry, fish, and game foods, such as rabbit.

Vegetables vary in kind and preparation according to region. They may be simmered, fried, grilled, stuffed, sautéed, or eaten raw. An Italian meal might include cauliflower, eggplant, cabbage, artichokes, peas, squash, or potatoes.

Salads may begin or end the meal. They are usually served with an oil and vinegar dressing. Salads, pickled vegetables, cheeses, and other appetizers are called **antipasto,** which means "before the meal."

Italy is famous for its cheeses, from the hard Parmesan and Romano, which must be grated, to ricotta, similar to cottage cheese.

At a production plant in Trentino, Italy, wheels of cheese are being carefully aged to just the right point.

A colorful assortment of pasta awaits an equally colorful array of sauces. Parmesan cheese and bread are typical accompaniments.

Greece

Lamb is the most popular meat in Greece. Fish and shellfish are also important, since Greece is located on the Mediterranean Sea.

Greek cooking often makes use of tomatoes, green peppers, garlic, lemon juice, and olive oil. Rice appears in many dishes. *Feta cheese*, made from sheep's or goat's milk, is widely eaten as an appetizer and in salads.

The history of Greece includes nearly four hundred years when it was ruled by Turkey. As a result, many Greek dishes, such as vine leaves stuffed with seasoned meat and rice, are similar to the foods of the Middle East.

Here are some other dishes popular in Greece:

* ❖ ***Avgolemono*** is a well-known Greek soup of chicken broth and rice flavored with eggs and lemon juice.
* ❖ ***Moussaka*** is a layered casserole made with seasoned ground lamb and sliced eggplant. A rich white sauce is poured over the mixture before baking.

Scandinavia and Northern Europe

Denmark, Norway, Sweden, and Finland make up the Scandinavian countries. Although these countries do not have a lavish cuisine, they have used the foods available to them creatively and tastefully.

The Swedish *smorgasbord* is perhaps the finest example of a bountiful buffet. Originally, smorgasbord meant a "sandwich board." Now it is a collection of assorted meats and fish dishes, raw vegetables, salads, and hot dishes.

Scandinavians rely heavily on fish for food. Dried and salted cod is a staple. Fish may also be fried, poached, or grilled, as well as used in soups and fishballs.

Smorrebrod are open-faced sandwiches which the Danes eat daily. They top thin slices of buttered bread with foods such as pickled herring, cooked pork, raw cucumbers, onion rings, apple slices, mustard, and horseradish.

Dairy products are also important to Scandinavian cooks. Each country seems to have a version of thick or sour milk which may be eaten with sugar. Milk, butter, and cream are essential ingredients in many dishes. For instance, the Danes are well-known for their rich, flaky, buttery pastries with touches of sugar, almonds, or jam. Scandinavians also bake an array of rye and white breads.

Because the local growing season is so short, Scandinavian meals are somewhat low in fresh fruits and vegetables. However, root vegetables such as potatoes, carrots, onions, and rutabagas are used regularly. Fresh berries (lingonberries, raspberries, and strawberries) are often used to accent desserts. *Fruksoppa*, or fruit soup, is a mixture of dried fruit and tapioca cooked in a sweetened liquid and served cold.

Christmas is special in Scandinavia. Weeks in advance, cooks prepare traditional sweet treats using butter, cream, almonds, eggs, and sugar. Swedes celebrate *Lucia Day* on December 13, when the eldest daughter, wearing a crown of seven white candles, serves coffee and Lucia buns, or *lussekake*, to her family.

Fish is a prominent part of this Swedish smorgasbord. Why is fish so common in Scandinavian cooking?

Eastern Europe

The countries of Eastern Europe have undergone changing borders and names in the late twentieth century. For ease in describing culinary history and tradition, general areas will be referred to by their traditional names. The following discussion will include the foods and culture of Russia, Poland, Czechoslovakia, Hungary, Bulgaria, Yugoslavia, and Rumania.

Russia

Russia is one of the many countries that once made up the Soviet Union. It covers a vast area, from Eastern Europe to the Pacific Coast in Asia.

Food in Russia differs from region to region, as it does in most countries. Over the years, Russian people have experienced many times of meager food supplies. Still, national dishes have evolved, based mainly on available staple foods. One example is Russian black bread, a dark, heavy, moist bread of rye and wheat flavored with chocolate, caraway, coffee, and molasses.

Hearty soups are also common. *Schchi* is a soup made from sauerkraut. Other popular soups are made with fresh cabbage and potatoes. *Borscht*, or beet soup, is one of the best known Russian soups. If available, meat or sausage is added. Most soups either contain sour cream or are served with it.

Russians have a fondness for sour cream and include it in many dishes. A popular combination is sliced cucumbers and onions with sour cream, seasoned with dill weed.

Fish is common in Russia. Sardines, salted herring, and salmon are especially popular.

Russia is noted for its caviar, the roe of eggs from certain fish. The roe is sieved, lightly salted, and served as an appetizer. Sturgeon roe is most expensive but considered the best.

Here are some other dishes common to Russian cuisine:

* ❖ *Piroshky* are little pies stuffed with meat, vegetables, or cheese.
* ❖ *Blini* are small yeast pancakes served with caviar or smoked salmon and sour cream.
* ❖ *Kasha* is crushed buckwheat, cooked and served as a side dish or used as an ingredient.

Tea is the most popular beverage. On cold evenings, you might find a gathering of Russians drinking tea and enjoying good conversation.

Easter has been one of the most important holidays. For Easter, Russians color eggs in beautiful, complex designs. *Kulich* is a sweet, fruit-filled yeast bread, drizzled with a thin white frosting.

Other Eastern European Nations

The food in other nations of eastern Europe has many similarities to that of Russia and, sometimes, the Middle East. The use of wheat, kasha, and cabbage, for example, is widespread.

In Poland, the national dish, *bigos*, is a stew of game meat with mushrooms, onions, sauerkraut, sausage, apples, and tomatoes. Barley is commonly used, especially in soup. *Krupnik* is a barley and vegetable soup to which sour cream and dill are added.

The Hungarian people enjoy grilled skewered lamb or beef in addition to the stew for which they are most famous, *goulash*.

Borscht is a well-known Russian dish. The colorful beet-based soup is served with a dollop of sour cream.

Holidays and family gatherings are an important part of life in Poland. Roast mutton cooked over a wood fire will be the main dish at this feast.

Goulash consists of simmered cubed beef, onions, paprika, potatoes, and perhaps garlic, caraway seeds, tomatoes, green peppers, and honey.

Hungarians also enjoy sauerkraut, pork-stuffed cabbage rolls, strudels, and *dobos torta*, a chocolate-filled sponge cake of many layers, glazed with caramel.

The Slovakian, Moravian, and Bohemian people of the Czechoslovakia area rely on dumplings as the cornerstone of their meals. Dumplings may be made from a variety of foods and come in many shapes and forms. A national favorite is liver dumplings in beef bouillon. Pork, beef, and game are common, as are cabbage and sauerkraut with caraway. One of the most famous Czech dishes is *kolacky*, yeast buns filled with fruit, cottage cheese, poppy seeds or jam.

In the region of former Yugoslavia, pilafs (seasoned rice dishes) are a favorite, as are cornmeal dishes, vegetables, and pasta. *Sarma*, the national dish, is rolled cabbage or sauerkraut leaves stuffed with a mixture of rice and ground pork. Also popular are thick, dark coffee, baklava, and desserts made with sweet noodles, dumplings, and fried yeast dough.

Corn is the mainstay of cooking in the area of Rumania. Cornmeal mush, the national dish, is served with melted butter, sour cream, or yogurt. Rumanian cooks also use peppers in their dishes and are known for their richly-flavored stews.

Meals in the Bulgarian region are some of the most healthy in this part of the world. Grains, vegetables, fruit, nuts, and yogurt are mainstays. Fresh vegetables are eaten widely in salads. Fruits, nuts, and herbs grow well in this region. The people prefer fish and lamb to other meats. A favorite dish is *potato musaka*, a casserole of vegetables, meat, potatoes, onions, garlic, tomato, eggs, cream, and grated cheese.

■ Section 22.3 Review ■

RECALL THE FACTS

1. Name five foods commonly found in the countries of Western Europe.

2. What is the difference between haute cuisine and nouvelle cuisine?

3. Name two characteristics of German cooking.

4. Identify five foods commonly found in Eastern European countries.

DISCUSS YOUR IDEAS

5. Discuss the similarities and differences among the foods of Western and Eastern Europe. What factors appear to have influenced food choices and how foods are prepared?

APPLY YOUR LEARNING

6. Choose a European country. Assume you are inviting two teens from this country to dinner with your family. Write a menu showing what you would serve to make these teens feel at home. Give reasons to support your selections.

Thinking About the Recipe

Read the recipe for "Scandinavian Marinated Cod" and answer the following questions.

1. What other varieties of fish might you substitute for the cod that would commonly be eaten by Scandinavian people?
2. Give two suggestions for reducing the fat in this recipe.

Scandinavian Marinated Cod

Customary	Ingredients	Metric
1 lb.	Cod fillets	454 g
1/4 cup	Olive oil	50 mL
2 Tbsp.	Lemon juice	30 mL
1/4 cup	Onion, finely chopped	50 mL
1 tsp.	Salt	5 mL
	Black pepper, freshly ground	
2 Tbsp.	Butter or margarine, melted	30 mL
2 Tbsp.	Vegetable oil	30 mL

Yield: 4 servings

Directions

Pans: Shallow baking dish, broiler pan

1. Wash cod fillets in cold water and pat dry. Place in shallow baking dish.
2. Combine olive oil, lemon juice, onion, salt, and a small amount of freshly ground black pepper in a small bowl.
3. Pour marinade over cod fillets. Allow fish to marinate 30 minutes (15 minutes on each side). Drain marinade from fillets and discard.
4. Blend melted butter or margarine with vegetable oil in a small bowl.
5. Brush cold broiler pan with 1 tablespoon of the butter and vegetable oil mixture.
6. Place cod fillets on cold broiler pan.
7. Broil fillets 10 minutes for each inch of thickness, turning halfway through cooking time. Occasionally brush fillets with butter and vegetable oil mixture to keep fish from drying out. Fish should flake easily with a fork when done.
8. Serve immediately.

Nutrition Information

Per serving (approximate): 146 calories, 20 g protein, 2 g carbohydrate, 6 g fat, 54 mg cholesterol, 348 mg sodium

Objectives

After studying this section, you should be able to:

❖ Identify foods common to the countries of Asia and the Pacific.
❖ Point out how culture and climate influence the foods of Asia and the Pacific.

Look for This Term

masala

Rice is the staple grain in most of Asia, the largest continent in area and in population. In Northern China and parts of India and Japan, wheat is the staple grain.

Wood is the main cooking fuel in most of Asia. Because fuel is often scarce and expensive, food is cut into small pieces that cook quickly. The basic cooking methods include boiling, steaming, and frying.

Main dishes are usually a mixture of fried or steamed vegetables, mixed with a small amount of meat, poultry, or fish. Flavorful sauces add variety and spice to meals in Asia.

Another staple is soybeans, which are used to make many products, such as soy sauce, tamari sauce, and tofu. Soybean sprouts are used fresh and in cooked dishes.

Coastal areas enjoy an abundant variety of seafood. Seaweed is an important part of Asian cooking. It is used in soups, sauces, and main dishes and also served as a side dish.

Traditional Asian cooking emphasizes grains and legumes and uses an abundance of fresh ingredients. As a result, most traditional Asian meals are generally healthy and nutritious.

A Japanese woman cleans vegetables at her family farm. Fresh ingredients are essential in Asian cooking.

The tea ceremony is a centuries-old Japanese custom. The tea is prepared and served in a ritual of grace and precision.

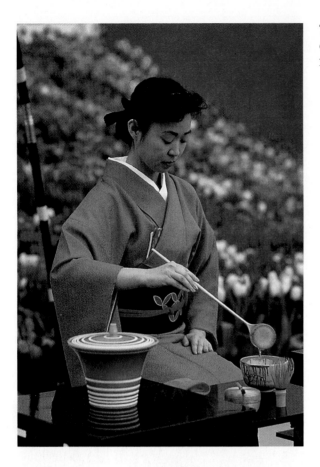

Sushi is popular in Japan. Cooked rice is flavored with vinegar, then combined with ingredients such as fresh raw fish, cucumber, and seaweed. The sushi is presented in artistically arranged, bite-size portions.

Japan

Japanese cuisine features foods that are economical, nutritious, and attractive in appearance. Traditionally, Japanese people have eaten mainly vegetables, seaweed, and fish, as well as some fruit. Popular seafood includes squid and eel.

Meals usually consist of small amounts of a variety of foods, since this is considered a healthy way to eat. The Japanese dietary guidelines recommend that a person eat 30 different foods a day. Here are a few of the dishes commonly found in Japan:

* ❖ *Sukiyaki* is a mixture of vegetables and meat cooked quickly in a wok.
* ❖ *Tempura* is the Japanese version of crispy, deep-fried vegetables and seafood which are batter-dipped before frying.
* ❖ *Soba* are buckwheat noodles, widely eaten for lunches and snacks.
* ❖ *Miso*, a paste made from soybeans, is often used as a flavoring.

In addition to having a pleasing flavor, Japanese food must also appeal to the eye. Foods and table settings are attractively arranged to provide beauty for the meal.

China

Chinese cuisine ranks among the best in the world. It dates back thousands of years.

Preparing and serving food reflects the philosophy of the people. Food preparation balances opposites, just as, according to Chinese philosophy, the universe is balanced. Ingredients are carefully selected and cut into pieces to retain the sense of harmony and symmetry. Whether for a banquet or a simple family meal, the food is a blend of simplicity and elegance.

China has always had a wide variety of foods. Instead of depending on expensive ingredients, the Chinese rely on their skill and cooking methods.

A Chinese meal does not have a main dish or a specific pattern. Instead, a variety of hot dishes are arranged in the center of the table. Each person is served a bowl of rice. The diners then help themselves to a small amount of each food. Soup is eaten during the meal or at the end of it, but never at the beginning. Hot tea is always served.

The variety of dishes in a meal depends on the number of people being served. If large amounts are needed, cooks prepare an additional number of recipes instead of making larger quantities of a few foods.

China is a such a large country that each region developed its own style of cooking. Generally, there are four different styles:

❖ **Northern or Peking** food is named after the capital, Peking, now called Beijing. The climate is dry and cold and the winters bitter. Wheat, the staple grain, is used to make dumplings, noodles, and steamed bread. The dumplings, known as *won ton*, are made from small sheets of dough filled with stuffings and folded into packets. The seasonings are usually mild, although spicy sweet and sour flavors are popular.

❖ **Coastal or Shanghai/Fukien** food comes from a region with a temperate climate. Fish and shellfish are the main foods in this area. Pork, chicken, and duck are also popular. They are mixed sparingly with large amounts of well-seasoned vegetables. *Red cooking* describes food simmered in a sauce that colors the food red.

❖ **Inland or Szechwan** food is prepared in central China, which also has a temperate climate. This area is noted for its hot peppers, which, along with garlic and ginger, create a zesty, spicy cuisine. Szechwan cooking also mingles sweet, sour, salty, and bitter flavors.

❖ **Southern or Canton** food is prepared in an area with a subtropical climate. Foods are generally steamed or stir-fried. Although meals are based on seafood, pork, or poultry, other ingredients include mushrooms, nuts, and chicken broth. Steamed dumplings stuffed with meat, seafood, or fruit pastes are popular. *Egg rolls* are small sheets of dough rolled around a flavorful filling, sealed with a water/flour mixture, and deep-fried.

A chef in Hong Kong (top photo) displays the noodles he has made by swinging the dough in his hands, a traditional Chinese method. At right, diners enjoy a buffet in Guangzhou City.

Dim Sum can be roughly translated as "hits the spot," or "heart's delight." They are an assortment of bite-sized snacks that include dumplings which are steamed, boiled, or fried. Dim sum is traditional for Chinese New Year's meals. Cooks often hide a coin inside one filled dumpling. The finder is assured prosperity for the coming year.

Korea

As in much of Asia, rice is essential in Korea. It is sometimes cooked with barley or millet, which adds nutrients, texture, and flavor to the rice.

Meals usually consist of a soup or stew plus a grilled or stir-fried dish. Fish and fish pastes appear regularly in Korean foods. Garlic, in many forms, is used in meals. In fact, some of the hottest foods in the world can be found in South Korea.

Pickles add interest and flavor to Korean dishes. They might be made from almost any foods, such as pumpkins, cabbage, or ginseng. They can be rich in minerals and vitamin C.

Southeast Asia

Southeast Asia includes Burma, Laos, Thailand, Vietnam, Cambodia, and Indonesia. These countries are in the tropics and have a variety of tropical fruits and vegetables, as well as a huge assortment of spices. The cooking reflects the influence of Chinese and European settlers.

Thailand

Coconut milk, the juice from coconuts, is frequently used as a liquid in Thai cooking, from main dishes to desserts. Noodles are a favorite and appear in casseroles and in soups. They are also mixed with sauces made of oysters, black beans, or fish. Then they are topped with chopped peanuts, coconut, and green onions.

Like many nations in Southeast Asia, Thailand is a blend of old and new, as this scene at a floating market shows.

Pad Thai is made with the flat noodles characteristic of Thai cooking.

The Philippines

The inhabitants of the Philippines are a blend of Chinese, Arab, and Indian people living on 7000 islands. The culture and food reflect the influences of those who have settled there, including the Spanish and Americans of the last few centuries.

The staple foods are fish, pork, and rice, which is made into cakes, noodles, and pancakes. Fish sauces are also widely used.

The national dish is *adobo*, which is pork marinated and browned in soy sauce, vinegar, garlic, bay leaves, and peppercorns.

Most food combinations in Thailand have four basic flavors—sweet, sour, salty, and spicy. They also meet four texture requirements—soft, chewy, crunchy, and crispy. The most popular dish is *pad Thai*, a well-seasoned mixture of noodles, shrimp, peanuts, egg, and bean sprouts.

Vietnam

Rice and fish are the staple foods in Vietnam. The Vietnamese eat rice every day, by itself and combined with other foods. Rice starch is used to make noodles and dumpling wrappers. Foods are usually seasoned with *nuoc-mam*, a spicy fish sauce.

Fish has always been the main source of protein for the Vietnamese. Fish and other foods are commonly seasoned with fresh ginger, coriander, lemon grass, and sweet basil. Many foods are rolled in lettuce or rice paper wrappers which are easily dipped into spicy sauces.

Indonesia

Indonesian foods are highly spiced. One of the most popular dishes is *nasi goreng*, which is a mound of fried rice surrounded by assorted meats, such as beef and shrimp, and vegetables. The diner mixes them to obtain a wide variety of flavor combinations.

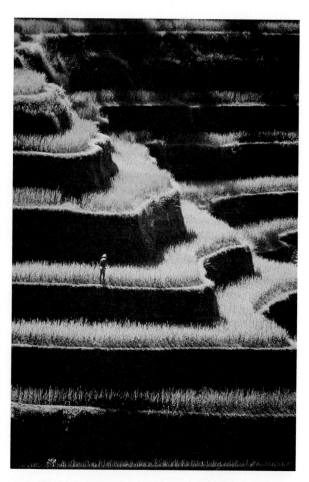

It takes a lot of rice to feed the great number of people in the world who depend on it as their staple grain. These terraced rice fields in Bali, Indonesia, are beautiful as well as productive.

India

Cooking in India varies from region to region, according to climate and culture. In the northern and central areas, wheat is the staple grain and lamb is the most common meat. In the south, rice is the staple grain and the food is much spicier.

The most common Indian seasoning is similar to American curry powder and is called **masala.** Most cooks grind and mix their own blend of spices and keep a jar on hand at all times. Yogurt is used widely.

Many people eat little or no meat. As a result, India has a wide variety of delicious, spicy, meatless main dishes. However, poultry and fish are popular wherever they are available. In northern India, for example, chicken stuffed with rice, almonds, and raisins is a favorite. Here are some other interesting foods found in meals in India.

- ❖ *Kebabs* are made of meat—often lamb—and herbs on a skewer.
- ❖ *Pilaf* is cooked, seasoned rice often mixed with chopped almonds, raisins, or yogurt.
- ❖ *Raita* is a salad which combines yogurt with several vegetables and spices.
- ❖ *Dal* is a dish of dry beans or lentils cooked in a seasoned broth.
- ❖ *Puri* is an Indian bread. (See the recipe on page 616.)

The food for an Indian meal is a pleasant blend of flavors and textures. It is served all at once. Indian people also enjoy candy made from sugar and almonds, rice flour, or coconut.

This spicy lamb dish is seasoned with masala. Rice and chapati, a flat Indian bread, complement its distinctive flavor.

Pavlova is a popular dessert in Australia and New Zealand. The meringue-like mixture is topped with whipped cream and berries or sliced kiwis.

Australia and New Zealand

The food in Australia and New Zealand is very similar to that of the European countries that contributed settlers to it. These include English in particular, but also Scottish and French people in some regions.

Menus vary according to location, from the outback of Australia to the large cities along its coasts to the smaller cities and rural areas of New Zealand. Meals usually feature foods which are locally available. Meat and seafood are plentiful. Many people eat steaks and chops (beef or mutton) for breakfast. New Zealanders enjoy toheroas, which resemble clams.

One uniquely Australian dish is *Pavlova,* a rich mixture of meringue, fruit, and cream. Pies and sweet rice dishes are also common desserts.

Shrimp and other seafood are widely eaten in Australia and New Zealand.

Section 22.4 Review

RECALL THE FACTS

1. What is the staple grain in Asia and the Pacific?

2. Give four examples of protein foods commonly used throughout Asia and the Pacific.

3. How does food preparation relate to Chinese philosophy?

4. What four food flavors are common to the foods of Thailand?

5. Name three foods eaten by the people of India.

DISCUSS YOUR IDEAS

6. Why do you think Asian cooking methods are popular in the United States today?

APPLY YOUR LEARNING

7. Plan a meal using foods from an Asian or Pacific country. Look up the calories, grams of protein and fat, and the amounts of vitamins A and C found in these foods. Are the foods in this meal a good source of these nutrients?

Thinking About the Recipe

Read the recipe for "Puri" and answer the following questions.

1. What other whole-grain flours might you substitute for whole wheat flour?
2. What foods of India might you eat with Puri for a meal?

Puri (Bread of India)

Customary	Ingredients	Metric
1¼ cup	Whole wheat flour	300 mL
1/2 tsp.	Salt	3 mL
1/4 cup	Margarine, softened	50 mL
3/4 cup	Low-fat yogurt, plain	175 mL
	Vegetable oil for frying	
	Honey	

Yield: About 2 dozen small biscuits

Directions

Pan: Deep saucepan
Temperature: Medium to medium-low heat

1. Mix flour and salt together in a bowl.
2. Cut in margarine until mixture resembles pea-size pieces.
3. Stir in yogurt and mix until well blended.
4. Roll dough out on a lightly-floured surface to 1/8 inch (3 mm) thickness and cut with a biscuit cutter.
5. Pour oil into deep saucepan, about 1 inch (2.5 cm) deep.
6. Heat oil until a small piece of dough sizzles quickly when dropped into the oil.
7. Lower biscuits into oil using a slotted spoon. Hold biscuits under the oil. (Otherwise they rise as soon as they begin to puff.)
8. Fry biscuits a few seconds until they turn golden brown.
9. Remove from oil and drain on paper towels.
10. Serve warm, plain or with honey.

Nutrition Information

Per serving (approximate): 62 calories, 1 g protein, 5 g carbohydrate, 4 g fat, trace of cholesterol, 75 mg sodium

CAREER PROFILE

Tab Sagi
Specialty Store
Owner

Current position:

"I'm the owner of a Middle Eastern grocery store located in a major city."

Responsibilities:

"I have family members and employees who help me, but I am ultimately responsible for maintaining the store's inventory and finances."

Skills:

"You need a variety of skills to successfully run your own business. You definitely need to be self-motivated and have leadership abilities, and you need to be skilled in management and accounting."

Education:

"My education has primarily been on-the-job, but my son, who will take over the business one day, has a bachelor's degree in food service management."

Work environment:

"You might think that by owning your own store you can take many days off! In reality I work very long hours, and my life often seems to revolve around the store."

Favorite part of the job:

"It's very satisfying for me to get to know my regular customers on a personal level. I enjoy being able to help them find particular items they are looking for, and to offer menu suggestions from time to time."

- What do you think Tab means when he says a business owner must be "self-motivated"?
- What aspects of Tab's job appeal to you? Why?

Summary

Section 22.1.
Latin America: Latin American cooking is a combination of native foods and European influences. Ccorn is the staple grain in most areas. Mexican meals include masa, rice, beans, and chili peppers. Staples in the Caribbean include fish, tropical fruits, and vegetables. Beef is popular in Brazil, Peru, and Argentina.

Section 22.2.
Africa and the Middle East: In Africa, staples include yams, cassava, and peanuts. Geography, climate, native traditions, religion, and foreign influence have shaped food customs. The same is true of countries in the Middle East. This region's location on trade routes from Europe to Asia brought many travelers who influenced food.

Section 22.3.
Europe: The cooking of the British Isles tends to be plain but hearty. The goal of French cooking is to blend flavors to enhance one another. Spanish foods are fairly simple and light. German cooking tends to be rich and heavy. Pasta is the national dish of Italy. Many Greek foods are similar to those in the Middle East. In Scandinavia, fish and dairy products are basic foods. Eastern European cooking emphasizes root vegetables, grains, and sour cream.

Section 22.4.
Asia and the Pacific: Rice, seafood, soybeans, and vegetables are the staples of Japanese and Chinese cooking. Foods in Korea and Southeast Asia are spicy and include tropical fruits and vegetables. Indian cuisine is known for its spicy, often meatless recipes. Australian and New Zealand cuisine has European roots.

REVIEWING FACTS

1. What is a plantain? How can it be prepared? (22.1)

2. Identify the two major influences on Brazilian cooking. Name two foods that reflect these influences. (22.1)

3. Name five foods that were introduced to Africa between the fourteenth and eighteenth centuries. (22.2)

4. Name and describe three dishes often eaten in Arab countries. (22.2)

5. Name three traditional condiments used in Israel. (22.2)

6. Name four foods commonly served at British tea. (22.3)

7. Identify two ways in which the cooking of northern Italy differs from that of southern Italy. (22.3)

8. Identify five mainstays of Bulgarian cooking. (22.3)

9. Name the four basic styles of Chinese cooking and give one characteristic of each. (22.4)

10. What is *nasi goreng*? How is it eaten? (22.4)

LEARNING BY DOING

1. **Foods lab:** Choose one popular food of Latin America. Find two recipes for preparing it: one traditional, the other as it is usually prepared in the United States. Prepare and sample both recipes. Tell how they differ in ingredients and flavor. Offer reasons for these differences. (22.1)

2. **Computer lab:** Design a table or database showing the dietary staples, their origins, and dishes made from these staples, for the different regions of Africa and the Middle East. Print out this information for the class. (22.2)

3. **Foods lab:** Find a French recipe that is traditionally considered haute cuisine. Modify the recipe to make it nouvelle cuisine. Prepare your new version. Be ready to explain how your modifications made this recipe nouvelle cuisine. (22.3)

4. **Demonstration:** Investigate the traditional ways of serving Japanese and Chinese meals. Then demonstrate these serving methods. Duplicate the foods, serving pieces, and serving styles as closely as possible. (22.4)

THINKING CRITICALLY

1. **Predicting consequences:** Review the dietary staples of the different regions of Latin America. For each region, identify one possible health advantage and one disadvantage of the typical way of eating. (22.1)

2. **Comparing and contrasting:** Find examples of bean-and-grain dishes served in several countries from different continents. How are they similar and different? (22.1,, 22.2, 22.3, 22.4)

3. **Recognizing bias:** Do people sometimes make assumptions about a national or ethnic group based on the foods they eat? What do you think about this practice? (22.3)

4. **Recognizing values:** You have read how Chinese meals reflect the Chinese people's traditional philosophy of life. What philosophies might meals in the United States reflect? (22.4)

MAKING DECISIONS AND SOLVING PROBLEMS

What Would You Do?

1. Your new neighbors are a Jewish family. You would like to invite them to dinner. However, you are not familiar with Jewish food customs and are unsure about what foods they may and may not eat. (22.2)

2. Your new acquaintance, an exchange student from Czechoslovakia, tells you that she is having trouble adapting to American foods. You wonder what common American foods might be similar to the foods she is accustomed to. (22.3)

3. One of your teammates on the basketball team is a practicing Hindu. When you play games in other cities and eat in restaurants, he has trouble finding foods that are acceptable. (22.4)

LINKING YOUR STUDIES

1. **Social studies:** Locate information on the controversy surrounding cattle raising in the rain forest regions of South America. What are the arguments of the opposing sides? What are the strengths and weaknesses of these arguments? Which side do you feel has the stronger case, and why? Share your findings with the class in a brief report. (22.1)

2. **Social studies:** Find out more about Jewish and Islamic dietary laws and customs. What foods are forbidden, and why? How else do these rules affect the cooking of Israel and Arab countries? (22.2)

3. **Literature:** Read the passages in Charles Dickens' *A Christmas Carol* regarding the Cratchits' Christmas pudding. Why is the family so concerned with its preparation and outcome? (22.3)

4. **Fine arts:** Learn more about how Japanese cuisine fits into the wider Japanese philosophy on the arts. How are the Japanese people's ideas about color, balance, and symmetry reflected in their art, music, and dance, as well as their meals? Make a presentation to the class using examples to support your conclusions. (22.4)

CHAPTER 23

Foods of the U.S. and Canada

Regional Foods of the East, Midwest, and South

Objectives

After studying this section, you should be able to:

❖ List foods common to the East, Midwest, and the South.

❖ Identify cultural and climate influences on the foods of the East, Midwest, and the South.

Look for This Term

roux

Cornbread, clam chowder, barbecued meat, key lime pie, grits, sourdough bread—do you think of these foods as typically American? Today, any of them can be enjoyed throughout the country. However, at one time each was known only in the region where it originated.

The Foundation of American Cooking

How did regional differences come about? As you learned in Section 13.3, the foods common to an area depend in part on the geography and climate of the region. The pattern of North American settlement also affected the development of food customs.

The first known inhabitants, the Native Americans, developed their own food customs based on locally available foods. Those foods are the foundation for American cooking. Later, immigrants from other parts of the world made additional contributions to the foods of America.

Corn, or maize, played an important role in the life of many Native American tribes. It is still a staple crop in the United States today. How many different uses for corn can you name?

Foods of the Native Americans

The philosophy of the Native Americans was to live in harmony with nature. They relied on hunting, fishing, and gathering local berries for meals. Some cultivated wild maize (corn) so that it would yield greater amounts of food and seed. They also stored the seed in dry places to protect it from moisture. The seed could be used as food in the lean months of winter. In a sense, Native Americans were early pioneers in food technology.

Corn was prepared in a variety of ways, some of which are still used today. Native Americans roasted and boiled the corn in the husk. Some removed the kernels and made them into a powder which was then made into flatbreads, drinks, and mush. Sometimes the Native Americans softened the kernels in homemade lye and made hominy, which was cooked with bits of meat.

Regional differences in climate and soil meant that different foods were available in different places. In the cold climates, food was dried, smoked, and frozen to use in the winter. *Pemmican,* for example, was dried meat, pounded into a paste with fat and preserved in cakes which were easy to carry when traveling.

In coastal areas, seafood was a staple. Fish were usually steamed or cooked over an open fire. Native Americans in the South concocted soups and stews from fish and small game.

In the Southwest, tribes grew peppers and beans to use in soups and chili-type dishes. They also made barbecue sauces to put on meat which was roasted over open fires. These foods are still part of the heritage of the region in which they originated.

Native Americans and the Immigrants

In the fifteenth century, immigration from Europe began. Immigrants coming to America brought their food customs with them. They tended to settle as groups in areas that reminded them of their homelands. These national clusters helped preserve their traditions.

Native Americans played an important role in the survival of the immigrants in the New World. They introduced the immigrants to such foods as maize, potatoes, tomatoes, peppers, pumpkin, squash, and many types of beans. Gradually, the immigrants adapted their favorite recipes to local produce and methods of cooking and preserving food.

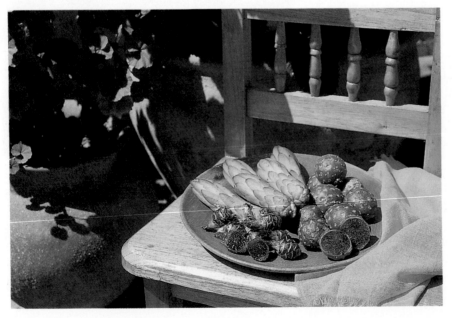

Foods of the Native Americans varied from region to region. For example, in the Southwest, locally available foods included the edible flowers and fruits of cactus plants.

Cultural exchange also occurred between different colonies and different immigrant groups. Over time, this process resulted in the unique cooking styles of each region of North America.

The Northeast

Among the first settlers in the Northeast were English, Dutch, French, and Germans. Native Americans taught early immigrants to use available foods such as deer, rabbit, wild turkey, and berries. They also taught the immigrants to plant native crops such as corn, beans, squash, and pumpkins. Corn and dry beans provided carbohydrates and protein to help the immigrants survive in the New World.

Dried corn was ground and made into breads, pancakes, puddings, mush, and fish batter. Corn cakes, called *journey cakes* or *Johnnycakes*, were a simple baked mixture of water and ground corn.

Baked beans also have their origins in these early days. The immigrants learned how to soak the beans and cook them slowly for hours. Over a period of time, through trial and error, they developed a tasty dish that is now known as *Boston baked beans.*

Seafood, which was plentiful along the Atlantic coast, was another source of protein for the early settlers. They learned to cook shellfish between layers of seaweed and heated rocks. They also cooked shellfish dishes called *chowders* in huge kettles hung in the fireplace. The most famous was clam chowder, made with milk, butter, onions, and clams. In some areas, cooks used tomatoes instead of milk. Either way, clam chowder is one of the most well-known dishes of New England.

The Irish came to the Northeast somewhat later than other immigrants. They introduced Irish stew and corned beef with cabbage, known throughout the United States as traditional Irish dishes.

Boston baked beans and pumpkin pie are two traditional New England dishes. Both beans and pumpkin were introduced to the European settlers by Native Americans.

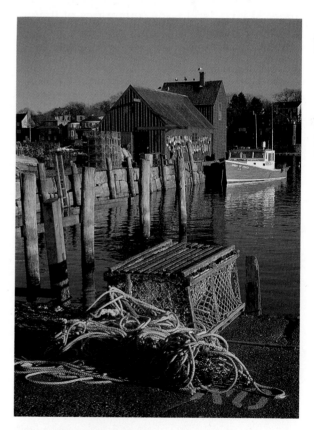

With miles of coastline, New England is rich in seafood. Here empty lobster traps await the next fishing trip.

Hearty and filling foods were a trademark of the Irish. These foods utilized a wide range of vegetables, including cabbage, carrots, and potatoes, which provided good sources of vitamins and minerals. Vegetables were combined with eggs, bread crumbs, butter, and spices to make puddings. Irish cooks also used leeks, onions, and garlic to flavor foods.

Pennsylvania Dutch

The early German, or *Deutsch,* immigrants to Pennsylvania were given a different name by the English settlers. The closest the English could come to pronouncing "Deutsch" properly was "Dutch." As a result, the Germans in this area became known as Pennsylvania Dutch.

These Germans were known for their hearty soups, stews, and homemade breads. They were farmers, which required hard physical labor and large quantities of flavorful, filling food.

The Pennsylvania Dutch immigrants continued to eat familiar foods from their homeland: pork, cabbage or sauerkraut, noodles, and sausage. Their meals included sweet and sour flavors from foods such as spiced fruit, pickled fruits and vegetables, and fruit butters.

The Pennsylvania Dutch are also known for tasty baked goods. Pies, cakes, rolls, and crumb-topped cakes were shared with neighbors over mid-morning coffee or *kaffeeklatsch.*

The Midwest

In the eighteenth century, as people in the East settled into a comfortable lifestyle, adventurous pioneers set out to explore the unknown land to the west. Settlers followed, opening up new lands in the Midwest. During the nineteenth century, newly arrived immigrants from Europe joined this westward movement.

Soon the prairies of the heartland were supporting farms and dairies. Settlers planted familiar crops that grew well in that climate—wheat, corn, other grains, fruits, and vegetables. Farms also produced beef, pork, and poultry. Fish was available from rivers and lakes.

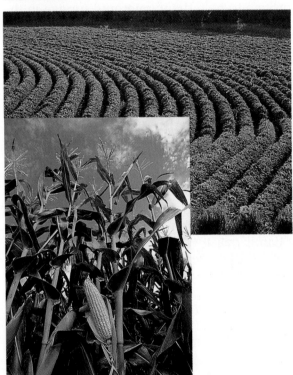

The Midwest is home to acres of rich farmland. Corn and soybeans are just two of the crops the region is famous for.

Rye bread with apple butter and pecan sticky buns reflect the Pennsylvania Dutch fondness for baked goods and sweets. Potato salad with a vinegar dressing provides one of the "sour" flavors included in each meal.

This bounty provided the basis for Midwestern cooking. It was also influenced by the cooking styles of settlers from the East and the food traditions brought by the new wave of immigrants from Europe.

In general, Midwestern menus were hearty and relied on the taste of the foods themselves rather than on much seasoning for flavor. The great supply of wheat made home-baked breads, cakes, and pies a way of life. Meat, potatoes, bread, vegetables, and dessert: this was food to provide energy for hard-working pioneers. It was simple fare, simply cooked, but a part of what is now known as American cooking.

The South

In the eighteenth century, life in the South generally revolved around the plantation and other rural areas. Crops in the South were bountiful because the earth along the lakes, rivers, and deltas was rich and the temperatures were warm. These lakes and rivers, as well as the ocean, provided fish and shell-

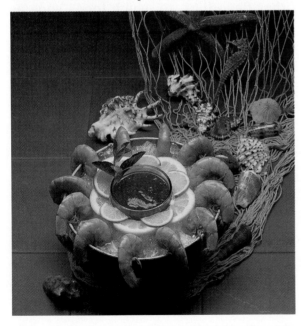

This appetizer features shrimp freshly caught along the southern coast of the United States.

fish. Corn was the staple food and was dried and ground so it could be used in a variety of recipes: cornbread, spoonbread, corn pone, fritters, cornmeal batters, grits, and hush puppies. These foods are still served in the South today.

The English were the primary settlers in the area. Food customs, however, were also influenced by the Africans, French, and Spaniards.

African-American Influence on Southern Cooking

African-American cooks on the plantations made their mark on Southern food. They incorporated turnip and dandelion greens, black-eyed peas, catfish, fried okra, yams, red beans, rice, and peppers into their cooking.

African-Americans developed their own special recipes for foods such as pig's feet and hog jowls. Chitterlings (small pieces of hog intestine) were fried and dipped into a spicy sauce. Pig tails were cooked with lima beans in a sweet-spicy sauce. Ham hocks (legs) and turnip greens became a popular dish. The backbone of the hog was simmered to make a tasty stew topped with dumplings.

The African-Americans had come to appreciate chili peppers, which had been transported to Africa from Latin America. They enjoyed spicy hot sauces and gravies. They also depended on one-pot cooking. Dishes were cooked in an iron pot and made with a wide variety of foods, including cooking greens.

African-American cooks also combined foods to make new recipes. *Hopping John,* for instance, is a mixture of black-eyed peas and rice. *Hush puppies,* made of cornmeal batter dropped by spoonfuls into hot oil, are often served with fried catfish. According to legend, hush puppies got their name in early days when they were thrown to silence barking dogs around campfires.

Creole jambalaya is a delicious mixture of rice cooked with tomatoes, onions, and other flavorings, to which foods such as shrimp, ham, sausage, and chicken are added.

African cooks helped create the special blend that is Southern cooking. Peanuts, yams, and peppers were familiar foods from their homeland. Here, they appear in an African-inspired peanut soup with red pepper garnish and a traditional Southern favorite, sweet potato pie.

Desserts were sweet and rich. They included pecan pie, sweet potato pie, and peach cobbler.

Creole and Cajun Cooking

Creole and Cajun are two specialized kinds of cooking that developed in the South. Creole cooking is typically found in Louisiana, especially New Orleans. Louisiana was the cultural crossroad of the New World. The fame of Creole cooking lies in the blending of flavors. This is only natural, as Creole cook-ing is the blending of four cultures: French, Spanish, African, and Native American.

Many famous Creole dishes owe their distinctive flavor to a **roux** (ROO), a mixture of browned flour and fat. It gives a subtle, dark, roasted taste to sauces and also thickens them. *Gumbos* (originally French bouill-abaisse), *jambalayas,* stews, and other dishes are commonly found in Creole territory.

Instead of roux, Native Americans in the area used a powder made of crushed sassafras leaves to thicken stews and to add a delicate flavor. This was called "filé powder" by the settlers.

The African-Americans brought okra to the cooking of this region and they used it to thicken stews. It is also often used in gumbos. The African-American method of simmering foods for a long time in iron pots also added to the Creole flavor.

Crayfish are a Louisiana specialty.

In the 1700s, the French Acadians were banished from Nova Scotia by the British. Eventually they found their way to Louisiana.

The French Acadians brought their culinary traditions to their new home and combined them with local foods for the beginning of Cajun cooking. The term *Cajun* is derived from the word *Acadian.*

Creole coffee is flavored with ground, roasted chicory root. *Beignets,* light, fried breakfast pastries, are another Creole specialty. They are still made fresh daily in the French quarter of New Orleans.

Cajun and Creole cooking are very similar, although Cajun foods contain more seasoning than Creole. Cajun foods are distinguished by a blend of herbs and spices which give them a distinctive flavor. Seafood is used abundantly and special spices draw out the unique flavors of crayfish, crab, shrimp, and oysters. The blending of hot peppers, spices, fish, rice, beans, corn, tomatoes, and vegetables results in food that is delicious as well as nutritious.

Section 23.1 Review

RECALL THE FACTS

1. Name two foods native to North America.

2. What are hominy and pemmican? What people made and ate these dishes?

3. Name three contributions made by the Africans to the American food culture.

4. What is roux?

DISCUSS YOUR IDEAS

5. What factors do you think encouraged the immigrants to try new foods?

APPLY YOUR LEARNING

6. Plan a dinner meal combining different foods from the South. (You may need to check some recipe books.) Survey a supermarket and gather ingredient prices for the foods in this meal. Which items were most or least expensive? Which were the easiest and most difficult to find? What does location have to do with the price and availability of food items?

Thinking About the Recipe

Read the recipe for "Creole Green Beans" and answer the following questions.

1. How might you adapt this recipe to use fresh green beans?
2. What suggestions do you have for lowering the sodium in this recipe?

Creole Green Beans

Customary	Ingredients	Metric
3 oz.	Ham, cubed	85 g
1	Onion, medium, chopped	1
1 clove	Garlic, minced	1 clove
1 lb.	Frozen cut green beans	454 g
1/2 cup	Water	125 mL

Yield: 4 servings

Conventional Directions

Pan: 3 qt. (3 L) covered saucepan

1. Sauté ham in saucepan over medium heat until lightly browned. Remove ham from saucepan and set aside.
2. Sauté onion and garlic in saucepan with ham drippings until tender, about 2 to 3 minutes.
3. Add green beans, ham, and water to saucepan. Cover.
4. Simmer over medium heat until beans are tender, about 12 to 15 minutes.
5. Serve hot in cooking liquid.

Microwave Directions

Pan: 3 qt. (3 L) microwave-safe baking dish
Power level: 100 percent power

1. Cook ham in covered baking dish 1 to 2 minutes at 100 percent power, stirring halfway through cooking time. Remove ham from baking dish and set aside.
2. Sauté onions and garlic with ham drippings in baking dish 1 to 2 minutes at 100 percent power, stirring halfway through cooking time.
3. Add green beans, ham, and water to baking dish.
4. Cook at 100 percent power for 10 to 12 minutes, stirring after 4 minutes and 8 minutes.
5. Serve hot with the cooking liquid.

Nutrition Information

Per serving (approximate): 80 calories, 7 g protein, 10 g carbohydrate, 2 g fat, 13 mg cholesterol, 334 mg sodium

Objectives

After studying this section, you should be able to:

❖ Identify foods characteristic of the western United States and Canada.

❖ Describe the cultural influences on foods of the western United States and Canada.

Look for These Terms

sourdough starter
hibachi

Early settlers in the American West brought with them the cuisine of their native homelands. In adapting their traditional recipes to the climate and foods available to them, these early settlers developed foods that are commonly found in these regions today.

The Southwest

Most people associate the Southwest with cowboys and huge cattle ranches. Spaniards introduced cattle to this area in the sixteenth century. By the 1800s, ranches dotted the Texas plains, raising large herds of Longhorn cattle tended by cowboys.

Long before the Spaniards arrived, Native Americans were raising crops such as corn, beans, pumpkins, squash, and chilies. They also had an abundant supply of fish and wild game as well as berries, nuts, and seeds.

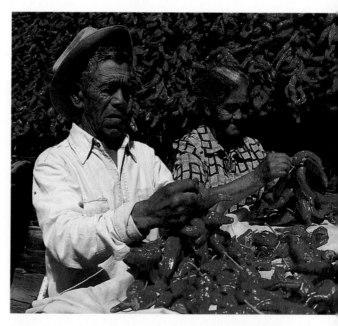

The use of chilies in Southwestern cooking illustrates the Native American influence, as well as the use of locally available foods.

While Native Americans and Spaniards influenced the cooking in the region, so did other cultures. These included Mexicans, French, English, and other settlers moving from the east. Settlers moving westward found rich soil for growing abundant crops.

Because cowboys couldn't come home for meals, a cook traveled with them. Food and essential equipment to cook over a campfire were carried in a chuckwagon.

At first, cowboy cooks prepared simple meals over the open campfires. Meat was cooked by roasting, barbecuing, or stewing in a pot. To save time in the morning, the cook made a biscuit mix the night before, mixing flour, salt, and baking powder in a sack. The next day he added fat and water and baked the biscuits over the campfire. For the cowboys, "dessert" consisted of biscuits topped with a sweet syrup. Very strong coffee completed the meal.

Before long, Mexican foods made their way across the Texas border and influenced Southwest cooking. Beans, corn, and chilies were added to the cowboys' meals. Soon other Mexican foods became popular, such as tamales, tacos, and tortillas. When the foods of the two cultures blended, the result was known as Tex-Mex. The seasoning in Tex-Mex can vary from mild to fiery hot. It depends on personal preference.

Many believe that Southerners moving to the Southwest introduced the barbecue. The word *barbecue* may be derived from the Spanish *barbacoa,* which refers to the grid on which meat is roasted in Latin America. However, records show that meat was barbecued in Virginia as early as the seventeenth century. Cowboy cooks bathed the roasting meat with a spicy tomato-based sauce. Soon, the barbecue was a major cooking method, especially in Texas.

There's a difference of opinion as to where *chili con carne* originated, in Texas or Mexico. There's little debate, however, over the popularity of chili, as it is now known. Originally, chili was made with diced beef cooked in a spicy sauce laced with red chilies and marjoram. Later, chili powder replaced the chilies and the beef was ground. Pinto beans, tomatoes, onions, cilantro, and spices were also added. Today, local contests are held yearly from coast to coast to find out who can make the best chili.

As in Mexican cooking, corn continues to be the mainstay of Tex-Mex cooking. Corn products are usually served at every meal. In addition, beans, chili peppers, fresh vegetables, and fruit, sometimes cooked with meats, are included in Southwestern meals.

Nachos are popular, made by smothering tortilla chips with refried beans, cheese sauce, and chilies. *Fajitas* (fah-HEE-tuhs) are tortillas wrapped around a thin, marinated, grilled steak. They are usually served with grilled onions and sweet peppers, guacamole, refried beans, and salsa.

Chili con carne is an all-American favorite, but nowhere is it more popular than in the Southwest. Many chili chefs create their own special blend of ingredients.

The Pacific Coast and the Northwest

Early settlers in the Pacific Coast and the Northwest found an abundant food supply. Natural resources such as seafood and game were plentiful. The settlers used simple food preparation methods to bring out the natural flavors of these foods. For example, elk, deer, and goat were grilled or roasted. Seafood was steamed, boiled, or grilled.

The coast also had a rich supply of tasty fresh fruits and vegetables. The temperate climate of Southern California provided the perfect growing conditions.

As with most seacoasts, great shipping ports grew on the Pacific Coast, including San Francisco, Seattle, and Los Angeles. When gold was discovered in California and Alaska, people from Asia flocked to the New World. These Japanese, Chinese, Russian, and Korean immigrants were joined by Mexicans, French, and Canadians.

The immigrants brought their food specialties with them and mingled them with local food customs. For example, *chow mein* is a dish created in California about 100 years ago. It is not an authentic Chinese dish, but an Americanized version of Chinese cooking.

Early sailing ships brought food from China, Japan, and the Polynesian islands to America. The influence of Asian cooking is still strong in the Pacific Coast and Northwest regions.

Sourdough bread today is considered one of the classic breads in America. Yet it had humble beginnings in the mid-19th century, during the days of the gold rush. Many early settlers in California and Alaska come looking for gold. Most of the prospectors were poor and relied on bread as their staple. They had no yeast, but made bread with a **sourdough starter,** a mixture of flour, water, and salt on which wild yeast cells grew. The mixture fermented and became a leavening agent.

The prospectors never put all their starter in the bread. A small amount was always left in a crock and then replenished by adding flour and water. In this way sourdough starter was always on hand and the prospector was assured of a food supply. As long as the prospector had the crock of sourdough starter, he knew he would not starve. Because they were so dependent on the starter, prospectors came to be known as "sourdoughs."

The Northwest corner of the United States was the last to be settled. Settlers in Oregon and Washington came to these Northwestern states by way of the Oregon Trail. Many brought seeds from fruit trees to begin orchards. Fruit orchards, which later became

San Francisco is the undisputed capital of sourdough bread.

Along the Pacific Coast, fish has always been a staple food. These cooks in Alaska are grilling salmon and other varieties for an outdoor festival.

profitable businesses for settlers, remain a major industry in the Northwest today. Along with raising fruits, such as pears, peaches, and apples, these settlers created delicious dishes from the abundance of fish and seafood. Dungeness crab and coho salmon were often steamed or served with creamy sauces.

Earth Watch

Today in the Pacific Northwest, the salmon which was once so abundant is less available. Environmental hazards, such as over-fishing and pollution, have taken their toll on the availability of this tasty fish. What suggestions might you have for preventing problems like this with other food sources?

Many tropical fruits, such as papaya (right), are grown in Hawaii. A tempting buffet (below) illustrates the bounty of the islands.

Hawaii

Hawaiian cuisine is a very complex blend of different cultures. Hawaii is a small chain of islands located in the middle of the Pacific Ocean, west of Mexico. For centuries, it has been the midway stopping point for ships traveling the long shipping lanes between Asia and North America.

The original inhabitants were Polynesian, but many other cultures have settled in the islands, bringing their food customs with them. Today, Hawaiian cooking is a blend of Polynesian, Chinese, Japanese, Korean, Fil-

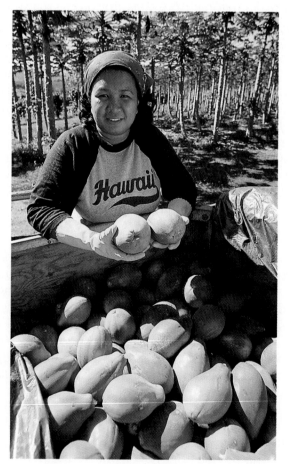

ipino, French, English, and Portuguese, as well as mainland American.

The rich soil and warm climate offer a wide variety of tropical fruits, including mango, papaya, pineapple, and bananas. The surrounding waters and inland streams provide a bounty of flavorful fish. Other foods were introduced by settlers. The Japanese introduced seaweed, teriyaki sauce for marinating, a new kind of noodle, and many rice and bean products. They also brought the **hibachi,** a small charcoal grill. The Chinese brought rice, soybeans, pork, and Asian vegetables such as Chinese cabbage. These, along with chicken, are the mainstay of Hawaiian cooking.

The early Polynesians had no pots and pans, so they invented techniques for preparing food. One was *poi* pounding. They pounded fruits or roots into a bland, sticky paste. This was their staple. Today, poi is made from ground taro root and is often used in cooking or served as a side dish. If allowed to ferment for several days, it develops a more sour flavor. Duck may be steamed in a banana leaf with cabbage, pineapple, and poi. Taro chips, similar to potato chips, are deep-fried thin slices of taro root.

Another cooking method was the open pit, which became famous as the *luau,* or feast. The luau is a tradition observed on special occasions, such as birthdays, marriages, and other events. Tourists visiting Hawaii are usually treated to the luau, which also features native entertainment.

The highlight of the luau is a pig roasted in an open pit. Fish and other meats are wrapped in leaves and roasted with sweet potatoes and bananas on the hot coals. Besides poi, other Hawaiian dishes that might be served include *lomi lomi salmon*—salted salmon with onions and tomatoes—and *haupia*, a sweet pudding made with arrowroot and coconut milk.

Canada

As in the United States, the foods of Canada reflect the nation's natural resources and cultural diversity. The natural resources include wild rice, fish, and beef. As for the people, Canada is populated by many nationalities that have, for the most part, retained their identities.

Ontario and the Western Provinces of Canada

Ontario is centrally located in Canada, lying to the north of Minnesota, Wisconsin, and Michigan. Over one-third of Canada's population lives in Ontario, making it the most heavily-populated province in the country.

Beef and dairy foods are among the chief products of Ontario. Poultry, eggs, fruits, vegetables, and maple syrup are also plentiful.

Food customs in Ontario are as varied as the people who live there. Many are of British, French, German, Italian, Ukrainian, or Asian descent, among others. In addition, more Native Americans live in Ontario than in any other province.

To the west of Ontario are the prairie provinces of Manitoba, Saskatchewan, and Alberta. Here, the traditional foods are similar to those in the Midwest of the United States.

In British Columbia, on the North Pacific coast, salmon is a staple. Vancouver, the largest city in British Columbia, is located just north of Seattle. It has a significant Chinese population and its own Chinatown. Foods from all regions of China can be found there.

The Northwest Territories stretch across northern Canada. Native Americans and Inuit (Eskimos) are the primary inhabitants. Until the 19th century, most Inuit hunted and fished for food. Seal meat, caribou, trout, and cod were staples.

Quebec

In 1534, Jacques Cartier landed in Gaspé, in what is now Quebec, and claimed the territory for France. The next year he traveled up the St. Lawrence River to the present site of Quebec and Montreal. By 1663, the area was under the firm control of Paris and was called New France.

One hundred years later, the Treaty of Paris gave Britain control of all of New France. By this time, though, French culture was firmly established and has continued to be dominant in the region.

Due to cultural and linguistic ties to France and Switzerland, Quebec shows the most European influence of any Canadian province. About a fourth of the population of Canada resides in Quebec. These French Canadians are proud of their language and heritage. French is spoken almost exclusively in that province.

It is not surprising, then, that food in Quebec displays a distinct French influence. Common dishes include French pastries, apple tarts, French breads, seafood soups, and special cheeses. Maple syrup, a local contribution, is a favorite in desserts. The cuisine of Quebec is considered some of the finest in North America.

Apples, pumpkins, and other produce are for sale at this orchard in Quebec. Besides fruits and vegetables, Quebec produces dairy products, pork, poultry, and beef.

Atlantic Provinces

Newfoundland, New Brunswick, Nova Scotia, and Prince Edward Island make up the Atlantic provinces. The ethnic origins of the people are largely English and French, with some German, Dutch, and Irish as well. Almost half of the people speak both English and French.

Fish is one of the most important foods of the region. The coast provides an abundance of lobster and crab, which are relatively common and quite inexpensive. Seafood provides great sources of protein and iodine. Fresh fruits and vegetables are grown locally, but the growing season is short due to the cold. Potatoes are raised on Prince Edward Island, showing the influence of the Irish who settled the region.

Blueberries are one of the main fruits grown in the Atlantic provinces. They are often featured in desserts and baked goods.

No matter what region you live in, you can find ethnic restaurants such as this one in major cities and even small towns. This is just one sign of the cultural diversity characteristic of the U.S. and Canada today.

Cultural Diversity Today

In recent decades, the United States and Canada have experienced much growth in their minority populations. Millions of immigrants have flocked to North America in search of a better life and settled in communities all across the country.

In addition to immigration, other factors that affect the cultural diversity in North America include:

❖ **Mobility.** People move from one region to another more often now than in the past. They carry their food traditions with them.

❖ **The media.** Through television, magazines, and other sources, people are exposed to various cultures and their traditions.

❖ **Technology.** Due to modern transportation and packaging methods, foods from many regions and cultures are available all across the U. S. and Canada.

For these and other reasons, today the food in a specific region is as diverse as the people who live there. Many food habits and patterns now reflect the traditions of individual families more than the area in which they live.

Section 23.2 Review

RECALL THE FACTS

1. Describe the special touch contributed to barbecued beef by inhabitants of the Southwest.

2. Explain two ways in which the geography of the Pacific Coast and Northwest affected the food supply.

3. Describe the contribution of the Polynesians to Hawaiian cuisine.

4. Identify one Irish influence on the foods of the Atlantic provinces of Canada.

DISCUSS YOUR IDEAS

5. Do you think the type of foods people were accustomed to influenced their decision about where to settle? Explain.

APPLY YOUR LEARNING

6. List ten foods that you enjoy eating. Identify the regional or ethnic source of each food.

Thinking About the Recipe

Read the recipe for "Southwest Guacamole" and answer the following questions.

1. How could this recipe be varied to suit individual tastes?
2. How might you adapt this recipe if you wanted to use a blender to make guacamole?

Southwest Guacamole

Customary	Ingredients	Metric
2	Ripe avocados	2
1 small	Tomato, diced	1 small
4-oz. can	Chopped mild green chilies, drained	112-g can
1/4 cup	Onion, minced	50 mL
2 Tbsp.	Lemon juice	30 mL
1 Tbsp.	Cilantro (fresh coriander leaves), minced	15 mL
1/8 tsp.	Garlic powder	0.5 mL

Yield: About 2 cups (500 mL)

Directions

1. Peel and seed avocados.
2. Mash avocados in a medium bowl.
3. Stir in tomato, chilies, onion, lemon juice, cilantro, and garlic powder.
4. Serve as a spread on warm tortillas, as a dip with baked tortilla chips, or as a condiment with Tex-Mex foods. To store, cover surface of guacamole with plastic wrap and refrigerate.

Nutrition Information

Per 1/4-cup (50-mL) serving (approximate): 87 calories, 1 g protein, 5 g carbohydrate, 7 g fat, 0 mg cholesterol, 174 mg sodium

CAREER PROFILE

Joyce Nitobe
Foods Writer

Current position:

"I'm a journalist assigned to the food section in a medium-sized newspaper."

Responsibilities:

"I'm responsible for producing a weekly page in the newspaper on regional food specialties. I write the articles and obtain photographs or arrange to have them taken. Of course it's necessary to be a good cook in this business. It also helps to be well-organized and personable."

Skills:

"First and foremost, you must be able to meet deadlines to be successful in this job. You also must have good interviewing skills, organizational skills, and writing skills. It helps to be knowledgeable about foods, although some of what you need to know can be learned on the job."

Education:

"I have a bachelor's degree in journalism and a background in foods and cooking that goes back to my high school years."

Typical day on the job:

"I spend a lot of time gathering information through mail I receive, my own research, and interviews. Often I test out recipes in my own kitchen. After I have the information I need, I spend time writing at a computer."

Favorite part of the job:

"I'm a natural born writer and I love to cook, so this is a perfect job for me! I enjoy learning so many new things in my job and being able to pass on that information to others."

- Why are organizational skills important in Joyce's job?
- What aspects of Joyce's job do you think you might enjoy? Why?

Summary

Section 23.1
Regional Foods of the East, Midwest, and South: Native Americans lived on fish and game, wild berries, and corn. They shared these foods with European immigrants, who adapted them to their own lifestyles and cooking traditions. British, Dutch, and German groups in the Northeast developed recipes to supply their energy needs and get them through the harsh winters. Midwestern farmers raised cattle, grains, and vegetables that became the basis of that region's flavorful food. Southern staples such as corn, catfish, and black-eyed peas were incorporated into new dishes by African-Americans living in the South. Creole and Cajun cuisines, which originated in and around Louisiana, are famous for their distinctively spiced, seafood-based recipes.

Section 23.2
Regional Foods of the West and Canada: Foods and preparation methods of the American Southwest reflect the influence of Native American and Mexican cultures. On the Pacific Coast and in the Northwest, shipping ports brought the influence of Asian cooking to native food supplies. Hawaiian cuisine combines Polynesian, Chinese, Japanese, Korean, and Filipino traditions. Foods in Canada's Western provinces show the influence of Native Americans, the French, British, and other immigrant groups. The cuisine of Quebec reflects its historical ties to France. Fish and potatoes are staples in the Atlantic provinces.

REVIEWING FACTS

1. Name three ways that Native Americans prepared corn that are still used today. (23.1)

2. Describe three ways in which regional differences affected the foods and preparation methods of Native Americans. (23.1)

3. Identify the three influences on the development of Midwestern cooking styles. (23.1)

4. What four cultures are blended in Creole cooking? (23.1)

5. Name six foods that are often combined in Cajun cooking. (23.1)

6. Why was grilling and barbecuing a common food preparation method among cowboys? (23.2)

7. *Chow mein* reflects a blending of what two cultures? (23.2)

8. How is sourdough bread made? What is the advantage to this method? (23.2)

9. Identify two uses of the taro root. (23.2)

10. Name three foods that show the French influence in Quebec. (23.2)

LEARNING BY DOING

1. **Foods lab:** Find and prepare an authentic recipe for one of the regional favorites described in this chapter. Compare its basic flavor to those of the foods you enjoy today. Describe and give reasons for the similarities and differences you find. (23.1)

2. **Foods lab:** Find and prepare a recipe for sourdough starter and bread. Experiment with different flavor combinations that show the influence of the different regions and ethnic cuisines that you have read about. (23.2)

3. **Foods lab:** Combine the preferences and cooking traditions of your lab group to create your own "regional" cuisine. Prepare a meal of these favorite recipes, explaining how each one became part of the group's "heritage." (23.1, 23.2)

THINKING CRITICALLY

1. **Recognizing alternatives:** Identify the traditional cooking methods used to prepare the regional foods described in this chapter. Suggest some modern methods that could replace the traditional methods. (23.1, 23.2)

2. **Analyzing behavior:** What personal qualities did immigrants and settlers show by trying new foods and developing new recipes? In what other situations did those qualities help them survive? How might people today benefit from trying new foods? (23.1, 23.2)

3. **Predicting consequences:** How do you think appreciating the food traditions of other cultures affects your attitudes and feelings toward the people of these cultures? (23.1, 23.2)

MAKING DECISIONS AND SOLVING PROBLEMS

What Would You Do?

1. You are spending a few months with friends in the South. You are concerned that many of the foods they prepare—fried chicken and fish, hush puppies, meat gravy—are high in fat and calories. You would like to suggest ways of preparing foods that are more healthful, but retain the flavors and textures your friends enjoy. (23.1)

2. You want to prepare *poi* for your family's dinner. However, taro root is not available where you live. (23.2)

3. A friend of yours, who grew up in Texas, has recently moved to Vermont. In one of her letters, she says she misses the flavor of an authentic outdoor barbecue, especially in the winter. (23.2)

LINKING YOUR STUDIES

1. **Literature:** In Willa Cather's *My Antonia,* find a passage related to food, or the lack of it. What does the scene tell you about meals, food supplies, and preparation methods of people of that time and place? What might the scene tell you about the characters involved? (23.1)

2. **Social studies:** Interview people of different cultural backgrounds who live in your community. What are some traditional foods of their ethnic group? If they originally came from another country or region, how has moving affected their cooking and eating habits? How have their cooking traditions affected the way they prepare common American dishes? (23.1, 23.2)

3. **Writing:** In diary form, describe your first encounter with some of the foods, recipes, and preparation methods of another region of North America. (23.1, 23.2)

CHAPTER 24

Special Ways with Food

Objectives

After studying this section, you should be able to:

❖ Describe how to use a variety of seasonings and marinades.
❖ Explain how to use your creativity in cooking.
❖ Describe ways to improve the appearance of foods with garnishes.

Look for These Terms

seasoning blends
julienne
en papillote

Once you learn the basics of food preparation, you can begin to use creative techniques that can easily turn simple foods into special meals. For instance, different seasonings can vary the flavor of any basic recipe. Other creative techniques include cooking in parchment paper and making garnishes.

Seasoning Secrets

Seasonings are ingredients that are used in small amounts to flavor foods. They include herbs and spices, condiments, and marinades. Seasonings can be helpful to health-conscious people who are limiting their use of salt and fat.

When you begin to experiment with seasonings, start out using a small amount. You can always add a little more. If you add too much at the beginning, there's little you can do to correct the flavor.

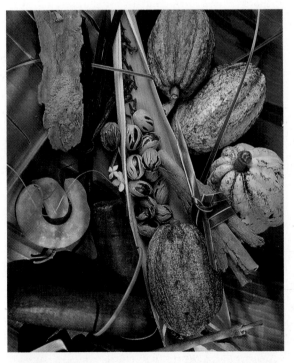

Would you recognize these objects as spices in their natural form? The seeds, bark, stems, and roots of certain plants yield seasonings that are essential for creative cooking.

Herbs and Spices

Herbs are the flavorful leaves and stems of soft, succulent plants that grow in the temperate zone. Some familiar examples include basil, oregano, sage, and bay leaf. They are usually sold dried, but some, such as parsley and basil, are available fresh.

Spices are usually dried, ground buds, bark, seeds, stems, or roots of aromatic plants and trees. Most grow in tropical countries. Some are sold whole or in pieces, such as whole nutmeg, peppercorns, or cinnamon sticks. A few are sold fresh, such as ginger root, which is commonly used in Asian cooking.

Seasoning blends are convenient combinations of herbs or spices. Most are used for specific purposes. For instance, Italian seasoning combines flavors typical in Italian cooking. You can buy blends or mix your own.

Because herbs and spices are used in such small amounts, consider buying them in bulk. That way, you can buy just the amount you can use in a short time.

Light, air, and heat are the main enemies of herbs and spices. Store them in tightly closed, opaque containers in a cool, dark place. Do not keep them next to the range.

Dried crushed herbs keep their flavor about six months. To test dried herbs for freshness, rub a small amount in the palm of your hand with your thumb for about five to ten seconds. If there is little or no aroma, the herb is probably too old to use. It might give food a bitter flavor.

Ground spices keep their flavor about a year. Whole spices may last as long as three years.

Here are some guidelines for using herbs and spices:

❖ Begin with a few basic herbs and spices as suggested on the chart on pages 644-645. Once you learn how to use them, you can add others.

❖ Herbs and spices vary in strength and are used in differing amounts. Dried herbs are more potent than fresh. As a rule, one tablespoon of fresh herbs can be substituted for one teaspoon of dried and crushed herbs.

You can grow your own fresh herbs in a garden or on a windowsill. Starter plants are available at many garden shops.

TIPS for Success

Drying Herbs

You can successfully dry your own fresh herbs. Here are two simple methods:

❖ **Air-dry method.** Rinse sprigs of herbs and shake off excess water. Tie herbs into bunches and label so you can identify them when they dry. Hang them in a dry, shady, well-ventilated place. They should dry in about two weeks.

❖ **Microwave method.** Place rinsed herbs between several layers of paper toweling. Microwave on 100 percent power, 15 to 30 seconds at a time, until the herbs are dry and can be crumbled.

Fresh herbs can be dried in the microwave oven. After drying, store herbs in airtight containers and use as needed.

* When adding herbs and spices to hot foods, let the mixture simmer or stand at least ten minutes before tasting. This gives the heat time to release the flavor. When adding the seasonings to cold mixtures, let them stand at least 30 minutes before tasting so flavors can be released.
* Herb flavors are lost if overcooked. Add them to foods during the last 45 minutes of cooking. For cold foods, however, add them several hours before eating.

Condiments

Condiments are liquid or semi-liquid accompaniments to food. They can also be used as flavorful seasonings. Condiments vary in flavors, such as sweet, salty, and spicy hot. Mustard, salsa, and ketchup are popular condiments. Here are some others.

* *Soy and tamari (tuh-MA-ree) sauces* are made from fermented soybeans. Soy sauce has a sharper, more pungent flavor than tamari. Low-sodium types are available.

* *Hot pepper sauce* is made from hot chili peppers. It's measured by drops because it is so strong.
* *Worcestershire (WOO-stir-sheer) sauce* is a dark, spicy sauce used in soups, stews, and meat mixtures.

Marinades

Marinades (MAIR-ih-nayds) are flavorful liquids in which food is placed before it is cooked. Marinades can tenderize less tender cuts of meat and can add flavor to food. Low-fat salad dressings can be used as marinades, or you can make your own.

Most marinades contain three basic ingredients—oil, an acid, and seasonings. Any mild oil can be used. It coats the outside of the food and keeps it from drying out as it broils or grills.The acid ingredient helps tenderize the food. Options include flavored vinegars, citrus juices, plain nonfat yogurt, and buttermilk. Seasonings add flavor. Try using herbs and spices or aromatic vegetables such as onions, peppers, garlic, and celery.

You can vary the flavor of marinades by the ingredients you choose.

Basic Herbs, Spices, and Blends

Herbs	Uses
Basil Mild, spicy-licorice flavor with a hint of mint.	Dishes containing tomatoes; meat and poultry; carrots; peas; rice.
Bay leaves Strong, aromatic, pungent flavor.	Braised meats, stews, soups, bean dishes. Use leaf whole. Remove before serving.
Dillweed Sharp flavor, similar to caraway seeds.	Cruciferous vegetables; carrots; green beans; cucumbers; fish; poultry; breads.
Marjoram Delicate, sweet, spicy flavor with hint of mint.	Soups; stews; poultry; stuffings; salads; tomato sauces.
Mint Strong, refreshing, aromatic flavor.	Yogurt dishes; tomato dishes; rice; bulgur; vegetables; lentils; fruits; tea.
Oregano Strong, clove-like flavor.	Italian and Mexican dishes; bean dishes; pork; poultry; salads; green beans.
Rosemary Strong, piney flavor. sauces; soups.	Poultry; lamb; pork; potatoes; breads; bean dishes; pasta
Sage Strong, slightly bitter flavor.	Poultry; pork; stuffings; potatoes; white beans; chowders.
Thyme Strong, clove-like flavor.	Poultry and stuffings; lamb; dry beans; stews; soups.
Spices	**Uses**
Cinnamon Sweet flavor.	Meat dishes; desserts; legumes; sweet potatoes; squash.
Cloves Strong, hot, pungent flavor.	Meat dishes; grains; legumes; fruit desserts.
Cumin Strong, musty flavor.	Mexican and Mideastern foods; legumes; tomato sauces and soups; rice.
Dry mustard Hot, sharp, spicy flavor.	Meat; poultry; soups; stews; egg dishes; salad dressings.
Ground ginger Hot, pungent, spicy flavor.	Stir-fries; stews; soups; squash; sweet potatoes; grains; legumes; desserts.

Basic Herbs, Spices, and Blends (continued)

Nutmeg Mild, spicy flavor; best if purchased whole and grated fresh.	Cooked spinach, zucchini, and carrots; sweet potatoes; soups; stews; ground meat; bulgur; fruits; desserts.
Blends	**Uses**
Chili powder Spicy hot, pungent flavor.	Tex-Mex cooking; chili; stews; soups; barbecue sauces; dishes made with corn.
Curry Powder Pungent, spicy flavor.	East Indian cooking; poultry; meats; fish; yogurt dishes; legumes.
Italian seasoning Blend of basil, marjoram, oregano, rosemary, sage, savory, and thyme.	Italian recipes.
Poultry seasoning Blend of lovage, marjoram, and sage.	Any recipes made with poultry, including stuffing.

Pour the marinade ingredients into a large container, such as a reusable glass jar, and shake well. Place the food into a glass or plastic covered container, pour the marinade over the food, and refrigerate. Occasionally turn and stir the food so it marinates evenly. Do not marinate food in metal pans—the acid may react with the metal and give an unpleasant flavor.

Marinating time depends on the food. Tender foods, such as fish, can marinate for an hour or less. Meat and poultry can marinate up to six or eight hours. Be careful not to over-marinate foods because they will get mushy. If you are marinating foods just for flavor, 30 minutes is long enough.

Before cooking, drain the food well. Discard marinade used for meat, poultry, and fish as it may contain harmful bacteria. If you want to baste with the marinade, make an extra batch for basting.

Using Your Creativity

What's the secret to making food look appealing? Using your creativity and your "meal appeal" skills—that's the secret! For many people, preparing food is more than just cooking. It's a form of self-expression. A creative cook may plan the appearance of a plate of food much like Michaelangelo or Picasso planned a painting. Think about the colors and shapes of food or how the flavors blend together. What would your edible "work of art" look like?

You might want to look in a variety of cookbooks for different ways to present food. Here are a few possibillities:

❖ Swirl whipped potatoes into a fluffy mound by using a pastry bag with a decorative tip similar to those used in cake decorating.
❖ Cut foods into **julienne** strips. Julienne strips are long, thin strips of food.
❖ Use a small scoop to mold fruits such as melons into balls.

Even simple foods can be served with a creative flair.

Garnishes

Garnishes are small, colorful, bits of food that are used to enhance the appearance and texture of any dish. They can be used on appetizers, salads, main dishes, vegetables, desserts, and beverages. Presenting foods that are attractive, as well as tasty, helps make mealtime an enjoyable experience.

Keep size in mind when garnishing foods. If a garnish is too large, it may overpower the food. Choose garnish colors and flavors that complement the food it is served with. Here are some ideas for simple garnishes:

❖ **Soups.** Float a spoonful of yogurt, cucumber slices, lemon slice, croutons, or chopped parsley or chives on soups.

❖ **Salads.** Add green pepper rings, cherry tomatoes, pimiento strips, red onion rings, tomato wedges, pickle fans, radish roses, chopped nuts, or seeds to salads.

Cooking in parchment paper, or cooking **en papillote** (ehn pah-pee-YOHT), is another method used by creative cooks. Fish and tender cuts of meat and poultry are often cooked by this method. One serving is placed in the center of a square of parchment paper along with other ingredients, such as vegetables, butter, or a sauce. The paper is folded around the food to form a package. The ends are tightly closed and folded under so food does not leak out. As the food cooks, flavors blend. The sealed package retains the flavor and aroma.

The packages are placed on baking sheets and baked in the oven. To serve, each package is placed on a dinner plate. An X is cut into the top of the paper, which is peeled back. As you read on about garnishes, think about ways you might dress up foods served en papillote.

Safety Check

Do not use brown paper bags for cooking. They are not made to withstand the high cooking temperatures and may burn. Chemicals in the paper also may be transferred to the food.

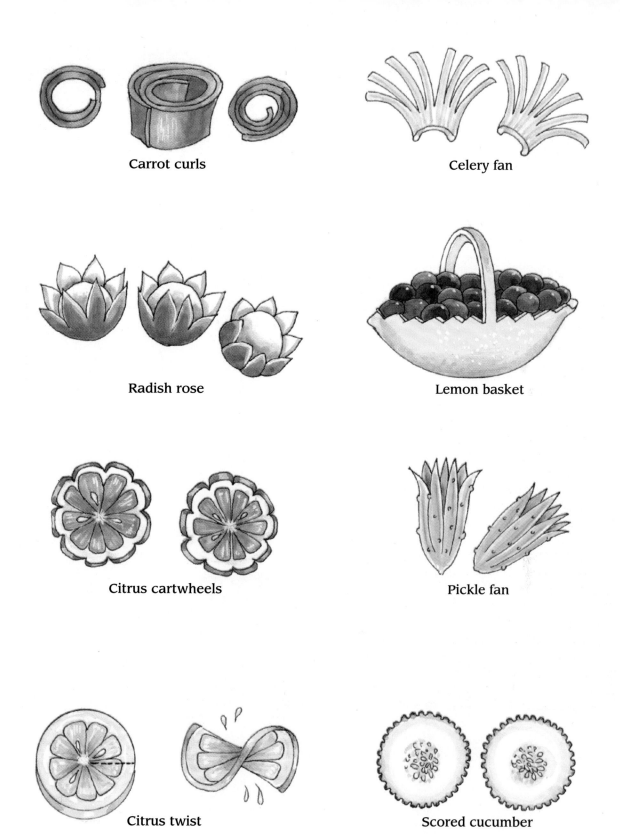

Carrot curls

Celery fan

Radish rose

Lemon basket

Citrus cartwheels

Pickle fan

Citrus twist

Scored cucumber

Garnishes add only a little extra time to food preparation, but a lot of appeal to the foods you serve. How might you use these garnishes?

- **Meat, poultry, and fish dishes.** Use citrus fruit slices, twists, or wedges, a small bunch of grapes, cranberry sauce, spiced crabapples, currant or mint jelly in lemon baskets, sprigs of parsley or fresh herbs, pineapple slices, or olives.
- **Sandwiches**. Use crisp, fresh vegetables, such as scored cucumber slices, carrot curls, celery fans, radish roses, and fruit slices or wedges.
- **Beverages**. Try citrus twists on a skewer, lemon or lime slices slipped on the edge of a glass, marshmallows or peppermint sticks in cocoa, or fruit slices and whole fruits frozen in an ice ring for punch.

Garlic and red peppers are among the vegetables that can add flavor to food mixtures such as stews and marinades. What others can you name?

Section 24.1 Review

RECALL THE FACTS

1. When should herbs and spices be added to hot foods and to cold foods?

2. Briefly explain how to marinate food.

3. Explain how foods are arranged and cooked en papillote.

4. Name one way to garnish each of the following dishes: tomato soup, tossed salad, roasted whole chicken, tuna sandwich, and iced tea.

DISCUSS YOUR IDEAS

5. How can seasoning with herbs and spices replace other methods of flavoring food that are higher in fat and sodium?

APPLY YOUR LEARNING

6. Make a list of herbs and spices your family uses regularly. Create a recipe using some of these herbs and spices. Explain how you would use them and describe the flavor they would give to the foods.

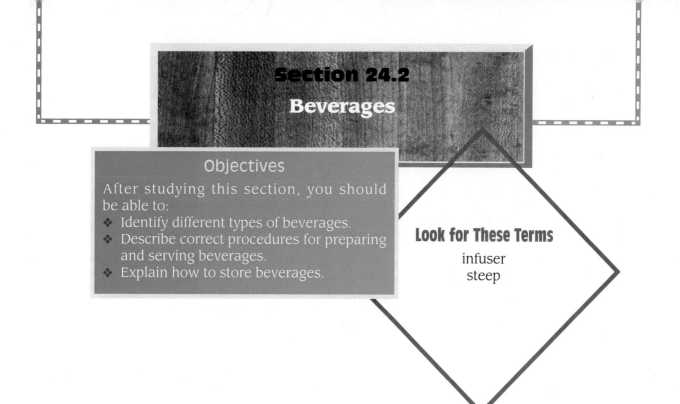

Objectives

After studying this section, you should be able to:

* Identify different types of beverages.
* Describe correct procedures for preparing and serving beverages.
* Explain how to store beverages.

Look for These Terms

infuser
steep

Beverages are refreshing any time of day. No meal is complete without one. Offering guests a beverage is a sign of hospitality. In this section, you will learn about several types of beverages including coffee, tea, and punch.

Coffee

Coffee is brewed from ground coffee beans, which are the seeds from trees grown in South and Central America, Asia, and Africa. Ground coffee can be made from just one variety of coffee beans or a blend of several. Gourmet coffee is more expensive because it is made from costlier beans.

Coffee contains caffeine, a mild stimulant to the nervous system. Most forms of coffee are also available in a decaffeinated (dee-KAFF-in-ay-ted) version.

Instant coffee is brewed coffee that has been dried and ground. It comes either as a powder or freeze-dried crystals, regular or decaffeinated. All you do is add hot water.

Besides regular and gourmet coffee, flavored coffees are also available. Flavors include mocha, vanilla, and assorted spices.

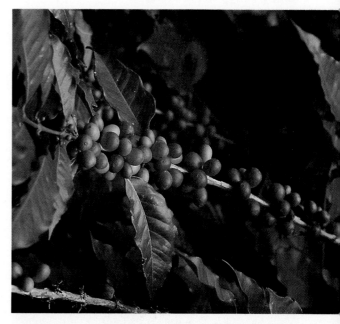

Coffee trees produce berries that turn red when they ripen. Inside each berry are two coffee beans, which are the seeds of the plant.

The type of coffee to buy depends on the way you plan to brew it. Popular coffeemakers include the electric percolator (left), the automatic drip coffeemaker (center), and the nonautomatic drip model.

Buying Coffee

Ground coffee comes in different grinds to suit the brewing method. For example, drip coffee brews quickly, so a fine grind is needed. Percolator coffee takes longer, so it requires a coarser grind. Some coffee manufacturers offer an all-purpose grind that can be used for several brewing methods. Buy the grind recommended for your coffeemaker.

Most ground coffee is sold in vacuum-packed containers. Gourmet shops and many supermarkets also sell coffee beans that can be ground to order. Specialty coffees are sold in bags that are not vacuum-packed.

Storing Coffee

Unopened containers of vacuum-packed coffee can be stored at room temperature for about a year. Once opened, refrigerate fresh coffee, whether ground or whole beans, in an airtight container. It will generally keep in the refrigerator up to two weeks. For longer storage, freeze. Instant coffee can be kept at room temperature.

Making Coffee

The most popular appliance for making coffee is the automatic drip coffeemaker. Most automatic drip coffeemakers have four parts—a water reservoir, a basket that holds a filter and coffee, a carafe that catches the coffee as it brews, and a hotplate which keeps the carafe and coffee warm. Some automatic drip coffeemakers are equipped with timers which can start the brewing cycle at a preset time.

Here are a few popular coffee beverages:

* ***Espresso*** (ehs-SPRESS-oh) is dark, strong coffee made by steaming in a pressure coffeemaker using a specially blended Italian coffee. The surface of the coffee has a thin layer of light-colored froth.
* ***Café au lait*** (kaff-FAY oh-LAY) is a French beverage made with equal parts of hot milk and regular coffee.
* ***Cappuccino*** (kap-oo-CHEE-noh) is the Italian version of café au lait. It is made with espresso coffee and frothy steamed milk or cream. The foamy top is often dusted with cocoa or cinnamon.

An espresso machine uses pressure and steam to produce the dark, frothy beverage.

Automatic drip coffeemakers are easy to use. Just put ground coffee into a filter inside the basket, pour cold water into the reservoir, and turn on the controls. The coffeemaker quickly heats the water which drips through the coffee grounds into the carafe.

How much coffee and water should you use? The final decision depends on your taste preferences. Begin by following the directions that come with the coffeemaker as well as those on the coffee container. If desired, change the amounts to get the strength of coffee you want. Coffeemakers usually have convenient markings on the carafe or sides of the reservoir so you can measure the water easily.

Clean the coffee carafe and basket in hot sudsy water after every use. Coffee contains oils that cling to the inside of the carafe and basket. They can give the next carafe of coffee an unpleasant flavor.

Serving Coffee

Serve coffee piping hot, right after it is made. If coffee is held at a high temperature for too long or reheated, it loses its flavor and aroma.

Coffee can also be served iced. Make double strength coffee and pour it over ice cubes.

Tea

Tea is a beverage made from the leaves of a shrub grown in tropical mountainous areas. Three basic types of tea are produced and used worldwide. *Black tea* is made from leaves that have been oxidized or fermented, which turns them black. Black tea has a dark, rich color and deep hearty flavor. *Green tea* is processed without being oxidized, so the leaves retain their green color. It has a delicate, light green color and a very mild flavor. *Oolong tea* is partly oxidized, so the

Most of the world's tea is grown in Asia. This tea estate is in Japan.

leaves are partly brown and partly green. Its flavor and color are between black and green teas. Tea is sold loose or in teabags.

Tea contains caffeine, although not as much as coffee. It is also available decaffeinated. The same processes are used to decaffeinate tea as coffee.

In addition to plain tea, you can also buy flavored and instant teas. Flavored tea includes fruit, herb, and spice flavors. Instant tea is brewed tea which has been dried and ground to a powder. It is available plain, flavored, and presweetened.

Herb Teas

Herb teas are made from herbs and other plants. They do not contain regular tea and are caffeine-free.

Buying Tea

Because there are so many different varieties, read labels carefully. Be certain you are buying the type and form of tea you want.

The many varieties of tea and herb teas can be purchased loose or in bags. What tea-making utensils are shown here?

Buy herb teas from reliable sources. Most supermarkets carry the major brands. Avoid teas that make health claims, such as weight-loss teas.

Storing Tea

Store tea in an airtight container at room temperature. Keep different flavored teabags in separate containers so the flavors don't intermix. Properly stored, tea will keep up to two years.

Brewing and Serving Tea

Begin by bringing fresh, cold water to a rolling boil. If the water has been standing or reheated, it gives tea a flat taste.

You can use a teapot or brew just one cup of tea. Preheat the pot or cup by rinsing it with hot water. This helps keep tea hot while brewing.

Put the tea or tea bags in the container. To make loose tea easier to use, put it in an **infuser**—a small container with tiny holes that let water in but don't allow the tea leaves to come out. The infuser is as easy to

remove as teabags at the end of the brewing time. As a rule, use one teaspoon of tea (about 5 mL) or one teabag for each cup.

Pour boiling water over the tea. The tea **steeps,** or brews in water just below the boiling point. Follow package directions for brewing time and set a timer. Do not judge the strength of tea by its color since different varieties brew to different colors.

Stir the tea before pouring or drinking to make sure it's uniformly strong. If the brewed tea is too strong, add a little hot water. Tea may be served with milk or lemon and sweetener.

To make iced tea, brew as for hot tea but use fifty percent more tea. That allows for melting ice when the hot tea is poured into ice-filled glasses. For six servings, use nine teabags or nine teaspoons (45 mL) of tea. Steep. Remove tea and pour into ice-filled glasses.

You can also use instant tea to make iced tea. Just follow the directions on the label.

Tea can be served hot or iced. How does the preparation for each differ?

Punch

A punch is generally a mixture of fruit juices and either carbonated beverages, such as ginger ale or seltzer, or tea. It is usually served in a punch bowl. Sherbet, ice cream, or fruit may be added. To serve the punch, ladle it from the bowl into small glasses or cups.

If the punch is to be served cold, combine all liquids except the carbonated beverages ahead of time and chill well. Chill the carbonated beverages separately and add them just before serving.

Fruit is often floated in the bowl as a garnish, the kind depending on the fruit flavors in the punch. Another popular garnish is an ice ring. Besides being decorative, it helps keep the punch cold. The ice ring is usually made with punch or water. Fruit is placed in the ring mold in a decorative design. You can also freeze fruit in ice cubes.

When making punch, mix and chill fruit juices ahead of time to blend flavors. Why should you wait until just before serving to add carbonated beverages?

Other Beverages

As you learned in Section 2.4, water is an essential nutrient. Beverages that can supply your body's need for water include plain water, milk, and fruit juices.

Fruit and vegetable juices are healthful choices because they supply vitamins and minerals as well as water. When shopping, remember that only products labeled "juice" are made of 100 percent juice. Others may contain large amounts of added sugar.

Many carbonated soft drinks are also high in sugar. In "diet" soft drinks, the sugar is replaced with artificial sweeteners and other additives. These beverages do not supply the natural vitamins and minerals of fruit juices.

Bottled specialty waters are popular. There are many different kinds, such as mineral water, spring water, seltzer water, and club soda. They vary in mineral content and flavor. Some are carbonated. Check the list of ingredients on the label.

Milk is not only a nutritious beverage in itself, but is the basis for many other beverages, such as cocoa. For information about milk and cocoa, see Section 18.2.

Section 24.2 Review

RECALL THE FACTS

1. What is decaffeinated coffee?

2. How should coffee be stored?

3. What is the difference between tea and herb tea?

4. What is punch? How is it served?

DISCUSS YOUR IDEAS

5. What are the nutritional drawbacks of coffee, tea, and punch? How do these compare with other beverage choices?

APPLY YOUR LEARNING

6. Look through cookbooks and magazines to find a punch recipe. How might you change the ingredients in this recipe to make it more healthful?

Thinking About the Recipe

Read the recipe for "Fruit Punch" and answer the following questions.

1. How could you serve punch if you didn't have a punch bowl?
2. What liquids and fruits could you use to make an ice ring for the punch?

Fruit Punch

Customary	Ingredients	Metric
6 oz.	Frozen lemonade concentrate, thawed	177 mL
6 oz.	Frozen orange juice concentrate, thawed	177 mL
32 oz.	Tropical fruit punch, canned, chilled	1 L
2 qt.	Ginger ale or lemon-lime soda	2 L

Yield: 32 servings (approximate)

Directions

1. Combine thawed juice concentrates and tropical fruit punch in a half-gallon (2L) pitcher. (Note: Do not put frozen juice concentrate directly into punch bowl—you may crack the bowl.)
2. Pour juice mixture into punch bowl.
3. Add ginger ale or lemon-lime soda and stir the mixture gently.
4. Garnish with citrus fruit slices or an ice ring.
5. Serve chilled.

Nutrition Information

Per serving (approximate): 54 calories, 0 g protein, 14 g carbohydrate, 0 g fat, 0 mg cholesterol, 11 mg sodium

Objectives

After studying this section, you should be able to:

* Identify ways to plan for entertaining.
* Develop menus and organize food preparation and cleanup for entertaining.
* Describe different methods of serving food depending on the occasion.

Look for These Terms

modified English service
service plate
reception

Entertaining is a way of expressing hospitality to people, making them feel welcome and special. Although food is generally served, entertaining involves much more than this.

Entertaining does not have to be elaborate. You can have a successful party with a simple soup-and-salad meal if the atmosphere is right. With planning and organization, entertaining can be just as much fun for the person giving the party as it is for the guests.

Planning for Entertaining

When you think about entertaining, what do you think of? Perhaps you think of a formal dinner party, a meal with a few close friends, a brunch, or even a potluck supper. Whatever the event or occasion, careful planning goes a long way.

Holidays and other special occasions are a perfect time for entertaining. This group of family and friends has gathered to celebrate Tet, the Vietnamese New Year.

Parties are more memorable when both the food and decorations relate to a theme. Besides a Mexican fiesta, what are some other possible themes? What foods and decorations would you choose to go with each?

Informal and Formal Events

Entertaining can be as simple or elaborate as you like. When you begin making your plans, think about the type of occasion. Is it an informal event such as a simple evening party, a family-style dinner with friends, or perhaps a buffet (buh-FAY) meal for a larger number of guests? You may be planning a formal sit-down dinner for a special event such as a birthday or graduation.

Whether the occasion is to be formal or informal affects the menu and the way you will serve food. Think about your skills in entertaining. If this is the first party you are giving, it's probably best to start with a simple, informal event.

Themes and Decorations

After you've decided whether you are having an informal or formal event, decide on a theme for the occasion. Most parties or get-togethers are more fun if they have a theme. A theme is a specific idea on which the occasion is based. Holidays, birthdays, and gradu- ations provide a ready-made theme. Be creative! You might want to choose an interest you and your guests share such as sports or old movies, or an ethnic theme such as a Mexican fiesta. After you have chosen your theme, plan the menu, activities, and decorations to go with it.

A pleasant atmosphere makes a party or meal more enjoyable for everyone. Whether you are serving snacks to your guests from a card table or eating a meal in the dining room, providing attractive decorations makes everyone feel comfortable.

TIPS for Success

Simple Decorations

Here are a few decorating ideas:
* A potted plant on a placemat.
* An arrangement of fresh or silk flowers.
* A grouping of seashells on a wicker mat.
* A basket of fresh fruit or colorful gourds.
* A fresh flower floating in water in a glass bowl beside some candle-holders.

Invitations

As you decide on a list of guests, try to put together a combination of people who are likely to get along and be interesting to one another. Look for a good blend of listeners and talkers. Avoid inviting people that you know don't get along.

For informal events, you will most likely ask your guests in person or by telephone about one week before the event. (Of course, impromptu gatherings are fun, too! Just be sure check with your parents first.)

Formal occasions or larger parties require a written invitation. This will help eliminate any mixups about the time or date. Send your invitations ten days to two weeks before the event is to occur. On your invitation, be sure to include the following information:

❖ The date, location, and time of the event.
❖ The occasion, if there is one.
❖ Your name as host or hostess.
❖ R.S.V.P. and your telephone number. This informs your guests that you would like them to "Reply, please." You might also include a date by which they are to reply so that you can buy the appropriate amount of food.

If, as an invited guest, you are asked asked to R.S.V.P., it is your responsibility to follow through with this request. If you can't reach a person by telephone, send a brief note in the mail.

Menus for Entertaining

Planning food for parties and other special occasions follows the same guidelines as planning meals. Choose a variety of nutritious, attractive foods. If you are planning foods for a special theme, try to choose some foods that are liked by many people. Here are a few guidelines for selecting foods for your menu:

❖ Find out about special food needs or preferences that your guests might have.

Help us celebrate
Westview High Marching Band's
first place trophy!

Please come to a Pizza Party
Saturday, November 9 at 7 p.m.
417 Ridgeway Road

Hosted by Sheila Wilson and Carlos Morales
R.S.V.P. to Sheila (555-9843)
by Thursday, November 7

Does this invitation include all the information a guest would need?

❖ Keep food choices simple. Choose foods that can be prepared ahead of time with a minimum of last-minute preparation. For example, you might want to prepare lasagne as the main course and do all the preparation except baking it the day before. Add a tossed salad, bread, beverage, and perhaps some fruit for dessert.
❖ You might want to select a simple appetizer, such as a dip and crackers or fruit, that your guests can nibble on while you make a few last-minute preparations.

Making a Schedule

After you have planned your meal or refreshments, the next step is to identify the tasks to be accomplished before the event.

You might start with a list organized by catgories such as food shopping and preparation, decorations, set-up, and clean-up. List the tasks in order, beginning with the one that must be done first. Think about ways to accomplish the items on your list efficiently. Some jobs can be done far ahead of the event. Make a special list for things to be done the day before and the day of the event. Cross each item off your list as it is accomplished.

Serving Food

There are several ways to serve food, depending on the type of event, the number of people eating, the time available for serving and eating, the menu, and your personal preference.

Informal Table Service

Informal table service may include several ways to serve food. Your menu and the space you have for serving will affect the method you choose.

Most people want to do something special when they have guests for a meal. Even with informal sit-down meals, you will want to set your table properly. (See pages 292-293.) In addition, you may want to add a bread and butter plate or a salad bowl above the forks on the left side of the cover.

Many people feel most comfortable serving a meal family style. Food is brought to the table in serving dishes and people help themselves. To avoid confusion, all foods should be passed to the right.

If space and tableware is limited, you might want to consider using plate service. As you learned in Section 10.1, this means food is portioned out on individual dinner plates and served to each person at the table. This eliminates the need for serving dishes and makes cleanup easier.

An attractive table setting helps make the meal special.

Formal Service

For formal occasions, there are several ways you might handle serving food. If your guest list is limited to eight people (including yourself), you can easily handle serving the meal yourself. For larger groups, you will need help serving the meal so that all of your guest are served quickly and efficiently.

For serving small groups yourself, use **modified English service.** Dinner plates and the food for the main course are brought to the table in serving dishes and placed in front of the host or hostess. If meat is to be carved, this is done by the person hosting. He or she places the meat and vegetables on the plate and passes it to the right. The first plate is passed down to the person at the end of the table. When all people on the right have been served, those on the left are served.

The salad is often served on individual plates from the kitchen and placed on the table before the guests are seated. Accompaniments, such as rolls and butter, are usually passed at the table.

Formal service for large groups is rarely done at home because additional help is needed to serve the meal. This style of service is often used in fine restaurants, at hotels for banquets, and other formal occasions.

For most formal occasions, the table is set with silver, glassware, and a service plate for the appetizer course. A **service plate** is a large and beautifully decorated plate used only for the first course. It is removed from the table before the main course is served. Food is never put directly on the service plate—it is served in a separate dish and place on the service plate.

As a rule, formal service includes a number of courses, each served separately on clean plates. Flatware is needed for each course. It is not uncommon to have three pieces of flatware on each side of the plate.

Buffet Service

A buffet is an easy, practical way to entertain if you don't have enough seating space at a dining table. For eating space, you can set up card tables or other small snack tables. People can also hold plates of food on their laps.

The prepared food is placed in serving dishes on a large table, kitchen counter, or perhaps on several card tables. When setting up the buffet, stack the plates where you want the guests to begin. After the plates, place the main dish, followed by vegetables, salad, rolls, and butter. The flatware, rolled up in a napkin, should be the last items your guests pick up.

When planning a buffet meal, choose foods that are easy to serve and that do not have to be cut with a knife. This makes the food easier to eat. Casseroles, stir-fries, sandwiches, and salads are good choices. You may want to serve beverages to your guests after they are seated.

Receptions

Receptions are social gatherings usually held to honor a person or an event, such as a wedding anniversary or a graduation. These gatherings are usually formal. Buffet service is most often used to serve food.

A reception table should be organized for the convenience of both servers and guests. This table is set up to handle two serving lines. What is the starting point for each line? Which direction would each line move?

A large table is generally used to serve food at a reception. It is covered with a floor-length tablecloth with an attractive centerpiece placed in the center of the table.

Indicate the starting point at the reception table by where you place the plates. For large groups, divide the table in half lengthwise and offer the same food on both sides of the table. This allows people to move in two lines instead of one.

Types of Foods to Serve

Hot beverages, such as coffee or tea, are generally served at one end of the table while a cool beverage, such as fruit punch, is served at the opposite end. Food choices often include small fancy sandwiches, nut-breads, cheese, crackers, small fruit kabobs, delicate cookies and small pastries, candies, and nuts that are attractively arranged on plates and trays.

When preparing foods for a buffet or reception table, remember to arrange and garnish them attractively. Also be sure to provide appropriate serving utensils.

Section 24.3 Review

RECALL THE FACTS

1. Identify two factors that help determine whether an occasion will be formal or informal.

2. What is one point to remember as you decide on a guest list?

3. Give three guidelines for planning a menu for a party.

4. How should you set up a buffet table for serving food?

DISCUSS YOUR IDEAS

5. Name three foods or dishes that you would include at a buffet and three that you would serve at a formal dinner. What factors influence your choice?

APPLY YOUR LEARNING

6. In small groups, brainstorm a list of themes that might be appropriate for a party for teens. Chose one theme and describe how you would carry it out with invitations, decorations, music, and menu. How would you serve the food?

Objectives

After studying this section, you should be able to:

- Describe how to choose and pack picnic foods.
- Identify ways to safely cook foods outdoors.
- Identify foods for outdoor cooking.

Look for This Term

micro-grill

Outdoor cooking is a favorite way to prepare meals for many families. It's a way for family and friends to gather and enjoy the out-of-doors while preparing and eating a meal.

You can apply many of the food preparation skills that you have already learned to outdoor cooking. Keeping food at safe temperatures is especially important when cooking and eating outdoors.

Picnic Foods

The food you choose for a picnic may depend on how far you have to travel. Avoid taking hot cooked food unless you know it will be eaten within two hours. For safety, keep hot foods in an insulated container.

Cooking foods on a grill at the picnic site is often safer than transporting hot food. Cook raw foods, like hamburgers, or warm up cold cooked foods. For safety, don't partially cook food at home and then finish cooking it at the picnic.

Outdoor cooking seems to add a special flavor to foods. What are some other reasons for its popularity?

A picnic can have almost any kind of food, as long as it is properly packed and kept at a safe temperature. How would you pack the foods shown here?

Packing the Picnic

If you're traveling to the picnic area, make a list of everything you will need, including food, tableware, and cleanup equipment. Don't forget such as premoistened cleaning wipes, can and bottle openers, a paring knife, paper towels, trash bags, and extra plastic bags to bring back dirty utensils. As you pack for the picnic, check off each item on your list.

Be sure to follow the same safety and sanitation precautions given for packing a lunch in Section 20.1, page 525.

Pack nonperishable items in a basket or any other container. Use an insulated cooler for chilled food. To keep the food chilled, put ice cubes in the cooler or a reusable frozen gel pack. Frozen food, such as sandwiches or boxed frozen juices, will help keep other food cold.

If you're taking raw meat or poultry to cook at the picnic, pack it in a separate cooler to prevent cross-contamination with ready-to-eat foods.

When packing the cooler and picnic basket, put the last item you will need on the bottom and the first one on top. To pack the cooler, start with the end of the meal, so put the dessert on the bottom (if it's fragile, put it

in a crush-resistant plastic container first). Packing food in this order eliminates the need to unpack the whole cooler every time you want something. Don't remove food from the cooler until you need it.

At the picnic site, keep the cooler in a cool, shady spot. Keep the cover on the cooler at all times. Don't leave the cooler in the sun, a hot car, or a car trunk. Even an insulated cooler won't stay cool under such conditions.

Buying an Outdoor Grill

When buying an outdoor grill, look for features that meet your needs and provide for safety during cooking. Here are some things to think about:

* **Consider durability.** Look for a grill made of heavy-gauge metal that will withstand regular use over a period of time.
* **Consider stability.** The body of the grill should be securely attached to sturdy, well-balanced legs.
* **Consider cost.** Buy the best quality for the money you have available and the amount of outdoor cooking you plan to do.
* **Consider size.** Buy a size that provides enough cooking area to meet your needs.

Outdoor Cooking

Grilling food outdoors is also called barbecuing. Before barbecuing, be sure you have the proper tools and understand how to use an outdoor grill safely.

Safety First

The simplest grill is a round, kettle-shaped metal container that holds burning charcoal. It is topped with a wire grid for holding food above the hot coals. There are many other kinds of grills that vary in price. Some cook with bottled (propane) gas instead of charcoal.

All grills cook by the same principle. Heat radiates upward and cooks the food held on the grid above. Grilling is a dry-heat method of cooking, similar to broiling. Cooking time depends on the kind and thickness of food and the distance from the heat.

In a basic grill, hot coals provide radiant heat that cooks the food above it.

Follow the directions in the owner's manual for using the grill. Methods vary, depending on the kind of grill you have.

Here are some guidelines for safe grilling:

❖ Use fireproof gloves and heavy-duty grilling tools with long handles. The long handles keep your hands away from the intense heat.

❖ Set the grill on a level surface so it won't tip over. Keep it away from flammables such as buildings, shrubs, and trash containers.

❖ Use a clean grill. Before using it, remove baked-on grime from the inside and the grid with a hard-bristled brush. Baked-on food and grease can cause flames to flare up when you light the fire.

❖ Apply enough of the starter fluid (if you use it) before striking the match. Never add more fluid after the coals have been lighted—it might explode.

❖ Never use kerosene or gasoline as firestarters—they can explode.

❖ Fat and meat juices dripping on coals can cause flare-ups. If that happens, raise the grid, cover the grill, or use a long-handled tool to spread the coals apart. You can also remove the food from the grid and use a pump-spray bottle filled with water to spray a mist on the flare-up. Then put the food back on the grid. Don't pour water on the burning charcoal—it might explode.

Use the proper tools to keep your cookouts safe.

❖ When you have finished grilling, let the coals burn out until only ashes are left. Douse the ashes with water and then put them in a metal trash can. Do not dump hot coals or ashes on the ground. They damage the grass and can even start a fire.

Food for Grilling

Grilling is used mainly for tender cuts of meat and poultry. Cook them thoroughly, turning after half the cooking time.

Fish is also easy to grill. Place fillets skin-side down on a lightly oiled grid so they do not stick. Grill until fish flakes easily. Thick pieces may have to be turned.

Most fruits and vegetables can be grilled. Thread small pieces of fruits and vegetables on metal skewers. Brush them lightly with melted butter or a basting sauce. Place them on the grid. Turn the skewers frequently until foods are hot and lightly browned.

Section 24.4 Review

RECALL THE FACTS

1. Give three safety tips for choosing and preparing picnic foods.

2. In what order should foods be packed in a cooler? Why?

3. Give four guidelines for safe grilling.

4. Briefly explain how to grill fruits and vegetables.

DISCUSS YOUR IDEAS

5. What are some advantages of outdoor cooking?

6. What effect might local government regulations have on outdoor cooking in your area?

APPLY YOUR LEARNING

7. Bring to class a favorite recipe for indoor cooking. Explain how it might be modified for preparation on a grill.

Kabobs are a popular food for grilling.

Objectives

After studying this section, you should be able to:
- ❖ Identify ways to safely freeze fruits and vegetables while retaining quality and nutrients.
- ❖ Explain how to safely can fruits and vegetables at home.
- ❖ List the benefits of drying foods at home.

Look for These Terms

antioxidant
blanched
processing
raw pack
hot pack
headspace

Preserving food at home serves several purposes for some families. For many families, it's a way to stretch the food budget. In other families, it's a way to spend time working together and have some fun while preserving food at the same time. People who garden usually preserve some of the food they have grown.

There are several ways to preserve food at home, including freezing, canning, and drying. Whichever method you use depends on personal preference and the equipment you have available.

If you do not grow your own food, you may be able to buy seasonal foods at lower rates and save money. Farmers often have lower prices for fruits and vegetables that people pick themselves. Stores may have specials on locally grown produce.

Always use ripe, high quality food. At best, freezing and canning do not improve the quality of the food. Buy only the amount you can process in the time you have available. Wash the food carefully and prepare it according to recipe directions, keeping cleanliness and sanitation in mind.

Why do people preserve foods at home? One reason might be to take advantage of low-priced, high-quality fruits and vegetables found at a farmer's market. What are some others?

Freezing Fresh Fruits and Vegetables

In Section 7.4, you read about freezing as a method for storing food. Follow those directions for packing, labeling, and freezing.

Freezing Fruits

Most fruits can be frozen. Pears, oranges, and bananas do not freeze well. Applesauce freezes better than apples.

Before freezing fresh fruits, enzyme activity must be stopped. Since enzymes need oxygen, cutting off the oxygen supply stops enzyme activity. Ascorbic acid is an **antioxidant**—a substance which slows down enzyme activity. It is used for fresh fruits that darken. Those that do not darken have enough natural ascorbic acid. Fruits can also be packed in syrup or water to eliminate the oxygen supply, but this limits the way they can be used.

❖ **Dry-pack plain.** Put prepared fruit on a cookie sheet, leaving space in between the pieces. Use this method for fruits that do not darken, such as most berries, melons, pineapple, and cherries. Freeze. Package food pieces when solidly frozen.

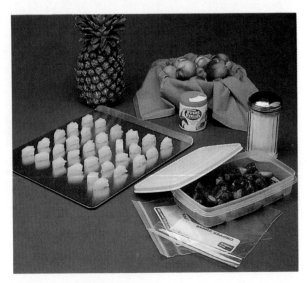

What freezing method is being used for each of these kinds of fruits? Why?

❖ **Dry-pack with ascorbic acid.** Sprinkle fruit with a ready-prepared ascorbic acid mixture according to package directions. Use for fruits that darken, such as apples, figs, peaches, nectarines, and plums. Freeze as directed for "Dry-pack plain."
❖ **Sugar-packed fruits.** Toss fruits in sugar until they are well coated. Pack in containers and freeze. Use this method whenever you want sweetened fruits or fruits in syrup to use as a sauce. When fruits defrost, their juices combine with the sugar to form a sweet syrup.

Freezing Vegetables

Vegetables must be **blanched**, or pre-cooked, to kill enzymes. Tomatoes do not need to be blanched. Work with 1 pound (500 g) of vegetables at a time.

To blanch vegetables, you will need the following items: a large pan of boiling water; about a gallon (4 L) of water to blanch 1 pound (500 g) of vegetables; a large strainer to hold the vegetables while blanching; a large pan of ice water; a supply of ice cubes; and clean, dry towels for draining vegetables.

Put the prepared vegetables into the strainer and immerse them in boiling water. Allow the water to return to a rolling boil and begin timing the vegetables. Timing depends on the type and size of vegetable pieces. The larger the pieces, the longer they must blanch. Follow the time recommended in a blanching chart.

When the time is up, remove the strainer of vegetables and plunge them into cold water until completely cooled. Be sure the water remains ice cold. Drain the vegetables on clean, dry towels and pat dry. Pack them into containers and freeze.

Vegetables may also be blanched in a microwave oven. Use the same method as for microwaving vegetables. Blanching times are generally similar to those for top-of-the-range blanching.

Canning Fruits and Vegetables

Before canning, make sure you have up-to-date recipes, instructions, and equipment. Canning methods have changed in recent years to prevent serious food-borne illness. A reliable source of information is your local cooperative extension service.

Follow the recipe directions and do not take shortcuts or change recipes. Sugar and salt in recipes may act as preservatives. If you want low-sugar or low-sodium foods, look for that type of recipe.

Jars and Lids

Only use jars made for home canning. Be sure they are all perfect. Discard any that have cracks or chips that might keep the lids from sealing tightly.

Use two-piece metal covers, which combine a flat lid with a screw band. The lid is used only once. The band may be reused. Follow the manufacturers' directions for preparing the covers. Do not use one-piece covers that seal with separate rubber rings, such as glass or metal with a porcelain lining. They do not seal properly.

If filled jars are to be heated more than 10 minutes, they do not need to be sterilized before packing the food. Others should be sterilized. Follow the recipe directions.

Processing the Food

When canning, the food is heated in specific ways to kill enzymes and harmful microorganisms. This is called **processing** food. Two different heating methods are used. *Water bath canning* is used for high-acid foods such as fruits and most tomatoes.

Metal Screw Band

Metal Lid With Sealing Compound

Seals Here

Two-piece metal covers provide a tight, safe seal for home-canned goods.

Home economists from the local cooperative extension service can provide information about home canning.

Acid protects canned food against the growth of harmful microorganisms. Low-acid foods, such as all vegetables, require *pressure canning* to be safe. A pressure canner is like a pressure cooker, only larger. It heats foods under pressure to temperatures above the boiling point to kill harmful microorganisms.

There are several methods you can use to pack the jars for processing. To **raw pack** jars, place raw foods into the jars and then pour in hot syrup, water, or juice. To **hot pack** foods, heat the food in liquid first, then pack it into the jars.

When packing jars, leave about 1/2 to 1 inch (1.3 to 2.5 cm) **headspace**, the space between the top of the food and the rim of the jar, for the food to expand. Run a spatula between the food and the jar to remove air bubbles. Wipe the jar top clean. Apply the covers. Screw the metal band on tightly by hand. Process the jars using one of the recommended processing methods. Do not process canned food in conventional or microwave ovens.

❖ *Canning fruits*. After raw packing or hot packing fruits into jars, process the jars in a boiling water bath canner for the time directed on recipe. The canner is a large, covered pot, with a rack to hold the jars.

A pressure canner contains a rack to hold jars, a steam-tight cover, a safety release valve, and a pressure gauge which measures accurate pressure during processing. To use a pressure canner safely:

❖ Read the manufacturer's directions for using the canner *carefully*.

❖ Process foods at the pressure indicated in the instructions for each type of food.

❖ Make sure the cover of the canner is fastened securely to avoid injuries.

❖ When the processing time is over, remove the pressure canner from the heat and allow it to cool until the pressure gauge returns to zero pressure. Open the safety release. If no steam escapes, the pressure is down and the canner can be safely opened. *Do not attempt opening the canner until the pressure is down and no steam escapes from the canner. Failure to do this could result in serious injury.*

A pressure canner heats foods to temperatures higher than 212°F (100°C). It is used for low-acid foods, such as vegetables.

Many people enjoy canning their own fruits, vegetables, and homemade jellies as a hobby. State and local fairs often give prizes for the best results.

❖ **Jams and fruit spreads:** Fill the jars with the prepared jam or fruit spread and apply the two-part covers. Process them in the boiling water bath canner for the time specified in the recipe. Do not seal jars with paraffin—it does not make a tight seal.

❖ **Canning vegetables:** After raw packing or hot packing the jars with vegetables, process the jars in a pressure canner.

After processing, let the jars cool on a rack or clean dish towel away from drafts until completely cool, usually about 12 hours.

Check the covers to make sure they have sealed. Press the center of the cover or tap it with a spoon. The cover should stay down and give a clear, ringing sound when tapped. If the jar has not sealed, reprocess or remove the food and refrigerate or freeze it.

Store home-canned foods in a clean, cool, dry place. Before tasting or using home-canned vegetables, boil them for 10 to 15 minutes to be certain that any harmful microorganisms are destroyed.

Drying Food

Drying food at home is a time-consuming process that requires special equipment. Most people find it easier to buy dried foods. Sun-dried tomatoes, for example, are popular. However, sun drying requires both a high temperature and a dry climate, which is difficult to find in the United States.

The easiest way to dry foods at home is with the use of a food dehydrator. A food dehydrator is similar in size, shape, and cost to a microwave oven. However, it functions much differently. Most food dehydrators have a 24-hour timer and an adjustable thermostat which allows you to dry foods between 90°F and 155°F (32°C and 68°C). Follow the manufacturer's directions for drying times and temperatures.

Foods such as fruits and vegetables, granola, and beef jerky can be dried easily at home. By taking advantage of lower seasonal prices on fruits and vegetables, you can save money, too.

Food dehydrators make it easy to dry fruits and vegetables at home.

Dried foods are convenient to store and make delicious snacks. They are especially popular with hikers because they are a lightweight, nutritious source of energy.

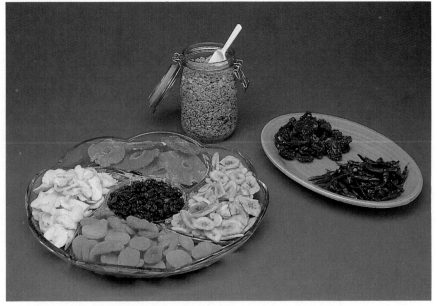

Section 24.5 Review

RECALL THE FACTS

1. Briefly explain why and how vegetables are blanched.

2. Give four guidelines for using a pressure canner safely.

3. What should you do with food in a jar that has not sealed?

4. Name two foods that can be easily dried at home.

DISCUSS YOUR IDEAS

5. Why do you think preserving food at home has remained popular even with today's busy lifestyles?

APPLY YOUR LEARNING

6. Brainstorm a list of all the frozen, canned, and dried products your family uses regularly. Identify those that you might preserve at home. Why might it be impractical or unwise to preserve the others at home?

CAREER PROFILE

Eugenia Snyder
Wedding Cake
Baker

Current position:

"I'm a baker specializing in wedding cakes."

Responsibilities:

"After helping customers pick out the right kind of cake to match their wedding, I bake the cake, decorate it, and deliver it to the reception site."

Skills:

"To be successful in this career, it helps to have some artistic ability. You also must be able to communicate with people and manage your own finances."

Education:

"I have a high school diploma and previous experience as a cook and baker. I took cake decorating classes to learn how to create the 'special effects' that are so important to wedding cakes. I've also taken a few accounting classes."

Typical day on the job:

"Most of my days are divided between preparing cakes and meeting with new customers. I also spend time ordering supplies and cleaning up the kitchen."

Favorite part of the job:

"I've always thought the wedding cake was an important part of any wedding reception, and I find a lot of pleasure in contributing to the bride and groom's special day."

- Does Eugenia seem to have the skills necessary for her job? Why or why not?
- What parts of Eugenia's job do you think you might find interesting? Why?

671

CHAPTER 24 REVIEW

Summary

Section 24.1
Creative Techniques: You can add flavor to foods with seasonings such as herbs, spices, condiments, and marinades. Cooking foods *en papillote* allows the flavor of several foods to blend in a sealed paper package. Garnishes are colorful bits of food that complement a dish's appearance and texture.

Section 24.2
Beverages: Coffee and tea come in several different varieties and are easy to prepare. Punch is a mixture of fruit juices and carbonated beverages or tea.

Section 24.3
Entertaining: Good planning helps make any occasion, whether formal or informal, a success. When you plan, consider the theme, decorations, invitations, and menu. Options for serving the food include modified English service, formal service, and buffet service. Receptions are usually formal gatherings at which buffet service is used.

Section 24.4
Outdoor Meals: Safety is especially important when planning and preparing outdoor meals. Pack foods with care and follow rules for safe grilling. Meats, fish, and fruits and vegetables can all be successfully grilled.

Section 24.5
Preserving Food at Home: When freezing fruits and vegetables, take steps to stop enzyme activity. To can safely, use up-to-date recipes and equipment and follow recipe instructions exactly. Some foods can be dried at home with a food dehydrator.

REVIEWING FACTS

1. Identify the three basic ingredients in a marinade and the purpose of each one. (24.1)

2. Give two reasons for not using brown paper bags for cooking foods *en papillote*. (24.1)

3. Identify the four basic parts of a coffeemaker. (24.2)

4. Compare the three basic types of tea for taste and appearance. What accounts for their differences? (24.2)

5. Give four suggestions for making a schedule of things to do when organizing a party. (24.3)

6. Describe modified English service. (24.3)

7. Give two guidelines for packing chilled food in a cooler. (24.4)

8. Explain how to handle grill flare-ups. (24.4)

9. Describe two differences between the dry-pack plain and sugar-pack methods of freezing fruits. (24.5)

10. Briefly describe how to prepare raw packed and hot packed jars for processing. (24.5)

LEARNING BY DOING

1. ***Foods lab:*** Create your own herb or spice blend or marinade. Experiment with different combinations and proportions of seasonings. Prepare a recipe using your blend or marinade. (24.1)

2. ***Demonstration:*** Design and demonstrate for the class the arrangement of two different table settings: one for a six-year-old's birthday party, the other for a formal dinner. Explain the differences between the two and the reasons for your selections. (24.3)

3. **Demonstration:** Demonstrate safe grilling practices. Include such things as using utensils properly, starting the fire, preparing different foods on the grill, cleaning up after grilling, and handling flare-ups. (24.4)

4. **Food science lab:** Blanche and freeze green beans. Freeze another batch without blanching. After one week, thaw and compare the two packages' appearance and texture. Cook the beans and compare their taste. How do you explain your findings? (24.5)

THINKING CRITICALLY

1. **Forming hypotheses:** Why do you think dried herbs are more potent than fresh ones? (24.1)

2. **Drawing conclusions:** Why are carbonated beverages added to punch mixtures just before serving? (24.2)

3. **Recognizing alternatives:** Suppose you wanted to host a sit-down dinner but had limited space. How might you creatively use the space available to seat your guests? (24.3)

4. **Recognizing fallacies:** You are cleaning up after a picnic with friends. One of your friends says you can leave your dirty paper plates at the picnic site, since paper is biodegradable. Do you agree? Explain your answer. (24.4)

5. **Forming hypotheses:** Why do you think fruits such as oranges and bananas do not freeze well? (24.5)

MAKING DECISIONS AND SOLVING PROBLEMS

What Would You Do?

1. You are doing the grocery shopping for a friend. He has written "tea" on his shopping list, but he hasn't specified any particular kind. (24.2)

2. Some of the guests at your dinner party do not seem to be enjoying themselves. They don't eat or speak much and generally seem uncomfortable. (24.3)

3. You have several items to pack in your cooler for a picnic for yourself and three family members: a large container of ham salad for sandwiches; a six-pack of soda; a chunk of cheese; a chocolate cake; and ice for the drinks. As you pack, however, you realize that there is not enough room in the cooler for everything. (24.4)

LINKING YOUR STUDIES

1. **Social studies:** Choose five different herbs or spices and find out where they are commonly grown. Make a display using a world map identifying the herb or spice, the region in which it is produced, and the geographic conditions that help it grow there. (24.1)

2. **Science:** Research the latest findings on the possible effects of caffeine on health. Summarize your findings in a brief report. (25.2)

3. **Fine arts:** From a library's music collection or your own, select music that would provide an enjoyable accompaniment to the following meals: a seven-year-old's birthday party; a neighborhood potluck dinner; an elegant anniversary dinner. (24.3)

4. **Science:** Find more information about one of the chemical processes involved in preserving food at home, such as oxidation, the action of enzymes, or dehydration. If possible, set up an experiment or other demonstration to illustrate the principles involved. (24.5)

CHAPTER 25

Careers in Food and Nutrition

Section 25.1
Career Opportunities

Objectives

After studying this section, you should be able to:

❖ Identify career opportunities in food and nutrition.

❖ Describe the training and education needed for various careers.

Look for These Terms

career
entry-level job
career ladder
entrepreneur

Carrie had always enjoyed preparing food for her family and friends. When she entered high school, she thought she might like to become a chef or a baker. After a few home economics courses, she discovered her opportunities in the foods area were even more varied. She could also choose from a career in food science, research and development, or communications, to name just a few. After thinking about her skills and interests, Carrie set herself a new goal. She decided she wanted to develop low-fat recipes for a large food corporation.

Thinking About Careers

Like Carrie, you can prepare for a career in the food and nutrition field. Now is the time to explore your opportunities, to learn about training requirements, and to develop good work habits.

A **career** is a profession or a life's work within a certain field. It usually begins with an **entry-level job,** one that requires little or no experience. These jobs often lead to better paying jobs with more responsibility.

An interest in food that starts as a hobby could someday turn into a career.

TIPS for Success

Choosing a Career

These guidelines can help you choose a career that you will enjoy and do well in:

❖ **Think about the classes and activities you enjoy.** Why do you like them?

❖ **List your skills and talents.** Do any point toward a specific career you might enjoy?

❖ **Identify your values.** They can direct you toward a career area.

❖ **Work in community service and part-time jobs.** Even though they may not be in the career area that interests you, they can provide you with valuable information about yourself, your abilities, and your preferences.

Many entry-level jobs are available in the food service industry. Employees who show motivation and pride in their work have a better chance of moving up to higher-paying jobs.

Employees advance in a career by mastering the skills needed for their job and showing they are qualified to take on new responsibilities. Many seek additional education or training throughout their lives to further their career.

Career Areas

A recent study on job growth for the coming years predicted great expansion in service industries, including food and nutrition. The job outlook for this field is bright. More people are eating out. Consumers are more interested in the relationship between food and health. The growing world population and other global factors make producing and utilizing quality food efficiently more important than ever. All this means a growing demand for service and information.

Here is a summary of some of the careers in food and nutrition.

Food Service

The food service industry includes all aspects of preparing and serving food for the public. It is expected to create more new jobs than any other retail industry in the next decade.

Jobs in food service can vary from serving food, to developing recipes, to merchandising food products. They are usually available in every part of the country. If you like to travel, you might even consider food service jobs with cruise lines or airlines, or even in different countries.

Educational requirements vary, depending on the job you want. Part-time, entry-level jobs are often a good start. Food preparation classes in high school can also provide a valuable foundation. For more training, consider vocational schools, junior or community colleges, and four-year colleges and universities. Many companies offer on-the-job training to help employees advance.

As a rule, more education and training allows you to start higher on the **career ladder**—a series of jobs through which a person can advance in a career. Food service offers many different career ladders. One is shown on this page.

Brent started working in a restaurant bussing tables. Through hard work and study, he moved up the ladder to become assistant manager. His goal is to become a manager.

Food service requires certain personal traits. Employees must enjoy and be able to work successfully with people. They must be willing to do their share as part of a team. Producing quality food on schedule can mean hard work and long hours. Good health, enthusiasm, ambition, and a sense of humor are essential. So are good work habits, such as punctuality and the ability to follow directions and accept criticism.

Having a long-range goal, such as becoming an executive chef, can help you plan your career. An entry-level job, such as kitchen helper, is often the first step. From there, you can work your way up the career ladder. Each promotion takes you a step closer to your long-term goal.

Home Economics

Home economics—called human ecology or family studies at some universities—involves using knowledge and skills to solve problems and make decisions about the home and family. Home economists with degrees in food and nutrition have many career options in addition to food service, including:

❖ *Teaching.* Home economists may teach in schools, colleges, and universities. They may teach classes ranging from nutrition to ethnic foods. Nutritionists may work for county or regional extension services, teaching consumers about food preparation and related topics. They are also needed by other government agencies and health organizations to teach consumers how to make wise food choices.

- ❖ **Communication.** This involves communicating information to the public through television, magazines, books, and newspapers. People with strong communication skills are needed to help write speeches, articles, and advertisements about food products and services. Food stylists create attractive arrangements of foods for photographs. Employers include food producers, manufacturers, government agencies, and trade associations.
- ❖ **Research and development.** Home economists help develop new products and appliances in test kitchens or research laboratories. They may work for universities, food producers, appliance manufacturers, or the government.

Jobs in home economics require at least a bachelor's degree. Some, such as teaching, research, and management, require higher degrees. Study and experience in related fields also helps. Home economists in communications, for example, might have a background in journalism or public relations.

Food Science

Food science is the study of the physical, chemical, and microbiological makeup of food. Food scientists develop food products and new ways to process and package them. They also test foods and beverages for quality and purity to make sure they meet company standards and federal food laws.

Food scientists are generally employed by the food processing industry. They may work in laboratories, test kitchens, or on the production line. The many careers in food science include basic research, product development, quality control, and sales.

Food scientists need at least a bachelor's degree with a major in food science, food engineering, or food technology. Higher degrees are needed for research and management jobs.

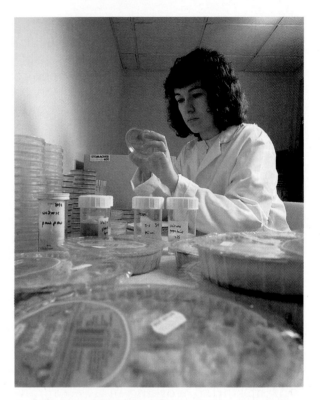

A college education can lead to a rewarding career as a food scientist or a home economist in research and development.

Dietetics

A dietitian (die-uh-TISH-en) is a professional who is trained in the principles of food and nutrition. Dietitians may work for large institutions such as hospitals, health maintenance organizations, company cafeterias, and food service companies. They help develop special diets and counsel groups or individuals in making wise food choices.

Dietitians must have a bachelor's degree in food and nutrition. They must then serve a one-year internship at an approved institution. A registered dietitian (RD) must pass the Registration Examination for Dietitians. Some community colleges offer two-year programs for dietetic technicians, who work as assistants to dietitians.

Food Production, Processing, and Marketing

A vast network of people is involved in producing food and getting it to the marketplace. Career opportunities vary from hydroponic farming to supermarket management.

Training and education also varies, but a combination of experience and formal education is best. Farmers, for example, need to know how to do the everyday work on the farm itself, but can also benefit from studies in related topics such as soil conservation and plant and animal genetics. A bakery owner must have experience in preparing the food as well and knowledge about business management, marketing techniques, and tax laws.

Owning a business takes hard work, but the results are worthwhile. Entrepreneurs feel the special satisfaction of building their own success. They also contribute to the strength and growth of their communities.

Entrepreneurship

Many people dream of owning their own business. A person who runs his or her own business is called an **entrepreneur** (on-truh-pruh-NOOR). Successful entrepreneurs share certain personal qualities. They are willing to work hard and take risks. They can make sound decisions, are well organized, and understand basic business management practices. Opportunities for entrepreneurs in food and nutrition include catering; running a snack shop; home delivery from restaurants or supermarkets; nutrition consultation; and preparing and selling food, such as homemade baked goods.

Entrepreneurs sometimes invest in a franchise, which allows them to own a business with an established name and guidelines. Some fast food restaurants are franchises. Not all franchises are reliable, however, so potential owners should investigate carefully before buying one. Also, a franchise cannot guarantee success. It's up to the businessperson to provide the skills and commitment needed to succeed.

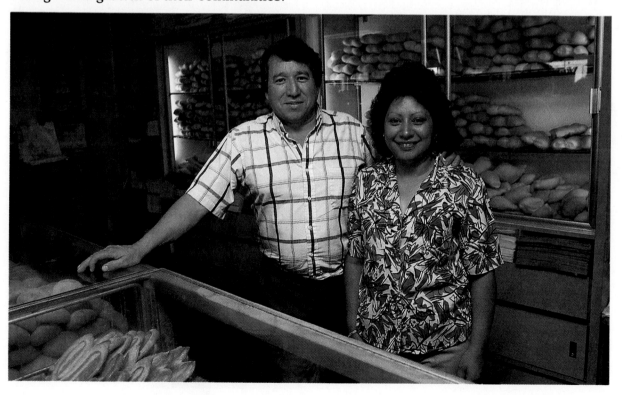

Sources of Food and Nutrition Career Information

The Council on Hotel, Restaurant, and Institutional Education (CHRIE)
1200 17th Street NW
Washington, DC 20036

American Home Economics Association
1555 King Street
Alexandria, VA 22314

The Institute of Food Technologists
221 N. LaSalle Street
Chicago, IL 60601

The American Dietetic Association
216 W. Jackson Blvd., Suite 800
Chicago, IL 60601

U.S. Department of Agriculture
14th Street and Independence Ave. SW
Washington, DC 20250

Small Business Administration
409 3rd Street SW
Washington, DC 20416

■ Section 25.1 Review ■

RECALL THE FACTS

1. List four types of education or training for a career in food service.

2. Name three food and nutrition career options other than food service.

3. Briefly describe the educational and training requirements for registered dietitians.

4. Name three business opportunities for entrepreneurs.

DISCUSS YOUR IDEAS

5. Discuss what social trends contribute to the increased need for workers in food and nutrition.

APPLY YOUR LEARNING

6. Choose one food that you enjoy. List as many workers as you can that are involved in producing, processing, and distributing that food.

A culinary arts school is just one example of the opportunities for education and training in the foods area.

Objectives

After studying this section, you should be able to:
- ❖ Identify qualities of successful workers.
- ❖ Describe the steps in applying for a job.
- ❖ Give guidelines for job interviews.
- ❖ Explain how to handle leaving a job.

Look for These Terms

networking
resumé
references

Even if you haven't decided on a career, having a part-time or summer job offers several advantages. Finding and keeping a job teaches responsibility and increases self-confidence. It sharpens your management and decision-making skills. It also lets you enjoy the benefits of earning a paycheck. In addition, working can also help you decide what type of career you might enjoy.

Qualities of Successful Workers

Recent surveys have identified some of the qualities employers look for. You can develop these skills while still in school:
- ❖ **Communication skills.** These include writing, reading, speaking, and listening. Employees often write reports. They must read and understand company bulletins and guidelines. They must listen carefully to instructions they receive or to customer requests.

Learning how to communicate effectively and becoming familiar with computers are two ways you can prepare for a career while you are still in school.

- ❖ **Computer skills.** Most jobs involve the use of a computer in some way. In many restaurants, for instance, servers use computers to send customer food orders to the kitchen.
- ❖ **Critical thinking and problem solving.** Employees who can analyze situations and suggest solutions to problems are valued by their employers.
- ❖ **Positive attitude.** Employees must be enthusiastic about their work and interested in what they do.
- ❖ **Math skills.** Even though computers and calculators are widely used, employees must understand basic math. They may have to make change, keep a time schedule, or solve math-related problems.
- ❖ **Teamwork and self-responsibility.** Employees must be willing to do their share, and more if necessary. They must work well with others to achieve common goals.
- ❖ **Ability to learn.** New technology will continue to cause rapid changes in the workplace. That means learning new skills will be a lifelong process for employees.

Develop good learning and work habits while you are still in school. Volunteer work, school projects, and social activities can provide opportunities to develop essential skills.

Looking for a Job

As a student, right now you may be looking for only a part-time job. Even so, the experience of finding and keeping a job will be valuable to you personally as well as professionally.

There are many ways to find a job. Check with your school employment or counseling office. Read the newspaper want ads and community bulletin boards. You can also contact employers directly and ask if they have any job openings.

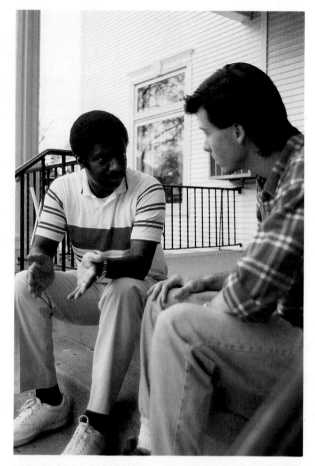

Networking can help you find a job. Ask teachers, neighbors, and friends for advice. The more people who know you are looking for employment, the more likely you will be to find out about any openings.

Another idea helpful to job hunting is **networking.** This means making connections among people who can provide information about job openings. When Anton began exploring careers in food science, his network included his home economics teacher, a nutritionist at the county extension office, and the writer of a foods column in the local newspaper. Remember, however, that other people can only help you find a job. Getting the job and keeping it are up to you.

Applying for a Job

Your next step is to apply for a specific job. This usually involves filling out a job application form or writing a letter of application.

A job application form requires basic personal information, such as your age and home address, and information about your education and experience. Remember to print your answers in ink, answering all questions as concisely as possible.

A letter of application serves the same purpose as an application form. However, you have a choice of what information to include. Include basic personal information plus any other helpful facts about yourself. As with the application form, focus on those things that will demonstrate your suitability for the job you are seeking. For example, being editor of the school yearbook shows that you can work well with people and delegate authority. Good grades in food science courses indicate your knowledge of foods and related fields.

For some jobs, you may need to submit a **resumé** (REH-zoo-may). This is a written summary of your past experience, skills, and achievements that are related to the job you seek. A chronological resumé lists jobs and experiences from most recent to the earliest. A functional resumé describes your skills and accomplishments as they relate to the job you are seeking. A sample of a functional resumé is shown on this page.

Although a resumé is more detailed than a letter of application, it should be brief—not more than one page—and contain only relevant information. If you have no previous work experience, don't mention it. Focus instead on those activities that show your skills and abilities.

When applying for a job, you may be asked for **references.** These are people who know you well and can give information about your previous work or your character. A teacher or former work supervisor might be good references. Be sure to ask them first. You will need their names, addresses, and phone numbers.

Employers are prohibited by law from asking, in person or on application forms, for certain information such as your race, gender, religion, or marital status. They may not ask questions about some aspects of your personal or past life.

An application form, letter of application, and resumé all demonstrate your ability to communicate in writing. All three should be carefully thought out and neatly written or typed. Be sure the grammar and punctuation are correct. Remember that this will be your potential employer's first—and possibly only—impression of you as a worker. Make it a positive one.

SAMPLE RESUME

Ginny Arnold   Social Security: 000-00-000
800 Southwest Street
Anytown, US 11111
Home Phone: (000)000-000

OBJECTIVE: Kitchen helper, part-time.

QUALIFICATIONS:
- Received high grades in food preparation class.
- Have ability to organize work.
- Know how to use a computer.
- Would like to become a chef.

EXPERIENCE:
- Help with Friday night suppers at church.
- Organized successful pancake breakfast for parents, sponsored by Home Economics Club.
- Worked at the Community Center soup kitchen, helping with meals for homeless.

EDUCATION:
- Junior at Anytown High School.
- Currently taking advanced food preparation class.

A well-written resumé is brief, but provides the information that employers need in order to consider you for the job.

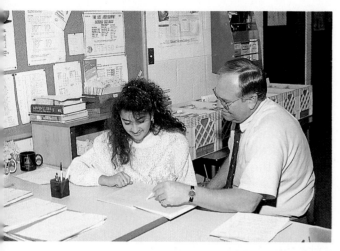

At many high schools, you can apply for a work permit in the school counseling office.

Interviewing for a Job

If the employer thinks you might be a good prospect for employment, you will be called for an interview. This is a meeting with the employer during which you can both get more information and perhaps reach a conclusion regarding the job.

The impression you make at the interview should continue the one you began in your application. You want to show that you are enthusiastic, qualified, and willing to work hard. You convey this by arriving on time and being neatly groomed and polite.

Interviews can be stressful, but try to relax. Let the interviewer direct the conversation. Show your interest in the job and familiarity with the company. Explain how you can help the company and be prepared to answer questions such as, "What are your strengths and weaknesses?" Remember to phrase your answers in ways that will stress your abilities and qualifications. Ask questions about the nature of the job, but don't focus on money or benefits yet.

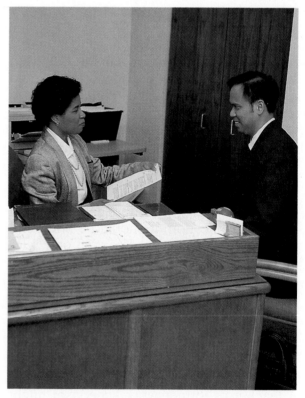

It's natural to feel a little nervous when going to a job interview. Think of the interview as an opportunity to visit a workplace, learn more about an interesting job, and meet new people. Try to make a good impression, but also relax and be yourself.

TIPS for Success

Preparing for an Interview

An interview can go more smoothly with a bit of advance preparation:

❖ Write down the time and place of the interview. Make sure you know how to get there and how long it will take. Be sure to arrive on time.

❖ Make up an interview package. Include your resumé (if needed), a good pen, and a small notebook for taking notes.

❖ Learn all you can about the company, including the job you are applying for.

❖ Go to the interview alone. Don't bring family members or friends.

❖ Dress neatly. Avoid jeans, excessive make-up, and too much jewelry.

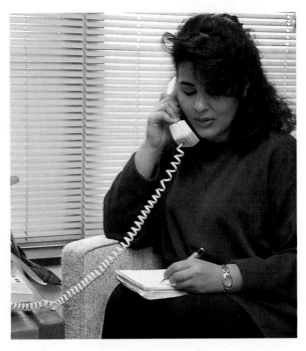

What questions should you ask when making an appointment for an interview?

At the end of the interview, thank the interviewer and repeat your interest in the job. If you are not told whether you are being offered the job, ask when you may call to find out about the decision. When you get home, write the interviewer a note of thanks, again expressing your interest in the job.

If you didn't get the job, you may politely ask why. Whatever the reason, use the interview as a learning experience.

If you are offered the job, you have completed the first step in reaching your career goals. Now you must work to continue making progress toward those goals.

On the Job

Once you have found a job, it is up to you to keep it. These tips can help you:

❖ Get to work on time and appropriately dressed.

❖ Follow company rules, such as those about taking breaks and eating on the job.

❖ Pay attention when receiving instruction or training.

❖ Don't be afraid to ask questions about your responsibilities.

❖ Accept criticism and suggestions without resentment.

❖ If you make a mistake, admit it and learn from it.

❖ Take pride in your work. Remember that even small jobs can make a big difference.

Balancing Your Life

Balancing the demands of school, work, and family life takes good stress management skills:

❖ Recognize that your life must include a balance of activities. Set your priorities and focus on the most important ones.

❖ Keeping fit and healthy helps you do your best. Make wise food choices and allow time for exercise.

❖ You also need rest and relaxation. Find time for your family, your friends, and quiet time for yourself.

When writing a letter of resignation, give careful consideration to what you say. In the future, a prospective employer may ask you for the name of a previous employer as a reference. If your letter of resignation was critical or angry, you'll wish you had left on a more positive note.

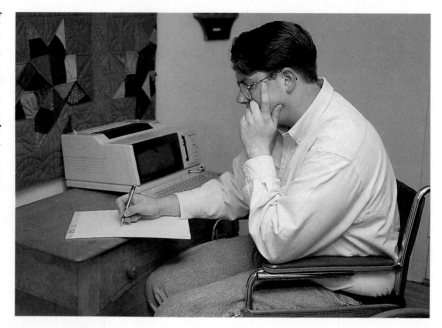

Leaving Your Job

There will probably come a time when you will want to leave your job. Here again you can make a good impression. At least two weeks ahead of time, inform your employer with a brief but polite letter of resignation. You may mention your reasons for leaving, but do not be negative. Thank your employer for the opportunity of having worked for the company.

Continue to do your best work until your last day. Remember, you may want to use your employer as a reference in the future.

If you are fired, find out exactly why. How can you improve your job performance so you won't have the same problem again?

When you interview for the next job, be honest about the reasons for leaving. If you were fired, explain why. Also explain how you plan to change so you won't have the same problem again. Employers are more willing to give employees a chance if they seem eager to improve and change.

Remember, success doesn't depend on just your skills and talent. It also depends on your attitude and commitment to do the best you possibly can.

Section 25.2 Review

RECALL THE FACTS

1. Name six qualifications of successful workers.

2. How are a job application form and a letter of application similar? How do they differ?

3. Give five suggestions for interviewing successfully.

4. How much notice should you give an employer before leaving a job?

DISCUSS YOUR IDEAS

5. What do you think is the most serious mistake people make when they interview for a job?

APPLY YOUR LEARNING

6. Review the qualities of successful workers described in this section. Using job listings from the newspaper want ads, give specific examples of how each skill might be needed in a particular job.

CAREER PROFILE

Debra Munson
Fast Food Worker

Current position:

"I'm a high school student working part-time at a fast food restaurant."

Responsibilities:

"I take orders from customers, take their money and give them change, and serve the food at the counter. Occasionally, I fill in as a cook in the kitchen."

Skills:

"It's important to be pleasant in this job, since you have to deal directly with customers. It also helps to be able to keep a clear head under pressure."

Work environment:

"Things can get pretty hectic during the breakfast, lunch, and dinner rush. But with all of us working efficiently as a team, we get through it smoothly."

Why I chose this job:

"I started looking for a job so I could save up some money for college. At first I didn't have anything particular in mind, except that I would need a job with evening and weekend hours. After checking the want ads and talking with friends about their jobs, I applied here. One of the things that appealed to me was their training program for entry-level workers."

Future plans:

"I haven't decided on a college major yet, but I plan to investigate home economics courses. I think I may be interested in a career in the food industry."

- Do you think Debra chose wisely in seeking this job? Why or why not?
- What aspects of Debra's job do you think you might enjoy? Why?

Summary

Section 25.1
Career Opportunities: Career opportunities in food and nutrition are growing and varied. Food service jobs include all those needed to prepare and serve food for the public. Home economists are needed to inform consumers about food, food choices, and related topics. Food scientists develop new foods and test foods for safety and quality. Dietitians help develop special diets for individuals or large groups. Many opportunities exist in food production, processing, and marketing. The food industry offers many options for entrepreneurs. The training and education needed for these careers also varies. Some require extensive formal education and advanced degrees. For others, a combination of on-the-job experience and additional training is most effective.

Section 25.2
The Successful Worker: Successful workers share certain qualities. They can communicate well, solve problems, and learn new things. They have a positive attitude and work well alone and with others. Applying for a job may involve filling out an application form, writing a letter of application, and submitting a resumé. These documents require you to give basic personal information and allow you to describe your strengths and qualifications. They should be brief, concise, and well-written. Interviews can be successful if you are relaxed, positive, and show an interest in the job and a willingness to learn. Even if you decide to leave a job or are fired, it can be a learning experience.

REVIEWING FACTS

1. Give three reasons for the expected job growth in food and nutrition. (25.1)

2. Name six personal traits needed to succeed in food service. (25.1)

3. Identify two career options for home economists in teaching and two in communications. (25.1)

4. What degrees and majors are needed to become a food scientist? (25.1)

5. Identify two risks of investing in a franchise. (25.1)

6. Name three benefits of having a job. (25.2)

7. Identify three instances when employees need good communication skills. (25.2)

8. What is networking? (25.2)

9. Give three tips for preparing for an interview. (25.2)

10. Give four tips for being a valuable employee. (25.2)

LEARNING BY DOING

1. **Computer lab:** Design and print a form that might be used by an entrepreneur in the food industry, such as an inventory or an employee schedule. (25.1)

2. **Foods lab:** Suppose you are a dietitian working in an institution. Think of some of the special diets that might be needed by people in an institutional setting. Create one such diet and prepare one or more of your recipes. (25.1)

3. **Demonstration:** Working in pairs, demonstrate how to successfully interview for a job. Have the rest of the class identify the positive points of the interview. (25.2)

THINKING CRITICALLY

1. *Recognizing fallacies:* A friend comments that he thinks bussing tables in a restaurant is an unimportant, dead-end job. How would you respond? (25.1)

2. *Comparing and contrasting:* How might the training and personal traits needed by a teacher in home economics be similar to those needed by a home economist in research and development? How might they differ? (25.1)

3. *Comparing values:* Which do you think is more important for a job—technical ability and experience, or enthusiasm and a positive attitude? Explain your answer. (25.2)

4. *Predicting consequences:* How can one employee's poor work habits affect other workers? (25.2)

MAKING DECISIONS AND SOLVING PROBLEMS

What Would You Do?

1. You have been working for almost a year as a cook in a fast-food restaurant and hoping to work your way up the career ladder. However, others who have been working at the restaurant less time than you are being promoted ahead of you. (25.1)

2. Your friend is an excellent baker. He would like to sell his baked goods for profit, but he cannot afford to start a business of his own. (25.1)

3. You and a friend work at the same restaurant. One day he asks you to tell your boss that he is sick so he can go to a concert that night. (25.2)

4. While filling out a job application form, you come to some questions that you feel are inappropriate. (25.2)

LINKING YOUR STUDIES

1. *Art:* Use your creative talents to arrange foods in an appealing manner. You may also photograph or make sketches of your arrangement. Bring your display or illustrations to class. (25.1)

2. *Economics:* Interview at least two local entrepreneurs about the economic aspect of their businesses. What economic factors encouraged them to start their business? What social and economic trends affect their business decisions? What role does their business play in the local or national economy? Do they feel the economy is a good one now for starting a business? If so, what kind? Write a transcript or a summary of your interview, including an explanation of what you learned from it. (25.1)

3. *Social studies:* Trace the history of child labor and child labor laws in this country. At what jobs and under what conditions have children worked in the past? How have attitudes toward child labor changed over time? What circumstances led to the enactment of child labor laws? How do these laws protect children in the workplace? Are there any disadvantages to these laws? Share your findings in a short report to the class. (25.2)

4. *Writing:* Choose a want ad from the newspaper. Write a letter of application for the job, using the suggestions given in this chapter. (25.2)

Glossary

A

additives. Chemicals added to food for specific reasons, such as to preserve freshness or to enhance color or flavor. (Section 13.2)

aerobic exercise (uh-ROW-bick). Exercise that gives the heart and lungs a workout. (Section 5.3)

a la carte (ah-lah-CART). On a restaurant menu, describes items that are priced individually. (Section 4.3)

albumen (al-BYOU-men). The thick, clear fluid inside an egg; also call the egg white. (Section 18.3)

al dente (ahl-DEHN-tay). Used to describe pasta that is tender, but still firm in the center. (Section 17.2)

amino acids (uh-MEE-no). Chemical compounds that combine to make up protein. (Section 2.2)

anabolic steroids (AN-uh-boll-ick STEER-oyds). Drugs used illegally by some athletes to build up muscles; have dangerous side effects that create serious physical and psychological health risks. (Section 5.4)

analogues (AN-uh-logs). Foods made from a vegetable protein and processed to resemble animal foods. (Section 15.1)

annual percentage rate (APR). The percent of interest that is charged per year on a loan. (Section 14.1)

anorexia nervosa (an-uh-RECK-see-yuh ner-VOH-suh). An eating disorder characterized by an irresistible urge to lose weight through self-starvation. (Section 6.3)

antioxidant. A substance that slows down enzyme activity; used to keep cut or pared fresh fruits from darkening. (Section 24.5)

antipasto (ahn-tee-PAH-stoh). An assortment of appetizers served before the main meal in Italy. (Section 22.3)

aquaculture. Method of growing fish or seafood in enclosed areas of water. (Section 13.1)

arcing. Electrical sparks produced when metal is used in a microwave oven; can damage the oven or start a fire. (Section 9.3)

aromatic vegetables. Flavorful vegetables, such as onions, garlic, celery, and green peppers, that are frequently sautéed to provide flavoring for other foods. (Section 20.3)

au jus. Describes meat served in its own juices. (Section 20.3)

B

bakeware. Containers used to cook food in an oven. (Section 9.1)

basal metabolism (BAY-suhl muh-TAB-oh-lih-zum). The amount of energy needed by the body to carry out automatic processes, such as breathing and digesting food. (Section 2.5)

base. A lining of salad greens on which the main part of a salad is placed. (Section 20.2)

behavior modification. Gradually making permanent changes in eating and exercise habits to lose weight and keep it at a healthy level. (Section 5.2)

berbere. A spicy seasoning mixture popular in Ethiopia. (Section 22.2)

binder. A liquid, such as broth or soup, used to hold a casserole together. (Section 20.4)

biotechnology. A method of improving the characteristics of plants and animals by modifying genes for specific traits. (Section 13.2)

blanch. To briefly cook vegetables to kill enzymes before freezing. (Section 24.5)

body. The main part of a salad. (Section 20.2)

bouillon (BOOL-yon). a clear, seasoned liquid made from cooking meat, poultry, fish, or vegetables. Also called broth or consommé. (Section 20.3)

bran. The outer protective coat or skin of a grain kernel. (Section 17.1)

budget. A plan for spending one's income. (Section 11.3)

bulimia nervosa (byou-LIM-ee-yuh ner-VOH-suh). Eating disorder characterized by episodes of binge eating (rapidly consuming large amounts of food) followed by purging (using self-induced vomiting, laxatives, and/or vigorous exercise to prevent weight gain). (Section 6.3)

bulk foods. Foods that are sold loose and displayed in covered bins or barrels; consumers buy as much or as little as they want. (Section 12.3)

C

calorie. A unit used to measure the energy that food supplies the body. (Section 2.1)

carbohydrates (kar-boh-HY-drates). Nutrients that are the body's main source of energy; commonly known as starches and sugars. (Section 2.1)

career. A profession or a life's work within a certain field. (Section 25.1)

career ladder. The steps from entry-level to top-level jobs through which a person can advance in a career area. (Section 25.1)

chalazae (kuh-LAH-zuh). The twisted, cord-like strands of albumen that anchor the yolk in the center of an egg. (Section 18.3)

chlorophyll (KLORE-uh-fill). The chemical compound that plants use to turn the sun's energy into food; gives plants their green color. (Section 16.3)

cholesterol (kuh-LESS-tehr-all). A fat-like substance present in all body cells and needed for essential body processes. (Section 2.3)

club sandwich. A layered sandwich made using three slices of bread and two types of fillings. (Section 20.1)

coagulate (koh-AGG-yoo-LATE). To cause a liquid to become a soft, semisolid mass, such as curdled milk or the white of a baked or poached egg. (Section 18.3)

code dating. A series of numbers and letters printed on food packages to indicate in code form where and when the product was packaged. (Section 12.2)

colostrum (kuh-LAW-strum). A thick, yellowish fluid produced by the mother's breasts the first few days after a baby's birth. (Section 6.1)

comparison shopping. Comparing prices of similar items to see which offers the best value. (Section 12.3)

complete proteins. Protein foods that supply all of the essential amino acids. Foods from animal sources supply complete protein. (Section 2.2)

conduction. A method of transferring heat by direct contact from one molecule to another. (Section 9.2)

contaminants. Substances that accidentally get into food as it moves from the farm to the table. Chemical pollutants and bacteria are examples. (Section 13.2)

continuous cleaning oven. An oven with special rough interior walls that absorb spills and spatters; residue can then be easily wiped off. (Section 14.2)

convalescence. The period of recovery after a serious illness or injury. (Section 6.2)

convection. A transfer of heat by the movement of currents in air or liquid. (Section 9.2)

convection current. A circular flow of air or liquid resulting from uneven heating. (Section 9.2)

cooking style. An individual's approach to food preparation as determined by personal feelings and priorities. (Section 11.2)

cookware. Containers used for cooking food on top of the range. (Section 9.1)

cover. Arrangement of a place setting for one person. (Section 10.1)

CPR. Stands for cardiopulmonary resuscitation, a first-aid technique used if a person's breathing and heartbeat stop. (Section 7.2)

critical thinking. Judging an idea on its soundness and truthfulness. (Section 3.3)

cross-contamination. Letting microorganisms from one food get into another. (Section 7.3)

cruciferous vegetables (crew-SIH-fur-uss). Vegetables in the cabbage family, including broccoli, brussels sprouts, cabbage, collards, kale, mustard greens, cauliflower, rutabagas, and turnips. (Section 16.1)

crustaceans (kruss-TAY-shuhns). Shellfish that have segmented bodies and limbs covered with a shell. Lobsters and crabs are examples. (Section 19.4)

cultural diversity. A variety of cultures in a single geographical area. (Section 1.3)

culture. The shared customs, traditions, and beliefs of a large group of people, such as a nation, race, or religious group. (Section 1.2)

cultured. Describes milk products to which a harmless bacteria culture has been added, causing fermentation, which results in a tangy, acidic flavor. (Section 18.1)

curing. A method of processing meat using a mixture of salt, sugar, nitrate, ascorbic acid, and water; extends shelf life and adds distinctive flavor. (Section 19.2)

cut. Refers to a piece of meat, poultry, or fish as it is sold in the marketplace. (Section 19.1)

cut in. To mix solid fat, such as butter or shortening, and flour using a pastry blender or two knives and a cross-cutting motion. (Section 21.2)

D

daily values. Reference amounts shown on the nutrition panel of food labels. Consumers can compare the amount of calories and nutrients in the food with the daily values, which are based on the recommendation of health experts. (Section 12.2)

dehydration (dee-high-DRAY-shun). Lack of adequate fluids in the body; can lead to serious health problems. (Section 5.4)

desired yield. When changing the yield of a recipe, the number of servings you want the revised recipe to make. (Section 8.3)

developing nations. Countries that are not yet industrialized or are just beginning to become so. (Section 13.3)

diabetes. A condition in which the body cannot control blood sugar properly. (Section 6.2)

dietary fiber. Mixture of plant materials that are not fully broken down in the digestive system; needed for good health. (Section 2.1)

Dietary Guidelines for Americans. A set of guidelines developed by the U.S. government to help people make healthy food choices. (Section 3.1)

digestion. The process of breaking food down into usable nutrients. (Section 2.5)

disposable. Refers to products that are thrown away after use. Examples include paper towels and food packaging. (Section 7.5)

doneness. Point at which food has cooked long enough so that it is both pleasurable and safe to eat. (Section 19.5)

dovetail. To fit tasks together in order to make the best use of time. (Section 8.5)

drop biscuits. Biscuits made by dropping sticky batter from a spoon onto a baking sheet. (Section 21.2)

drupes. Fruits with a central pit enclosing a single seed. Cherries and peaches are examples. (Section 16.1)

dry heat. Cooking food uncovered without added moisture. (Section 9.2)

E

eating disorder. Extreme, unhealthy behavior relating to food, eating, and weight. (Section 6.3)

eating patterns. Patterns that individuals follow when it comes to eating meals and snacks (such as what they eat, where, when, and how much). (Section 4.1)

electrolytes. The minerals potassium, sodium, and chloride, which work together to help maintain the body's fluid balance. (Section 2.4)

emulsion. An evenly blended mixture of two liquids that do not normally stay mixed, such as oil and water. (Section 20.2)

endosperm. The part of the grain kernel that contains the food supply for the embryo or germ; made up mostly of proteins and starches. (Section 17.1)

EnergyGuide label. Label on a large appliance that gives consumers information about estimated yearly energy costs. (Section 14.1)

en papillote (ehn pah-pee-YOHT). Describes technique for cooking foods in parchment paper. (Section 24.1)

enrichment. Adding nutrients to a product to make up for those lost in processing. (Section 17.1)

entree (AHN-tray). Main course in a meal. (Section 4.3)

entrepreneur (AHN-truh-pruh-NOOR). A person who runs his or her own business. (Section 25.1)

entry-level job. A beginning-level job that requires little or no experience. (Section 25.1)

enzymatic browning (EN-zie-MATT-ik). Browning that occurs in cut fruit when it is exposed to air. (Section 16.2)

equivalent. The same amount expressed in different ways by using different units of measure. For example, 4 tablespoons is the equivalent of 1/4 cup. (Section 8.2)

ergonomics (urr-guh-NAHM-iks). The study of how to make tools and equipment easier and more comfortable to use. (Section 1.4)

esophagus (ih-SOFF-uh-gus). The long tube connecting the mouth to the stomach. (Section 2.5)

ethnic group. A cultural group based on a common heritage. (Section 1.3)

extender. A starchy food, such as a grain or vegetable, used in a casserole to thicken it. (Section 20.4)

F

fad diets. Current, popular weight-loss methods that ignore good nutrition. (Section 5.2)

famine. Food shortages that continue for months or years, frequently resulting in starvation. (Section 13.3)

fat. Nutrient that provides a concentrated source of energy, provides essential fatty acids, and carries fat-soluble vitamins. (Section 2.1)

fat-soluble vitamins. Vitamins that dissolve only in fat, not in water; include vitamins A, D, E, and K. (Section 2.4)

fetus (FEE-tus). The unborn baby in the mother's womb. (Section 6.1)

finance charge. The total amount a person is charged for borrowing money; includes interest plus any service charges or insurance premiums. (Section 14.1)

foam cakes. Light, airy cakes that are leavened (made to rise) with beaten egg whites. Angel food, sponge, and chiffon cakes are examples. (Section 21.4)

food allergy. Condition in which eating even a small amount of a certain food causes an unwanted reaction, such as itching, rash, hives, nausea, or difficulty breathing. (Section 6.2)

Food Guide Pyramid. A guide developed by the U.S. government to help people make wise food choices. It divides foods into five food groups, plus a Fats, Oils, and Sweets category, and indicates a range of the number of servings needed daily from each group. (Section 3.2)

food record. A record kept over a specific period of time that lists all the foods one eats, the amount, and when it was eaten. (Section 4.2)

food science. A scientific study of food and its preparation. (Section 1.4)

formed product. A food product that is processed, flavored, and shaped to resemble a more expensive food. (Section 15.1)

fortified. Describes a food to which the manufacturer has added 10 percent or more of the daily value for a particular nutrient to make the food more nutritious. (Section 17.1)

freezer burn. Condition that results when food is improperly packaged for freezing or stored in the freezer too long; food dries out and loses flavor and texture. (Section 7.4)

frying. Cooking food in fat. (Section 9.2)

G

generic. Describes products in plain labels with no brand name; less expensive than name brands or store brands. (Section 12.3)

germ. The embryo in a grain kernel. The germ can sprout and grow into a new plant. (Section 17.1)

giblets (JIB-lets). Edible poultry organs, such as the liver and gizzard (stomach). (Section 19.3)

glucose. Blood sugar; the body's basic fuel supply. The body breaks carbohydrates down into glucose during digestion. (Section 2.5)

gluten (GLOO-ten). A protein in flour that affects the texture of a baked product and helps determine how it will rise. (Section 21.1)

glycogen (GLIE-kuh-juhn). The stored form of glucose; stored in the liver and muscles. (Section 2.5)

grazing. Eating five or more small meals throughout the day instead of three larger ones. (Section 4.1)

grounding. A method of providing a safeguard against electrical shock in case of electrical problems in appliances and equipment. (Section 14.3)

H

haute cuisine (HOAT kwee-ZEEN). The classic cooking of France, characterized by rich sauces, exotic ingredients, and puff pastries. (Section 22.3)

headspace. The space left between the food and the cover of the container when packing food for freezing or canning. (Section 24.5)

Heimlich Maneuver. A first-aid technique used in case of choking. (Section 7.2)

hibachi (hih-BAH-chee). A small cast iron charcoal grill. (Section 23.2)

high tea. In England, a light meal served in the late afternoon or early evening. (Section 22.3)

homogenized (huh-MAH-jen-ized). Used to describe milk that has been processed so that the fat does not separate. (Section 18.1)

hot pack. A method of filling jars for canning. The food is first heated in liquid, then packed in jars. (Section 24.5)

hot spots. Areas of intense heat, as in a microwaved food. (Section 9.3)

hydrogenation (hi-DRAH-juh-NAY-shun). A process used to turn vegetable oils into solids; makes fat more saturated. (Section 2.3)

hydroponic farming (high-druh-PAH-nik). Using nutrient-enriched water to grow plants without soil. (Section 13.1)

I

impulse buying. Buying an item you did not plan on and don't really need just because it seems appealing at the moment. (Section 12.1)

incomplete protein. Protein lacking one or more essential amino acids. Foods from plant sources provide incomplete protein. (Section 2.2)

industrialized nations. Countries that use machines and equipment to manufacture many products and process foods. Also called "developed countries." (Section 13.3)

infuser. A small container with tiny holes that holds loose tea while brewing. (Section 24.2)

insoluble fiber. Type of dietary fiber that contributes bulk to help move waste through the large intestine. (Section 2.2)

interest. The amount of money a lender charges as a fee for a loan; equals a specific percentage of the amount borrowed. (Section 14.1)

inventory. An up-to-date record, as of food stored in the freezer. (Section 7.4)

irradiation. Exposing food to gamma rays to increase its shelf life and kill harmful microorganisms. (Section 13.2)

island. A freestanding kitchen counter. (Section 14.3)

J K L

julienne. Term for long, thin strips of food. (Section 24.1)

kibbutz (kih-BOOTS). An Israeli communal organization that raises its own food. (Section 22.2)

knead. To work dough with the hands (or an appliance) to further mix the ingredients and develop the gluten. (Section 21.1)

lacto-ovo vegetarians. People who do not eat meat, poultry, or fish, but do eat dairy products and eggs in addition to foods from plant sources. (Section 4.4)

lacto-vegetarians. People who do not eat meat, poultry, fish, or eggs, but do eat dairy products in addition to foods from plant sources. (Section 4.4)

leavening agents. Substances that produce the air, steam, or gas that helps baked products rise. (Section 21.1)

legumes. Edible seeds that develop in pods of plants; include dry beans and peas, lentils, and peanuts. (Section 17.3)

life cycle. The various stages of life a person passes through from the prenatal stage through old age. (Section 6.1)

life-span design. Designing kitchens to be adaptable to people of various ages and degrees of physical ability. (Section 14.3)

lifestyle. A person's typical way of life; includes how one spends one's time and one's values and attitudes. (Section 1.2)

M

macrominerals. Minerals that are needed in relatively large amounts; include calcium, phosphorus, magnesium. (Section 2.4)

maize. Another name for corn. (Section 22.1)

major appliance. A large electrically- or gas-powered device that performs a specific task, such as cook foods, keep foods cold, or wash dishes. (Section 7.1)

malnutrition. Serious health problems caused by poor nutrition over a long period of time. (Section 2.1)

management. Specific techniques that help one use resources wisely. (Section 1.5)

marbling. Small white flecks of fat that are visible within the muscle tissue of meat. (Section 19.1)

masala. A common seasoning powder used in India; similar to American curry powder. (Section 22.4)

mature fruits. Fruits that have reached their full size and color. (Section 16.1)

meal appeal. Characteristics that make a meal appetizing and enjoyable. (Section 11.1)

media. Channels of mass communication, such as newspapers, television, and radio. (Section 1.2)

meringue (mehr-ANG). A foam made of beaten egg whites and sugar, used for desserts. (Section 18.4)

micro-grill. A combination cooking method in which food is partially cooked in a microwave oven and then immediately placed on an outdoor grill to finish cooking. (Section 24.4)

microorganisms. Tiny living creatures, such as bacteria, that are visible only through a microscope. (Section 7.3)

minerals. Nutrients that help the body work properly; many become part of the body's bones, tissues, and fluids. (Section 2.1)

moderation. Avoiding extremes, as in eating moderate (average or medium size) amounts of a wide variety of foods. (Section 3.1)

modified English service. A method of serving food in which the host or hostess serves the main course at the table. (Section 24.3)

moist heat. Method for cooking food that involves using either liquid or steam. (Section 9.2)

mollusks. Shellfish with soft, unsegmented bodies that are enclosed in a rigid outer shell. Clams and oysters are examples. (Section 19.4)

monounsaturated (MAH-no-uhn-SAT-chur-ay-ted). Term for fatty acids, found mainly in olive oil and certain other foods, that appear to lower only LDL ("bad") cholesterol levels. (Section 2.3)

multicultural. Describes a society that includes many cultures. (Section 1.3)

myths. Beliefs that are not based on fact. (Section 3.3)

N

net weight. The weight of the food itself without the weight of its container or any packaging. (Section 12.2)

networking. When job hunting, making connections among people who can provide information about job openings. (Section 25.2)

nonfat milk solids. Solids in milk that contain most of the protein, vitamins, minerals, and lactose (milk sugar). (Section 18.1)

nouvelle cuisine (new-VELL kwee-ZEEN). Modern French cooking, which uses less flour, sugar, and fat than the classic cooking. (Section 22.3)

nutrient deficiency. A severe shortage of a nutrient, which can cause illness or interfere with normal growth or development. (Section 2.1)

nutrient-dense. Describes a food that is low or moderate in calories, yet rich in nutrients such as complex carbohydrates, protein, vitamins, and minerals. (Section 3.2)

nutrients. Chemicals in food that the body uses to carry out its functions. (Section 1.1)

nutrition. The study of nutrients and how they are used by the body. (Section 1.1)

O

obstetrician. A physician who specializes in pregnancy. (Section 6.1)

open dating. A date on a food product that can be understood by consumers, such as a "sell by" date or an expiration date. (Section 12.2)

open stock. Pieces of tableware that are sold individually rather than in a set. (Section 14.2)

osteoporosis (AH-stee-oh-puh-RO-sis). Condition in which human bones gradually lose their minerals, causing them to become weak and fragile and break easily. (Section 2.4)

ovo-vegetarians. People who do not eat meat, poultry, fish or dairy products but do eat eggs in addition to foods from plant sources. (Section 4.4)

oxidation. Process in which fuel is combined with oxygen to produce energy. In the body, the fuel is glucose. (Section 2.5)

P

parasites (PAIR-uh-sights). Organisms that get their nutrients from other living organisms (their hosts). Some parasites, when found in food, can cause food-borne illness. (Section 7.3)

pasteurized. Describes milk or other substance that has been heat-treated to kill enzymes and harmful bacteria. (Section 18.1)

patterns. Designs used in dinnerware, flatware, and glassware. (Section 14.2)

pediatrician. A physician who cares for infants and children. (Section 6.1)

peninsula. An extension of a kitchen counter. (Section 14.3)

perishable. Refers to foods that spoil quickly at room temperature. (Section 7.4)

peristalsis (PAIR-uh-STALL-suhs). Muscular action whereby muscles alternately contract and relax, creating wavelike movements that force food through the digestive system. (Section 2.5)

place setting. The pieces of tableware (dinnerware, glassware, flatware, and napkin) needed by one person to eat a meal. (Section 10.1)

poach. To simmer whole food, such as eggs or fish, in a small amount of water until done. (Section 9.4)

polarized plug. An electrical plug designed, as a safety measure, with one wide prong and one narrower one; may not fit in some older electrical outlets. (Section 7.2)

polyunsaturated (PAH-lee-uhn-SAT-chur-ay-ted). Term for certain fatty acids that seem to help lower cholesterol levels. Many vegetable oils are high in polyunsaturated fatty acids. (Section 2.3)

preheating. To turn an oven on for about 10 minutes before using it so it will be at the desired temperature when the food is put in. (Section 9.4)

pre-preparation. Food preparation tasks done before one begins to actually assemble a recipe. Measuring the ingredients is an example. (Section 8.5)

principal. The amount of money that is borrowed from a lender. (Section 14.1)

processing. Heating filled canning jars at boiling temperatures or above to kill enzymes and harmful microorganisms. (Section 24.5)

proteins. Nutrients that help the body to grow and to repair tissue; also provide energy and help fight disease. (Section 2.1)

psychological. Having to do with the mind and emotions. (Section 1.1)

Q

quacks. People who promote a particular food, diet, or supplement as a health aid without some scientific evidence. (Section 3.3)

quiche (keesh). A main-dish pie with a custard filling that contains foods such as chopped vegetables, cheese, and chopped cooked meat. (Section 18.4)

quick-mix method. Method for mixing yeast bread dough in which the active dry yeast is mixed with the dry ingredients before warmed liquid and fat are added. (Section 21.2)

R

radiation. A method of transferring heat by waves of energy called infrared rays. When the rays strike an object, the object is warmed. (Section 9.2)

raw pack. A method of filling jars for canning in which raw foods are placed in jars and covered with hot liquid. (Section 24.5)

RDA. Recommended Dietary Allowances. Scientifically-developed guidelines that specify the amounts of protein and certain vitamins and minerals needed daily by people, according to their age and gender. (Section 2.1)

rebate. A partial refund paid to the buyer after an item has been purchased. (Section 12.1)

reception. A social gathering to honor a person or an event, such as an anniversary or a graduation. (Section 24.3)

reconstitute. To add back the liquid that was removed from a food or beverage during processing. (Section 15.2)

references. People a job applicant knows well who can give information about the applicant's previous work or character. (Section 25.2)

refined sugars. Sugars that have been removed from plants and processed to be used as sweeteners, such as table sugar and maple syrup. (Section 2.2)

reservations. Arrangement made by calling a restaurant ahead of time to have a table set aside for you and any of your guests for a particular time. (Section 10.2)

resources. Objects and qualities that can help one reach one's goal. Time, money, skills, knowledge, and equipment are examples. (Section 1.2)

resumé (REH-zoo-MAY). A written summary of skills and past experiences and achievements that are related to the job a person is seeking. (Section 25.2)

retail cuts. Smaller cuts of meat into which wholesale cuts are divided for sale to consumers. Steaks, roasts, and chops are examples. (Section 19.2)

ripe fruits. Tender fruits that have a pleasant aroma and fully developed flavors and are just ready to eat. (Section 16.1)

ripened cheese. Cheese made from milk curds to which ripening agents, such as bacteria, mold, yeast, or a combination of these, have been added; the cheese is then aged, or ripened, for a certain period of time. (Section 18.1)

rolled biscuits. Biscuits made by rolling dough out to an even thickness and cutting it. (Section 21.2)

roux (ROO). A mixture of browned flour and fat; thickens sauces and gives them a subtle roasted taste. (Section 23.1)

S

sanitation. Keeping disease-causing bacteria down to as small a number as possible through cleanliness and proper food handling. (Section 7.3)

saturated. Term for fatty acids that appear to raise the level of LDL ("bad") cholesterol in the bloodstream. Meat, poultry skin, whole-milk dairy products, and tropical oils (coconut, palm, and palm kernel oils) are high in saturated fatty acids. (Section 2.3)

sauté (saw-TAY). To brown or cook foods in a skillet with a small amount of fat, using low to medium heat. (Section 9.4)

scalded milk. Milk that has been heated to just below the boiling point. (Section 18.2)

science. Research to develop knowledge of a particular part of nature. (Section 1.4)

scones. A tasty variation of biscuits popular in parts of Britain. (Section 22.3)

seasoning blends. Convenient combinations of herbs or spices, such as Italian seasoning. (Section 24.1)

self-cleaning oven. An oven with a special cleaning cycle that uses high heat to burn off food stains. (Section 14.2)

self-esteem. A healthy recognition of your strengths and weaknesses and the ability to accept yourself as you are. (Section 1.1)

serrated. Refers to a knife with sawtooth notches along the edge of its blade. (Section 8.4)

service contract. Insurance purchased to cover repair and maintenance of a product for a specific length of time. (Section 14.1)

service plate. A large, decorative plate on which the dish containing the first course of a formal meal is placed; removed before the main course is served. (Section 24.3)

serving pieces. Tableware used for serving food. Platters and large bowls are examples. (Section 10.1)

shelf life. The length of time a food can be stored and still retain its quality. (Section 7.4)

shelf-stable. Describes processed foods that can be stored at room temperatures up to 85°F (29°C). (Section 7.4)

shirred eggs. Baked eggs. (Section 18.3)

shortened cake. Rich, tender cake, usually made with a solid fat and leavened with baking powder or baking soda. (Section 21.4)

small appliance. A small electrical device used to perform tasks such as mixing, chopping, and cooking. (Section 7.1)

snacks. Small amounts of food eaten between meals. (Section 4.1)

soluble fiber. Type of dietary fiber that may help lower blood cholesterol levels. (Section 2.2)

soufflé (soo-FLAY). Dish made by folding stiffly beaten egg whites into a sauce or batter, then baking the mixture in a deep casserole until it puffs up. (Section 18.4)

sourdough starter. A mixture of flour, water, and salt, which when allowed to sit for a few days, ferments and grows wild yeast cells, turning the mixture into a leavening agent; used to make sourdough bread. (Section 23.2)

spores. Cells that will develop into bacteria if conditions are right. (Section 7.3)

standing time. The amount of time a food must stand after microwave power is turned off. The heat inside the food causes the cooking process to continue during this time. (Section 9.3)

staple foods. Locally grown foods that make up the basic food supply of a particular region. (Section 13.3)

staples. Items you use on a regular basis, such as flour, honey, and margarine. (Section 12.1)

steep. To allow tea leaves to soak in hot water until the flavor is extracted from the leaves. (Section 24.2)

stew. To cover small pieces of food with liquid and simmer until done. (Section 9.4)

store brands. Packaged foods specially produced for the store; also called "private labels." (Section 12.3)

stress. Physical or mental tension triggered by an event or situation in one's life. (Section 6.2)

study. A scientific experiment conducted on a specific group of people or animals. (Section 3.3)

subsistence farming. A farming method in which people grow and raise their own food supply on small plots of land; common in many developing countries. (Section 13.3)

supplements. Nutrients people take in addition to those that are in the food they eat; usually in the form of pills, capsules, liquids, or powders. (Section 2.1)

sustainable farming. A farming method that uses few, if any, chemicals. (Section 13.1)

T

table etiquette. Rules for polite, appropriate mealtime behavior in a particular culture. (Section 10.2)

task lighting. Bright, shadow-free light over specific work areas, such as counters and sinks. (Section 14.3)

technology. The practical application of scientific knowledge to develop new or improved products and processes. (Section 1.4)

texture. The way food feels when you chew it, such as soft, hard, crispy, or chewy. (Section 11.1)

tip. Extra money given to the server in a restaurant in appreciation for good service. (Section 10.2)

tolerance levels. Maximum safe levels of certain chemicals that may be present in food. By law, foods cannot contain more of a chemical than the tolerance level set for it. (Section 13.2)

toxins. Poisons produced by bacteria. (Section 7.3)

trace minerals. Minerals that are needed in small amounts; include iron, copper, zinc, iodine, and selenium. (Section 2.4)

tuber (TOO-burr). Thickened, fleshy part of an underground stem that stores a plant's nutrients. Potatoes are an example. (Section 16.1)

U

ultra-pasteurization. Heating milk to a higher temperature than in normal pasteurization so the milk can be kept refrigerated longer than regularly pasteurized milk. (Section 18.1)

unitized. Describes produce that is held together with a rubber band or plastic tie and sold as a single unit. (Section 16.1)

unit price. Cost per ounce, quart, pound, or other unit of measurement. (Section 12.3)

unripened cheese. Cheese made of milk curds that have not been aged, or ripened; highly perishable. Cottage cheese and cream cheese are examples. (Section 18.1)

UPC symbol. Universal Product Code. A bar code on food labels and other products; it carries coded information (such as the price of the product) that can be "read" by a laser scanner. (Section 12.2)

utensils. Tools or containers used for specific tasks in food preparation. Examples include measuring cups, peelers, and cookware. (Section 7.1)

V

vacuum bottle. Container with two walls enclosing a vacuum (empty space), which provides insulation; used to keep heated foods and beverages hot for several hours. (Section 20.1)

variety meats. Edible animal organs, such as liver and kidneys. (Section 19.2)

vegans (VEE-guns *or* VEE-juns). People who eat only foods from plant sources. They do not eat meat, poultry, fish, eggs, or dairy products. (Section 4.4)

vegetarians. People who do not eat meat, poultry, or fish; some also do not eat dairy foods or eggs. (Section 4.4)

vent. To allow steam to escape from food as it cooks by slightly rolling back one edge of a plastic wrap cover on a dish to be microwaved. (Section 9.3)

vitamins. Chemicals in food that are needed in small amounts to help the body function properly and to help other nutrients do their jobs. (Section 2.1)

volume. The amount of three-dimensional space something takes up. (Section 8.2)

W

waist-to-hip ratio. Waist measurement divided by hip measurement; helps determine how weight is distributed in the body. (Section 5.1)

warranty. Manufacturer's written guarantee that for a specified period of time, it will repair or replace a product that does not perform properly. (Section 14.1)

water-soluble vitamins. Vitamins that dissolve in water, not in fat; include B vitamins and vitamin C. (Section 2.4)

watts. Units by which electrical power is measured. (Section 9.1)

wellness. Taking responsibility for one's own health by making choices and developing habits that help one become and stay physically, emotionally, and mentally healthy. (Section 1.1)

white sauce. A milk-based sauce thickened with starch. (Section 20.3)

wholesale cuts. Large pieces of meat into which an animal carcass is divided. Examples include flank, rib, and loin. (Section 19.2)

wok. A special pan used for stir-frying. It is wide at the top and has a narrower, rounded bottom. (Section 9.4)

work center. An area in the kitchen designed for specific tasks; includes equipment needed for the task and adequate storage and work space. (Section 7.1)

work flow. The sequence of movement from one area of the kitchen to the next while performing food preparation tasks. (Section 14.3)

work plan. A list of all the tasks required to complete a recipe in the order they must be done; includes an estimate of how long each task will take. (Section 8.5)

X Y Z

yield. Number of servings or amount a recipe makes. (Section 8.1)

"yo-yo" dieting. Repeated cycle of losing weight while dieting and then gaining weight when the diet stops. (Section 5.2)

Appendix: Nutritive Value of Foods

Nutrients in Indicated Quantity

Item No.	Food Description	Approximate Measure	Weight (Grams)	Food energy (Calories)	Protein (Grams)	Fat (Grams)	Cholesterol (Milligrams)	Calcium (Milligrams)	Iron (Milligrams)	Sodium (Milligrams)	Vitamin A value* (Retinol equivalents)	Vitamin C (Milligrams)
	Beverages											
9	Club soda	12 fl oz	355	0	0	0	0	18	Tr	78	0	0
10	Regular cola	12 fl oz	369	160	0	0	0	11	0.2	18	0	0
11	Diet, artificially sweetened cola	12 fl oz	355	Tr	0	0	0	14	0.2	32	0	0
12	Ginger ale	12 fl oz	366	125	0	0	0	11	0.1	29	0	0
20	Fruit punch drink	6 fl oz	190	85	Tr	0	0	15	0.4	15	2	61
21	Grape drink	6 fl oz	187	100	Tr	0	0	2	0.3	11	Tr	64
	Dairy Products											
	Natural Cheese											
32	Cheddar, cut pieces	1 oz	28	115	7	9	30	204	0.2	176	86	0
34	Shredded Cheddar	1 cup	113	455	28	37	119	815	0.8	701	342	0
	Cottage cheese											
35	Creamed (4%)	1 cup	225	235	28	10	34	135	0.3	911	108	Tr
38	Lowfat (2%)	1 cup	226	205	31	4	19	155	0.4	918	45	Tr
43	Mozzarella, part skim milk	1 oz	28	80	8	5	15	207	0.1	150	54	0
46	Parmesan, grated	1 tbsp	5	25	2	2	4	69	Tr	93	9	0
52	Pasteurized process American cheese	1 oz	28	105	6	9	27	174	0.1	406	82	0
	Milk, fluid:											
78	Whole (3.3% fat)	1 cup	244	150	8	8	33	291	0.1	120	76	2
79	Lowfat (2%)	1 cup	244	120	8	5	18	297	0.1	122	139	2
81	Lowfat (1%)	1 cup	244	100	8	3	10	300	0.1	123	144	2
83	Nonfat (skim)	1 cup	245	85	8	Tr	4	302	0.1	126	149	2
85	Buttermilk	1 cup	245	100	8	2	9	285	0.1	257	20	2
86	Canned, condensed, sweetened milk	1 cup	306	980	24	27	104	868	0.6	389	248	8
88	Evaporated skim milk	1 cup	255	200	19	1	9	738	0.7	293	298	3
	Dried, nonfat, instantized:											
90	Envelope, 3.2 oz. net wt.	1 envelope	91	325	32	1	17	1,120	0.3	499	646	5
91	Cup	1 cup	68	245	24	Tr	12	837	0.2	373	483	4
	Milk beverages:											
94	Chocolate milk, lowfat (1%)	1 cup	250	160	8	3	7	287	0.6	152	148	2
104	Shakes, thick: Chocolate	10 oz	283	335	9	8	30	374	0.9	314	59	0
105	Shakes, thick: Vanilla	10 oz	283	315	11	9	33	413	0.3	270	79	0

#	Food	Measure										
	Milk desserts, frozen:											
	Ice cream, vanilla, regular (about 11% fat):											
107	Hardened	1 cup	133	270	5	14	59	176	0.1	116	133	1
109	Soft serve (frozen custard)	1 cup	173	375	7	23	153	236	0.4	153	199	1
	Ice milk, vanilla:											
113	Hardened (about 4% fat)	1 cup	131	185	5	6	18	176	0.2	105	52	1
114	Soft serve (about 3% fat)	1 cup	175	225	8	5	13	274	0.3	163	44	1
116	Sherbet (about 2% fat)	1 cup	193	270	2	4	14	103	0.3	88	39	4
	Yogurt, made with lowfat milk:											
117	Fruit-flavored	8-oz	227	230	10	2	10	345	0.2	133	25	1
118	Plain	8-oz	227	145	12	4	14	415	0.2	159	36	2
	Eggs											
	Eggs, large (24 oz. per dozen):											
	Raw:											
121	Whole, without shell	1 egg	50	75	6	5	213	25	0.7	63	95	0
122	White	1 white	33	15	4	0	0	2	Tr	55	0	0
123	Yolk	1 yolk	17	60	3	5	213	23	0.6	7	97	0
	Cooked:											
124	Fried in margarine	1 egg	46	90	6	7	211	25	0.7	162	114	0
125	Hard-cooked, shell removed	1 egg	50	75	6	5	213	25	0.6	62	84	0
	Fats and Oils											
129	Butter (4 sticks per lb) (1/8 stick)	1 tbsp	14	100	Tr	11	31	3	Tr	116	106	0
138	Margarine (1/8 stick)	1 tbsp	14	100	Tr	11	0	4	Tr	132	139	Tr
141	Margarine, soft	1 tbsp	14	100	Tr	11	0	4	0.0	151	139	Tr
147	Corn oil	1 cup	218	1,925	0	218	0	0	0.0	0	0	0
	Salad dressings, commercial											
162	French, Regular	1 tbsp	16	85	Tr	9	0	2	Tr	188	Tr	Tr
163	French, Low calorie	1 tbsp	16	25	Tr	2	0	6	Tr	306	Tr	Tr
164	Italian, Regular	1 tbsp	15	80	Tr	9	0	1	Tr	162	3	Tr
165	Italian, Low calorie	1 tbsp	15	5	Tr	Tr	0	1	Tr	136	Tr	Tr
166	Mayonnaise, Regular	1 tbsp	14	100	Tr	11	8	3	0.1	80	12	0
167	Mayonnaise, Imitation	1 tbsp	15	35	Tr	3	4	Tr	0.0	75	0	0
168	Mayonnaise type	1 tbsp	15	60	Tr	5	4	2	Tr	107	13	0
	Fish and Shellfish											
176	Crabmeat, canned	1 cup	135	135	23	3	135	61	1.1	1,350	14	0
177	Fish sticks, frozen, reheated, (stock, 4 by 1 by 1/2 in.)	1 fish stick	28	70	6	3	26	11	0.3	53	5	0
181	Haddock, breaded, fried	3 oz	85	175	17	9	75	34	1.0	123	20	0
182	Halibut, broiled, with butter and lemon juice	3 oz	85	140	20	6	62	14	0.7	103	174	1
193	Shrimp, French fried (7 medium)	3 oz	85	200	16	10	168	61	2.0	384	26	0
195	Tuna, canned, oil pack, chunk light	3 oz	85	165	24	7	55	7	1.6	303	20	0
196	Tuna, canned, water pack, solid white	3 oz	85	135	30	1	48	17	0.6	468	32	0

Item No.	Food Description	Approximate Measure	Weight	Food energy	Protein	Fat	Cholesterol	Calcium	Iron	Sodium	Vitamin A value*	Vitamin C
			Grams	Calories	Grams	Grams	Milligrams	Milligrams	Milligrams	Milligrams	Retinol equivalents	Milligrams
Fruits and Fruit Juices												
198	Apples, raw, unpeeled, 2-3/4-in. diam.	1 apple	138	80	Tr	Tr	0	10	0.2	Tr	7	8
202	Apple juice, bottled or canned	1 cup	248	115	Tr	Tr	0	17	0.9	7	Tr	2
204	Applesauce, canned, unsweetened	1 cup	244	105	Tr	Tr	0	7	0.3	5	7	3
215	Bananas, raw, without peel, whole	1 banana	114	105	1	1	0	7	0.4	1	9	10
229	Fruit cocktail, canned, juice pack	1 cup	248	115	1	Tr	0	20	0.5	10	76	7
230	Grapefruit, raw, without peel, 3-3/4-in. diam.	1/2 grapefruit	120	40	1	Tr	0	14	0.1	Tr	1	41
233	Grapefruit juice, canned, unsweetened	1 cup	247	95	1	Tr	0	17	0.5	2	2	72
237	Grapes, Thompson Seedless	10 grapes	50	35	Tr	Tr	0	6	0.1	1	4	5
239	Grape juice, canned or bottled	1 cup	253	155	1	Tr	0	23	0.6	8	2	Tr
242	Kiwifruit, raw, without skin	1 kiwifruit	76	45	1	Tr	0	20	0.3	4	13	74
250	Mangos, raw, without skin and seed	1 mango	207	135	1	1	0	21	0.3	4	806	57
251	Cantaloup, orange-fleshed, 5-in. diam.	1/2 melon	267	95	2	1	0	29	0.6	24	861	113
253	Nectarines, raw, without pits	1 nectarine	136	65	1	1	0	7	0.2	Tr	100	7
254	Oranges, raw, whole	1 orange	131	60	1	Tr	0	52	0.1	Tr	27	70
260	Orange juice, frozen concentrate, diluted	1 cup	249	110	2	Tr	0	22	0.2	2	19	97
262	Papayas, raw, 1/2-in. cubes	1 cup	140	65	1	Tr	0	35	0.3	9	40	92
263	Peaches, raw, whole, 2-1/2 in. diam.	1 peach	87	35	1	Tr	0	4	0.1	Tr	47	6
267	Peaches, canned, fruit and juice	1 cup	248	110	2	Tr	0	15	0.7	10	94	9
273	Pears, raw, with skin, cored, Bartlett, 2-1/2-in. diam.	1 pear	166	100	1	1	0	18	0.4	Tr	3	7
283	Pineapple, chunks or tidbits, juice pack	1 cup	250	150	1	Tr	0	35	0.7	3	10	24
287	Plantains, without peel, cooked, boiled, sliced	1 cup	154	180	1	Tr	0	3	0.9	8	140	17
288	Plums, raw, 2-1/8-in. diam.	1 plum	66	35	1	Tr	0	3	0.1	Tr	21	6
294	Prunes, dried, uncooked	4 extra large	49	115	1	Tr	0	25	1.2	2	97	2
297	Raisins, seedless, cup, not pressed down	1 cup	145	435	5	1	0	71	3.0	17	1	5
303	Strawberries, raw, capped, whole	1 cup	149	45	1	1	0	21	0.6	1	4	84
309	Watermelon, 4 by 8 in. wedge	1 piece	482	155	3	2	0	39	0.8	10	176	46
Grain Products												
	Breads:											
311	Bagels, plain or water, enriched	1 bagel	68	200	7	2	0	29	1.8	245	0	0
314	Biscuits, from mix, 2 in. diameter	1 biscuit	28	95	2	3	Tr	58	0.7	262	4	Tr
316	Breadcrumbs, enriched, dry, grated	1 cup	100	390	13	5	5	122	4.1	736	0	0
319	Cracked-wheat bread (18 per loaf)	1 slice	25	65	2	1	0	16	0.7	106	Tr	Tr
332	Pita bread, enriched, white, 6-1/2-in. diam.	1 pita	60	165	6	1	0	49	1.4	339	0	0
337	Raisin bread, enriched (18 per loaf)	1 slice	25	65	2	1	0	25	0.8	92	Tr	Tr
346	White bread, enriched (18 per loaf)	1 slice	25	65	2	1	0	32	0.7	129	Tr	Tr

No.	Food	Measure	Grams	Calories								
353	Whole-wheat bread (16 per loaf)	1 slice	28	70	3	1	0	20	1.0	180	Tr	Tr
355	Bread stuffing, dry type, from mix	1 cup	140	500	9	31	0	92	2.2	1,254	273	0
356	Bread stuffing, moist type, from mix	1 cup	203	420	9	26	67	81	2.0	1,023	256	0
	Breakfast cereals:											
359	Cream of Wheat®, cooked	1 cup	244	140	4	Tr	0	54	10.9	5	0	0
365	All-Bran®	1 oz	28	70	4	1	0	23	4.5	320	375	15
367	Cheerios®	1 oz	28	110	4	2	0	48	4.5	307	375	15
368	Kellogg's® Corn Flakes	1 oz	28	110	2	Tr	0	1	1.8	351	375	15
383	Shredded Wheat	1 oz	28	100	3	1	0	11	1.2	3	0	0
384	Special K®	1 oz	28	110	6	Tr	Tr	8	4.5	265	375	15
386	Sugar Frosted Flakes, Kellogg's®	1 oz	28	110	1	Tr	0	1	1.8	230	375	15
388	Total®	1 oz	28	100	3	1	0	48	18.0	352	1,501	60
390	Wheaties®	1 oz	28	100	3	Tr	0	43	4.5	354	375	15
	Cakes prepared from cake mixes:											
394	Angelfood, 1/12 of cake	1 piece	53	125	3	Tr	0	44	0.2	269	0	0
396	Coffeecake, crumb, 1/6 of cake	1 piece	72	230	5	7	47	44	1.2	310	32	Tr
398	Devil's food with chocolate frosting, 1/16 of cake	1 piece	69	235	3	8	37	41	1.4	181	31	Tr
	Cakes, commercial:											
	Snack cakes:											
416	Devil's food with creme filling (2 small cakes per pkg)	1 cake	28	105	1	4	15	21	1.0	105	4	0
417	Sponge with creme filling (2 small cakes per pkg)	1 cake	42	155	1	5	7	14	0.6	155	9	0
423	Cheesecake, piece, 1/12 of cake	1 piece	92	280	5	18	170	52	0.4	204	69	5
	Cookies, commercial:											
424	Brownies with nuts and frosting	1 brownie	25	100	1	4	14	13	0.6	59	18	Tr
426	Chocolate chip, 2-1/4 in. diam.	4 cookies	42	180	2	9	5	13	0.8	140	15	Tr
429	Fig bars, square, 1-5/8 in. square	4 cookies	56	210	2	4	27	40	1.4	180	6	Tr
430	Oatmeal with raisins, 2-5/8-in. diam.	4 cookies	52	245	3	10	2	18	1.1	148	12	0
437	Corn chips	1-oz pkg.	28	155	2	9	0	35	0.5	233	11	1
	Crackers:											
444	Graham, plain, 2-1/2 in. square	2 crackers	14	60	1	1	0	6	0.4	86	0	0
447	Saltines	4 crackers	12	50	1	1	4	3	0.5	165	0	0
448	Snack-type, standard	1 cracker	3	15	Tr	1	0	3	0.1	30	Tr	0
449	Wheat, thin	4 crackers	8	35	1	1	0	3	0.3	69	Tr	0
450	Whole-wheat wafers	2 crackers	8	35	1	2	0	3	0.2	59	0	0
	Doughnuts, made with enriched flour:											
456	Cake type, plain, 3-1/4-in. diam.	1 doughnut	50	210	3	12	20	22	1.0	192	5	Tr
457	Yeast-leavened, glazed, 3-3/4-in. diam.	1 doughnut	60	235	4	13	21	17	1.4	222	Tr	0
458	English muffins, plain, enriched	1 muffin	57	140	5	1	0	96	1.7	378	0	0
461	Macaroni, enriched, cooked	1 cup	130	190	7	1	0	14	2.1	1	0	0
	Muffins, 2-1/2-in. diam., commercial mix:											
467	Blueberry	1 muffin	45	140	3	5	45	15	0.9	225	11	Tr
468	Bran	1 muffin	45	140	3	4	28	27	1.7	385	14	0
496	Corn	1 muffin	45	145	3	6	42	30	1.3	291	16	Tr
470	Noodles (egg noodles), enriched, cooked	1 cup	160	200	7	2	50	16	2.6	3	34	0
471	Noodles, chow mein, canned	1 cup	45	220	6	11	5	14	0.4	450	0	0

Item No.	Food Description	Approximate Measure	Weight Grams	Food energy Calories	Protein Grams	Fat Grams	Cholesterol Milligrams	Calcium Milligrams	Iron Milligrams	Sodium Milligrams	Vitamin A value* Retinol equivalents	Vitamin C Milligrams
	Pancakes, 4-in. diam.											
474	Plain, from mix (with enriched flour), egg, milk, and oil added	1 pancake	27	60	2	2	16	36	0.7	160	7	Tr
	Piecrust, flour and vegetable shortening, baked:											
476	From mix, 9-in. diam.	for 2-crust pie	320	1,485	20	93	0	131	9.3	2,602	0	0
	Pies, 9-in. diam:											
478	Apple, 1/6 of pie	1 piece	158	405	3	18	0	13	1.6	476	5	2
484	Creme, 1/6 of pie	1 piece	152	455	3	23	8	46	1.1	369	65	0
488	Lemon meringue, 1/6 of pie	1 piece	140	355	5	14	143	20	1.4	395	66	4
490	Peach, 1/6 of pie	1 piece	158	405	4	17	0	16	1.9	423	115	5
494	Pumpkin, 1/6 of pie	1 piece	152	320	6	17	109	78	1.4	325	416	0
	Popcorn, popped:											
497	Air-popped, unsalted	1 cup	8	30	1	Tr	0	1	0.2	Tr	1	0
498	Popped in vegetable oil, salted	1 cup	11	55	1	3	0	3	0.3	86	2	0
499	Sugar syrup coated	1 cup	35	135	2	1	0	2	0.5	Tr	3	0
500	Pretzels, stick, 2-1/4 in. long	10 pretzels	3	10	Tr	Tr	0	1	0.1	48	0	0
	Rice:											
503	Brown, cooked, served hot	1 cup	195	230	5	1	0	23	1.0	0	0	0
505	White, enriched, cooked, served hot	1 cup	205	225	4	Tr	0	21	1.8	0	0	0
	Rolls, enriched, commercial:											
509	Dinner, 2-1/2-in. diam.	1 roll	28	85	2	2	Tr	33	0.8	155	Tr	Tr
510	Frankfurter and hamburger	1 roll	40	115	3	2	Tr	54	1.2	241	Tr	Tr
512	Hoagie , 11-1/2 by 3 by 2-1/2 in.	1 roll	135	400	11	8	Tr	100	3.8	683	0	0
514	Spaghetti, enriched, cooked	1 cup	130	190	7	1	0	14	2.0	1	0	0
	Wheat flours:											
521	All-purpose flour, enriched	1 cup	125	455	13	1	0	20	5.5	3	0	0
524	Whole-wheat, from hard wheats	1 cup	120	400	16	2	0	49	5.2	4	0	0

Legumes, Nuts, and Seeds

Item No.	Food Description	Approximate Measure	Weight Grams	Food energy Calories	Protein Grams	Fat Grams	Cholesterol Milligrams	Calcium Milligrams	Iron Milligrams	Sodium Milligrams	Vitamin A value* Retinol equivalents	Vitamin C Milligrams
526	Almonds, shelled, whole	1 oz	28	165	6	15	0	75	1.0	3	0	Tr
	Beans, dry, cooked, drained:											
527	Black	1 cup	171	225	15	1	0	47	2.9	1	Tr	0
528	Great Northern	1 cup	180	210	14	1	0	90	4.9	13	0	0
529	Lima	1 cup	190	260	16	1	0	55	5.9	4	0	0
530	Pea (navy)	1 cup	190	225	15	1	0	95	5.1	13	0	0
531	Pinto	1 cup	180	265	15	1	0	86	5.4	3	Tr	0
536	Black-eyed peas, dry, cooked (with cooking liquid)	1 cup	250	190	13	1	0	43	3.3	20	3	0

Item No.	Foods, approximate measures, units, and weight	Measure	Grams	Food energy (cal)	Protein (g)	Fat (g)	Cholesterol (mg)	Calcium (mg)	Iron (mg)	Sodium (mg)	Vitamin A	Vitamin C (mg)
544	Chickpeas, cooked, drained	1 cup	163	270	15	4	0	80	4.9	11	Tr	0
550	Lentils, dry, cooked, with peanuts	1 cup	200	215	16	1	0	50	4.2	26	4	0
553	Mixed nuts, dry roasted, salted	1 oz	28	170	5	15	0	20	1.0	190	Tr	0
555	Peanuts, roasted in oil, salted	1 cup	145	840	39	71	0	125	2.8	626	0	0
557	Peanut butter	1 tbsp	16	95	5	8	0	5	0.3	75	0	0
559	Pecans, halves	1 cup	108	720	8	73	0	39	2.3	1	14	2
564	Refried beans, canned	1 cup	290	295	18	3	0	141	5.1	1,228	0	17
565	Sesame seeds, dry, hulled	1 tbsp	8	45	2	4	0	11	0.6	3	1	0
	Soy products:											
567	Miso	1 cup	276	470	29	13	0	188	4.7	8,142	11	0
568	Tofu, piece 2-1/2 by 2-3/4 by 1 in.	1 piece	120	85	9	5	0	108	2.3	8	0	0
569	Sunflower seeds, dry, hulled	1 oz	28	160	6	14	0	33	1.9	1	1	Tr
570	Tahini	1 tbsp	15	90	3	8	0	21	0.7	5	1	1
573	Walnuts, pieces or chips	1 cup	120	770	17	74	0	113	2.9	12	15	4

Meat and Meat Products

Item No.	Foods, approximate measures, units, and weight	Measure	Grams	Food energy (cal)	Protein (g)	Fat (g)	Cholesterol (mg)	Calcium (mg)	Iron (mg)	Sodium (mg)	Vitamin A	Vitamin C (mg)
	Beef, cooked, braised, or pot roasted:											
575	Chuck blade, lean and fat, piece	3 oz	85	325	22	26	87	11	2.5	53	Tr	0
577	Round, bottom, lean and fat, piece	3 oz	85	220	25	13	81	5	2.8	43	Tr	0
578	Lean only from item 577	2.8 oz	78	175	25	8	75	4	2.7	40	Tr	0
580	Ground beef, regular, broiled, patty	3 oz	85	245	20	18	76	9	2.1	70	Tr	0
585	Round, eye of, lean and fat, roasted	3 oz	85	205	23	12	62	5	1.6	50	Tr	0
587	Sirloin, steak, broiled, lean and fat	3 oz	85	240	23	15	77	9	2.6	53	Tr	0
590	Beef, dried, chipped	2.5 oz	72	145	24	4	46	14	2.3	3,053	Tr	0
	Lamb:											
593	Chops, loin, broiled, lean and fat	2.8 oz	80	235	22	16	78	16	1.4	62	Tr	0
	Pork, cured, cooked:											
599	Bacon, regular	3 slices	19	110	6	9	16	2	0.3	303	0	6
601	Ham, light cure, roasted, lean and fat	3 oz	85	205	18	14	53	6	0.7	1,009	0	0
	Luncheon meat:											
605	Chopped ham (8 slices per 6 oz pkg)	2 slices	42	95	7	7	21	3	0.3	576	0	8
	Pork, fresh, cooked:											
610	Chop, loin, pan fried, lean and fat	3.1 oz	89	335	21	27	92	4	0.7	64	3	Tr
614	Rib, roasted, lean and fat	3 oz	85	270	21	20	69	9	0.8	37	3	Tr
	Sausages											
618	Bologna, slice (8 per 8-oz pkg)	2 slices	57	180	7	16	31	7	0.9	581	0	12
620	Brown and serve, browned	1 link	13	50	2	5	9	1	0.1	105	0	0
621	Frankfurter cooked (reheated)	1	45	145	5	13	23	5	0.5	504	0	12
	Veal, medium fat, cooked, bone removed:											
627	Cutlet, braised or broiled	3 oz	85	185	23	9	109	9	0.8	56	Tr	0

Mixed Dishes and Fast Foods

Item No.	Foods, approximate measures, units, and weight	Measure	Grams	Food energy (cal)	Protein (g)	Fat (g)	Cholesterol (mg)	Calcium (mg)	Iron (mg)	Sodium (mg)	Vitamin A	Vitamin C (mg)
	Mixed dishes:											
629	Beef and vegetable stew, home recipe	1 cup	245	220	16	11	71	29	2.9	292	568	17
630	Beef potpie, home recipe, baked, 1/3 of 9-in. diam. pie	1 piece	210	515	21	30	42	29	3.8	596	517	6
631	Chicken a la king, cooked, home recipe	1 cup	245	470	27	34	221	127	2.5	760	272	12

Nutrients in Indicated Quantity

Item No.	Food Description	Approximate Measure	Weight (Grams)	Food energy (Calories)	Protein (Grams)	Fat (Grams)	Cholesterol (Milligrams)	Calcium (Milligrams)	Iron (Milligrams)	Sodium (Milligrams)	Vitamin A value* (Retinol equivalents)	Vitamin C (Milligrams)
633	Chicken chow mein, canned	1 cup	250	95	7	Tr	8	45	1.3	725	28	13
636	Chili con carne with beans, canned	1 cup	255	340	19	16	28	82	4.3	1,354	15	8
639	Macaroni and cheese, home recipe	1 cup	200	430	17	22	44	362	1.8	1,086	232	1
640	Quiche Lorraine, 1/8 of 8-in. diam. quiche	1 slice	176	600	13	48	285	211	1.0	653	454	Tr
642	Spaghetti in tomato sauce with cheese, home recipe	1 cup	250	260	9	9	8	80	2.3	955	140	13
644	Spaghetti with meatballs and tomato sauce, home recipe	1 cup	248	330	19	12	89	124	3.7	1,009	159	22
	Fast food entrees:											
645	Cheeseburger, regular	1 sandwich	112	300	15	15	44	135	2.3	672	65	1
648	English muffin, egg, cheese, bacon	1 sandwich	138	360	18	18	213	197	3.1	832	160	1
649	Fish sandwich, regular, with cheese	1 sandwich	140	420	16	23	56	132	1.8	667	25	2
651	Hamburger, regular	1 sandwich	98	245	12	11	32	56	2.2	463	14	1
653	Pizza, cheese, 1/8 of 15-in. diam.	1 slice	120	290	15	9	56	220	1.6	699	106	2
654	Roast beef sandwich	1 sandwich	150	345	22	13	55	60	4.0	757	32	2
655	Taco	1 taco	81	195	9	11	21	109	1.2	456	57	1

Poultry and Poultry Products

Item No.	Food Description	Approximate Measure	Weight (Grams)	Food energy (Calories)	Protein (Grams)	Fat (Grams)	Cholesterol (Milligrams)	Calcium (Milligrams)	Iron (Milligrams)	Sodium (Milligrams)	Vitamin A value* (Retinol equivalents)	Vitamin C (Milligrams)
	Chicken:											
	Fried, flesh, with skin and bones:											
656	Breast, 1/2 breast, batter dipped	4.9 oz	140	365	35	18	119	28	1.8	385	28	0
657	Drumstick, batter dipped	2.5 oz	72	195	16	11	62	12	1.0	194	19	0
	Roasted, flesh only:											
660	Breast, 1/2 breast	3.0 oz	86	140	27	3	73	13	0.9	64	5	0
662	Stewed, flesh only, light and dark meat	1 cup	140	250	38	9	116	20	1.6	98	21	0
	Turkey, roasted, flesh only:											
665	Dark meat, piece, 2-1/2 by 1-5/8 by 1/4 in.	4 pieces	85	160	24	6	72	27	2.0	67	0	0
666	Light meat, piece, 4 by 2 by 1/4 in.	2 pieces	85	135	25	3	59	16	1.1	54	0	0
667	Chopped or diced	1 cup	140	240	41	7	106	35	2.5	98	0	0
	Poultry food products:											
669	Chicken, canned, boneless	5 oz	152	235	31	11	88	20	2.2	714	48	3
671	Turkey, roll, light	2 slices (2 oz)	57	90	11	4	28	24	0.6	331	14	0
672	Gravy and turkey, frozen	5-oz pkg	142	95	8	4	26	20	1.3	787	18	0
673	Ham, cured turkey thigh meat	2 slices (2 oz)	57	75	11	3	32	6	1.6	565	0	0

No.	Food	Measure	Grams									
676	Turkey roast, boneless, frozen, seasoned, light and dark meat, cooked	3 oz	85	130	18	5	45	4	1.4	578	0	0

Soups, Sauces, and Gravies

No.	Food	Measure	Grams									
	Soups, condensed											
	Canned, prepared with milk:											
679	Cream of mushroom	1 cup	248	205	6	14	20	179	0.6	1,076	37	2
680	Tomato	1 cup	248	160	6	6	17	159	1.8	932	109	68
	Canned, prepared with water:											
681	Bean with bacon	1 cup	253	170	8	6	3	81	2.0	951	89	2
682	Beef broth, bouillon, consomme	1 cup	240	15	3	1	Tr	14	0.4	782	0	0
684	Chicken noodle	1 cup	241	75	4	2	7	17	0.8	1,106	71	Tr
693	Vegetarian	1 cup	241	70	2	2	0	22	1.1	822	301	1
	Dehydrated, prepared with water:											
697	Onion	1 pkt (6-fl-oz)	184	20	1	Tr	0	9	0.1	635	Tr	Tr
	Sauces:											
	From dry mix:											
699	Cheese, prepared with milk	1 cup	279	305	16	17	53	569	0.3	1,565	117	2
700	Hollandaise, prepared with water	1 cup	259	240	5	20	52	124	0.9	1,564	220	Tr
	Ready to serve:											
703	Barbecue	1 tbsp	16	10	Tr	Tr	0	3	0.1	130	14	1
704	Soy	1 tbsp	18	10	2	0	0	3	0.5	1,029	0	0
	Gravies:											
708	Brown, from dry mix	1 cup	261	80	3	2	2	66	0.2	1,147	0	0
709	Chicken, from dry mix	1 cup	260	85	3	2	3	39	0.3	1,134	0	3

Sugars and Sweets

No.	Food	Measure	Grams									
	Candy:											
711	Chocolate, milk, plain	1 oz	28	145	2	9	6	50	0.4	23	10	Tr
712	Chocolate, milk, with almonds	1 oz	28	150	3	10	5	65	0.5	23	8	Tr
715	Chocolate, semisweet, small pieces	1 cup	170	860	7	61	0	51	5.8	24	3	Tr
717	Fondant, uncoated (mints, other)	1 oz	28	105	Tr	0	0	2	0.1	57	0	0
718	Fudge, chocolate, plain	1 oz	28	115	1	3	1	22	0.3	54	Tr	Tr
720	Hard candy	1 oz	28	110	0	0	0	Tr	0.1	7	0	0
722	Marshmallows	1 oz	28	90	1	0	0	1	0.5	25	0	0
723	Custard, baked	1 cup	265	305	14	15	278	297	1.1	209	146	1
724	Gelatin dessert	1/2 cup	120	70	2	0	0	2	Tr	55	0	0
726	Honey, strained or extracted	1 tbsp	21	65	Tr	0	0	1	0.1	1	0	Tr
727	Jams and preserves	1 tbsp	20	55	Tr	Tr	0	4	0.2	2	Tr	Tr
731	Popsicle, 3-fl-oz size	1 popsicle	95	70	0	0	0	0	Tr	11	0	0
	Puddings											
	Canned:											
732	Chocolate	5-oz can	142	205	3	11	1	74	1.2	285	31	Tr
	Dry mix, prepared with whole milk:											
739	Vanilla, instant	1/2 cup	130	150	4	4	15	129	0.1	375	33	1
740	Vanilla, regular (cooked)	1/2 cup	130	145	4	4	15	132	0.1	178	34	1

Nutrients in Indicated Quantity

Item No.	Food Description	Approximate Measure	Weight (Grams)	Food energy (Calories)	Protein (Grams)	Fat (Grams)	Cholesterol (Milligrams)	Calcium (Milligrams)	Iron (Milligrams)	Sodium (Milligrams)	Vitamin A value* Retinol equivalents	Vitamin C (Milligrams)
	Sugars:											
741	Brown, pressed down	1 cup	220	820	0	0	0	187	4.8	97	0	0
742	White, granulated	1 tbsp	12	45	0	0	0	Tr	Tr	Tr	0	0
745	White, powdered, sifted	1 cup	100	385	0	0	0	1	Tr	2	0	0
	Syrups:											
748	Molasses, cane, blackstrap	2 tbsp	40	85	0	0	0	274	10.1	38	0	0
749	Table syrup (corn and maple)	2 tbsp	42	122	0	0	0	1	Tr	19	0	0
	Vegetables and Vegetable Products											
750	Alfalfa seeds, sprouted, raw	1 cup	33	10	1	Tr	0	11	0.3	2	5	3
	Beans, snap, cooked, drained:											
761	From frozen (cut)	1 cup	135	35	2	Tr	0	61	1.1	18	71	11
	Broccoli:											
771	Raw	1 spear	151	40	4	1	0	72	1.3	41	233	141
772	Cooked	1 spear	180	50	5	1	0	82	2.1	20	254	113
	Cabbage, common varieties:											
778	Raw, coarsely shredded or sliced	1 cup	70	15	1	Tr	0	33	0.4	13	9	33
	Cabbage, Chinese:											
780	Pak-choi, cooked, drained	1 cup	170	20	3	Tr	0	158	1.8	58	437	44
782	Cabbage, red, raw, shredded	1 cup	70	20	1	Tr	0	36	0.3	8	3	40
	Carrots:											
784	Whole, 7-1/2 by 1-1/8 in.	1 carrot	72	30	1	Tr	0	19	0.4	25	2,025	7
786	Cooked, sliced, drained, from raw	1 cup	156	70	2	Tr	0	48	1.0	103	3,830	4
	Celery, pascal type, raw:											
792	Stalk, large outer, 8 by 1-1/2 in.	1 stalk	40	5	Tr	Tr	0	14	0.2	35	5	3
	Collards, cooked, drained:											
795	From frozen (chopped)	1 cup	170	60	5	1	0	357	1.9	85	1,017	45
	Corn, sweet:											
	Cooked, drained:											
796	From raw, ear 5 by 1-3/4 in.	1 ear	77	85	3	1	0	2	0.5	13	17	5
798	From frozen kernels	1 cup	165	135	5	Tr	0	3	0.5	8	41	4
	Canned:											
799	Cream style	1 cup	256	185	4	1	0	8	1.0	730	25	12
800	Whole kernel, vacuum pack	1 cup	210	165	5	1	0	11	0.9	571	51	17
801	Cucumber, with peel, slices 1/8 in. thick, 2-1/8-in. diam.	6 slices	28	5	Tr	Tr	0	4	0.1	1	1	1
806	Kale, cooked, drained, from raw	1 cup	130	40	2	1	0	94	1.2	30	962	53
	Lettuce, raw:											
813	Crisphead, as iceberg, chopped	1 cup	55	5	1	Tr	0	10	0.3	5	18	2
814	Looseleaf, chopped or shredded	1 cup	56	10	1	Tr	0	38	0.8	5	106	10

No.	Food	Measure										
824	Onion rings, breaded, par-fried, frozen, prepared	2 rings	20	80	1	5	0	6	0.3	75	5	T
830	Peas, green, frozen, cooked, drained	1 cup	160	125	8	Tr	0	38	2.5	139	107	16
832	Peppers, sweet, raw	1 pepper	74	20	1	Tr	0	4	0.9	2	39	95
	Potatoes, cooked:											
834	Baked, with skin	1 potato	202	220	5	Tr	0	20	2.7	16	0	26
	French fried, strip, frozen:											
838	Oven heated	10 strips	50	110	2	4	0	5	0.7	16	0	5
839	Fried in vegetable oil	10 strips	50	160	2	8	0	10	0.4	108	0	5
	Potato products, prepared:											
840	Au gratin, from dry mix	1 cup	245	230	6	10	12	203	0.8	1,076	76	8
845	Mashed, from dehydrated flakes, water, milk, butter, and salt added	1 cup	210	235	4	12	29	103	0.5	697	44	20
849	Potato chips	10 chips	20	105	1	7	0	5	0.2	94	0	8
852	Radishes, raw	4 radishes	18	5	Tr	Tr	0	4	0.1	4	Tr	4
853	Sauerkraut, canned, solids and liquid	1 cup	236	45	2	Tr	0	71	3.5	1,560	4	35
	Spinach:											
856	Raw, chopped	1 cup	55	10	2	Tr	0	54	1.5	43	369	15
858	Cooked, drained, from frozen (leaf)	1 cup	190	55	6	Tr	0	277	2.9	163	1,479	23
	Squash, cooked:											
861	Summer, sliced, drained	1 cup	180	35	2	1	0	49	0.6	2	52	10
862	Winter, baked, cubes	1 cup	205	80	2	1	0	29	0.7	2	729	20
863	Sweet potatoes, baked in skin, peeled	1 potato	114	115	2	Tr	0	32	0.5	11	2,488	28
	Tomatoes:											
868	Raw, 2-3/5-in. diam.	1 tomato	123	25	1	Tr	0	9	0.6	10	139	22
869	Canned, solids and liquid	1 cup	240	50	2	1	0	62	1.5	391	145	36
870	Tomato juice, canned	1 cup	244	40	2	Tr	0	22	1.4	881	136	45
877	Vegetable juice cocktail, canned	1 cup	242	45	2	Tr	0	27	1.0	883	283	67
Miscellaneous Items												
885	Catsup	1 cup	273	290	5	1	0	60	2.2	2,845	382	41
889	Chocolate, bitter or baking	1 oz	28	145	3	15	0	22	1.9	1	1	0
894	Mustard, prepared, yellow	1 tsp	5	5	Tr	Tr	0	4	0.1	63	0	Tr
895	Olives, canned, green, medium	4	13	15	Tr	2	0	8	0.2	312	4	0
	Pickles, cucumber:											
901	Dill, medium, whole, 3-3/4 in.	1 pickle	65	5	Tr	Tr	0	17	0.7	928	7	4
903	Sweet, small, whole, 2-1/2 in. long	1 pickle	15	20	Tr	Tr	0	2	0.2	107	1	1
906	Vinegar, cider	1 tbsp	15	Tr	Tr	0	0	1	0.1	Tr	0	0

*1 RE = 3.33 IU from animal foods or 1 mcg retinol.
1 RE = 10 IU from plant foods or 6 mcg beta carotene.
Tr = Trace amount.
Source: USDA Home and Garden Bulletin No. 72, "Nutritive Value of Foods"

Index

A

Acids
   ascorbic, 71, 73, 419, 666
   mixing, with milk, 458, 462
Additives, food, 354, 355-357
Adolescence, nutrition during, 168
Advertising
   evaluating, 104-106
   influence of, on food choices, 29
Aerobic exercise, 151
Aflatoxins, 359
Africa, foods of, 591-595
African-Americans, and Southern food, 625-626
AGA seal, 373
Air, as leavening agent, 553
A la carte, 123
Alcohol, and pregnancy, 165
Allergy, food, 173
Altitude, high, and recipes, 236-237
American cooking, 621-633
Amino acids, 64, 82
Anabolic steroids, 157-158
Analogues, 396
Anemia, 75
Annual percentage rate (APR), 372
Anorexia nervosa, 176, 177
Antipasto, 604
Appeal, in meals, 307, 646-647
Appetizer salads, 531, 604
Apple Bran Bars (recipe), 578
Apples, baking, 424
Apple-Tuna Sandwiches (recipe), 528
Appliances
   buying, 372-379
   for cooking, 255-258, 271, 272, 378-379
   gas, 192, 256, 373
   grounding, 386
   for kitchen cleanup, 197
   major, 185, 255-258, 376-379
   safety with, 43, 189-190, 191-192
   small, 185, 258, 379
Applying for a job, 683
Aquaculture, 350
Arab foods, 595-596
Argentina, foods of, 589
Aromatic vegetables, 536
Artificial sweeteners, 356-357
Ascorbic acid
   as nutrient, 71, 73
   to prevent browning of fruit, 419, 666

Aseptic packages, 352, 456
Asia, foods of, 609-614
Asian influences on cooking, 631, 633
Assistance programs, food, 320-322
Athletes
   nutritional needs of, 154-157
   and steroids, 157-158
Atmosphere, mealtime, 292
Au jus, 539
Australia, foods of, 615
Austria, foods of, 603

B

Bacteria
   in cultured dairy products, 457
   and food-borne illness, 196-203. *See also* Food-borne illness
Baked apples, 424
Baked eggs, 470
Baked Potatoes, Microwave (recipe), 278
Baker, career as, 671
Baked products
   basic ingredients in, 551-554
   biscuits, 561-563
   cakes, 571-574
   cookies, 574-575, 578 (recipe)
   fiber in, adding, 560
   gluten in, 552, 554
   and high altitude cooking, 237
   leavening for, 552-553, 631
   microwaving, 557
   muffins, 559-560
   nutrients in, 559, 560
   pan materials for, 555
   pies, 575-577
   quick breads, 559-564
   storing, 207, 208, 558
   texture of, factors affecting, 552, 560, 562
   yeast breads, 554, 565-570
Bakery manager, career as, 579, 679
Bakeware, 259, 263
Baking. *See also* Baked products
   apples, 424
   eggs, 470
   fish, 510-511
   general discussion, 281-282
   in high altitudes, 237
   meat, 510-511
   pan placement when, 282
   potatoes, 278, 426
   poultry, 510-511
   squash, 426
   vegetables, 426

Baking powder, 553
Baking soda, 425, 553
Barbecues, 630
Bar code, 338
Bar cookies, 574, 578 (recipe)
Barley, 436, 440
Basal metabolism, 84
Batter, 555, 562
Beans, dry, 446, 447-449
Beans and Rice, Western (recipe), 443
Beef. *See also* Meat
   cholesterol and fat in, 485
   cuts of, 490, 492
   description of, 489
   grades of, 493
   ground, 485, 493, 509, 518 (recipe)
   internal temperature of, and doneness, 509
   lean cuts of, 491
Beef Patties with Herbs (recipe), 518
Behavior modification, 145-148
Beta carotene, 40, 71, 73, 412
Beverages
   for athletes, 156
   carbonated soft drinks, 653
   cocoa, hot, 453
   coffee, 649-651
   garnishes for, 646
   for infants, 166
   juices, fruit and vegetable, 416, 653
   milk, 456-457. *See also* Milk
   punch, 653, 654 (recipe)
   shakes, 231, 525
   soy milk, 132
   tea, 651-652
Binge eating, 176
Biotechnology, 41, 358, 366
Biotin, 73
Biscuit and pastry method, 556, 561-562
Biscuits, making, 561-562
Blanching vegetables, 666
Blood pressure, and sodium, 94
Blood sugar, 80, 173
Body-fat test, 141
Boiling, 280
Bone shape, and cut of meat, 491, 492
Botulism, 199
Bouillabaisse, 602
Bouillon, 535
Braising, 285, 542
Bran, of grain kernel, 433
Brands of foods, and shopping, 341-342